LEEDS COLLEGE OF BUILDING LIBRARY
CLASS NO. 721.0467   T 33758
BARCODE   GRE 720.47 GRE

The Green Building Bible

All you need to know about ecobuilding

3rd Edition, Volume 1

LEEDS COLLEGE OF BUILDING
WITHDRAWN FROM STOCK

ISBN 1-898130-03-05

Publishing editor: Keith Hall

D1584504

Includes listings of green building professionals, tradespeople, product suppliers and organisations in the UK & Ireland

Green Building Press

www.greenbuildingbible.co.uk

www.greenbuildingpress.co.uk

the Green building bible

3rd edition, Volume 1

Copyright

This edition, layout and format is copyright of Green Building Press. All text and submissions are joint copyright of the respective authors and the publisher. No reproduction in any form without prior approval of the publisher.

Publishing editor: Keith Hall
Green Building Press, PO Box 32,
Llandysul, SA44 5ZA
Tel: 01559 370798
E-mail: keith@greenbuildingpress.co.uk
Web Site: www.greenbuildingpress.co.uk
Advertising: Jerry Clark 01208 895103
jerry@greenbuildingpress.co.uk

Disclaimer

The views expressed in this book are not necessarily those of the publisher. No guarantee is given as to the accuracy of any information contained herein.

The authors and the publisher do not accept any responsibility, or liability, for any error, omission, loss, damage, injury of any kind incurred as a result of the use of the information contained in this book, or reliance upon it. It is suggested that readers should always seek professional advice when embarking on any building project.

The publisher also accepts no responsibility what-soever for any individual or company, for whatever reasons, selected from the adverts, listings or weblinks held within this book. Readers should obtain references and details of past projects prior to making any decision to employ.

Extra copies of this book or Volume 2 can be ordered at: www.newbuilder.co.uk/books or by post - send cheque or postal order, made payable to *Green Building Press*, for £9.95 (incl p&p) per copy. Send to *Green Building Press*, PO Box 32, Llandysul, SA44 5ZA.

Cover photo: The Wintles at Bishop's Castle, Shropshire
Cartoons: Jo Burt, Mike Flanagan

DO YOU MIND? YOU'RE BLOCKING THE SOLAR PANELS!

Advertising Policy of the Green Building Press

Advertising space will only be offered to companies whose products or services (in our opinion) offer clear environmental advantages over similarly available products for the same purpose.
In particular we will not accept adverts for products that:
- include ozone destroying gasses
- are wasteful of energy or are high energy consumers
- contain components that are considered harmful to human health, either by passive or active exposure
- are racist or sexist in nature.
The product selection criteria used for our GreenPro database forms the basis of our advertiser selection process.
www.newbuilder.co.uk/greenpro/

The Green Building Press is a member of Green Ink.

The public lending rights (PLR) of this title have been assigned to the World Land Trust.

The World Land Trust identifies and conserves vital wilderness areas under threat. Its strategy is to purchase such land and then work with non-governmental organisations to manage it in the most environmentally sensitive way.

GREEN INK
Authors, Artists & Publishers Helping The Environment

WORLD LAND TRUST
www.worldlandtrust.org

Contents

Contents

Printed on Era silk paper and board; an FSC product which contains 50% recycled fibre, by Cambrian Printers, an FSC Accredited company (TT-COC-2200): 01970 627111 www.cambrian-printers.co.uk
No reproduction in any form without prior approval of the publisher.
Cover design © Green Building Press.

All web links in this book were checked and live as at October 2006.

FSC

TT-COC-2200

Acknowledgements

This book would not have been possible without the willing help of numerous people. Thank you Jay Abrahams, Peter Aceston-Rook, Steve Allin, Ben Bamber, Dave Barton, Adrian Birch, Gavin Blakemore, Graham Bond, Kevin Boniface, Bill Bordass, Katy Bryce, Jon Broome, Roger Budgeon, Jo Burt, Anita Bradley, Iain Calderwood, John Cantor, Isabel Carmona, Jerry Clark, Stan Crawford, Trevor Davies, Bill Dunster, David Elliot, Clive Frewins, John Garbutt, Mike George, Beccy Gillham, Mark Gorgolewski, Leonie Green, Sally Hall, Gavin Harper, Féidhlim Harty, Cath Hassell, Alan Heeks, Chris Herring, Mischa Hewitt, Kerry Hughes, Derek Hunt, Carla Jameson, Paul Jennings, Gavin Killip, Chris Laughton, Adrian Leaman, Robert Lewin-Jones, Howard Liddell, Michael Littlewood, Oliver Lowenstein, Stephen Lowndes, Tom MacKeown, Chris Morgan, David Nettleton, Richard Nicholls, David Olivier, Richard Oxley, Rupert Paul, Jane Powell, Olwyn Pritchard, Sue Roaf, Gideon Richards, Paola Sassi, Rob Scott McLeod, Bob Tomlinson, John Shore, Michael Smith, Doug Stewart, Geoff Stow, Judith Thornton, Nick White, Rachel Shiamh Whitehead, John Willoughby, Adam Wiseman, Sarah Villiers, Andrew Yeats and Louise Zass-Bangham.

I would also like to extend my thanks to all of the advertisers who have supported this edition. Their input has enabled us to keep the cover price affordable and because of our strict advertising policy, (see page 4) these businesses add to the usefulness of this book.

I must give very special thanks to my close friend Jerry Clark for his hard work, total commitment and dedication to this project, like my wife Sally, often working for hours on end without breaks in order to keep to my demanding deadlines. My son Keith Jnr. also deserves a mention for his patience, help and support.

Finally I dedicate this book to my wife Sally who is the backbone of ALL my work. Throughout our thirty years together, Sally has supported me. Without her dedication to professionalism and timekeeping, you would not be reading this book.

Keith Hall - Publishing Editor

web: www.stonehealth.com
e-mail: info@stonehealth.com

Supplier of a Wide & Full Range of products for Building Conservation & Restoration

'Latex' Cleaning, Stone Care Treatments, Graffiti & Paint Removal, Iron, Aluminium, Copper Oxides & Soot Removal, Gum Repellants, Anti-Graffiti & many more etc...

Torque ... to ...

DOFF

Operates the TORC & DOFF Approved Register,

Check the Trained & Inducted Authenticity of an Operator - Prior to Commencement of a Project, to Safeguard Standards & Results...

Clean-Film

Bowers Court, Broadwell, Dursley Gloucestershire, GL11 4JE
tel: (0044) 01453 540600
fax: (0044) 01453 540609

Welcome to the future part 1

Welcome to Volume 1 of the third edition of the Green Building Bible. As in previous editions, my aim has been to provide a comprehensive snapshot of the 'green building' movement in the UK. I am pleased to say that I believe that, with the willing help of the many professionals and contributors who have been involved, this has been achieved admirably.

My hope is that this book will be your helping hand, your first port of call to help you 'get to grips' with one of the most vitally important aspects of our society - the built environment. I, like many others, believe we need to learn how to live sustainably. We have to build and remodel our living environments in such a way as to drastically reduce our burden on the planet. As each year passes by, the opportunities to make a difference decrease, and most scientists are now agreed on this point. The time left to embrace a lower impact lifestyle is ticking away.

There are no easy answers and many different approaches, but in this book (and its companion, Volume 2) you will find encouraging, practical and immediately useful hands-on information from both the long-term green building professionals and enthusiastic newcomers to the movement. The new 'Industry trends' chapter will provide you with a snapshot of where we are now and how things are likely to develop in the near future.

Although this is a big book, we have been unable to cover every subject area in the detail I would have liked, therefore we have included many references and suggestions for further reading and contacts. Many of these are web-based as the internet has proven to be an excellent resource. If you do not have a computer many local libraries allow free access.

Volume 2 goes beyond the introductions and delves into the more in-depth design detailing of buildings. It also provides easy to understand explanations of how some of the new technologies actually work. The book covers areas such as site layout, building envelope and fabric, renewable technologies, environmental factors, lighting strategies, heating and cooling systems and lots more. If you don't already have a copy, you can order it from any of our web sites.

Finally I would like to extend a personal thank you, to all those who have contributed to, and supported, the production of this third edition. You know who you are!

Authors

There are profiles and contact details of the authors that contributed to this book on page 449.

Keith Hall - publishing editor
keith@greenbuildingpress.co.uk

if you think outside the box, you don't want to live in one

Thinking of building an unconventional home with the environment in mind? Contact the Ecology - specialists in mortgages for ecological homes.

Mortgages are available...

... up to 90% of value
... for renovations, conversions & new builds
... on the land or unimproved property value
... in stage payments as the work progresses

Call 0845 6745566
email loans@ecology.co.uk
www.ecology.co.uk

Ecology Building Society understands the use of traditional and ecological building techniques and materials and will consider all projects that benefit the environment.

Ecology Building Society
Ref: GBB, FREEPOST BD714
KEIGHLEY, BD20 0BR

Authorised and regulated by the Financial Services Authority

Ecology
Building Society

An early repayment charge is payable if you repay all or part of this mortgage within the first four years

YOUR HOME MAY BE REPOSSESSED IF YOU DO NOT KEEP UP REPAYMENTS ON YOUR MORTGAGE

Introduction

> **"The world has only one generation, perhaps two, to save itself"**
>
> *Worldwatch Institute* [1]

For sustainability read survivability

The world is changing fast. The hot summers, fiercer floods and our rising gas, and electricity bills at home, ring alarm bells for all of us. The discussions we had a decade ago of 'sustainability' have now become peppered with concerns about the more urgent issue of 'survivability'! **Sue Roaf** discusses the pressing drivers for an 'eco-society', and an overview of what the characteristics of an eco-society might be, and how we, as ordinary citizens, might adapt our life-styles to become part of it ...

We know what the problems are, we have the technologies and the understanding of what changes are necessary, but all we seem to lack is the will to implement the already prepared action plans for change. We have around ten years in which to build an 'eco-society' that is capable of putting the planet, the global common good, and 'survival' at the top of its agenda. This article outlines how individuals can play a part in building such an eco-society and at the same time a more 'sustainable' lifestyle for themselves[2]. The four greatest challenges that this society faces are climate change, peak oil, resource depletion and pollution.

Climate change

In 1988 the United Nations Environment Programme and the World Meteorological Organisation established the Intergovernmental Panel on Climate Change (IPCC)[3], consisting of hundreds of leading scientists and experts on global warming. Since 1990 the Panel has published numerous reports on how the growing accumulation of human-made greenhouse gases in the atmosphere is 'enhancing' the greenhouse effect, and how humanity can, and must, respond to climate change. In 1992, at the Earth Summit in Rio de Janeiro, the United Nations Framework Convention on Climate Change (UNFCCC)[4] was adopted. The treaty called for industrialized countries to take the first steps to prevent 'dangerous anthropogenic interference' with the climate by voluntarily reducing their emissions to 1990 levels by the year 2000. These voluntary measures have not proved effective, despite the fact that the Kyoto Treaty was ratified on 16th February 2005.

The world is very far from being able to meet its required greenhouse gas emission reductions to meet the swingeing 90% reduction targets that many bodies propose as necessary if we are to stabilise climate change by the end of this century[5]. To achieve this many scientists now believe we must keep carbon levels in the atmosphere below 450 parts per million (ppm). We are already at 380ppm and rising at around 2-3 ppm, year on year. The urgency of the challenge is obvious[6].

Peak oil

Since the beginning of the Industrial Revolution

*Produced and predicted oil and gas reserves
for the UK Source: UK Department of Trade and
Industry, via www.peakoil.net*

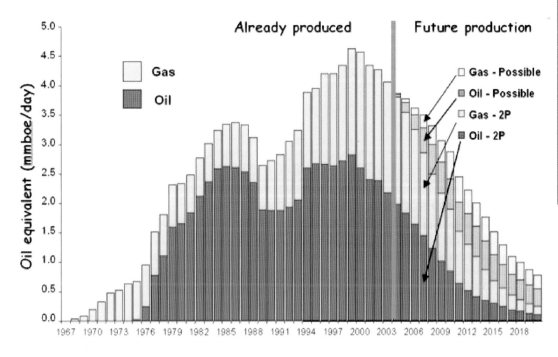

we have relied on cheap energy to power our factories, transport and lifestyles. Unfortunately we have reached the end of cheap oil and gas and as the global consumption soars, global supplies are declining rapidly, making energy more and more expensive, year on year[7]. In Britain we will have run out of our own supplies by around 2020 and will then be dependant on fossil fuels from some of the least stable regions of the world. We will also be at the end of the global supply lines, making us even more vulnerable to shortages.

Resource depletion

The systems of the planet itself are beginning to buckle under the challenge of not only providing more resources for more people but also under the strains of a rapidly changing climate that threatens not only our vital water sources but also the plant and animal species on which we are mutually dependant for survival. There is currently concern that the greatest individual ecosystem of them all, the Amazon Basin is on the brink of being turned into a desert[8]. As the ecological footprint of human beings goes up, the number of other species declines dramatically.

Pollution

As the sheer scale of our plundering and processing of the earth's resources accelerates, so does the scale of our pollution of its atmosphere. The vast range of pollutants that we generate, touch much of the planet's surface and range from agricultural fertilisers to industrial and vehicular air-pollution[9]. Today, nearly one-third of the World's population lives with chronic shortages of water that directly threaten human health, agriculture and economic development. More than 1 billion people lack access to safe drinking water and more than 2 billion, adequate sanitation. Some 6,000 children die every day from water related diseases. By 2025, nearly two-thirds of the World's population will experience some form of water-related stress[10].

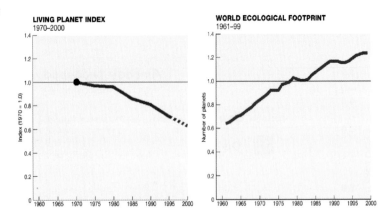

As the consumption of resources by mankind increases, the numbers of other species we share our planet with declines rapidly Source: World Wildlife Fund.

Building an eco-society

If we are to survive with our society and planet largely intact in the coming years, our challenge is to build a society that values the good of the global commons. One that is equiped to face the enormous challenges of reducing consumption and the rate of climate change; to adapt to survive the impacts of extreme weather without fossil fuels; to reduce our need for non-sustainable resources and minimise the pollution we inflict on the planet. What would such a society look like?[11]

There would be a shared understanding of the values of an eco-society. An eco-society should, for instance, act as a protector, not destroyer, of the environment. It would be built on the fundamental values of equality, responsibility, respect for human dignity and our fellow species. It would recognise the importance of happiness; well being; quality of life, joy, health and beauty. The only way to build such values into our lives would be through the medium of thriving communities that work together to improve the lot of the individuals within them, based on altruistic action, openness, truth and democratic politics. There would inevitably also have to be clear leadership and enforced adherence to strategies that limit the impacts of that society to levels that do not cause social or ecological devastation and that afford individuals within that society a fair earth share of the available resources. A new economic system would have to be built to support this society[12].

Resources are valued as finite by an eco-society that is economical, using minimal resources, efficient, resourceful, understanding the available resources and able to use them innovatively, optimising the 'yield' potential of our finite resources. Resources are shared and re-used and re-cycled. Renewable materials and energy are chosen in preference to finite resources and waste is minimised, with users employing conservation strategies and closed resource loops where possible. Non-toxic and non-polluting materials and processes are used where possible in a value-driven, sufficiency-oriented, native economy.

Buildings in an eco-society would enhance nature, the environment and the community and help people connect with them. Buildings would be built to have minimal impact on the eco-sphere and be designed to promote peace. They would generate their own energy, use local materials and be designed to provide shelter and comfort even when the infra-structures of societies begin to break down. They would be designed to minimise the risk of failure in the event of extreme weather, so not be too exposed to the revenge of the climate, be robust and resilient to reduce the vulnerability of their occupants at difficult times. In America there is already a movement towards 'passive survival' buildings which could survive when centralised systems fail and the climate becomes even more extreme[13].

Citizens within an eco-society would have to not only be educated and self-aware of their own local impacts but would also understand how their actions impacted on the rest of the world. They would thus be well 'connected' to others, and also more self dependant than today's generation that is very vulnerable to the changes ahead we face. They would be eco-consumers knowing what the impacts of their own life style are and actively working to reduce those impacts for transport, energy use, resource purchases in their day to day lives,[14] living in a local culture that promotes communal activities singing, dancing, art, and communal fun. They would be wise, engaged in working to build ideas, understanding and consensus and a safe and secure local, regional and global society.

Conclusion

So now we know what an eco-society should be like, it is up to us to all go out and help to build it. The Green Building Bible has been written to help you build an eco-society.

References

1. State of the World report, 2003: www.worldwatch.org/taxonomy/term/38

2. 'Adapting Buildings and Cities for Climate Change' by S Roaf, D. Crichton and F. Nicol (2005). This book contains a fuller account of the issues outlined in this article, available from: www.newbuilder.co.uk

3. For a complete explanation of the processes of climate change and the related publications of the International Panel on Climate Change: www.ipcc.ch How climate change affects UK: www.ukcip.org.uk For a potted and well informed history: www.doc.mmu.ac.uk/aric/eae/Global_Warming/global_warming.html

An excellent book on climate change: 'The Weather Makers' by Tim Flannery (2005).

4. For a full state of play on the climate conventions see http://unfccc.int/index.html

5. See the Global Commons Institute site for an outline of the carbon reduction challenge: www.gci.org.uk/contconv/cc.html

6. Our only hope is if we can 'contract' our greehhouse gas emissions, and 'converge' to a universally held global fair earth share of emissions, to a level commensurate with survival. See www.gci.org.uk

7. See www.peakoil.net and www.energycrisis.com Good book resource is 'Half Gone: Oil, Gas, Hot Air and the Global Energy Crisis' by Jeremy Leggett (2005).

8. 'The Last Generation' by Fred Pearce (2006).

9. See http://en.wikipedia.org/wiki/Pollution

10. See http://en.wikipedia.org/wiki/Clean_water

11. The section on Building an Eco-society resulted from discussions at the 2006 Summer retreat of the Society of Buildings Science Educators, in the USA in Pingree Park in the Colorado Rockies in July. For more information: www.sbse.org

12. www.neweconomics.org

13. www.buildinggreen.com/press/passive-survivability.cfm

14. See: www.bestfootforward.com/footprintlife.htm for a general carbon lifestyle calculator. For information on how to environmentally rate resources for buildings see many of the specialist sites on Google and also the chapter on materials in 'Closing the Loop, Benchmarks for Sustainable Buildings' by S Roaf, A. Horsley and R.Gupta (2004). For low impact ecohousing see 'Ecohouse 2: A Design Guide' by S Roaf, M. Fuentes and S. Thomas (2003) available from: www.newbuilder.co.uk

Most of the books mentioned above are available from the Green Shop 01452 770629 www.greenshop.co.uk

Best Foot forward:	www.bestfootforward.com/carbonlife.htm
Centre for Alternative Technology:	www.cat.org.uk/carbongym
Choose Climate:	www.chooseclimate.org/flying/mapcalc.html
Climate Care:	www.co2.org/living/calculator_info/index.cfm
Carbon Neutral Company:	carbonneutral.com/calculators/index_world_calculator.asp
ICLEI:	www3.iclei.org/co2/co2calc.htm
National Energy Foundation:	www.nef.org.uk/energyadvice/co2calculator.htm
SafeClimate:	www.safeclimate.net/calculator/index.php
Travel Calculator:	www.travelcalculator.org
Climate Outreach Information Network:	www.coinet.org.uk/projects/challenge/measure
Climate Crisis (USA):	www.climatecrisis.net
Carbon Coach Calculator:	www.carboncoach.com/countdown_01.html#2
British Gas:	www.house.co.uk/energysavers

Carbon footprint calculators.

A green building philosophy

Sustainability and quality of life are highly influenced by the buildings in which we live and work. At their best, buildings can be inspiring, efficient structures which facilitate health and creativity, and enable us to live in harmony with one another and the planet. **John Shore** explains ...

Green buildings should aim to cause the minimum possible harm to the environment and users - throughout their design, construction, use, upkeep and eventual end of life recycling. Despite green and sustainable construction becoming increasingly popular, this comprehensive, cradle to cradle philosophy is not yet common currency.

So perhaps the first rule of green design should be to avoid the need to destroy, replace or abandon as unsuitable without proper consideration. Adaptability and loose-fit may be more appropriate than a design which costs the environment dearly by requiring regular modification and renovation. A sustainable house, for example, might be designed to service the needs of many generations of diverse users – from infancy to old age, from lively teenagers sharing space and facilities, to disabled people or elderly relatives. Such long-life green buildings need to be part of a sustainable community infrastructure to deliver their full potential.

Green building, as a concept, is straightforward and makes perfect sense. It means making thoughtful design choices and using ecological materials in ways that create quality, long-lasting environments with minimum damage to the planet. Natural ambient resources can often be used for services – energy – heating – cooling – water etc.

A vision for a green future

Imaginative and enlightened planning is essential if we are to achieve this. Current thinking must adapt to our needs for thicker, insulated walls, equal access to sunshine, decent sized gardens, green spaces and trees, space to work from home, a softer infrastructure, less need to travel...

We need to rethink current housing policy based on simplistic, polarized thinking and out-dated concepts. Such unsustainable development builds impoverished communities and additional long-term social costs. People need environments that are worth caring for.

Low energy buildings provide us with an easy way to combat climate change. New buildings can be designed to be zero-heat and zero-carbon. With the application of external wall and warm-roof insulation, existing buildings can also make a massive contribution. Cities and urban areas will need to be greened - less buildings and more nature, more local fresh food production. Rural areas could benefit from sensitive development, so they become less isolated and more sustainable. Independently serviced buildings would allow use of the extensive existing rural road network. As we begin to develop our use of natural resources, more people will need to live and work in the countryside.

Building to a green agenda now has widespread support and there is no shortage of products and techniques. Whether you are drawn to use timber from sustainable sources, strawbale or earth, lime-based renders, plasters and paint – or to harvest the rain, sun and wind – you will find amazing products and people who can help you.

Green buildings will become the new vernacular form if we are not afraid to design with integrity and use materials with a new honesty. Simple, economical forms require less materials, energy and maintenance. The ever-increasing bureaucracy of building should be resisted, in order to encourage local solutions and building diversity. High standards in construction are essential, but building regulation should not stifle innovation or make buildings so unaffordable that they become unsustainable. Enabling affordable land for self-build might be an ideal way to develop green building skills and green communities without the curse of identi-kit houses. Affordable green buildings could help deliver a step-change in the way we live and work, freeing up time for us to create a more caring and sane society.

Challenges for green design

For green buildings to make a real difference, they must be practical designs which we can all have and afford. Cost-efficiency is a pre-

requisite for sustainability, because income generation usually has environmental consequences. Green designs do not have to be complex or costly.

Many ordinary buildings are often described as green or ecological without real justification. Some are little more than 'business as usual' buildings, extravagantly 'decorated' with green gestures and renewable energy devices. Simple building designs which enable us to reduce our

An innovative neighbourhood of 35 affordable homes, designed as a template for rural, sustainable social housing. Architects: Gale and Snowdon

ecological footprint are so much more important than being seen to look green. We should
design and build with integrity and responsibility. Complex and costly multiple-layer walls, or a
wall or roof of south-facing glazing may not be
the most efficient or sustainable building form.
The technologies needed to make a building
autonomous have always been tempting, but
unless they are cost-effective, simple and
reliable, they may not deliver any benefit.

Well designed, easy to build, robust buildings that are healthy to live in and perform well
year after year without causing harm to the
planet are urgently needed. We must rise to
the challenge of climate change – but without
resorting to building in unecological materials!
A building is not just a machine or a lock-up for
our possessions, but something we intimately
live with, that we care for and love.

There are a number of key aspects to the
design of green buildings:
- cost-efficiency (a pre-requisite for
  sustainability)
- conservation of energy and resources
- ecological foundations and minimal site
  intervention
- reduction of infrastructure; roads; pipes;
  lighting...
- elimination/reduction of material and
  resource wastage
- elimination/reduction of toxic materials and
  processes
- use of renewable/biological materials and
  energy
- use of safe, recycled materials and products
- vapour-diffusive – air and wind-tight
  construction
- super insulation and ecological thermal
  energy storage
- use of natural (passive) heating and cooling
- use of natural lighting (for health and energy
  saving)
- minimisation of electro-magnetic fields
- long life – low maintenance, robust design
- adaptable, inclusive (access for all) design
- green surroundings – design with nature and
  climate.

Get the design right!

Be clear about your design strategy. A south-
facing passive solar building will demand a
different approach than an east-west-axis
building. Houses which achieve a U-value of
0.1 to 0.15 are often described as zero-heat,
which means they do not require a conventional
heating system. But even when combined with
passive solar space heating they will still usually
require small amounts of back-up heating for
short periods. A zero-heat house will require a
thickness of 235-300mm insulation in the wall,
300-400mm in the roof and 200-250mm in the
floor, depending on the properties of the other
elements used.

Good natural lighting and solar space heating
can be achieved without massive areas of
high-embodied-energy glass. Glazing areas
should be sized appropriately for the orientation, construction and type of building, together
with the provision of adequate shading and
ventilation to avoid summer overheating. Double
glazing with a 1.5 U-value (frame+glass) is
now common and can be supplemented with
low energy blinds. Insist on the use of non-
conductive glazing spacers (superspacer) and
pay attention to air-tightness, the quality of
seals, materials and fittings used for doors and
windows. The Supply-Air window is an interesting development, where air is drawn into
the building between two panes of glass by
a passive stack system. The air captures the
heat lost across the window and brings it into
the building. With U-values as low as 0.7W/mK,
these windows have great potential, providing
stack heat loss can be carefully controlled.

Ventilation is an increasingly challenging area
of design. We need systems that can provide
adequate fresh air in winter, without heat loss
in varying weather conditions, but can also
provide summer cooling during heat-waves.
Are passive pipes and ducts – or active micro-
processor-controlled fans, heat-exchangers and
filters (which all require cleaning and maintenance) – the way forward, or can we develop
much simpler and greener ideas?

>>>

© Green Building Press

Gaia Architects

Ecological designers for 20 years throughout the UK and Europe. Projects include all building types, plus research, community consultation, masterplanning and feasibility study services in rural and urban contexts.

The Monastery
2 Hart Street Lane
Edinburgh
EH1 3RG

Tel: 0131 557 9191
Fax: 0131 557 9292
Email: architects@gaiagroup.org
Website: www.gaiagroup.org

Ensure that internal materials and finishes are robust to eliminate the need for wasteful renovation. Reduce water use by fitting aerating taps, showers and low flush toilets. Installing professionally engineered dry (composting) toilets may actually be more eco than a rainwater harvesting system used to flush ordinary water closets. Keep wiring simple and pipework compact and eliminate unnecessary pumps, boilers and techno-gizmos. Design to allow the easy reuse of materials in the future – buildings do not have to be irreversible.

Sustainable energy

Buildings have an unhealthy appetite for energy, and energy consumption is increasing despite use of more efficient technology. There is massive potential for the development of new energy-efficient appliances and for new ways of living and working which can reduce our energy use. Solar and wind energy are available to all buildings and we should make better use of these independent resources. Using renewable energy makes us more dependent on climate, but reduces our vulnerability to scarce, imported and costly fossil fuels. Driving down energy demand makes it much easier for a building to be self-sufficient through using ambient energy sources. The increasing use of green electricity from the national grid makes it essential and urgent that we harvest more renewable energy for grid connection.

Up to 50% of the solar energy falling on a roof or wall can be harvested just by sucking the pre-heated air from behind the tiles or claddings. Solar water heating is one of the most cost-effective and reliable renewable energy systems and an increased collector area could be used in winter to boost performance. Photovoltaic (PV) electricity panels are gradually falling in cost while gaining in efficiency and can be easily mounted on the roof and walls of buildings. PV is increasingly used to pump solar water heating systems and to feed appliances in buildings or export to the electricity grid during times of excess.

Small-scale wind turbines are more cost effective than PV modules and can work both day and night, but for best results they are mounted on tall towers – away from trees or buildings. New, quiet, slow-speed turbines are becoming available and some can be building-mounted (with great care!) Be cautious and realistic though – urban wind-speeds are very low, and some manufacturers are making equipment of questionable quality and unsubstantiated performance claims. Wind turbines can also be used to heat buildings and pump water without the need for battery storage. If well designed and maintained, a wind turbine system can have an unlimited life.

Given appropriate site layouts, it is possible to heat buildings using windows, walls or roofing as solar collectors. Green electricity can be used for the small amount of back up heat required. We should be designing buildings which do not need conventional active heating or cooling systems. For more energy-dependent buildings, efficient wood chip and pellet stoves can be used. Green buildings have the potential to become energy producers rather than users. The key to making these systems cost-effective is to use them as part of an integrated design where they replace and eliminate the need for conventional energy systems.

For both healthy living and quality of life, we need to green not just our homes, but also our places of work and our surroundings. We also need to drastically reduce our need for travel and change the way we work to enable more flexibility and the use of local, natural resources. For a society that can develop spacecraft, micro-computers and mobile telephones this should not be too great a challenge? ☯

© Green Building Press

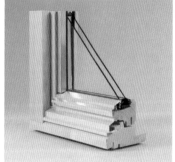

High performance timber & aluminium clad windows and doors

NorDan: Norwegian for quality

NorDan windows and doors offer superb quality, craftsmanship and design. Able to produce 1500 windows/doors daily, NorDan has the capacity of a major world exporter. Their five large factories have a work force in excess of 850 with computer controlled production lines. This enables manufacturing in volumes sufficient for the largest projects while remaining competitively priced.

Eco-friendly

More than 95% of the timber used in the manufacture of NorDan windows and doors is sourced from managed forests. For each tree that is used in the production, more trees are planted to meet future demands.

Energy saving

Although the NorDan standard U-value for the UK is 1.6 W/m²K, NorDan can achieve a U-value as low as 1.0 W/m²K with the added benefits of a secondary sash. With the facility to produce their own glazing units (circa. 400,000 per year) NorDan are more than capable of meeting your requirements.

Security

NorDan UK Ltd provide windows and doors to the police preferred specification of Secured by Design. Furthermore, NorDan also manufacture windows and doors to ISO9001 which guarantees the consistent quality of each and every product.

NorDan®

NorDan UK Ltd, Green Farm Business Park, Falcon Close, Quedgeley, Gloucester, GL2 4LY

T: 01452 883131
F: 01452 883739
E: info@nordan.co.uk
W: www.nordan.co.uk

POLICE PREFERRED SPECIFICATION

Cover story

The Wintles

The Wintles is a small eco-development of 40 houses built on a south-facing slope on a 15 acre plot on the edge of Bishops Castle in Shropshire. The man behind this project, Bob Tomlinson, established a development company called 'Living Villages' back in the mid 90s, a company that builds, promotes and encourages sustainable building at the development level. This project is the second scheme by the organisation which created a limited company to design and build these houses. **Sally Hall** reports...

"One of the reasons for purchasing the Wintles site", said Tomlinson, "was to save it from being developed as a 'typical soul-less housing estate' by a national housebuilder. At Living Villages, we believe that building energy-efficient new housing and encouraging an eco-friendly lifestyle is vital for the future of the planet and of our children."

This project follows on from a smaller but similar project of five houses on the other side of the village. The local planners have been very supportive of both eco-schemes. The careful landscaping and low densities helped keep objections from local residents to a minimum.

Few details escaped the careful green scrutiny during the design of the houses in this development. It is a model eco-build for the middle class homebuyer. The houses use a super insulated, engineered timber frame structure and have been designed to take advantage of the natural south facing aspect of the site, with passive solar design playing a large part in the layout of the site. The design philosophy was 'to provide attractive, energy efficient homes set within safe, quiet pedestrian zones connected by pathways with direct access to the open countryside beyond.' Every house is different and the aim has been to echo the nature and form of the houses found in the old town of Bishops Castle. The internal layouts are designed to be flexible. Modifications could be agreed during the building process and rooms can be easily formed from attic areas if required in the future.

The designers hope that the high performance, triple glazed windows and doors, and heat exchange systems will create a 'zero heat' house. Just in-case they are not, highly efficient

© Green Building Press

gas condensing boilers have been installed to provide under-floor heating on the ground floor and bathrooms. Solar panels for hot water heating are fitted as standard kit. The houses are even plumbed ready for water re-cycling! As you might expect with a spec like this, natural, local and reclaimed materials have all been carefully chosen and incorporated, as have low energy appliances and lighting (where fitted). Every house is well insulated to far exceed current building regulations and good use is made of natural light.

Value

Tomlinson says that their efforts to create quality ecohomes has paid off because demand for the properties has way exceeded supply. The premium prices achieved for the properties are reflecting a true regard for 'sustainability' by purchasers. Sustainability that has been addressed in both the buildings and external landscaping. The build costs for this development, were higher than for a conventional build. It is clear that these are homes for downshifters (or sideshifters may be a more accurate description) rather than your run of the mill executive. Most of the houses are being bought and occupied by '40 somethings' with young children seeking a better quality and healthier lifestyle.

Landscaping and site management

The scheme is designed to favour pedestrians rather than cars, although it is possible to drive up to each front door if necessary. Parking is on allocated spaces. There are no garages (now that is radical!) although there are car shelters. Each house has a private garden but the houses are in groups and each

group of houses has a shared garden area.

3,000 trees have been planted around the edge of the site and a balancing pond has been worked into the scheme for flood alleviation and wildlife value. Allotments are available and there are community woodlands, orchards, gardens and recreational spaces.

A residents' management company has been set up to care for and manage the common areas and facilities. All houses get one share (this always remains with the house) in this company. It is hoped that the company will be used for schemes such as car sharing, bulk food purchasing etc. There is an emphasis on resident satisfaction with owners being requested to complete questionnaires after a few months; comments and feedback being taken into account for future builds. ☯
www.livingvillage.com

Decentralise our energy

Many designers and managers of buildings recognise the importance of mitigating climate change. With energy use in buildings associated with around a half of total CO_2 emissions, 'climate champions' have emerged, like Bill Dunster, with his zero emission development in Sutton - BedZED. Greenpeace's report 'Decentralising Power' puts such energy innovation in buildings at the centre of a grand master plan for transforming the power sector in the UK. **Leonie Greene** of Greenpeace reports ...

The vision is bold: entire professions at the very frontline of a wholesale revolution in the outdated electricity systems that dominate the developed world and that pose such a serious threat to climatic stability. In the Greenpeace vision buildings are the power stations of the future and at the very centre of a network and technology revolution.

For all their fancy debates on the minutiae of future power generation options, politicians routinely neglect the fact that centralised power systems are the embodiment of technological inertia, performing little better today than they did in the 1970s. Almost two-thirds of primary energy is wasted in the UK's centralised electricity system, mostly in the form of heat and in volumes that exceed the entire thermal energy needs for space and water heating of every building in the UK. And that's before power encounters the staggering energy inefficiency of the average UK home. In the face of climate change and mounting security concerns, this is indefensible – particularly since the knowledge and technologies to address this have been with us for decades.

In 'Decentralising Power', Greenpeace argues to end this wastage in the centralised power model and to deliver an electricity system fit for the challenges of the 21st century. The potential to reduce the overall demand for electricity through energy efficiency measures has been endlessly analysed, but weakly pursued. Less well rehearsed, and still less acted upon, is the potential to reduce energy wastage and CO_2 emissions by remodelling our electricity system. Furthermore, decentralising our electricity system presents an opportunity to deliver on all four key energy policy goals set out in the 2003 Energy White Paper: improving security of supply, tackling fuel poverty, and enhancing competition, as well as emissions reduction.

Decentralised energy (DE) is not a difficult concept, it is simply energy generated at or near the point of use. The link with buildings is obvious. By enabling the capture of waste heat through proximity, and establishing an infrastructure and regulatory regime responsive to the characteristics of renewables and other decentralised energy (DE) technologies, a decentralised model has the potential over the coming decades to at least halve our electricity system's contribution to climate change – much more if renewables make up a greater proportion of the mix and they should increasingly do so as direct application will drive market innovation. DE technologies supported by Greenpeace include those you would expect; photovoltaics, biogas and biomass cogeneration and trigeneration and geothermal, wind, wave, tidal and small-scale hydroelectric power. DE also includes dedicated heating technologies like ground source and air source heat pumps, solar thermal and biomass heating. However, Greenpeace also supports natural gas cogeneration (or trigeneration) as a bridging technology. This is able to achieve efficiencies of over 90% and can offer a complementary energy profile to more intermittent renewable technologies.

In the long run, a decentralised pathway may actually be cheaper – and that's a certainty when the environmental costs of electricity production are internalized. There are many economic benefits to DE, like reduced skills

© Green Building Press

training costs or reduced lead-in times to plant construction – see Amory Lovins' weighty tome 'Small is Profitable'[1] for over 200 benefits. But one of the most striking economic benefits of DE is it obviates the need for the current level of investment in hugely expensive high-voltage transmission and distribution networks. For example, the International Energy Agency estimate that the EU will invest some $1.35 trillion in electricity infrastructure to 2030, nearly half of which ($648 billion) will be spent on transmission and distribution networks. DE technologies simply do not require such expensive centralised infrastructure, since their energy sources are so highly dispersed and varied.

A decentralised pathway delivers a more secure network configuration, improving security of supply. The vulnerability of brittle, centralised electricity systems has been demonstrated dramatically around the world in recent years – 2003 was a particularly sobering year for the centralised power industry, with over 100 million people affected by breathtakingly widespread blackouts across North America, Italy and, to a lesser extent, London. Twinkling in the darkness of New York's blackout were lights powered by decentralised cogeneration plant. Fretting in the darkness of London's underground were passengers who probably didn't know that London Underground's dedicated local power plant had been closed only months earlier, leaving passengers exposed to the fragility of a national grid. Power failures are not only stressful and potentially dangerous, but expensive. They cost the US economy a staggering $80 billion a year. Moreover, the vulnerability of centralised systems is set to increase as a result of climate change impacts, and our dependence on energy imports. Our society's growing reliance on electronic technology makes the potential consequences of this system vulnerability all the more catastrophic.

Demand reduction measures and DE have a natural synergy; DE technologies can help drive energy efficiency at the point of use. When energy consumers become their own producers those consumers are incentivised to reduce their energy demand to minimise the capital and running costs of plant. Energy efficiency purists often bemoan the designer's easy love affair with 'sexy' renewables, but their undeniable appeal should be celebrated - and harnessed - to drive energy efficiency forward in parallel with DE. There is nothing like seeing local working alternatives to wasteful centralised power – the silver glint of a pv roof or a turbine in motion - to propel climate change out of the abstract and into the real world of everyday people. Action by the building professions, however individually modest, can weave a spell around hearts and minds as people increasingly encounter local low-carbon generation on their doorsteps, understand energy options better and develop a sense of responsibility for their own energy foot prints. It's the start of a virtuous circle, with increased exposure to DE driving increased demand for a stake in the action.

Decentralising energy democratises energy. It offers a means to turn lip service paid to the value of local political leadership on climate change mitigation into reality. Opening up the networks to ready DE access means that local government would be able to take active responsibility for overseeing the reduction of CO_2 emissions in its catchment area – local political champions can emerge to put central government's ineffectual posturing to shame. Crucially, devolving and democratising energy decision-making promises to curb the influence of the hugely powerful vested interests that currently have so much sway over policy.

The benefits of a decentralised pathway are most striking from an international perspective; billions of people lack access to basic energy services, frustrating human development. DE is highly flexible; it allows solutions to be tailored to unique local opportunities and budgets without first investing in an over-specified phenomenally expensive centralised infrastructure that invariably leads to fossil-fuel dependence. Wealthy Western governments face an obligation and a considerable challenge to promote globally a far more sustainable energy model than they themselves have

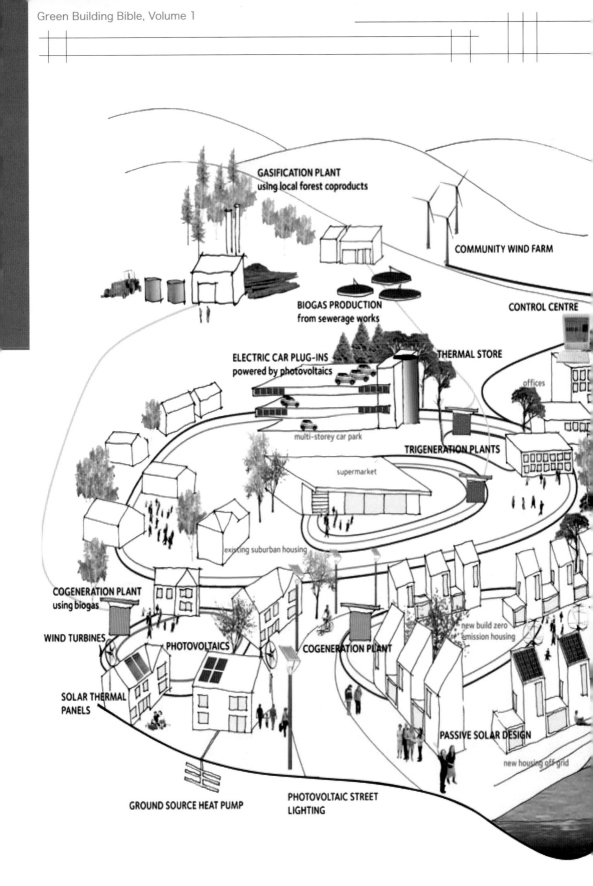

GASIFICATION PLANT
using local forest coproducts

COMMUNITY WIND FARM

BIOGAS PRODUCTION
from sewerage works

CONTROL CENTRE

ELECTRIC CAR PLUG-INS
powered by photovoltaics

THERMAL STORE

offices

multi-storey car park

TRIGENERATION PLANTS

supermarket

existing suburban housing

COGENERATION PLANT
using biogas

new build zero
emission housing

WIND TURBINES

PHOTOVOLTAICS

COGENERATION PLANT

SOLAR THERMAL
PANELS

PASSIVE SOLAR DESIGN

new housing off-grid

GROUND SOURCE HEAT PUMP

PHOTOVOLTAIC STREET
LIGHTING

© Green Building Press

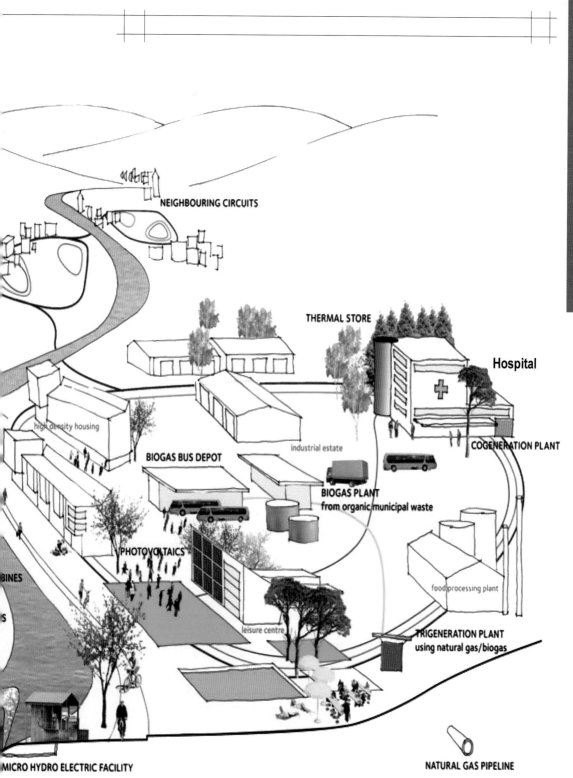

NEIGHBOURING CIRCUITS

THERMAL STORE

Hospital

high density housing

industrial estate

COGENERATION PLANT

BIOGAS BUS DEPOT

BIOGAS PLANT
from organic municipal waste

PHOTOVOLTAICS

food processing plant

BINES

leisure centre

S

TRIGENERATION PLANT
using natural gas/biogas

MICRO HYDRO ELECTRIC FACILITY

NATURAL GAS PIPELINE

A vision of a decentralised society - image courtesy of Greenpeace.

achieved thus far. This is best done through domestic leadership, recognising a moral duty and a legitimate self-interest in incubating and disseminating technologies, skills and knowledge appropriate to both international development and climate change mitigation.

Despite ticking all the boxes for the UK's stated energy policy goals, barriers to DE remain immense. Market 'liberalisation' rests on the unspoken presumption that expensive centralised infrastructure should be taken as given in the UK electricity markets, where meaningful competition thrives only at the wholesale level. The only real choice is between different providers of centralised power. The regulatory regime acts as a ring of steel around

tory regime is therefore needed, alive to the needs of the small and innovative.

The lack of any such framework is painfully predictable given the bizarre misalignment between the electricity regulator Ofgem's remit and the stated key energy policy goals set out in the 2003 Energy White Paper. Ofgem has just a singular primary remit to protect consumer interests - no one needs a crystal ball to predict the outcome. The government' failure to correct this misalignment in turn reflects the reality of its own fractured approach to energy policy in which disparate grant-aided initiatives are layered over a fundamentally faulty system.

Readers may be familiar with the local low-

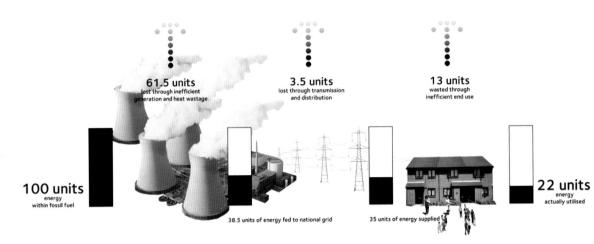

61.5 units
lost through inefficient generation and heat wastage

3.5 units
lost through transmission and distribution

13 units
wasted through inefficient end use

100 units
energy within fossil fuel

22 units
energy actually utilised

38.5 units of energy fed to national grid

35 units of energy supplied

Centralised energy infrastructures waste more than two thirds of the energy available from fossil fuels. This accounts for more than 20% of the UK's CO_2 emissions. Diagram courtesy of Greenpeace.

business as usual; far from supporting technological advance and market innovation, the UK's model of liberalisation serves to entrench an outdated system because its rules perpetuate and reward the characteristics of old technologies. DE faces real barriers to fair competition at the retail level where it encounters protectionism, totally inappropriate regulation and a failure to reflect the economic benefits of DE back to the DE provider. Under a DE scenario a million potential consumers of energy are also a million potential suppliers. A whole new regula-

carbon networks set up by Woking Borough Council. Woking overcame many of the barriers to DE through the use of private electricity wires. These are relatively cheap to lay – particularly in a new build situation. Yet, in typical fashion, the use of private wires is unfairly constrained by regulation – a situation described as anti-competitive by a House of Lords Select Committee. Greenpeace agrees and wants to see these barriers lifted to enable the investment community to back massive innovation in the Energy Services Company

© Green Building Press

sector (or indeed in the existing electricity sector) where entire local low-carbon micro-grids could be established, free to sell their power directly to thousands of consumers.

Much remains to be done to make low carbon electricity networks common place. While some small steps in support of DE have recently been taken by Ofgem, full implementation of a DE model demands an explicit primary obligation on the regulator to deliver a sustainable electricity system. The electricity market needs fundamental reform to promote meaningful competition and support and stimulate technological advances. At the same time the economic regulation of the electricity sector must be overhauled to discourage the currently profitable expansion of the centralised grid.

Crucially alongside instigating regulatory reform, the government must urgently take systematic measures to empower the new generation of energy actors who can offer the real alternative to dirty centralised power. These new actors include architects and building mangers who have such a critical role to play in driving forward the DE revolution.

The UK's ambitious house-building programme presents an exceptional and immediate opportunity to pump-prime the DE marketplace and to experiment with low carbon microgrids. Unfortunately the government has not introduced any mandatory measures for low or zero carbon technologies for new buildings in the recent revision to Part L of the Building Regulations. So much for sustainable communities. Some hope had been invested in the government's Microgeneration Strategy consultation. Why not support the full range of DE technologies like the 130kW cogeneration plant deployed at BedZED or indeed, massive DE plant in industrial buildings that can deliver significant emissions reduction in one shot?

UK CO_2 emissions are on the rise for the third year running. Scientists at the government's own conference on the science of climate change held in Exeter in 2005, warned we have just 20 years to put CO_2 on a steep

downward trajectory if we are to avert committing ourselves to 'dangerous' climate change by 2050, with appalling consequences for billions around the world. Climate change is simply too important to be left to politicians and industry insiders. The battle for the climate will never be won in the global political circus with its grand conferences and grand rhetoric. Nor will it be won by pleading for the good will of the immensely powerful global centralised power industry. It will be won on the ground by real people with real projects, making real changes to the practices of real professions.

The Decentralising Power agenda draws a neat battle line in the fight for the future. On one side of the line is the old industry with its antiquated systems and practices and its staggering political influence. On the other are increasing numbers of people demanding to be empowered to take the necessary action in the face of climate change. Phenomenal resources and influences are pitched against those of us seeking sharp cuts in emissions. The pressure is on to form new networks and alliances around a common agenda and to collectively make our demands heard loud and clear above the clamour of vested interests. 'Decentralising power' is the strategy Greenpeace has put forward to unite us. We urgently need those in the buildings professions to take their place at the frontline of the energy battle. ◔

References
1. Small is Profitable, Amory Lovins et.al. ISBN 1881071073 Earthscan.

Greenpeace: www.greenpeace.org.uk

See also: 'Minimise electricity use' in Chapter 7.

Clean, green energy

Green energy is energy that comes from clean, renewable, sources such as the sun, wind, waves, water (hydro) biomass and geothermal energy from the ground. The 'clean' refers to the fact that it has negligible emissions, not only of the key greenhouse gasses that are driving climate change, of which the main one is carbon dioxide[1], but also that it does not produce polluting gases, such as sulphur dioxide that causes acid rain, or nitrogen dioxide that is an important constituent in air pollution. **Sue Roaf** examines the market of clean green energy ...

The term renewable describes sources of energy that are driven by the sun, and the resulting climate and weather systems it creates on the planet. The two main influences on climate are latitude and the location of a site in relation to land and water masses. Weather is driven by the climate, and the regional and local micro-climates of a site, shaped by its location in relation to the local and regional geomorphology. The available energy from the sun, wind, waves and water will result from the climate and weather of a site while the biomass energy sources are additionally influenced by man's management of the land and water. Geothermal energy is also available, based on heat from the Earth's interior.

All renewable energy sources arise from repeating natural processes, in contrast to the very finite nature of the global fossil fuel reserves. The latter are largely past their 'peak' of production, forcing oil and gas prices up globally and providing a strong impetus for the swift move to renewable energy use[2]. This is most important for the built environment that uses up to 50% of all energy produced on the earth.

Some sources also include nuclear power and energy from waste incineration as green power but neither are anywhere near carbon neutral power supplies due to the high energy costs of maintaining these large plants, and

their highly polluting processes. Energy purchased from green energy suppliers cannot be technically counted as 'green' energy because the carbon emission reductions of the suppliers have typically already been included in the supplier's quotas and cannot then be double counted into the customer's carbon quotas. What is important for a site is what its potential energy yield is from the different sources of energy.

Energy yields

The site: every site will have a different range of opportunities to harvest green energy. For wind energy, the continental location of a site is important, as coastal sites typically have far higher windspeeds than inland locations, also the micro-climate (for wind generators). This is discussed at length in Volume 2 of the Green Building Bible. It is vital that turbines are not shaded by an adjacent building, mountain or trees. The temperature of the geothermal heat available to a building will depend not only on latitude, but also on the location of the system. Ground temperatures on the cold side of a mountain can be many degrees lower than those on its sunny side. Solar energy is considered the best renewable source for cities, as the PV systems can be fitted to building roofs with minimal infra-structural costs, although the higher levels of air pollution over a city may lower the overall yield.

The building: for solar energy, latitude plays a major role in the potential yield of a solar array, as will the terrain and weather around a building. But for solar, the design of the building itself is key. The angle of a roof on which the panels are located, and the building orientation, help in optimising the potential yield of the solar systems of buildings[3], as does its location in relation to adjacent structures that may shade it from the sun.

Temporal yields: in designing renewable

This page and next: various views of community renewables installed on and around homes and offices in Kirklees, as part of a drive to make the region less dependant on grid power. The initiative has won the authority an Ashden award 2006.

energy systems in the rapidly changing climates of the 21st century it is vital to design for the future as well as the present. There is no use designing micro-hydro systems for rivers that have catchment areas that are vulnerable to summer droughts for instance, or are supplied by rapidly disappearing snow and ice reserves. In the UK we are lucky to have excellent scenarios of what future climates might look like[4] and a very well informed Environment Agency that has detailed information on the seasonal flows and trends of all the rivers in the UK[5]. For those who want to design for future climates, see the excellent design weather guide produced by CIBSE[6].

A major characteristic of any weather driven renewable energy system is that it is impossible to predict the weather. The supply of wind, water or sun are intermittent and so are their resulting energy supplies. The UK national system of energy supply is dominated by a monolithic 'national grid' supplying either gas, or electricity, generated from coal, hydro, gas or oil fuelled power stations. This system is hugely inefficient, with only around 20%-40% of the original energy source being actually delivered to the building due to losses in the generating plant (up to 70%) and the distribution network (around 10-20%).

Electricity blackouts are becoming more common around the world as regional grids buckle under the strain of excessive demand, and the cut back on generation capacity imposed by privatised energy companies driven by the need for shareholder profits. 20th century society became dependant, for its ordinary functioning, on a constant, and high quality, supply of electricity that is totally reliable (without interruptions); with a high power quality (relating to frequency and voltage stability, waveform abnormalities etc.) and rapidly repairable. This type of supply will be increasingly difficult to produce and we are becoming more concerned with issues of the security of supply and the environmental impacts of the supply in light of the climate change and peak oil challenges. In this emerging '21st century' market micro-grids, supplying embedded generation, are a very attractive social, environmental and commercial proposition.

Embedded generation (also known as distributed embedded or dispersed genera-

© Green Building Press

tion) is electricity generation connected to a local distribution network, rather than the high voltage national transmission network, or grid. distributed generators are mostly - though not exclusively - those generating power from environmentally friendly renewable energy sources, (including small hydro, wind and solar power) or from combined heat and power (CHP) plants.

Historically, distribution networks have been designed to take electricity from the high voltage transmission system and to deliver it to customers. The management of this one-way flow of energy has been termed 'passive'. In order for the networks to accommodate increased levels of distributed generation, the energy flow in both directions has to be managed - both to the customer and from the distributed generator. This is termed 'active' management. This move from 'passive' to 'active' management is a major challenge.

The nature of distribution networks today means that many smaller generators find it difficult and expensive to connect to networks that were not designed to accommodate them. The output from a single PV house into the grid is little more than noise on the line, but when the whole street has solar hot water systems and PV arrays, then the solar contribution to powering houses down the street becomes significant, especially if the householders are out all day at work during the week but at home during the week end. Matching the load profiles to the electricity supply becomes a real challenge, as a range of very 'frisky' energy sources cutting in and out of the supply, causes difficulties and is the subject of extensive research.

In order to solve the supply and quality issues associated with distributed micro-grids much work is currently being done in the UK but there is no reason why in the coming years we should not move back to the old 20th century systems of the local 'municipal grid'. Perhaps in the 21st century, as we adapt to live with the rapidly changing climate, and to kick our addiction to dwindling fossil fuels, we will increasingly move to community owned and controlled grids, to supply our energy from a

cocktail of embedded, clean, renewable energy generators, many of which may be located in or around our own homes. ✆

References

1. For extensive and authoritative information on climate change and its impacts see:
www.ukcip.org.uk and www.ipcc.ch

2. For more information on the Peak Oil and Gas issue see: www.peakoil.net and www.energycrisis.com and for books see:
www.eci.ox.ac.uk/renewables/UKWind-Report.pdf

3. www.macslab.com/optsolar.html

4. www.ukcip.org.uk

5. www.environment-agency.gov.uk

6. www.cibse.org/index.cfm?go=publications.
view&PubID=317&L1=164
www.lboro.ac.uk/crest/education-modulespecs.html

A good place to start researching your own local renewable energy needs and potential is the website of the Centre for Alternative Technology - a pioneer in this field, providing information, education, courses and consultancy: 01654 705989 www.cat.org.uk; or email: info@cat.org.uk

Grants

Low Carbon Building Programme: 0800 915 7722 www.lowcarbonbuildings.org.uk Grant scheme covering wind, hydro, solar PV and more. Grants for householders, small businesses, community schemes, and larger projects.

Scottish Householders and Community Renewable: 0800 138 8858 www.est.org.uk/schri

Energy Saving Trust: You may be eligible for additional local grants: 0800 512 012 www.est.org.uk/myhome

Related organisations

British Photovoltaic Association, information about permissions and approvals (G83/1) needed for grid connected systems: 01908 442291
www.greenenergy.org.uk/pvuk2/

British Wind Energy Association promote wind power. Web site includes advice on siting a turbine and connecting it to the grid: 020 7689 1960
www.bwea.com

British Solar Trade Association: 01908 442290;
www.greenenergy.org.uk/sta/

Green energy suppliers

Two companies who both supply and buy back electricity from renewable sources:

Ecotricity: 0800 0326 100
www.ecotricity.co.uk

Good Energy: 0845 456 1640
www.good-energy.co.uk

OFGEM (Office of Gas and Electricity Markets) regulates renewable obligation certificates (ROCs): 020 7901 7000 www.ofgem.gov.uk

Buildings are for life!

Just like human beings, buildings need to be allowed to develop over time, to mature, grow and evolve; otherwise they often deteriorate and become obsolete. In the very interesting book How Buildings Learn, Stewart Brand talks about 'blue jeans buildings' – buildings that age honestly and elegantly over time. But to create such buildings we need to accept them as evolving entities, whose design and construction phase is just the start of a long process of evolution over their life. Yet this is alien to the current ways in which buildings are designed and procured in most countries. **Mark Gorgolewski** reports ...

For most buildings, it is impossible to consider or even to know, at the design stage, all the different potential activities and uses that they may be used for over an extended life. The modernist idea of form following function becomes redundant when we accept that a building may have many changing functions over its operational life, and that even if it is used for the same purpose, such as an office building, for example, the nature of office work changes at such a pace that the building is likely to accommodate a variety of different activities over its life. All we have to do is think of the changing nature of work over recent years to see how the demands on buildings are changing.

Shifting business practices, new technologies, and new management processes mean that buildings quickly become obsolete. Employers want working environments that are closed and private one day, then open and collaborative the next. Spaces that cannot accommodate this frustrate occupants and hamper business objectives. Adaptable interior workspaces are essential for companies likely to face uncertainty and change as markets shift.

So how should building designers respond to this challenge? First of all we must get away from the glossy journal notion of buildings

as style icons. So many buildings are photographed and reported in journals at the time they are completed, often before they are furnished and unoccupied. They are presented and analysed as abstract forms which are assumed to be at their best the moment they are completed, rather than functional and useful objects which develop, change and improve over time. There is little consideration of how well they actually work. Although recent interest in building performance, including the Probe studies[1], increased interest in how buildings operate, nevertheless there is little consideration by designers or critics of how well buildings work over time, and it is rare for an architectural magazine or journal to go back and look at how a prominent building is performing over time.

Right from the start of the design process, there is a need to consider how buildings will perform and change over time. This inevitably requires that buildings can adapt and change over their life to meet new demands on their spaces, structures and systems. As Croxton[2] (2003) has written: "If a building doesn't

The Millennium Dome in London which was apparently built with little consideration for what may happen to it after the initial short term use was finished!

support change and reuse, you have only an illusion of sustainability. You may have excellent building orientation and other energy-saving

© Green Building Press

systems, but the building must also be able to be flexible to meet a change in curriculum."

Buildings are complex assemblies of many different resources, with a large investment of materials, labour, and energy. A building which allows its parts to change over time will place a lighter load on natural resources and provide better value to future generations. Buildings that are not adaptable, are destined to become lost resources more quickly. Adaptability takes advantage of the embodied energy of the components, as less processing or transport is required if a building's life is extended.

Open building

A building is more adaptable when it can be easily modified, extended, and strengthened to allow a new or changed use. So how can a designer help to achieve this? 'Open building' is an approach to the design of buildings that recognises that the contemporary built environment must allow both stability and change. The open building approach includes the idea that the built environment is in constant transformation and that change must be recognized and understood. It recognises that the built environment is the product of an ongoing, never ending design process that includes many partici- pants, including users / inhabitants making design decisions as well as professionals. Open building[3] suggests that buildings should be separated into the 'base building' which consists of the more permanent parts, and 'fit- out' that changes more often. To achieve this, the connections between technical systems must allow easy replacement of one system, with another performing the same function. This approach allows the designer to consider strategies for both long term and short term change.

Design for adaptability

Terrence Riley, in The Un-private House[4] (1999), suggests that a "rigorous distinction between structural and pragmatic elements in planning and construction . . . would allow for transformation of houses over time as owners'

situations change". This suggests a clear sepa- ration between different systems in the building and the possibility of easily replacing and updating systems when they become redundant without significantly affecting the rest of the building.

Early in the design process, the design team should identify what type of changes may take place and how these could be accommodated in the building. Through this process alternatives should be discussed and a range of possibilities developed that will help achieve adaptability. The possibilities will vary for each project. The following are a series of approaches identified from various technical studies that can help to make a building more adaptable:

- minimize the number of internal structural components (columns and load bearing walls) to create flexible open space
- optimise structural grids to allow changing uses of space. Use simple structural grids with clear support lines
- allow some redundancy so that additions and changes to the building can be accommodated. Over-designed structural capacity may be appropriate to allow alternative uses and the option of extending the structure. Ensure that floor loads used in design reflect foreseeable changes in occupancy patterns
- separate structure and cladding to allow independent alteration and replacement.
- allow for good vertical circulation by lifts and stairs, and for service routing
- separate services into clearly accessible locations to allow easy change and upgrade. Raised floors can also permit easy upgrade of services. Integrate heating and electrical systems so they can easily be upgraded or replaced. These systems generally require far more regular replacement than other components of the building. Some over- provision of flexibility in service routing allows for future upgrade
- design with a building depth to allow for daylighting of the main spaces, and for a variety of different ways to divide up the spaces
- provide a "loose fit" to allow some

redundancy to accommodate future additions/changes
- consider what are appropriate floor to ceiling heights; offices require greater ceiling heights than residential buildings
- integrate finishes so they can be easily upgraded and replaced, without making access to other components difficult
- keep designs simple to help with future change; independent systems allow changes where necessary. Strong inter-dependence reduces the scope for change
- provide sufficient space for machinery needed for dismantling, renovation, and addition

expense to meet the evolving needs of occupants. It means designing a building to allow its different parts to change, each in its own timescale. Incorporating adaptability into a building during initial construction can save time, money, and inconvenience when changes are needed or desired later in the life of a building, and can significantly extend its life. ◔

References

1. *www.usablebuildings.co.uk*
2. Croxton, (2003) Architectural Record, Aug 2003, pg 147.
3. *http://open-building.org*
4. Riley, Terrence. (1999). The Un-private House. New York: Museum of Modern Art.

This building, in the suburbs of London, has been used for many different functions over the last 30 years, showing the ability to be adapted to a variety of uses.

- avoid irreversible processes. Reversible mechanical fixings - bolts and screws - can usually be removed; adhesives, welding, and cement often cannot
- avoid complex composite materials that are difficult to separate. This includes some treatments and finishes applied on site.
- incorporate each component so that it can easily be removed and recycled when obsolete. Use demountable internal partitions
- consider drainage carefully as this often limits changes to building plan.

Adaptable building incorporates, at the design and construction stage, the ability to make future changes easily and with minimum

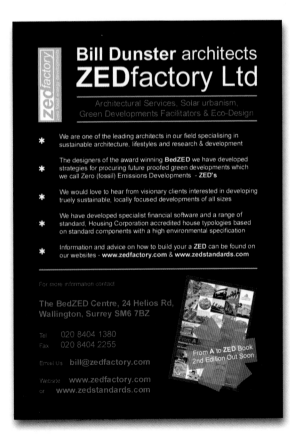

zedfactory

Bill Dunster architects
ZEDfactory Ltd

Architectural Services, Solar urbanism, Green Developments Facilitators & Eco-Design

* We are one of the leading architects in our field specialising in sustainable architecture, lifestyles and research & development

* The designers of the award winning BedZED we have developed strategies for procuring future proofed green developments which we call Zero (fossil) Emissions Developments - ZED's

* We would love to hear from visionary clients interested in developing truely sustainable, locally focused developments of all sizes

* We have developed specialist financial software and a range of standard, Housing Corporation accredited house typologies based on standard components with a high environmental specification

* Information and advice on how to build your a ZED can be found on our websites - www.zedfactory.com & www.zedstandards.com

For more information contact

The BedZED Centre, 24 Helios Rd, Wallington, Surrey SM6 7BZ

Tel   020 8404 1380
Fax   020 8404 2255

Email Us   bill@zedfactory.com

Website   www.zedfactory.com
or   www.zedstandards.com

From A to ZED Book 2nd Edition Out Soon

© Green Building Press

SOLAR HEATING

Thermal storage system

◆ Instant hot water on demand
◆ Rapid heat up from solar input
◆ Large heat storage capacity
◆ Solar contribution to space heating
◆ Ecologically friendly construction
◆ Buffer store for wood boilers

The only water store your building needs

Consolar large capacity thermal stores, with their patented stratification system, enable immediate use of solar heated water. The volume of hot water available is up to three times greater than conventional thermal stores

Greenshop Solar Ltd, Bisley, Gloucestershire GL6 7BX
T: 08452 235440 F: 01452 770115 E: info@consolar.co.uk
www.consolar.co.uk

AURO
NATURAL PAINTS AND WOOD FINISHES

NATURAL PAINTS FROM START TO FINAL FINISH

YOU'LL BE HEAD OVER HEELS WITH OUR NATURAL PAINTS.

• Using only natural, plant and mineral raw ingredients we have a closed cycle of sustainability.

• Manufactured using solar energy and wind power to lower CO_2 factory emissions.

• Certified organically grown linseed oil is a major component of our paints and wood finishes.

• So pure, any left over paint can be dried and composted

• All of our finishes are micro-porous, allowing wood and plaster to breathe for a healthy living environment.

• Our water based, solvent free paints and wood finishes are hypoallergenic, making them great to use for allergy sufferers.

Please see our web for details of nearest stockists nationwide, or give us a call for a brochure, pricelist and expert advice.

www.auro.co.uk
tel: 01452 772020

*Auro UK, Cheltenham Rd, Bisley, Nr stroud Gloucester, GL6 7BX
email: sales@auro.co.uk*

Preserve and Enhance your Environment

the Green shop
PRODUCTS FOR A SUSTAINABLE FUTURE

Quality Environmentally Friendly Interior Paints and Finishes

- Auro Natural Paint
- Green Paints
- Earthborn Clay Paints
- Lime Earth Paints
- OS Colour Wood Treatments
- Holkham Linseed Paint
- La Tienda Pigments

+ 100's of other environmental products from solar torches and wind up radios to books and bodycare.

Go online or phone for a catalogue to see our full range

www.greenshop.co.uk
tel: 01452 770629

The Green Shop, Holbrook Garage, Cheltenham Rd, Bisley. Glos, GL6 7BX

the Green shop
PRODUCTS FOR A SUSTAINABLE FUTURE

a greener lifestyle for you and your home

natural paints
high quality, safe to use decorating products

body and home care
soaps, lotions and potions, eco-friendly cleaning

green books
green living, building, home and garden, crafts

energy saving
solar hot-water, light bulbs, battery chargers, PV panels

gifts and toys
solar radios and torches, fairtrade and recycled gifts

water saving
rainharvesting, low-flush loos

gardens
furniture, wormeries solar fountains and lights

visit us: at Holbrook Garage on Cheltenham Rd, near Bisley
01452 770629
enquiries@greenshop.co.uk
www.greenshop.co.uk
The Green Shop, Cheltenham Rd, Bisley, Glos, GL6 7BX

shop online or ask for our free catalogues

The COOPERATIVE BANK

move your
mortgage
somewhere greener

If you'd like a mortgage that's as good for the environment as it is for you, then switch to The Co-operative Bank.

Bank of England base rate plus 0.14%

4.64%
variable 2 year Tracker Mortgage

6.14%
standard variable rate after 2 years

6.1% APR
overall cost comparison

£499 application fee
Early repayment charges apply for the first 2 years

For every mortgage we arrange we make an annual donation to Climate Care, an organisation dedicated to helping stop climate change. These donations, equivalent to £250,000 in 2005, are used to offset over one fifth of the carbon dioxide generated by our customers' homes.

And it's not just the environment that benefits – remortgage with us and you'll naturally receive a great service and a range of additional benefits:

- Easy and hassle-free application
- Free legal and standard valuation fees
  (on a standard remortgage case using our recommended solicitors)
- Flexible repayments
- Daily interest calculation to keep your repayments as low as possible.

So if you'd like a mortgage that's better for both you and the planet, switch to The Co-operative Bank – it will be a great move.

YOUR Mortgage
yourmortgage.co.uk
2005-2006 AWARDS
EDITOR'S SPECIAL AWARD
THE CO-OPERATIVE BANK

to switch your mortgage call today on
0800 169 8652
www.co-operativebank.co.uk
we are here 8am to 9pm Mon to Fri and 9am to 5pm Sat. ref: 64363

YOUR HOME MAY BE REPOSSESSED IF YOU DO NOT KEEP UP REPAYMENTS ON YOUR MORTGAGE

The Co-operative Bank plc, (Registered No. 990937), P.O. Box 101, Balloon Street, Manchester M60 4EP. Calls may be monitored or recorded for security and training purposes. The Co-operative Bank plc is authorised and regulated by the Financial Services Authority.

The **CⓄOPERATIVE BANK**

[imagine]

Phil Basten with Richard Topham, Charles Topham Group Limited - 129 unit residential development Deakins Park Bolton

A bank that genuinely understands the needs of property professionals.

Now hold that thought.

If you're looking for property funding, The Co-operative Bank's Property Finance Unit offers fast decision making, flexibility and a creative approach.

Talk to us anytime, call
Phil Basten 07789 867380
Rob Dawson 07786 126045
www.co-operativebank.co.uk/corporate

PS 87% of our existing customers feel so good about their relationship with us that they would happily recommend us. (Source: Dataquest survey 2006)

Calls may be monitored or recorded for security or training purposes.
The Co-operative Bank is authorised and regulated by the Financial Services Authority (No.121885), subscribes to the Business Banking Code, is a member of the Financial Ombudsman Service and is licensed by the Office of Fair Trading (No.006110). Registered Office: The Co-operative Bank p.l.c., Head Office, P.O. Box 101, 1 Balloon Street, Manchester M60 4EP. Reg No. 990937.

charities | **property finance** | syndicated finance | public sector | asset finance | relationship banking | ethics as standard

Trends and direction

Politics

See also: 'A code for sustainable homes' later in this chapter.

Due to ongoing and predicted lifestyle changes, such as single occupancy homes, it is estimated that by 2016 we will need around three and a half million more new houses. Building new homes consumes vast amounts of energy, in terms of material production and transport – around 90,000kWh for the average new home. **Keith and Sally Hall** wonder how this consumption can continue ...

One of the findings of a report[1] carried out for the government revealed that the building of 50,000 new homes per year would add 6.4 million tonnes of CO_2 (on top of the 154 million tonnes already emitted by the domestic sector). It was suggested that eco homes could reduce this by 17%.

The One Million Sustainable Homes campaign, led by WWF, identified several barriers to the widespread adoption of more sustainable housing in the UK.

1. There is a lack of significant fiscal incentives and consumer demand and government grant schemes to encourage the installation of energy saving technologies have been slow, under-funded and overly bureaucratic.
2. Current building regulations and planning legislation do little to encourage sustainable building. The planning system could be changed to enable planners to refuse permission for projects that fail to reach high environmental standards.
3. Most investors and businesses just want a quick return and high profits. Few will do anything unless forced to do so as a result of legislation or encouraged by financial incentives.
4. There is little 'perceived' consumer demand for sustainable homes. However, a survey

in 2004 of home owners and occupiers by WWF and others[2] found an overwhelming (87%) interest in sustainable homes with 84% stating they would be prepared to pay up to 2% more for such a home.

5. Many feel that it costs too much to build sustainable homes but this is not always the case, as revealed in WWF's report 'One Planet Living in the Thames Gateway'[1]. This study compared current building standards of developing 200,000 homes with EcoHome, an environmental assessment scheme and Z2 (zero fossil energy, zero waste). The EcoHome 'Very Good' standard achieved a 32% reduction in CO_2 but cost only 2% extra to build. The Z2 (zero fossil energy, zero waste) achieved a 99% reduction in CO_2 emissions with just 10% extra build costs.

If future household expenditure is factored in, living in a sustainable home would actually be cheaper as well as offering the environmental and associated health benefits.

So what is the government doing? Surely, the government could sweep in the changes that we need to build eco homes? Sadly, there are too many businesses with vested interests, keen to make noises about sustainability but actually holding back the delivery of the necessary legislation and codes of conduct.

The government is certainly making a lot of noises about sustainability but it is clearly pushing with one hand and pulling back with the other. In 2003 its white paper on UK Energy established the need to tackle climate change as one of the central aims of energy policy, with an aim to reduce CO_2 emissions by 60% over the next 50 years; including the

© Green Building Press

use of renewable energy options and energy efficiency improvements. In the government's 2005 pre-budget report on 'Protecting the Environment', it accepted that climate change is one of the most serious risks facing the world and a major challenge for all countries. If it is not tackled the consequences are projected to be extremely damaging for the environment and the economy. In 2006[2] the government won a legal bid to force the EU to consider an increase in the amount of climate-changing pollution the UK can emit under the EU Emissions Trading Scheme (ETS). The UK wants to pump out an extra 20 million tonnes of CO_2 under the ETS between 2005 and 2008!

The government claims it is "committed to delivering sustainable growth and a better environment and to tackling the global challenge of climate change." However, despite apparently widespread support for tackling climate change, in reality signs are that 'we' remain disengaged and the government seems more intent on relying on voluntary measures. Whilst it supposedly recognises the significance of climate change, according to many eco groups and individuals, it is not doing enough to combat the effects. This certainly seems to be so when it fails to meet sustainability targets within its own departments. The Sustainable Development Commission's findings revealed that in the same year the government pledged to take a global lead on climate change, CO_2 emissions from its departments increased and the cabinet office was the worst polluter![3]

The government also believes that a building constructed to the new building regulations (spring 2006) will be 40% more energy efficient than ones built 5 years ago. However, the forthcoming regulations do not go far enough and the UK is still lagging far behind other European countries. A further concern, according to research by the BRE, is that up to 50% of new houses, supposedly built to the latest building regulation standards, still have problems with badly installed insulation resulting in significant heat losses[4]. There is therefore an urgent need to address this issue and ensure building regulation inspections check workmanship quality properly during construction.

It was disappointing to see the dropping of a well-supported proposal to include a clause in the last update of the building regulations (spring 2006) which would have ensured that all extensions needing planning consent would only be approved if energy efficiency measures were undertaken in the existing building. The government apparently scuppered the proposal because it was perceived to be too bureaucratic and regulatory for homeowners[4].

Organised foot dragging

As a result of pressure from big business and house builders only a voluntary Code for Sustainable Homes (put forward by a 'handpicked' group made up of business and organisation representatives) has been proposed, possibly based on the existing EcoHomes scheme. However, the voluntary nature of the code will probably ensure that it has as little take-up as the previous schemes it is likely to replace! For more information about the Code see 'Too little, too late or just the next stage?' later in this chapter.

Home information packs

Home information packs (HIPs), a government initiative, will be mandatory from 1 June 2007, for those selling property in England and Wales. The HIPs will include the terms of sale, evidence of title, copies of planning permissions and building regulation consents, warranties, guarantees, searches and an energy performance certificate. Voluntary home condition reports can also be included, but following a government u-turn these will not be mandatory.

References

1. *www.wwf.org.uk/sustainablehomes/*

2. *www.newbuilder.co.uk/news/NewsFullStory. asp?ID=1068*

3. *Leading by Example?* *www.sd-commission.org.uk/watchdog/*

4. *Radio 4, report 11 December 2005*

Regulation and legislation

Amendments to the Approved Documents (AD) of the Building Regulations are the big change in legislation, or you would certainly think so from the clamour created by their introduction in April 2006. But not so, says **Michael Smith**, they are not even legislation; the Approved Documents set out detailed practical guidance on ways of complying with the Building Regulations.

There are other pieces of legislation, however, already published in 2006, and some still in committee, which will affect the construction industry just as much as the Approved Documents seem to have done. Construction related legislation, which comes into force this year, is set to have wide ranging effects; some will support the Approved Documents, and other legislation will be entirely independent. This overview will centre on the Building Regulations and Approved Documents, and then work outwards. But first, who gave the go ahead to change the Building Regulations?

Section 1 of the Building Act 1984 (as amended), that's who! This enables building regulations to be made to secure the health, safety and welfare of building users, enhancing the conservation of fuel and power, protection of the environment, and facilitating sustainable development. The Building Regulations themselves, impose general functional requirements for building work carried out and are supported by technical guidance in the form of the Approved Documents, which are not legislation, but which set out detailed practical guidance on ways of complying with the Building Regulations.

The introduction of the **Approved Documents 2006** was a consequence of the application of the Building and Approved Inspectors (Amendment) Regulations 2006, which amends earlier building legislation. In particular the 2006 legislation implements articles 3 to 6 of the Energy Performance of Buildings Directive, and makes various unrelated amendments to the Building Regulations and Approved Inspectors Regulations. Approved Document L, 2006 – conservation of fuel and power, came into force on the 6th April, and is now split into 4 parts, New build L1A/L2A and Refurbishment L1B/L2B. AD L aims to ensure that reasonable provision is made for the conservation of fuel and power in buildings by limiting heat losses through the fabric of the building. Approved Document F, 2006 – Ventilation, also came into force on 6th April 2006. This new edition is mainly performance based, and focuses on ventilation of buildings with low air permeability, extra for domestic ventilation systems and for ventilating basements, and recommended air supply rates for offices.

Legislation not attached to the 'Approved Documents'

There are several sustainability issues that have been legislated for during this year. Of those currently in force; the Natural Environment and Rural Communities Act 2006, and the Climate Change and Sustainable Energy Act 2006, and are among the most important, as they seek to look after environment, and community.

The Natural Environment and Rural Communities Act, is primarily intended to implement key aspects of the government's Rural Strategy, published in July 2004. It also addresses a wider range of issues relating to the natural environment. The Act establishes an independent body, Natural England, responsible for conserving, enhancing and managing England's natural environment for the benefit of current and future generations. The Act makes provisions in respect of biodiversity, pesticides harmful to wildlife and the protection of birds. It also alters enforcement powers in connection with wildlife protection, and extends time limits for prosecuting certain wildlife offences.

© Green Building Press

The Climate Change and Sustainable Energy Act, focuses more on community, commissioning an annual report on greenhouse gas emissions, identifying national targets for microgeneration (modifying section 1 of the Sustainable Energy Act 2003), changing permitted development orders for residential microgeneration, reporting on the energy efficiency of residential accommodation, extending time limits for prosecutions relating to environmentally unfriendly emissions, and reporting on advances in dynamic demand technologies. The Act further intends to monitor and reduce carbon emissions by promoting community energy projects and electricity from renewable sources.

There are always, in any year, many new Statutory Instruments (SI). These cover amendments to existing legislation, and updates to certain areas of Acts, not considered at the time of original drafting. There are relatively few SIs relating to sustainability, due to the massive amounts of legislation in this area in recent years.

The Boiler (Efficiency) (Amendment) Regulations 2006 (SI 2006/170), aims to exempt combined heat and power (CHP) units, from the requirements of the Boiler (Efficiency) Regulations 1993. This amendment affects cogeneration units of all sizes, but is most likely to affect microCHP units, which have an electrical output below 50kW.

Landfill Tax (Amendment) Regulations 2006 (SI 2006/865) came into force on 1st April 2006, amending regulation 31 of the Landfill Tax Regulations 1996, increasing the maximum credit that landfill site operators may claim against their landfill tax liability when contributing through the Landfill Tax Credit Scheme (LTCS).

The Contaminated Land (England) Regulations 2006 (SI 2006/1380), seek to consolidate the provisions of the Contaminated Land (England) Regulations 2000 and the Contaminated Land (England) (Amendment) Regulations 2001. The regulations also set out provisions relating to the identification and remediation of contaminated land under Part 2A of the Environmental Protection Act 1990.

Bills

Bills are pieces of legislation, which are still being heard by the House of Commons or House of Lords, and are yet to be voted upon. There are a lot of bills pending, whether this is due to filibustering or a plain lack of parliamentary sittings, only time will tell. The following are a roundup of UK public bills, relating to sustainability, which were due to be heard or voted on around 2006.

The Climate Change Bill (No 45 of 2005) aims to combat climate change by setting annual targets for the reduction of carbon dioxide emissions until 2050 and to place duties on the prime minister regarding the reporting on, and achievement of, those targets. The Bill also aims to provide certain powers to MPs, with regard to ensuring carbon dioxide emissions are reduced, and to set targets for energy efficiency, the generation of energy from renewable sources, combined heat and power and microgeneration.

Climate Change (Contraction and Convergence) Bill (No 92 of 2005), aims to make provision for the adoption of a policy of combating climate change in accordance with the principles of contraction and convergence.

Dynamic Demand Appliances Bill (HL) (No 184 of 2005-06), which will make provision about the possibilities for implementation and use of domestic and commercial dynamic demand appliances.

The Energy Bill (No 129 of 2005-06) seeks to establish a Renewable Energy Authority, and to lay upon the Authority a duty to promote the use of renewable energy and energy conservation.

The Greenbelt Reform Bill (No 44 of 2005-06), seeks to further protect, from unwanted development, the area of green belt around

Britain's cities.

The Management of Energy in Buildings Bill (No 22 of 2005-06) seeks to make provisions for the promotion of renewable and sustainable energy, energy efficiency in buildings and the alleviation of fuel poverty.

The Sustainable Communities Bill (No 122 of 2005-06), intends to make provisions for local authorities to submit plans in connection with promoting the sustainability of local communities, to provide for parish councils and other persons to participate in the formulation of such plans, and to specify the indicators by which the sustainability of local communities may be measured.

Don't be fooled, however; there will not be time to hear every bill due to be placed before parliament, so some will not be heard; some may indeed time out altogether. It is up to MPs to push for hearings, and lobbying your own MP will help this process immensely.

Further reading

Climate Change and Sustainable Energy Act 2006 (Ch.19): www.opsi.gov.uk/acts/acts2006/20060019.htm

Natural Environment and Rural Communities Act 2006 (Ch. 16): www.opsi.gov.uk/acts/acts2006/20060016.htm

Building and Approved Inspectors (Amendment) regulations 2006 (SI 2006/652): www.opsi.gov.uk/si/si2006/20060652.htm

Contaminated land (England) (Amendment) Regulations 2001 (SI 2001/663): www.opsi.gov.uk/si/si2001/20010663.htm

Building (Approved Inspectors etc) Regulations 2000 (SI 2000/2532): www.opsi.gov.uk/si/si2000/20002532.htm

Building Regulations 2000 (SI 2000/2531): www.opsi.gov.uk/si/si2000/20002531.htm

Contaminated Land (England) Regulations 2000 (SI 2000/227): www.opsi.gov.uk/si/si2000/20000227.htm

Energy Performance of Buildings Directive (EPBD) (2002/91/EC): http://digbig.com/4mbes

The EcoHouse - Britain's Original and Leading Green Showhome

eco house

• Eco showhome
• Hundreds of ideas for your new build or existing home
• Organic, permaculture garden

Open Wed-Fri: 2pm-5pm
Sat & Sun: 10am-5pm
Contact: 0116 254 5489 or
ecohouse@gwll.org.uk

www.gwll.org.uk/ecohouse

Putting the heat back into Ventilation

Kair™
Ventilation Limited
DOMESTIC HEAT RECOVERY VENTILATION

UP TO 90% HEAT RECOVERED
INCREASED SAP RATING
IMPROVED AIR QUALITY
PART F 2006 COMPLIANT
EST APPROVED PRODUCTS
INCREASED HEATING PERFORMANCE
HEAT RECYCLING
LOW ENERGY USE
WHISPER QUIET OPERATION
SECURE & HEALTHY VENTILATION
INCREASED ECOHOME RATING

www.kair.co.uk
CONTACT TEL - 08451 662240

SINGLE ROOM THROUGH THE WALL SOLUTIONS

APARTMENT AND BUNGALOW SOLUTIONS

WHOLE HOUSE SOLUTIONS

Enhanced capital allowances

Enhanced Capital Allowances (ECAs) are a tax relief given through the tax system by reducing the taxable profits of the business. The ECA scheme builds on existing statutory provisions, under which businesses may obtain tax relief, in the form of capital allowances, for their investment in plant and machinery. Capital allowances allow the costs of capital assets to be written off against a business's taxable profits.

The Energy Technology list (ETL) is part of the ECA scheme for energy saving investments, which the Carbon Trust manages on behalf of Defra. The ECA scheme is a tax relief that enables businesses to claim 100% first-year capital allowances on investments in energy saving equipment listed on the Energy Technology List.

For those of you in business, this means that any product you buy that is listed on the ETL, whether it's a boiler, refrigerated display cabinet or air conditioners, you could claim an ECA against your taxable profits during the period of investment.

The criteria for the ETL changes annually, yet new products are added each month.

Whether you are a purchaser or manufacturer wanting to register your product for inclusion on the ETL, to find out how you can save your business money: **www.eca.gov.uk/etl**

There is also a Water Technology List for water saving technologies installed by businesses: **www.eca-water.gov.uk**

ARCHITYPE

20 years experience of cutting edge sustainability and high quality design

Taplow Meditation Centre

National Memorial Arboretum

Seashells Children's Centre

Stroud Cohousing

The Genesis Project

Community Media Centre

contact

london office   t 020 7403 2889 e london@architype.co.uk
west office   t 01594 825775   e west@architype.co.uk

www.architype.co.uk

Conserving fuel and power

It has been a long time coming, but in recent years the government has acknowledged that action is crucial if we are to preserve the environment and achieve a sustainable future for ourselves and generations to come. It has followed this through with legislation aimed at cutting CO_2 emissions, and has set challenging targets to be met by 2010 and 2050. But if they have seen the light, have they also found the way to reach it? **John Garbutt** reviews the new building regulations (England & Wales) for the conservation of fuel and power & proposed building standards (Scotland) for energy.

It is widely recognised that there are four main global environmental sustainability issues: global warming, non-renewable resource depletion, toxic pollution and ozone depletion, and that these global issues far outweigh any local environmental sustainability issues in their need for immediate attention and potential impact from inaction.

Recent studies have shown that the first three issues are essentially one. The extraction and consumption (burning) of fossil fuels is by far the most significant contributor to global warming, non-renewable resource depletion and toxic pollution.

60% of fossil fuels are used to heat buildings in the UK, half of this in housing. Therefore it is argued that environmental sustainability comes down to two main issues: reduce fossil fuel use and specify zero ODP products.

By far the most economical method of reducing fossil fuel use is to reduce space heating demand. The investment for renewable energy sources only becomes convincing once space heating demand is minimised, as capital costs may be prohibitive to most. Furthermore, the renewables industry, arguably, does not have the capacity to meet mass market demand.

There are two main methods of reducing space heating demand: reduce heat losses through the building fabric and reduce heat losses from unintentional air-leakage. There is a whole raft of incentives that can be used to achieve this aim. The 'way' of course, is through legislation, and one of the biggest legislative weapons in this instance is the use of building regulations and standards to make our buildings, both domestic and non-domestic, much more energy efficient.

To this end new Approved Documents L (ADLs) to the Building Regulations for England & Wales were launched in April 2006. It is claimed that the new Approved Documents will lead to an improvement in the energy efficiency of new buildings (and hence a reduction in

© Green Building Press

the carbon emissions they would otherwise produce) of around 20%.

The 'truth', however is a slightly different matter. The construction industry struggled to implement the 2002 edition of ADL. The main problem appeared to be the sheer lack of capacity within the building control system to ensure that Approved Documents L were being adhered to. It is early days, but the building control system does not appear to have taken kindly to the new Approved Documents either.

Research has uncovered that a majority of building control officers (BCOs) consider that the new Approved Documents are far too complicated and unwieldy and that many building control bodies (BCBs) expect to take at least six months to get their heads around the complexities. Indeed I am aware of stories of a small number of BCBs that are point blank refusing to adopt the new Approved Documents and are instead 'inventing' their own set of elemental Standards for people to apply or simply retaining the old 2002 version of the Approved Documents. So much for progress!

Now, call me smug, but the Office of the Deputy Prime Minister (now metamorphosed into the Department for Communities and Local Government, or DCLG, since the demise of John Prescott), which was responsible for the new Approved Documents L, was warned that the proposed ADLs were far too complicated for BCOs to implement and builders to compre-hend. But pig-headedly, it was determined to stick to the course that it had set. Well now the chicken is well and truly coming home to roost. Will the ADLs achieve a 20% reduction in CO_2 emissions? I doubt it. Maybe 5% if the DCLG is lucky.

The saddest thing is that Scotland actually listened and the consultation for the new 2007 version of Section 6 (Energy) to the Building Standards deals with the issues, that London arrogantly ignored, in a wonderfully simple and elegant fashion. True Scot's pragmatism in action.

Approved Documents L have been split further into 4 parts, with newbuild and refur-bishment being treated separately for both dwellings and non-domestic constructions. This gives Approved Document L1a for new dwellings, Approved Document L1b for work on existing dwellings and similarly Approved Document L2a and Approved Document L2b for buildings other than dwellings. The docu-ments themselves give relatively minimal information compared with previous editions, with supplementary documents providing the detailed guidance.

There is no longer be a simple elemental or target U-value method of compliance, as the Energy Performance of Buildings Directive demands that performance standards are set for buildings as a whole, rather than for construction and services elements. This, in itself, is a logical next step towards optimizing energy performance. New methods of calcula-tion for 'whole building CO_2 emissions' have been introduced and compliance for new-build can be demonstrated using only these methods. These calculations consider a very wide range of performance issues, e.g. fabric U-values, air-tightness, heating system efficiency, lighting ...

The new method of calculation for new-build dwellings (SAP 2005) is relatively straightfor-ward, based on the old Standard Assessment Procedure (SAP), modified to include the ability to account for renewable energy supply. A target CO_2 emissions figure is calculated by putting the dimensions of your proposed building into SAP 2005 as if it were designed to the 2002 Approved Document L1, calculat-ing the CO_2 emissions and then taking 20% off the resulting figure. A building meets the requirements of ADL1a if its CO_2 emissions, as determined by SAP 2005, meets or betters this target figure.

There is similarly one standard calcula-tion methodology for new-build non-dwellings called SBEM or simplified building energy model, although others may be used if they meet certain criteria. Compliance targets will work in much the same way as for the new

Approved Document L1a. Approved Document L2a (new-build) will contain a set of notional values for the parameters in the calculation method. These notional values have been set at the 2002 Approved Document L2 elemental method standards. By assigning these notional values to the elements of a building, a user will apply the calculation method to produce a base target. The base target is then reduced by a factor to reduce CO_2 emissions from 2002 levels, and a factor to encourage renewables, and the resulting figure is the actual target. The performance of all elements can then be varied and, provided that the final building meets or beats the target when it is put through the calculation method, compliance is achieved.

However, unlike SAP 2005, official software for SBEM has yet to be finalised, which has left the market in limbo. The gap has been filled by commercial software suppliers, but the costs of this commercial software may be beyond the pockets of many. This, more than any other, is symptomatic of the unholy shambles that is the implementation of the new ADLs.

In recognition of the fact that energy use should be minimised before renewables are considered, fall back or worst allowable values are given for building fabric U-values and air-tightness. These have been set at the Elemental Method U-values from the 2002 Approved Documents L1 & L2.

Wall U-value	0.35W/m²K
Roof U-value	0.25W/m²K
Floor U-value	0.25W/m²K
Glazing U-value	2.20W/m²K

However, it has been and will continue to be argued by many commentators, that these values are too high if combined with renewables to force a building into compliance. And that is the real loop-hole that has been left wide open.

Firstly, designers could end up creating buildings that have relatively poor fabric measures and compensate with the specification of oversized renewable energy sources. The overall capital cost would be much greater and it would be difficult to cost-effectively improve the fabric

performance at a later date.

The second consideration is that fabric measures by their very nature tend to be long term assets (60 to 100 years minimum). Heating systems, including renewables, tend to be relatively short term (10-20 years). Most buildings that incorporate renewable energy supply will still require a secondary heating system. What happens to a building's Approved Document L compliance when the renewable supply breaks down and the owner can't afford to replace it or have it fixed? Reliance is placed on the secondary system, which will almost certainly have a much greater CO_2 impact.

The obvious solution would be to assume the CO_2 emissions of the secondary heating system in proving compliance for the building, but this would ignore the benefits of renewable supply. This, being politically unacceptable, means that the fall back U-values should have been tightened to a level which obviates the possibilities illustrated above. It is suggested that the following would be more appropriate:

Wall U-value	0.30W/m²K
Loft U-value	0.14W/m²K
Other roof U-value	0.22W/m²K
Floor U-value	0.25W/m²K
Glazing U-value	2.00W/m²K

The nature of the calculations themselves, and the many possible different permutations, bring much greater complexity to the whole process than in the past. No longer will anyone be able to use a straightforward set of U-values to be certain of complying. Far from the apparent freedom of trading off the thermal efficiency of the building fabric against other CO_2 efficient elements, people are forced to design by complex calculation methods, which will prove extremely problematical. In reality a designer may have to make 5 to 10 attempts at a calculation to get to a stage where the building in question complies with Approved Documents L.

The complexity of calculating (let alone achieving) compliance, and inadequate guidance, spell bad news for the smaller builder/designer. What was required was a set of robust simple rules embedded in the Approved Documents which, if used, would guarantee compliance with Approved Document L in 99% of cases when the building in question is put to the test via the calculation methods.

And that is exactly what Scotland has proposed. The consultation paper for the new 2007 Section 6 (Energy) takes a very similar approach to compliance and integration of the Energy Performance of Buildings Directive (EPBD), with one small but enormously significant change. Instead of using the elemental parameters from the current Section 6 to create an emission rate, which is then reduced by a percentage to create the target emission figure, it is proposed that a set of new 2007 elemental standards are used for the notional building put into SAP, and that the emissions figure created becomes directly the target. This means that if a designer creates a building to

the proposed 2007 elemental values, then when it is put through SAP, it is guaranteed to comply. If the designer wishes to change some of the parameters, he is free to do so, as long as the target emissions is equalled or bettered. Thus we get a simple set of values to design to, with guaranteed compliance, and the flexibility and whole building emissions led approach required by the EPBD. Simple, understandable, effective, buildable and enforceable!

I wonder how long it is since Scotland got one over on the English with so much global importance as this. Perhaps we all should lobby for direct rule from Edinburgh in all matters relating to building! ☙

Some of the issues raised here are discussed in more detail in 'Confusing Building Regulations' in Chapter 4.

ecoarc

ecological architecture practice

Eco Arc enjoys working with clients to design beautiful and healthy zero CO_2 buildings built to the highest technical and spatial standards incorporating best practice in low energy solar design, utilizing renewable wind & solar technologies all within a holistic frame work.

Past Projects include: The National Trust's Autonomous Gibson Mill, Lockton 'Green Beacon' Youth Hostel & David Johnson's Autonomous Eco House.

Please Contact Andrew, Lucy or Eric via our web site **www.ecoarc.co.uk** or email us: **ecoarc@ ecoarc.co.uk** or telephone us on **01904 468752**

A code for sustainable homes

Despite having been anticipated as a significant step towards mainstreaming sustainable buildings, the new Code, as being delivered, is a bitter disappointment to those working in the sustainable development sector. Some suspect it has been devised so that the government can declare vast swathes of new housing in the south east (in particular the Thames Gateway) as being sustainable communities.
Jon Broome reports ...

Regrettably, the long awaited Code for Sustainable Homes (CSH), formerly known as the Code for Sustainable Buildings, may not make the significant contribution towards reducing the environmental impacts of buildings that many had hoped for. Prior to its launch it was expected that the Code would cover all publicly funded buildings, including hospitals, schools and other public buildings. This is now promised for some unspecified date in the future. Regrettably the current document covers new housing only.

However, publicly funded new homes are already going to be built to the highest standards of environmental performance of any sector of the building industry. English Partnerships, and from April 2006 the Housing Corporation, require all new homes that they fund or provide site for, to be built to the Building Research Establishment's EcoHomes, Very Good standard. This equates to Level 3 of the proposed Code.

So do we need it?

One might wonder, therefore, why we need a new code. In the short term the only difference will be that 'higher levels of the CSH' will apply to homes developed with direct funding support from any of the ODPM's growth areas. The real significance lies in the aim of seeing the voluntary application of the Code to all new housing. The expectation is for local government to provide encouragement in this area.

The minimum standards, Level 1 of the Code, have been set so that house builders can meet the Code at minimum cost. The Code introduces voluntary standards of water efficiency, construction waste management and the use of materials. The minimum standards are modest; producing and implementing a Site Waste Management Plan, to record which materials are used in the construction and to reduce water consumption by an average of 18%.

However, the other 3 of the 6 minimum standards are already controlled by the Building Regulations and the Code does not raise standards in any real way above that of minimum compliance with current standards of energy efficiency, surface water disposal or household waste management. Meanwhile, the government has responded to the overwhelmingly adverse comment to the consultation by proposing to raise the threshold standards above the minimum mandatory level required by the building regulations.

One can argue that introducing new areas of standards, even if on a purely voluntary basis, has the effect of broadening the house building industry's awareness of environmental issues, and there is an expectation that in time they will opt to implement measures to improve performance in these areas. However, there seems to be no point in reproducing minimum compliance standards; this merely increases bureaucracy without raising performance, and increases costs without benefits.

Meanwhile, one part of local government is taking a much more pro-active role. The Supplementary Planning Guidance to the London Plan on Sustainable Design and Construction is due to be adopted. This will require developers of major residential and commercial developments to adopt much more far reaching standards. These include providing 10% of energy requirements from on-site renewable sources and 50% of timber to be

© Green Building Press

from sustainably managed forests, for example. The guidance goes further and includes higher preferred standards which suggest, for example, that all major developments should have zero carbon emissions and that all insulation materials should be from natural rather than man-made sources. These are radical standards and it remains to be seen how effective the planning system will be in implementing them. However, early signs are that developers are becoming much more aware of energy and emissions and are considering the implications from the inception of a project.

The CSH relies on the market and developers to push for sustainable homes but there are limitations to this approach. Firstly, the housing market is controlled far more by supply, rather than demand, and the suppliers (i.e the house builders) are notoriously resistant to change. Secondly, whilst there may be interest in solar power and other visible add-ons, it is not clear that there is substantial demand for truly sustainable building, which is a complex subject involving the detailed appreciation of waste and water, and the environmental impacts of materials and so on.

Introducing new standards at a relatively low level, with the expectation that they will be raised in subsequent years, has proved a successful strategy for raising standards in the medium term. It has been used to increase the standards of energy efficiency demanded by the building regulations Part L, and by the Housing Corporation to increase standards of sustainability to EcoHomes 'Very Good'. However, the suggestion is that the implementation of the Code will rely on the market to drive up standards. It is not clear how effective this may be.

Benefits of a CSH

The proposed CSH has two significant advances over EcoHomes. Firstly, a number of elements are essential for compliance, whereas it is possible (although difficult) to obtain an EcoHomes assessment without addressing the fundamental issues of energy or water effi-

ciency, for example. However, the converse of this is that external private space, security and guidance on using your home in a sustainable manner are not considered essential features of a sustainable home. There is no commitment to make issues such as these essential elements of a sustainable home in the future.

The second feature of the CSH which is good, is that it is assessed after completion, unlike EcoHomes which only includes an option for a post completion assessment and which is generally awarded on a design which may or may not be amended during design development and construction.

Nevertheless, introducing the Code has not addressed the question of broadening an understanding of the features of sustainable homes to include what many would regard as essential features, such as adaptability to enable homes to respond to changing needs and expectations without becoming obsolete. Measures to provide adaptability might include easy access to change and upgrade services, increased space, the use of frame structures and lightweight construction, such as timber for example.

Also fundamental to any sustainable housing system is the concept of resident consultation and involvement in the design and management of buildings. In Britain mass housing built by volume housebuilders does not have a proper role for residents. This is in contrast to Japan, for instance, where the prefabricated house industry offers residents a wide range of choices. Other issues which are not considered include potential health impacts, indoor air quality, durability, ease of maintenance and the sustainable treatment of ground contamination.

EcoHomes ignores the social and economic aspects of sustainability and is limited to indicators that can be easily measured and there is no suggestion that the CSH will be broadened out to embrace these fundamental issues in the future. The Code for Sustainable Homes is to be read in conjunction with the forthcoming Sustainability Checklist published by the South

East of England Development Agency, SEEDA. This deals with the more strategic planning issues, including the transport and ecological implications of development. This tool will be available on the internet soon.

To summarise, the new Code is a lost opportunity at a number of levels. In the short term it does not extend a commitment to sustainable building beyond the housing sector. In the medium term the minimum standards do little to improve performance within the housing sector and merely impose additional costs for marginal benefits. In the longer term the new Code ignores many of the fundamental aspects of sustainable building. ☙

Further information

www.breeam.org/ecohomes
www.odpm.gov.uk/index.asp?id=1162094
www.sustainabilityworks.org.uk

The future for green building standards

Our built environment accounts for over half of the carbon dioxide emissions in the UK. When we consider the contributing effect that carbon dioxide has on climate change, it is important to note that we can have a dramatic effect on reducing our environmental impact by choosing to build green. The problem is what standards will the UK adopt to dictate, quantify and assess how valuable our efforts are? **Gavin Harper** investigates ...

Deciding to build green is a positive step in the right direction. However, how do you know that your building is truly green and not just a triumph of marketing over substance? Building assessment methods provide an objective way of comparing your building to others in the field. Using standardised assessment techniques, they are able to evaluate your development against core criteria laid down in the standards, providing some objective measure of the building's environmental impact and whether it has met its sustainable goals. Using a building assessment method is important, as it validates the achievements of the building through impartial third-party review.

One of the commonalities to all of the environmental assessment methods presented here, is that it is important that the criteria of the method(s) to be applied are considered at an early stage in the design process in order to maximise opportunities for developing the building to conform to the relevant criteria.

Why use building assessment methods

Building assessment methods provide a common metric on which similar building types can be assessed. This is useful for a number of reasons.

They allow the client to specify how sustainable they want their building to be, using an easily understood format, which is much simpler than specifying a list of criteria. It also allows planners, developers and housing agencies to specify a level that a building should meet in a simple and accessible manner.

It is also a good tool for designers as it allows them to check that they have evaluated all relevant criteria in turn, and it can lead to investigation of gaining more skills where knowledge gaps are highlighted. The comprehensive nature of many building assessment methods

50

ensures that 'all bases are covered'.

When selling, leasing or letting a property, an indication of the building's environmental performance can be a good selling point – future occupiers may be conscious of the amount of energy the building will require in use.

BREEAM

Building Research Establishment Environmental Assessment Method

The BREEAM series of assessment methods have been established for well over a decade and as such have a good reputation for benchmarking buildings.

There are a number of different assessment methods which are tailored to different building types. The options that are currently available are:
- residential units (EcoHomes)
- retail units
- industrial units
- offices
- schools

Most buildings fit into one of the above classifications. However, because there is such a wide range of different buildings with different purposes and requirements, it is important to consider that the scope of one of the above might not be broad enough to include certain building functions. If the building does not fit one of the above criteria well, it is possible to tailor an assessment method to the building's function. This service provided by the BRE is known as 'Bespoke BREEAM', and has been applied successfully to churches, courts, leisure centres, shared accommodation and other applications that do not readily fit into one of the other BREEAM categories.

The BREEAM assessment method assesses a building's performance against a number of criteria, namely these are:
- management
- energy use
- heath and well being
- pollution
- transport
- land use
- ecology
- materials
- water

The output of the BREEAM process is that buildings are given a rating of 'pass', 'good', 'very good' or 'excellent', and a certificate is awarded to this effect.

EcoHomes

EcoHomes is the name given to the the version of BREEAM specifically designed for homes and residential dwellings. It follows the same pattern as the other BREEAM standards in that buildings are assessed against a similar range of criteria, the output from the process being a rating of 'pass', 'good', 'very good' or 'excellent'.

An addition to the EcoHomes armoury is the EcoHomes XB standard, which has been introduced to monitor existing building stock. The standard has been adapted to the needs and constraints of existing buildings, and can take one of two forms. There is a basic appraisal level, which can be undertaken using basic information that might be held on file by an organisation, for example a housing association, that owns a portfolio of property and holds information about that property on file. The next step up is the advanced level assessment, which will necessitate visits to the site and a more in-depth evaluation.

The scoring system for EcoHomes XB will differ slightly, to take better account of the incremental improvements that can be made to housing stock – which will have a smaller impact than changes at the design stage of the building. This flexibility takes into account the variable nature of housing stock, and the sometime sub-optimal designs that do not necessarily lend themselves directly to reduced environmental impact.

If you are looking at building an EcoHomes compliant dwelling, a good starting point is to get hold of the 'Developer Sheets' from the

BRE. These are a fairly mild introduction to EcoHomes for the untrained and provide a gentle introduction with tables and tick boxes for those without prior knowledge of the assessment method.

In the days before EcoHomes, the only real driver, in terms of standards and legislation, towards reducing environmental impact, was Part L of the Building Regulations. Hopefully, with its increasing adoption, EcoHomes, amongst other building assessment methods, will prove a valuable tool in improving the UK's housing stock.

Does EcoHomes have a future?

EcoHomes may well be replaced by the Code for Sustainable Homes (CSH)[1], which the UK government wants to run and as such, are in negotiations with the BRE over rights and possible compensation (unconfirmed rumours suggest that a seven figure sum may change hands). The BRE are understandably concerned because a government-led scheme would not be very fair competition. Why? Well the government controls the Housing Corporation (HC) and the HC dictate which environmental standard homes that they fund should meet. Therefore a failure to meet an agreement with the government could leave the BRE and their EcoHomes standard (which currently enjoys favour from the HC) out in the cold with far less customers than it attracts at present.

LEED

Leadership in Energy and Environmental Design
LEED is an assessment method from America devised as a voluntary assessment tool by the US Green Building Council, a consortium divided into 52 'Chapters' spread around the US, not all by state.

The US Green Building Council asserts that LEED was created to:
- define 'green building' by establishing a common standard of measurement
- promote integrated, whole-building design practices
- recognize environmental leadership in the building industry
- stimulate green competition
- raise consumer awareness of green building benefits
- transform the building market.

LEED is not simply an energy assessment, it takes a number of things into account when assessing the sustainability of a development:
- suitability of the site for a sustainable development.
- water management and economy
- energy efficiency and conservation
- suitable selection of environmentally responsible materials
- quality of the indoor environment.

One of the strengths of LEED, and a feature that is common to a number of other assessment methods, is that there is an array of different standards designed to meet the needs of different building types.

A building can earn one of four possible LEED ratings. A 'LEED certified' building meets the minimum environmental standards, a 'LEED silver rated' building is an improvement on the basic standards, 'LEED gold rated' being higher still, and 'LEED platinum' represents the paragon of the green building trade. LEED has been highly successful in the United States, and this may lead to its further adoption in the UK. The system is worked on a points basis.

As with BREEAM, if you are thinking of applying for the LEED scheme, it is recommended that your building is registered as early as possible in the design process in order to help the accreditation process[2].

AECB – CarbonLite

A relative newcomer to the green building standards game, the AECB (the sustainable building association) wants to 'up the game' by making post occupancy evaluation an integral part of the standard.

The AECB wants people to become 'Carbon Literate', by engaging with their buildings and living within a sensible home carbon budget – although some people argue that this is a step too far. Whilst Yvette Cooper argued on Radio 4 that building regulations are intruding into people's lives is too much, the AECB argue that their standard is aiming to inform and educate, empowering people to make intelligent considerations about how they interact with their buildings, not trying to constrain or restrict them.

By raising the bar for green building standards, the AECB is hoping that the BRE and EST will tighten up their standards and make them more stringent. The AECB's position is that many other standards are 'partial' standards, whereas their proposals (based on the German Passihaus standards) are for the 'whole home'. They want the home to be assessed on two years monitored energy use, post-occupancy, to ensure that the house does 'exactly what it says on the tin'.

This competition for the standard of choice can only result in a higher quality product for consumers. The AECB plans to award buildings a rating which is easily understood – bronze, silver, gold or platinum, based on the building's energy performance. The AECB is certainly one to watch in the future. As a 1300 member strong organisation, it is in a good position to lead the way, particularly as, at the moment, the organisation feels that leadership is not coming from government or industry[3].

EST - Best Practice

The Energy Saving Trust (EST) has been working on a set of enhanced energy standards. Its proposals are not so different from those already covered above and offers three categories better than the current Building Regulations; 'good', 'best' and 'advanced'.[4]

SAP - Standard Assessment Procedure

The Standard Assessment Procedure has now become a compulsory assessment that must be carried out on all new buildings, or converted buildings that have undergone a change of material use. This was made compulsory

under the amendments made to the Building Regulations Part 1, which came into place on April 2002. SAP 2005 is used as the government's standard assessment procedure in order to show compliance with Part L of the Building Regulations. It replaces the older SAP 2001 standards.

SAP is used to give a building a rating from 0 to 120 based on the annual energy costs of the building. The procedure also outputs a Carbon Index, which is a measure from 0-10.0. This is expressed as a 'National Home Energy Rating' – a certificate can be issued to this effect giving a simple indication of the home's energy needs for space heating and hot water.

The outputs of the SAP Procedure are:
- a measure of the energy consumption per unit floor area of the building
- a SAP rating (energy cost rating)
- environmental impact rating
- DER (Dwellings Emission Rate) which is the rate at which a building produces CO_2.

The SAP procedure looks at the amount of energy that is needed for space heating and water heating – this is one of its limitations – it does not take into account electrical loads and many other factors. Most of the existing UK housing stock would come out with an average SAP[5] rating of between 40 and 50. A house which met the BRE EcoHomes standard could be expected to come out with a score somewhere around 80. ☙

References

1. The Code for Sustainable homes is discussed in the story preceeding this.

2. A free LEED pre-evaluation checklist downloadable from www.usgbc.org which allows you to quickly evaluate what LEED rating your building might attain.

3. More information and draft standards can be viewed at: www.aecb.net/energyinbuildings.php

4. EST: www.est.org.uk/bestpractice

5. The SAP 2001 Specification can be downloaded from: http://projects.bre.co.uk/sap2005/pdf/SAP2005.pdf

Uniting the green building movement

In 2005, a meeting of a Sustainable Building Task Group (brought together by the UK government) recommended that the disparate green building campaign groups should form a single entity that would provide not only a much better conduit for dialogue with government, but also a way of motivating the UK construction sector to start taking green buildings more seriously. **Ben Bamber** reports ...

The proposed structure of a united organisation could be similar to the US Green Building Council. The USGBC has been highly successful in galvanizing all sectors of the construction industry, from architects to contractors, throughout the United States.

Certainly in the United States, since the formation of the USGBC in 1993, there has been an explosion of interest in the architectural and building professions. Designers and construction companies are designing and building low environmental impact buildings and the demand for 'green' construction products is stimulating major competitor activity and innovation. This has resulted in the development of lower environmental impact products, often with higher recycled content.

However, in mainland Europe there has been great interest in green building and a widespread development of ecological products for very many years, without the need for a collective group to demand or promote it, certainly not at a national level. So you may well ask, why do we need an overseeing group in the UK?

Well the baton for orchestrating the formation of a UK Green Building Council (UKGBC) was picked up by Dr David Strong, Managing Director of BRE Environment, who believes there is a real opportunity. "The whole prospect of establishing a UK Green Building Council is potentially hugely important but I don't underestimate the problems of getting such a thing

off the ground. I've already had pledges of support from a number of organisations who all recognise the desperate need for an entity of this sort." He continued, "I went along to the US Green Build Conference in Atlanta; there were over 10,000 delegates there, what they have achieved in the US is quite phenomenal. I believe there are real prospects for something similar to be established in the UK." The US Green Building Councils Leadership in Energy and Environmental Design (LEED) certification has become a single and auditable benchmarking system in the US.

Strong is hopeful the new Council will be formed in the near future. "We are in a much stronger starting position in the UK in that we have a very well established and robust environmental assessment method for buildings. There are now over 2000 trained assessors for BREEAM and EcoHomes across the country."

Strong is not the only one hopeful that a new organisation can be created. Commenting on the proposal, Bill Gething, Chairman of the Royal Institute of British Architects (RIBA) Sustainable Futures Group said: "What the industry does need is an organisation that pulls it together. This needs to be properly funded and to be proactive - to do things rather than merely talk about doing them. The entire building industry needs to buy into this; therefore it must be attractive and beneficial to them and give something back in return. If the UK Green Building Council is a way of achieving this it will be fantastic."

If established, the UKGBC will join the ranks of the current World Green Building Council member countries of Australia, Canada, India, Mexico, Taiwan and the US. The World Green Building Council was established to share the latest technical knowledge and advancement of national green building information.

© Green Building Press

The list of emerging member countries includes Brazil, Chile, Germany, Guatemala, Israel, New Zealand and the United Arab Emirates. Visit **www.worldgbc.org** for more information.

Problems ahead

A scoping study put together by Cranfield University, at the request of David Strong, examined the potential for a UKGBC, revealing some possible problems. Because the UK has such a broad range of organisations already monitoring and regulating green building stand-ards and practices, they concluded that the UKGBC faces an uphill struggle to find its place among the other organisations. They also iden-tified that one of the largest problems is which environmental assessment tool to use (see previous story for discussions of the options).

The study suggested that there are 'theo-retically' no barriers to the new UKGBC to take on an alternative to the BRE's BREEAM or EcoHomes assessment methods. Jules Saunderson, a co-author of the report, says 'Whatever system the UKGBC decided to go with, an arrangement would need to be worked out with the organisation that controls that system…so the relationship between BREEAM and the UKGBC would have to be negotiated.'

The financing of the UKGBC was identified as a problem too. The report says 'It is clearly not in the interests of a UKGBC to allow thousands of potential paying customers to be repre-sented by proxy through their membership to a trade association'. The potential membership for the new UKGBC is not a clearly defined area in this report. Its financial projections are extremely vague, leading me to presume that the current trade associations present a clear threat to the viability of the UKGBC.

The report '…expressed concern at the plethora of bodies in the field, and (recom-mended) that these should be reviewed and simplified', implying that the UKGBC should automatically take the lead role among the existing organisations; something which could

upset the other groups.

All in all the report is vague in parts and presumptuous in others, leading me to think that the scoping study wasn't in depth enough to really give a full picture of what is being asked. It also seems that they have presented the basis of argument to support the idea that a UKGBC isn't needed. It does go on to say that 'Strategic alliances need to be formed between members, key industry stake holders, research and technology organisations and government at national and local level'.

In summary it appears a UKGBC will initially struggle to find a role for itself. It will need a dedicated and determined team to make it a success. An alternative may be the expansion of existing organisations, otherwise the UKGBC is in danger of repeating work already being done and failing to achieve the financial stability it needs.

Opinions

We asked representatives of seven established UK organisations and businesses with an interest in 'green building' what they thought of the idea of a UKGBC. Firstly would they join?

The answers weren't that diverse. Those that answered said they were willing to sign up to UKGBC, but all were cautious, wanting more information before committing. We then asked whether they feel a united organisation is necessary or did they feel it is repeating the work of organisations already in exist-ence? Most were more enthusiastic about this question saying it was a good way to coordinate and deliver a green message to the wider world.

Chris Twinn from consulting engineers, ARUP, gave a lengthy answer saying, 'Any organisation must be structured somewhat differently to the others round the world because we already have a plethora of organisa-tions… there is a role needed for an umbrella representation body to provide a single voice for the industry to government and to the public. Secondly, as done by the USGBC it should also oversee the establishment of a baseline cross discipline accreditation/qualification for professionals. This latter aspect has been very powerful in the USA for getting sustainability into wider public circles...'

RIBA's Brendan O'Conner, said that 'A united, well-funded organisation with permanent staff would be a great asset to co-ordinate efforts in sustainable construction', and that 'being part of a global movement would similarly have great benefits.'

However, the National Energy Action (NEA) spokesman, David Bootle, was a lot more negative, saying, 'We're amenable to the whole concept of sustainable buildings, but at the moment we are more preoccupied with people that live in already established housing - often of an inadequate nature unfortunately.' Their reluctance to commit in principle, as most of the others have, shows that not all organisations feel that a UKGBC would add a significant element to the green building movement.

From the AECB, Liz Reason, says that 'The evidence is not clear from other GBCs that there is any real improvement in practice as opposed to business as usual with a bit of green attached. The real gap in the UK market is the actual performance of buildings in operation.'

A multi layered green movement means that duplication of campaigns and roles are a danger. The Micropower Council said 'There is a significant risk that work of other organisations may be repeated'. But incoherence among the various organisations may well be solved by a UKGBC. The wider global movement doesn't see the UK as a major player though. The World GBC seems more interested in encouraging growth countries like China, to sign up to the scheme. David Strong of BRE doesn't even think that the organisation should be named in the same way as the others. He prefers a 'coalition', rather than a 'council'. This underlines a suspicion that a UKGBC would be somewhat separate from the global schemes, currently being developed. ✎

Organisations that were asked: Institute of Civil Engineers (ICE), ARUP, RIBA, Micropower Council, Green Register, NEA, AECB.

The above report was collated from a much longer report on a website, entitled 'UKGBC Watch' which is operated by the Green Building Press www.ukgbc.co.uk

The Merton Rule

The London Borough of Merton was the first local authority to adopt, as part of its unitary development plan, a policy mandating the inclusion of renewables in large scale newbuild. Since its introduction in the borough (from which it takes its name), the Merton Rule, which mandates that 10% of energy consumption is to be met from renewable sources on new non-residential buildings over 1000 square metres, has rapidly gathered momentum. **Gavin Harper** reports ...

What began as just a small 'local' initiative, the concept has, and will increasingly be adopted by many local authorities right across the UK – dramatically demonstrating that local action can have national (and potentially global) knock-on effect.

The Merton Rule, was borne out of a desire to meet LA21 objectives, following a growth in awareness of how local action can have global environmental consequences. Interestingly, the driver for the introduction of the renewables policy was an attempt to encourage new businesses by helping to lower energy costs, demonstrating that green building, sensible economics and planning policies can go hand in hand.

The policy was implemented in October 2003 in the London Borough of Merton's unitary development plan (UDP). For planning consent to be obtained for a development, the policy must be applied and the developer

© Green Building Press

must provide evidence of compliance. 10% (+) renewables is a condition of the planning consent being obtained; failure to meet this obligation would mean failure to meet the terms of the planning consent – which would make the development illegal.

The Merton Rule was the catalyst for change and from it came Planning Policy Statement 22 (PPS22), Planning Guidance on Renewable Energy, issued by the Office of the Deputy Prime Minister in 2004. This statement clarified matters by maintaining that it was the ODPM's view that it was not only the right of local authorities to implement such didactic policy relating to renewable energy, but it was also the desire of the ODPM that this sort of legislation was adopted.

The two sections in PPS22 that explicitly state this guidance are sections 8 and 18.

Section 8 "Local planning authorities may include policies in local development documents that require a percentage of the energy to be used in new residential, commercial or industrial developments to come from on-site renewable energy developments."

Section 18 "Local planning authorities and developers should consider the opportunity for incorporating renewable (sustainable) energy projects in all new developments ... Local planning authorities should specifically encourage such schemes through positively expressed policies in local development documents."

The website, **www.themertonrule.org** states that this guidance helped to overcome a "psychological barrier" that was proving an impediment to change.

The first project to be completed under the Merton Rule guidelines, was a small light industrial development at Willow Lane in Mitcham, which used solar pv and wind turbines to fulfil the requirements of producing on-site electricity from renewables.

Meeting the rule

Merton define renewables as:
- photovoltaic energy
- solar-powered and geo-thermal water heating
- energy crops and biomass
- wind power.

However, they explicitly exclude energy from domestic or industrial waste.

Where a combined heat and power (CHP) system is installed, it is recognised that this helps to reduce carbon emissions significantly – as more primary energy is converted to useful, delivered energy. As a result, the 10% requirement can be met in many cases, for developments incorporating CHP.

This flexibility is good as it allows the developer to decide what forms of renewable energy are most appropriate for the site, as different sites will be suitable for a different blend of renewables, depending on orientation, access to light, average wind speed, availiability of biofuels etc.

Feedback from developers to the Borough of Merton indicate that the cost of new build has increased, but only by a relatively modest amount of 3-4%. When this initial investment

The Merton Rule in plain english

"This Council will encourage the energy efficient design of buildings and their layout and orientation on site. All new non-residential developments above a threshold of 1,000 sq metres will be expected to incorporate renewable energy production equipment to provide at least 10% of predicted energy requirements. The use of sustainable building materials and the re-use of materials will also be encouraged. As will the use of recycled aggregates in the construction of buildings. This will be subject to the impact on the amenity of the local environment, taking into account the existing character of the area."

is taken into account over the lifetime of the development, it can be seen that this is a small price to pay for our future. The policy represents a shift from the previous stance in the UK of 'encouraging' the uptake of renewables to one of 'requiring' the installation of renewables. This has helped to overcome the apathy in the mainstream UK building industry.

The London Borough of Merton has set an interesting precedent. In taking the lead it has created a domino effect that has rippled throughout the UK. If successfully implemented, this framework could set a precedent for Europe and the rest of the world.

London Mayor, Ken Livingstone, has extended the Merton Rule in his 'London Energy Plan' to also include residential developments of ten dwellings or more, although why can't all projects be included?

Concern has been expressed that the enforced adoption of renewables might scare developers away from certain regions, as the increased cost imposed by adopting renewables might act as a disincentive to build in poorer areas. This argument has been countered by the emphasis that it is precisely those sort of areas that would benefit from reduced energy costs. Again, **www.themertonrule.org** asserts that any developer citing that the implementation of renewable energy would make their development uneconomical is merely trying to establish a bargaining position. Evidence from local authorities suggests that there has been no decrease in the amount of developments – disproving arguments against the rule.

So far, forty nine local authorities have adopted the Merton rule in its entirety – some setting higher targets for the adoption of renewables in their locale, whilst seventy one have included variations of the Merton Rule in their draft unitary development plans. Fifty seven boroughs report making 'active progress', and one, Belfast, is currently assessing feasibility.

Some local authorities have decided to adopt targets that are higher than Merton's 10%. This 'one-up-manship' among local authorities trying to 'outgreen' each other can only be more encouraging for the wider environmental debate.

Merton's strategy initially focussed on energy. However, this has not been without debate – there has been a strong case made for measuring the reduction in carbon rather than energy. This has a number of inherent advantages:

- the government's Energy White Paper talks in terms of 'carbon' rather than energy – the UK's stated aim being to reduce 'carbon' emissions by 2050
- part L of the building regulations works in 'carbon' terms rather than 'energy terms', carbon is thus more congruous with this.

Concern has also been expressed that already 'overstretched' planning departments will not be able to deal with the extra work created by the Merton Rule – yet it is an incorrect assumption that a planning officer needs to be an expert in renewable energy to implement the rule. All that needs to happen is that the planners need to identify the predicted energy use and CO_2 emissions of the building, and verify that the proposed renewables will meet that target.

Plain sailing?

Making controversial policy, like the Merton Rule, a reality is rarely plain sailing. There were a number of initial objections to the Merton Rule. Two were:

- the policy was unjustified and placed undue burden on developers as they did not believe energy was a land-use issue
- before including in a UDP, the feasibility of the scheme should be demonstrated.

The case against these two arguments was robustly put and it was argued that energy was as much an issue of land use as: 'employment potential, wildlife protection and protection of an area's character', which are already considered in many UDP's. Furthermore, the 'burden'

© Green Building Press

placed on developers would be lightened by the increase in saleability and revenue from properties with embodied energy generation.

Following a financial evaluation of how the rule would affect a new development, the decision was reached that the rule was both feasible and reasonable and supported government instruments, such as the climate change levy, that were already in place.

So what effect might this rule have in the near future?

Certainly having a statutory instrument in place will be a boost for renewables - we can expect to see an increase in the growth of micro generation in those areas where the policy has been implemented.

This ruling will serve to greatly increase the visibility of renewable energy production, which in the context of rising energy prices, can only speed its adoption by consumers. The adoption of the Merton Rule by many local authorities will help renewables to gain widespread acceptance and be seen as 'mainstream' rather than alternative.

The other effect it will have is to educate developers as to the benefits of renewable technologies. If they are 'forced' to implement these technologies in certain areas, then it follows that they will become 'renewable-literate' en-masse, which we would hope would lead to them using these technologies in areas which are not governed by the rule – but voluntarily.

There are economies of scale to be gained – whilst the initial learning curve can be expensive, this expenditure can be spread over many developments and applications. If a developer is made to learn how to implement these technologies in areas like Merton, then they will have crossed the 'knowledge barrier' – removing one more obstacle for future installations.

Getting developers to become fully-conversant in the language of renewable energy is only

the start. Once developments that integrate renewables begin to proliferate, we should see an increased knowledge of renewable energy techniques amongst the general public and a growing desire to own homes that include them.

Developments where the amount of carbon saved, as a result of the embodied renewable energy generating technology, is displayed on a prominent public-facing display, such as that in North Haringey Primary School. This is a great tool for motivating the public to think about the environment – whilst also earning owners of such buildings environmental kudos and possibily future income from any exported power. ✪

Further information

www.themertonrule.org

http://en.wikipedia.org/wiki/Merton_rule

www.merton.gov.uk/living/planning/plansandprojects/10percentpolicy.htm

www.merton.gov.uk/renewable_energy_presenta-tion_jul_06.ppt

The link below has a fully interactive map that allows you to zoom in and see what your local authority is doing about the Merton Rule:
http://themertonrule.org/map

Compliance dodging

One of the unintended consequences of setting targets in terms of CO_2 emissions is the opening up of new loopholes that quick-witted developers, with an eye on profitability and speed of compliance, are seeking to exploit. The root cause of these loopholes is the concept of trade-offs – allowing a reduced performance in one aspect of building design in exchange for compliance beyond the minimum elsewhere. **Gavin Killip** explains ...

Trade-offs were allowed in the 1990s when elemental U-values were still the preferred measure of compliance. The thermal performance was deemed to be a function of thermal performance and total area, which led to a flurry of homes being built with small windows and lower levels of insulation in the walls. The thinking behind this was that, as windows are generally less insulating than walls, the performance of the whole structure would be improved if the area of wall was increased and the area of glazing decreased. Then the thermal performance of the walls need not be so tight for the entire envelope to achieve the same thermal properties. With the gift of hindsight, we know that the resulting designs provide poor levels of daylight (adding to electric lighting loads) and a legacy of sub-optimal wall constructions that would be very costly and disruptive to improve. This is one of the down-sides to having regulations that are blind to design.

As previously discussed, Merton Borough Council pioneered a planning policy that required 10% of energy to be generated from on-site renewables in developments over a certain size. It takes courage for a local authority to be innovative in this way but, once the national government had retrospectively endorsed the policy in its revised Planning Policy Statement 22 (PPS22), published in 2004, there was a rush among other forward-thinking local authorities to follow Merton's lead. Instead of getting their fingers burned or their wrists slapped, Merton Council was rewarded with a level of fame that it had never had before. It seems to be part of the culture in large public sector organisations that, when it comes to doing something pioneering, everybody wants to be second.

In the game of catch-up that followed, there are now several dozen local authorities in England with similar policies to Merton's. Some require 10% on only the largest developments; some ask for slightly higher percentages; some apply the rule to all developments, including the very smallest; some have stated publicly their intention to make the requirement more stringent over time: for example, Kirklees in West Yorkshire wants 30% by 2011 and the Greater London Authority (GLA) has set a ramp to reach 30% across London by 2025.

In the rush to join in, and in a probably unavoidable spirit of one-upmanship between different councils, there is a danger that developers end up faced with a different set of building codes in each area.

The pace of change is being pushed forward by local government action, but the plethora of individual initiatives will surely reach a point where some consolidation is required. Perhaps, following the example of PPS22, the UK government will retrospectively apply its stamp of approval and draw up a national consensus document in the process. Or maybe the government will simply decide to use the existing national consensus document – Part L of the Building Regulations?

Anomalies and loopholes are already appearing in the gaps between local and national policy development. For instance, a 'server farm' is a building full of servers (computers) providing IT capability to thousands of users remote to the building. This is a class of development that will seriously challenge on-site renewable energy policies. With potential electrical loads of several megawatts in one modest-sized building, how realistic or sensible is it to demand that 10% (let alone 30%) be generated on-site? The size of PV array required could easily be larger than the building itself. Or, if wind were the preferred option, the technically logical answer would be one or more large turbines. However, these work best away from the low-speed, turbulent air-flows that predominate around buildings. This tension between energy-intensive facilities like server farms and the diffuse nature of all renewable energy sources will need to be resolved. We may need to agree that certain classes of buildings providing energy-intensive services are exempted or treated differently.

In the process of building new buildings, developers deal first with the planning regime and only address building regulations later on. The requirement to achieve a percentage of on-site renewable energy supply has led some developers to complain that this effectively rules out the possibility of applying for 'outline' planning approval, as the detailed work needed to show how much renewable energy will be generated is the same as doing a full planning application. This may be a change of practice that is unavoidable. In terms of loopholes, planning officers also need to keep an eye open for potential double-counting. If a developer has incorporated on-site renewable energy sources to meet the 10% planning requirement, how is that reflected in their calculations to show compliance with Part L? Given that the measure for Part L is now carbon dioxide emissions (rather than U-values), there is scope for developers to argue for looser standards on insulation or airtightness in a building which has renewable energy technology built in. Adrian Hewitt, Senior Planning Officer for Merton Borough Council, is clear that these trade-offs should not be allowed, and that his council's requirement is additional to the requirement to comply with Part L. Clear guidance for planning officers will be needed and, in most cases, additional training will be required to provide the skills for the technical assessments. This is particularly challenging against the back-ground of generally low morale among planners, increasing workloads and poor recruitment and retention in the profession.

In another twist to the unfolding 'doing a Merton' story, some developers have begun to look beyond their own development, arguing that they can achieve more for climate change by retro-fitting insulation in existing homes nearby, rather than adding expensive, unfamil-iar renewable energy technology to their own scheme. Insulating a few dozen lofts down the road is cheaper and a lot less hassle for the developer than really getting to grips with low CO_2 emissions from their own development.

This argument makes sense in the context of a single development, but not in the wider context of national or regional CO_2 reduction targets. We need to reduce CO_2 emissions from both new and existing buildings: doing only one is not enough. Resources and policies need to be found to upgrade the existing stock, but not at the expense of improved quality in new-build. Allowing a developer to trade off the impact of their own development by picking off the cheap, quick improvements in a housing estate down

the road will only serve to continue the legacy of under-performing new buildings.

The devil is in the detail

Much of the detail of 'doing a Merton' will emerge over the coming months and years as all parties in the planning process become more familiar with it. For climate change policy, it is crucial that superficially plausible trade-offs are resisted. The AECB, among others, has argued cogently that the thermal performance of new floors and walls is particularly important to get right, as retro-fit improvements are both costly and disruptive.

A U-value in the range 0.1 - 0.15W/m²K for floors anwalls is about what is needed for genuinely low CO_2 emissions in our northern temperate climate. However, achieving comfort in hotter summers without recourse to carbon-intensive air-conditioning is a design challenge that will need to be met using appropriate thermal mass and control of solar gain through shading devices. This new design brief is beyond the conventional 100mm masonry cavity wall, and the construction industry has successfully fought against such standards for that very reason: genuinely low-emissions build-ings require new methods, new products and a shake-up in the whole supply chain. ☙

Architectural trends

2006 may be remembered as the year that the sustainable design agenda began finally to impact on a much wider architectural community than the usual green 'mission driven' practices. This is perhaps part to do with a breakthrough in awareness amongst the general public and client sector - including architects - who are at long last "getting" climate change. **Oliver Lowenstein** reports ...

This impact is also a consequence of the whole industry having to take on Part L of the Building Regulations, which came into effect in April 2006. That said, sustainable architecture has been moving up the priority list for all practice types: large, medium and smaller. At the largest end of the scale, the big four: Rogers, Fosters, Hopkins, and Grimshaws, along with all the other big companies jostling for pole position, have all developed sustainability as key parts of their portfolios.

Whatever their actual beliefs, sustainability is seen as an increasingly essential marketing element for practices presenting themselves to clients. In March 2006, Grimshaws Jolyon Brewis, told Building Design, "In the UK the best, most creative firms have embraced sustainability as a driver for innovative design. We very much see sustainability as a driver of design and it does make a difference in gaining work." At present, one effect of this has been that British firms are picking up lots of work in the States, based on their sustainability know-how, compared to comparatively inexperienced American practices. Europe and Britain is seen as far ahead in experience, technical expertise, and regulatory guidelines. One commentator stated that it is a 'symbolic act' to be seen as green. The irony of travelling thousands of miles, to practice green architecture, wasn't mentioned.

Of course huge practices, with offices all round the planet are one thing: on the ground, sustainability is another. It all depends where one draws the line. Look at the environmental architecture magazine, EcoTech. It seems a world away from Building for A Future magazine. But things are changing, that's for sure. Ken Shuttleworth, the ex Fosters' partner, in charge of both the Swiss Re Tower 'Gherkin' in London, and the Eco tower, which preceded it for Frankfurt Commerz Bank, declared that Part L meant the eclipse of glass and steel palaces, and by implication a whole realignment towards much more use of brickwork, smaller window areas, double and triple facades and a re-found emphasis on heavier thermal massing.

This appears ironic, when a countervailing trend is the arrival of high-rise eco-towers onto the British cityscape. Although none are yet built, many of the more sizeable cities up and down the country are clamouring for their very own high-rise quarter, and 'eco-towers' are seen as the way forward. This feeds into ongoing debates about density levels, affordable homes and city regeneration. It is only now, years since the publication of the Urban Task Forces Towards an Urban Renaissance that the remarkable consensus on residential brownfield building, infill development, may be beginning to fracture. New arguments are being fielded. For instance, that housing density needs to be defined by rooms rather than dwellings per hectare; that a variety of dwelling unit sizes needs to be factored in, and that much more attention needs to be paid to what are being called sustainable densities; projects predicated on infrastructure, transport links, health and education projects, and by implication and, theoretically at least, planning concerns of less car space, and more generous provision for families. Some describe this as hyper-density.

Right: the Swiss RE Gherkin building, by Fosters and Partners, is a hi-tech concrete/glass hybrid that cannot fail to impress all that glance at it. The Gherkin polarises opinion, reflecting the spectrum of sustainability. Photo: Nigel Young/Fosters and Partners

© Green Building Press

What it shows, perhaps, is the influence of a development such as BedZED, seeping into elements of mainstream thinking. So, the concept of sustainable cities is moving closer to envisaging, planning and realising more nuanced environments. As for ZEDfactory, Dunster and his gang are involved in negotiating an annual delivery of 1000 zero energy houses for Ken Livingstone's Greater London Authority. And Poran Desai of Bioregional, BedZED's former partner, is now working with various big time developers and advocating significant scaling up from BedZED size projects.

Not completely dissimilar is the respected architect, Richard MacCormack's recent rereading of suburbia. "We are keen on testing whether it's possible to meet the sustainable housing agenda using the suburban housing idiom", he states of his practice's experiments with sustainable suburbia. One thinks of the 200,000 new homes the government is claiming are needed in the South East. But, I would guess, on many planning minded architects minds, the big test, however, is the Thames Gateway development and how this is dealt with. Ken Yeang has become a partner in the recently formed Llewelynn Davies Yeang, with an immediate major project of a series of eco-towers in the Thames Gateway.

Not surprisingly, Part L, along with various other regulatory requirements, have been widely reported in the architectural press. Again, this plays into a wider general realisation that the ways cities needs are built and fuelled, needs to change. In London there are mutterings about how practical the 10% onsite renewables (see the Merton Rule) demanded of new developments is. The director of the big Kings Cross development masterplan, Argent's Roger Madelin, said that it was only technically possible to site 42 microturbine's on this huge development; it would need over 500 to meet the required 10%. If renewables are contentious, green roofs are generating interest for city based architects and developers. Ciria, another large developer, is looking at sedum and other green and brown roofing seriously,

Below and right: Dunster's SkyZED twin petal shaped towers, which would have supported enough wind turbines to make the building close to carbon neutral, failed to get approval in London. This is far more radical than anything being proposed by others, using ZEDfactory's ZED standards guidelines, which leave the BREEAM ratings standing. Images courtesy of ZEDfactory.

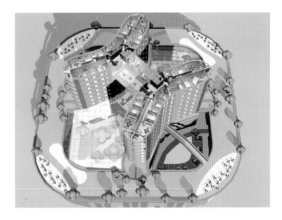

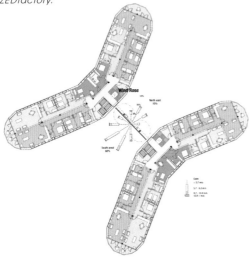

while RRP, having been commissioned by Livingstone's GLA, produced the Living Roofs report. Detractors again point to whether such roofs could survive various unusual weather patterns. But the substantive point: trying to find ways to check and change megacities, such as London's, heat island effect - is beginning to be looked at. Similarly, others point out

Renewables and green roof in harmony. Features such as these are beginning to pop up on commercial architecture as seen here on the Hasting's community centre, called 'The Bridge'. Photo; BBM.

that security of renewable energy, for instance, biomass for CHP's, just isn't assured. What is repeatedly stated, admittedly by doubters, is that sustainability at a high density city level simply hasn't been tested.

A second area of unease amongst some architects looking through Part L, is over the emphasis on technical fixes. This will not come as a worry to many in the profession, given the architectural love-in with technology and kit. But those green architects who have been caught up with sustainability for a long time may find their lower tech approaches are constrained by such technical emphasis. Saying that, it is interesting to note that in recent school buildings, Feilden Clegg Bradley (FCB) have begun replacing natural ventilation with hybrid mechanical-natural systems, which Peter Clegg claims, is currently both the healthiest and the most energy efficient approach to apply. Hearing this from most practices I would have taken it with a pinch of sceptical salt. But with FCB, who have done more research than most in natural lighting and ventilation, it remains an intriguing switch in strategy.

A third concern amongst some architects regarding Part L, has been that the regulation may act as a straight-jacket to their architectural creativity – limited by the need to meet new carbon emissions calculations restrictions. This is an old chestnut for architects, rolled out time again, that sustainability limits the ability for expression. But again there are sustainable architects who demonstrate, repeatedly, that

© Green Building Press

Haverstock Academy, NW London. Where FCB have begun replacing natural ventilation with hybrid mechanical-natural systems, which Peter Clegg claims, is currently both the healthiest and the most energy efficient approach to apply.

Photo: Feilden Clegg Bradley.

creativity and ingenuity can make for more interesting buildings designed and built from local materials, than the need to use hi tech materials and build in a signature architect style. BBM Sustainable Design in Sussex, is but one example, integrating aesthetic elements across a range of buildings and building types, while using locally available materials. What is odd perhaps, is why so few younger practices coming through and garnering a degree of national attention, promote themselves as sustainable practices.

Noticeably, none of the ten younger architects trail-blazed by the Architect Journal earlier this year, did so on an explicitly green pitch. Yet look at the architectural schools. Those doing urban design are 'designing in' climate change, hence, apparently, a profusion of floating technologies/floating communities student projects. Again and again one finds mid-sized practices

with sustainability completely embedded in their work: for instance Sarah Wrigglesworth Associates, one of the new stars, work from a straw bale live-work house in North London. Or another London based practice, Walters and Cohen, whose portfolio displays one after another green-hewed project.

What this tells us, the optimists suggest, is that sustainability in architectural design is becoming mainstream, that architects are literate and knowledgeable about the range of sustainability issues which need to be considered when exploring a client's brief. Others would argue that the development of sustainable architecture is still in its infancy, demonstrated by a palpable absence of fully-fledged, mature ecological aesthetics. True or not, as FCB's Clegg points out in his ecological iconographies essay last year, that with global warming actually beginning to effect the UK's weather, the balance of aesthetics will change anyway, shifting with the weather. So attention is no longer to be focused on the Nordic north's knowledge of reducing warmth-bringing energy, but on the Mediterranean south, where architects will be able to learn from centuries of experience of dealing with hotter climates. The art of shading, says Clegg, will become of prime importance.

This suggests locality and location as remaining important, and that sustainability within architectural debates will be carried out as part of the larger - for the architectural world - argument between the regional and the international. In a sense this a fault-line which divides architects by type, illustrated well by the return to favour over the last eighteen months of a kind of neo-modernism, highlighting locality and local material. Almost an identifiable movement, termed by some the new materialists, suggest that complete internationalisation and interchangeability between place, geography and materials, often forecast as inevitable, has been overplayed. Its most vocal advocate in this country is Patrick Lynch, though others, spread around Europe - are probably most visibly represented by the Swiss Regionalists, with Peter Zumthor as its hero.   >>>

Given their susceptibility to visual detailing, the new materialists aren't explicitly ecological, but even so a degree of common cause can be construed in both architectural parties shared attraction to variations of the regional. Set against this are yet more prefab construction initiatives, with one even surfacing at the 2006 Ecobuild Trade Fair; and making the seemingly unbelievable claims that this homogenising agent could be developed not merely for the European context, but the whole planet, never mind climate, never mind geography!

For some, Part L's influence includes being a counter-weight against such ultimate globalised fantasies, while also nurturing the possibilities of regaining traditional design studies, along with breathing new life into vernacular architecture, alongside new relationships to local culture. Such regionalist agenda's may well be aided by the Sustainable Procurement National Action Plan, published in June 2006 by the Sustainable Procurements Task Force. Noting that the government spend in the public sector comprises over £150 billion, the Task Force argues that if procurement chains for sustainable materials became easier, this would assist in shifting the market considerably further towards a sustainable economy, triggering many developments in environmental technologies, materials, and skills.

If applied to the government's major current public build priorities, principally the vast fifteen year £42 billion plus Building Schools for the Future programme and more sharply focused 2012 green Olympics - they could underscore a significant shift in building materials' procurement. This is part of the three big public spending areas in construction: healthcare, schools and the sustainable communities bandwagons. If these, as they have been repeatedly hyped, meet their sustainability criteria, they are where the current new generation of sustainable architects are most likely to cut their teeth, where new solutions will come through, and where, from a grassroots, rather than top-down, perspective the seedling sustainable architectural community will most likely realise itself.

All these elements - from sustainable procurement, through to architectural practices increasingly branding themselves as green, and, of course, Part L - feed the accelerating pace of the shift from development pure and simple, to sustainable development. What largely doesn't seem to get discussed is questioning the very clothes of this new emperor - sustainable development - and the new, sustainable ways of doing business, for example, importing organic sheep wool insulation from New Zealand. Any alternative perspective, which views sustainable development as not such a benign answer, finds hardly any voices in an architectural firmament which is dependent on its various paymasters to provide buildings to build.

By contrast, in the developing world, respected housing and poverty authorities argue passionately that sustainable development has now taken its place alongside disease and famine as a major generator of urban insecurity and fear. Questions on this level, seem to be just too much to consider for the vast majority of the 35,000 or so strong British architectural community, though also the small core sustainable architectural fraternity. There appears neither appetite nor interest, particularly at a time when workloads are gathering pace, for taking a long cool look at questioning the basis of sustainable development. In other words, whether all the building and design work is either actually needed, or the most genuine and propitious sustainable way forward. ❧

© Green Building Press

Mobile
07877 499901

Telephone
01245 380667

Acteson-Rook
Environmental Building
Consultancy

BRE accredited EcoHomes Assessor

Materials selection/sourcing

Eco Self-build Consultant
Guidance on a wide range of interior and
exterior materials for whole house well-being
to create your perfect eco home

info@acteson-rook.com
www.acteson-rook.com

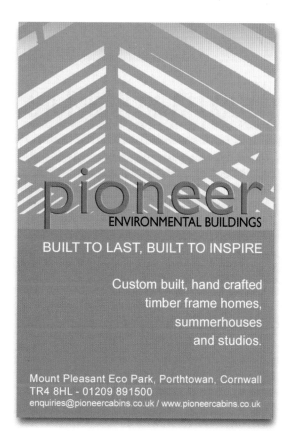

pioneer
ENVIRONMENTAL BUILDINGS

BUILT TO LAST, BUILT TO INSPIRE

Custom built, hand crafted
timber frame homes,
summerhouses
and studios.

Mount Pleasant Eco Park, Porthtowan, Cornwall
TR4 8HL - 01209 891500
enquiries@pioneercabins.co.uk / www.pioneercabins.co.uk

VISQUEEN ECOMEMBRANE
100% RECYCLED

New Visqueen EcoMembrane® Guaranteed 100% recycled post-use polyethylene waste.

Specifying recycled products helps to keep reusable material in the economy, diverts waste from landfill and conserves resources. Produced exclusively from 100% post use consumer waste; New Sustainable Visqueen EcoMembrane® is a high performance DPM that does not compromise on traditional DPM characteristics. The first DPM tested to the new rigorous European Standard EN 13967 Flexible Sheets for Waterproofing and to be Accredited by the BRE certificate No. 112/04.

For further technical information, contact us now on -

T: 01685 840672
F: 01685 842580
E: enquiries@visqueenbuilding.co.uk
W: visqueenbuilding.co.uk

Certificate No.
112/04

Wood in architecture

Today it is recognised that the specification of timber, both as construction and cladding material, has been steadily returning to favour among many architects, after many years out in the wilderness. This has been aided by a variety of ground-breaking and attention grabbing buildings with reasonable sustainable credentials, which have high-lighted, says **Oliver Lowenstein**, how timber can be applied in an architecturally exciting way.

That the majority of these buildings may not be sustainable projects through and through, hasn't dulled the realisation in the profession that timber has the potential to hold many sustainability credentials that concrete, steel and brick cannot compete with, if a whole life, rather than a 'here and now' approach is adopted.

Despite this, the indigenous British timber industry is hardly in the rudest of health. As many will know, approximately 80% of wood materials, primarily softwood, is imported from the Nordic region; with 60% of the remaining British production, also softwood, going into sawn timber. This feeds the principal market, timber frame housing, the use of which continues to gradually increase year on year. Across the most wooded parts of the country, saw mills continue to close down, unable to compete with usually higher quality European woods. The Forestry Commission priority is of forest amenity value, although strategies towards mixed and biodiverse replantation are maturing. There are many apocryphal stories of orders for locally sourced timber being abandoned because there just wasn't the wood available, or being transported half way across the country, as appropriate preparation technologies aren't available close to build sites.

Set against this, more and more architectural applications for low-grade timber, wastewood and thinnings are beginning to pay dividends, and an overall awareness and interest in both

the structural and engineered use of timber seems to be more widespread. As with so many parts of the profession, computers in engineered timber projects have come into their own. For those interested in how timber is influencing architecture it is these technological changes, converging with the influence of Part L, which is of interest in how sustainability questions are meeting architectural understanding of designing and completing buildings. Leaving to one side the mainstream timber frame industry, the unremarked maturing of these technological developments can be seen in any number of projects, from showcase, to large to medium scale. All this suggests that timber in construction has been given a new lease of life.

And the perception is that timber is, little by little, being increasingly specified by architects who only ten years ago wouldn't have considered it as a credible material. Evidence comes from all across the architectural sector, from major to small projects. It is no longer a fringe interest, and you only have to look at how two of the UK's leading practices Richard Rogers Partners (RRP) and Grimshaws, have each produced large-scale showcase projects featuring structural and cladding timberwork as part of their design brief.

For Rogers, it was the National Assembly for Wales building in Cardiff, completed and opened in 2006 after years of extended wrangling. The Assembly employs natural passive heating and cooling, an earth heat exchange system and a wood fired boiler. Its visual focus is a remarkable timber based roof-deck; a series of elliptical domes flowing over the main building's site, involving complicated roof geometries. Western red cedar is used to panel this deck and also as cladding for the funnel at the heart of the building. Although FSC sourced, and receiving a BRE 'excellent' rating, the cedar was imported.

One of the proto-typical hi-tech practices,

© Green Building Press

The National Assembly for Wales building in Cardiff, completed and opened after years of extended wrangling. The Assembly building employs natural passive heating and cooling, an earth heat exchange system and a wood fired boiler.

Photo: Redshift Photography

RRP's apparent conversion to timber is open to question, and previous efforts, most notably the North London Mossbourne Academy's use of a wet timber system, suggested minimal experience of the material and an approach which uses it like steel, rather than for its inherent properties. Grimshaw's Eden Project CORE building also used timber as a structural material, but did so by building on various continental precedents, even down to employing the German timber engineer giant, Merck. With the design informed by organic form in the shape of the sunflower spirals, its complex geometry eventually delivered the variation on a lamella of the roof system.

A third example, opened in 2006, is the new Savill Gardens gridshell in Windsor Great Park, designed by the Birmingham practice Glen Howells Architects. This is the first

major gridshell in Europe, since the much feted Cullinan's Weald and Downland Museum gridshell building of 2000. Keen to emphasise it as a low energy rather than sustainable exercise, Savill Gardens, none the less, exhibits the ongoing fascination certain groups of architects, engineers and designers in this country have with the gridshell form. Savill Gardens is essentially a timber deck, rather than building, twice the size of, and much lower in aspect than Weald and Downland gridshell. From above, the shape is somewhat reminiscent of a leaf-form, though modelled in the abstracted space of computers. The deck is another example of the team spirit behind the design: engineers, Buro Happold and carpenters, Green Oak Carpentry, meeting again after their collaboration on Weald and Downland. It will be interesting to see whether the arrival of this new grand scale gridshell will trigger a new round of attempts to get smaller – and unambivalently sustainable - gridshell projects off the ground in the next months and years.

These differing showcases highlight the fault line emerging in the timber engineering architectural world. Gridshells derive part of their fascination from their lightweight structural nature. Savill Gardens expands this avant-garde tradition in a most high-profile and, most would accept, conservative setting. But the other two buildings, particularly the Wales Assembly, where concrete is the core structural material, suggests timber as ancillary. Yet the visual centrality of timber in such showcase buildings marks, arguably, a coming of age of 'timber-build': signalling its new acceptability as a sustainable twenty-first century material. But does its crossing of a threshold also signal the

Housing is not missing out on the timber architecture trend. This new development in Angel Town in East London, designed by Anne Thorne Architects, makes extensive use of FSC certified cladding, frame and internal timbers.

disappearance of timber-build's more radical and experimental energies?

There have been many other showcased buildings in the last year, the rebranding and higher profile of the Wood Awards are evidence of this. From healthcare to education, new buildings applying structural timberwork can be found all over the country. The Scottish based Maggies centres, although not focusing on sustainability, have made most of the connection between the tacit warmth of wood as a material, and its 'healing qualities' used in a healthcare context. So far NHS buildings, with their focus on huge newbuild, have not provided quite as many examples as might be expected, especially compared to the education sector.

Here there are many examples to pick from. For instance, the corporate practice, BDP, involved in both higher education (HE) buildings, the new academies programme, as well as schools, have taken to applying timberwork both structurally and as part of their façade

© Green Building Press

Grimshaw's CORE building at the Eden project used timber as a structural material, but did so by building on various continental precedents, even down to employing the German timber engineer giant, Merck. The design is informed by organic form in the shape of the sunflower spirals for its complex geometry.

or foyer materials. South Bank University in Kennington, London, features an open foyer façade, comprising glulam beams and props. Study pods made from Finnish Kerto LVL, (a sturdy beam and panel product made by gluing together softwood veneers) hang mid-air on each floor. Another of BDP's recent HE projects is the Faculty of Education library building at Cambridge University. Similarly, the building here employs curved glulam and LVL floor deck aimed at a reminiscence of older wooden libraries, and integrated with a variety of sustainable features; a natural ventilation system which cools by chilled beams, along with a sustainable urban drainage system (SUDs), aiming to halve rainwater runoff.

At the soon to be completed Ramsgate Academy, the foyer canopy comprises a chunk of a torus, in effect a partial lamella, the structural form derived from Germany, but only just beginning to be used here. There are many other examples of school buildings being templates of timberbuild design. To mention only three; White-Design's award winning Kingsmead primary school in Cheshire is a study in glulam, and is repeated in a series of further iterations of the design, in Sheffield's St Anne's primary school and also with a series in Gwynned, South Wales. Walters and Cohen's new building at Bedales school, uses Douglas fir to provide structural supports for a concrete frame (for thermal mass), while clad in untreated larch; along with timber doors and the semi-mandatory natural lighting and ventilation. Finally the London based Greenhill Jenner continue to produce economic, pleasing and socially inspired buildings. Walthamstow's Queens Road community centre - with SureStart nursery facilities wrapped into various other functions - again employs concrete for its massing properties, but is complemented with dry-lined timber and externally untreated Douglas fir cladding.

What many of these projects demonstrate, is that engineered timber, from the Nordic and Baltic countries has established itself in Britain, be it Glulam, Kerto or Thermowood. However although this may well be the case, it still

comprises only a small part of the total timber market. Some say that it is too small for home-grown Glulam to take off – though the Eden Project's new visitor centre now features a film explaining the comparable sustainable advantages of Glulam to any interested member of the general public. And homegrown glulam, this time from waste wood chestnut, is beginning to make its mark, at least in the South East, where chestnut beams and columns are being produced by In-Wood, in Sussex, and feature in BBM Sustainable Design's community centre, 'The Bridge' in Hastings. In-Wood has also been the company behind developing the technology for the long length laths for both the Gridshells, another area which is gradually growing. On the ground the experiments started by Hooke Park in the eighties are apparently beginning to feed through, with waste wood and thinnings being looked at seriously by several organisations.

If the Nordic engineered timber is currently safe in its market share, a new timber laminate is currently being met with much interest. Another school building, a south London sports hall by DRMM architects is one of the first to apply cross panelling, by KLH, up to 3m high and 240mm long, fitted together with 300mm long screws. The system derives from Austria and is being taken up by a number of British practises. For instance Edward Cullinan Architects are using it for their Edinburgh Botanic Gardens post and frame visitor centre.

Of course, this doesn't fully deal with the more pressing question, how does Britain start using a larger proportion of its own harvested timber, short circuiting part of the embodied energy equation? How might it reduce its dependence on imported woods, whether certificated or not? Indeed the southern counties surrounding London, contains one of the most wood covered areas in England, with many small independent foresters whose stands, although not necessarily sustainably certificated (because of cost, usually), both grow and know the quality of their wood. But overall, for the industry, timber origin is something of a non-question, and for some in the sustainable design world it is also not central. If the wood

© Green Building Press

Making fantastic use of traditional homegrown timber, the community centre called 'The Bridge', in Hastings, features chestnut beams and columns which have been produced by 'In-Wood', in Sussex. Photo courtesy of BBM architects.

is coming from the Nordic areas, transport miles are not having a big impact, according to Bjorn Berge author of The Ecology of Building Materials, when I posed this question to him some years ago. Rome is nearer to Oslo than the northern borders of Norway, he added. But Britain has (at present) a different climate, with much more potential for broadleaf growth.

Although the years are running out, sizeable replanting of hardwoods could provide a materials' insurance, of a kind, later into the century. There are some who appear to be working around versions of such a premise, permaculturalist and cult cruck-frame self-builder, Ben

Law, for one. But overall it doesn't appear to have taken root among the wider architectural community. That the penny might drop within this community, given the mini resurgence in timberbuild, might be one hoped for spin-off, leading to a much more widespread debate about the benefits of re- and afforestation across the country. ✑

Useful information

Some contact addresses for engineered wood products:

www.finnforest.co.uk/default.asp?path=200;256;1317
www.in-wood.co.uk
www.klh.at

Micro-generation CHP

The last year or so has seen a lot of interest emerge in micro-generation - the generation of power by consumers in their own homes. A lot of very different technologies are bundled together in the micropower category, and not all may be equally viable. **Dave Elliott** looks at this emerging field ...

Micro-wind and domestic scale solar PV may have their detractors, given that they are expensive, PV in particular, and you may get more carbon reductions from other types of larger investment (e.g large scale wind farms), but once they are installed, they are at least carbon free supply technologies. By contrast micro-combined heat and power units use natural gas to power a Stirling engine or fuel cell, and that means there are direct carbon emissions. In theory, since they generate electricity and heat, they should be more efficient than say a conventional gas boiler, so micro-CHP should produce less emissions. However, in summer, when you don't need heat, you will not generate much electricity, so the overall energy efficiency will be reduced. Detractors say the electricity conversion efficiency averaged over the year can be as low as 11%, and translated into carbon emission avoidance that may mean you might do better with a gas condensing boiler - which would also be cheaper. But as yet only a few hundred micro-CHP systems have been installed for testing, so we are only now beginning to have an idea of what their actually performance is like over time.

Nevertheless, as was mentioned in Building for a Future magazine Vol. 15, No. 4 (Spring 2006)[1], the Carbon Trust reported some preliminary results from practical consumer trials, and they did not look very good[2]. Whereas some earlier modeling work had predicted up to 40% emission savings, the trials have found that in practice, over the full year, some of the units have only averaged 18% reductions and in some case much less. Indeed,

in some cases the units yield 18% lower reductions than achieved by conventional systems. The Trust says that 'more trials are needed, since only a relatively few units were available for test, but even so the emerging trial data indicates there is unlikely to be a significant carbon emissions reduction opportunity from wide deployment of the technology at this stage in its evolution. From the results of the trial to date, carbon savings are in the range of plus or minus 18%. The reasons behind this are being investigated but appear to relate to the interaction of the devices with the heating system, building and occupancy'. It adds that, 'if this trend continues for the full trial, there will be a material risk of an increase in emissions if micro-CHP is deployed at scale without regard to the different performance characteristics of specific technologies and the circumstances of their installation, maintenance and use.'

It seems that part of the problem is that the technology is still at a relatively early stage of development. In its initial publicity, the British Gas offshoot Microgen claimed their micro-CHP unit would have an overall efficiency of 90% or more, and could typically lead to a 25% annual reduction in CO_2 emissions. However, subsequently they announced that, 'following a comprehensive review' of the programme, they had decided that they needed to invest 'more time on product design and reliability testing before launching the Microgen system'. This, they said 'together with confirming energy savings and CO_2 performance' was 'of paramount importance to the success of Microgen and micro-CHP generally'. Further stringent field-tests were undertaken in 2005. This has inevitably delayed the commissioning of volume production. It was hoped that the commercial launch date would be spring 2007. The hope is that, as the technology and experience with using it improves, higher performance will be achieved.

Certainly, a review of micro power technology produced in November 2005, for the Energy Saving Trust,[3] was upbeat about the longer term prospects of micro-CHP. It says that by 2050, micogeneration, including micro-CHP, solar PV, micro wind, heat pumps and micro-biomass, if widely adopted by consumers, could potentially provide at least 25% of UK electricity and around 220GWh of heat per annum, with micro-CHP dominating. This assumes regulatory incentives, subsidies and proper payment for any excess power exported to the electricity grid (i.e net metering or as the EST report calls it 'energy export equivalence'). On this basis, the EST report finds that by 2050, overall, micro-generation could reduce UK emissions by 14.5% (based on 2005 levels). They see Stirling engine micro-CHP as being one of the likely leaders, particularly in larger houses. They put its likely breakthrough date, when costs become competitive with conventional sources, as 2010. By 2020 they say that there could be 16GW of micro-CHP capacity in place - 20% of UK electricity generating capacity. By 2050, they say that, assuming proper support, 8 million domestic units could

Though early trials of Sterling engine micro CHP units were inconclusive, the EST believes they will be popular options for larger homes in the future.

be installed, supplying 40% of domestic heating and 6% of UK electricity, but, interestingly, only cutting UK emissions by 1.9%. Fuel cell micro CHP will, they say, develop a bit more slowly, with a cost breakthrough date of 2017. By 2050 there could be 8GW(e)[4] in place supplying 9% of UK electricity and cutting emissions by 3% per annum. Micro wind has a cost breakthrough date of 2015 and by 2050 there could be 15GW(e) in place, supplying 4% of UK electricity and cutting emissions by 6%. Despite its costs, and a breakthrough date of 2049, PV solar could also be supplying 4% by 2050 - cutting emissions by 3%. The prospects for solar water heating and micro biomass, however, are not seen as very good (perhaps 6Twh pa and 4.5Twh pa respectively by 2050), but ground source heat pumps are seen as doing well - 12TWh pa by 2050. Finally, micro hydro supplies are forecast to be 100MW(e) by 2050.

Well there is some way to go before we can expect anything like that. The EST report noted that there are currently under 100,000 micro-generation units in the UK, mostly solar water heaters installed pre-2000, and that micro-CHP was only just beginning to enter the market - there were around 950 micro-CHP units in place. The big issue is whether this will grow and from the results so far, that is far from clear.

References

1. www.buildingforafuture.co.uk

2. For the Carbon Trust Trials preliminary report see: www.thecarbontrust.co.uk/carbontrust/about/publications/181105_01.pdf

3. For a summary of the report to EST see: www.dti.gov.uk/energy/consultations/pdfs/microgeneration-est-summary.pdf

4. (e) denotes electricity production

Note: *1MW = 1000kW*

     1GW = 1000MW

     1TW = 1000GW

Biomass industry review

'Biomass' a term bandied around liberally by the government, the renewable energy sector and co-firing electrical generators, but what is it? And why can biomass play such an important part in reversing the UK's impact on climate change? **Gideon Richards** investigates ...

Biomass is defined as 'organic matter used as a fuel, especially in a power station for the generation of electricity'. The Oxford Concise English Dictionary must have been provided this definition by the UK government, who find it difficult to appreciate the true benefits that biomass heat can bring to solving energy security and demand.

In real terms, for the domestic and smaller scale market, biomass is predominantly from the woody material, supplied either as a bi-product from the wood processing and manufacturing industry, or from virgin material, such as logs and woodchips.

Where we talk about wood pellet fuel, this has almost certainly been produced from residues (bi-products) from some other process. However, more and more, we are seeing other feedstocks being introduced to the market, like, straw, grain, miscanthus (elephant grass) and there is talk about using rape meal, the bi-product of the pressed rape from the rapeseed oil pressing.

Over the last 3 years the UK has seen an emergence of modern, highly efficient, highly controllable boilers using woodfuel. These have come in a number of designs, using various fuel forms. However, it is noticeable that predominantly, most of the technology comes from abroad - Austria and Italy. This emergence has been brought about from a number of fronts:
- the prices for fossil fuels have and are increasing in large steps
- the co-firing market has stimulated the

development of supply chains
- the renewable obligation certificates (ROC)[1] has supported the co-firing and electrical generation markets. This has created a demand for larger volumes of woodfuel (and other biomass), which in turn has created economies of scale to create an economic value for the fuels
- the EU and UK Emissions Trading Scheme (ETS) provides a mechanism for biomass to be valued as an offset in carbon reduction targets.

The above points are all at a large scale. For the domestic and smaller boiler user it may seem remote and of little consequence. However, in their way, these points have been an instrumental part of creating the stimulus within the market and will continue to do so. As policy and legislation develops to include more small scale biomass systems, utilizing the like of agencies and aggregation of systems, the mechanisms above will feel more real.

- There are grants to help offset the differential in cost between fossil fuel burning appliances and biomass boilers
- there is more choice of stoves and boilers in the UK
- fuel is becoming more readily available and the distribution networks are starting to develop around clusters, enabling economies of scale to stabilize and reduce the price of the fuel in comparison to individuals ordering on their own
- climate change is focusing people's attention and biomass is a CO_2 neutral way of heating a building without making an impact on the planet
- the market structure is becoming such that biomass supply is seen as less of a risk
- a major influencing factor in some council areas, and particularly the London boroughs, has been the so called 'Merton Rule', which requires new buildings over

© Green Building Press

1000m² to generate 10% of their energy from on-site renewable energy sources, (either electricity or heat or a combination of the two). This policy has been developed out of PPS22 – Renewable Energy.

This last point is developing across the UK rapidly through council policies, Regional Spatial Strategies (RSS) and Local Development Frameworks (LDF), and will be a growing feature of planning policy over the coming years as the policies come into force. Being statutory policies will mean that there is a requirement to deliver the on-site generation. Planning will not be refused unless there is a very good reason why it can't be done. This point has been reinforced by Yvette Cooper, the Housing and Planning Minister, during a statement following a review of local authorities implementing planning policies in line with PPS22.

Additional to these, the European Commission published the EU Biomass action Plan in December '05 , which focuses on the development of biofuels for transport and biomass for heating. The UK has also had a government backed task force, looking at how we can utilise biomass (Biomass Task Force Report to Government - Oct '05)[1] and a subsequent response from the government on the task force's recommendations (June '06)[2].

As a direct result of the Biomass Task Force report and the new Climate Change and Sustainable Energy Bill, 2006, the government's response has been to review and start developing a mechanism for a heat obligation of some form. This is important as 70% of energy used in domestic buildings, and between 30-35% of energy used in commercial buildings, is for heating and hot water and could well provide a major renaissance in community heating schemes.

While the above may appear very complex and obscure, the important fact is that biomass will play an ever-increasing role in the renewable energy mix and contribution to the government's target of 20% CO_2 reduction by 2010, once it is understood that biomass used in

modern appliances is very different to burning coal in existing solid fuel appliances.

Technology

Enough said about the policy drivers for now, how has the technology developed and what are the options in the market?

The technology used to heat buildings with biomass has moved on a pace from the open fires, roomheaters and solid fuel stoves and cooking appliances of the past. These still exist, however, increasingly the requirements for more efficient and cost effective heating systems are putting the squeeze on these types of appliances and are likely to continue to do so, due in part to the new Part L of the Building Regulations on Conservation of Fuel and Power, and the requirement from 2007 that mandatory 'Home Information Pack' (HIP'S) will require the seller to declare energy performance information.

Appliances fall broadly into four categories:

Space heaters – which heat the room the appliance sits in, although there are systems that allow hot air to be circulated by ducting to other rooms.

Space heaters with back boilers - stoves and cooking appliances - which do a combination of space and hot water heating. These can run a small radiator heating system, but some are limited in output. The output efficiencies vary greatly dependant on the type of appliance being used.

Boiler systems – these can be from 2kW for very well insulated buildings, through to large multiple boiler systems. Some use heat stores and accumulator tanks, to buffer the heat loads. Boilers are usually highly efficient, with many of them being highly automated, to a degree where they automatically de-ash, can clean the heat exchanger tubes, provide heat metering and auto switching on and off.

>>>

CHP or combined heat and power systems
- which have been developed at various sizes, however, at present require a constant heat load to make the economics stack up. It is the intention of the government that all multi-use schemes should consider CHP as a first option, if the heat load is there, i.e. what is commonly known as good quality combined heat and power. The UK has a checkered past in district heating (now often called community heating schemes); however, biomass systems are used all over Europe very effectively and give the control and metering directly at the property, through heat exchangers, internal and external thermostatic temperature controls and timers.

With the increasing requirements for builders to squeeze more properties onto a plot of land, there is a great opportunity to use biomass community heating schemes, which maximize the useable space and hence the saleable floor area in the individual buildings. It will also reduce the energy requirements of the buildings, through matching the energy demand better with one appliance, instead of having larger than actually required, gas boilers for each building to cover every eventuality. In turn this will reduce the carbon footprint for the development by requiring less energy and finally cost the end-user less money as fossil fuels energy costs keeps spiraling upwards.

Fuel

As the technology develops, the one question that always arises is that of the fuel availability. While there has and in some circumstances, there still is, an issue with getting fuels of the appropriate quality and volume, this is changing substantially, month on month, in the UK.

Fuel quality

The three predominant forms of fuel being used are logs, woodchips and wood pellets. All have had issues with regards to quality in the past. However, these are becoming a thing of the past as suppliers and end-users are becoming more competent at specifying the quality required, including new European Standards

to support the trading and use of the fuels. There are also a number of good reference documents dealing with biomass fuel quality available[3].

The UK government, in its response to the Biomass Task Force (BTF) report, announced that it will adopt the new European standards. With this endorsement, it is important that end-users, fuel producers and the equipment manufacturers and installers, use fuels to the standards, and that there is an understanding of what the standards mean. In addition to incorporating the standards, the industry is working on a Woodfuel Certification Scheme, which should help provide confidence to users of the fuel.

Installers

To solve the probem of rogue installers the REAL Assurance Scheme[4] was launched in July 2006 to provide a consumer code for companies supplying microgeneration products to end-users. This scheme will be Office of Fair Trade certified, and once again, is designed to provide buyers with the confidence to pick companies which are prepared to provide a quality service and support structure.

Grants

There are a number of grant schemes available for biomass schemes and equipment. The Low Carbon Building Programme[5] (LCBP) has recently been launched (for all microgeneration products) to replace the DTI Clear Skies and Solar PV grant programmes. This scheme allows individuals, communities and developers wanting financial support with their schemes to apply for a grant. The scheme is split into two streams. In the first phase; stream 1 being for householders and communities, with a £10.5 million pot over the three years, and stream 2 for larger scale developments, with an £18.5 million pot, which will be allocated through a bidding process. The latter scheme is hoped to generate enough volume in the market to bring economies of scale into the renewables industry, thereby reducing equipment costs.

© Green Building Press

The second phase is for £50 million and is being developed to support public sector projects, with a particular emphasis on education.

Additional to the LCBP there is also the Bio-energy Capital Grants Scheme, Bio-energy Infrastructure Scheme and regional development agencies have various support structures in place for biomass projects.

Future trends

At this point it would be good to do some crystal ball gazing. How is it anticipated that the industry will develop and what new products will be developed?

These are difficult questions to accurately answer; however, the biomass industry is developing rapidly. If the government continues to support biomass, and fossil fuel prices keep rising, the industry will continue to grow. This growth will start in the public sector as more and more local authorities incorporate biomass-heating schemes into their own building stock. As this develops and the supply chains strengthen, commercial and domestic users will grow. This can already be seen in councils such as Barnsley MBC who have introduced a biomass policy, which has been instrumental in them winning the prestigious Ashden Award in 2006 for a biomass supply chain project.

The development of a heat obligation, in whatever form, is likely to be a stimulus for the heat market, and the biomass industry in particular. However, there is considerable concern from environmental groups that the biomass industry is developed in a sustainable manner, which also takes account of biodiversity.

In terms of the technology, it is likely that biomass microCHPs, biomass condensing boilers, biofuel and potentially micro biogas boilers will be developed and introduced to the UK market over the next 5 – 10 years. Along with this, heat meters and smart meters will develop for the smaller scale heating appliances to enable them to benefit from energy supply contracts (companies supplying energy).

With the introduction of building performance data for the HIPs and tightening of air quality requirements it is likely that energy generating appliances will require labels, in much the same way as white goods do. This information would demonstrate the appliance's efficiency and emission levels against the current regulatory levels, and the fuel required for a standard building (whatever that may be).

Conclusions

The biomass industry can contribute considerably to the energy mix in the UK and play a major part in reducing CO_2 emissions. Biomass is the only renewable energy source that is not intermittent. This gives it an advantage over other renewable energy sources. However, due to the space required for fuel storage in comparison to other technologies, it may find it hard to take its rightful place for smaller individual domestic properties. That said, the way building developments have been reducing their footprints, the opportunity to provide community heating is growing all the time.

Current ossil fuel prices, and confidence that fossil fuel prices won't come down, can only be a good thing for the biomass industry. The development of a robust supply chain over the coming years, and homegrown fuels such as wood pellets, can only help the confidence in the market.

Don't be surprised if the next house you buy is supplied by a biomass heating system! ✆

References

1. http://ec.europa.eu/energy/res/biomass_action_plan/green_electricity_en.htm

2. www.defra.gov.uk/farm/crops/industrial/energy/biomass-taskforce/index.htm

3. See Biomass Energy Centre Website:
www.forestry.gov.uk/fr/INFD-6P8G8E

4. REAL Assurance Scheme:
www.renewablepowerassociation.org/article_flat.fcm?articleid=20

5. The Low Carbon Buildings programme:
www.est.org.uk/housingbuildings/funding/lowcarbon-buildings

A review of eco-building organisations

The AECB

The AECB, the independent sustainable building association, was founded in 1989 to facilitate environmentally responsible practices within building. Its members are committed to reducing the environmental impact of buildings and there is a vast range of knowledge and expertise within the organisation. Many of its members are at the forefront of sustainable design and represent the organisation on many different groups. Its members get together each year at the AECB's annual ecobuilding conference held at different venues across the UK and where workshops and debates run in tandem with networking. There are also local groups planned for some areas.

The organisation is currently focusing much of its resources on measures to tackle climate change. 50% (excluding air travel) of CO_2 emissions are currently from buildings, so reducing energy consumption in buildings is a vital step forward. The AECB's new CarbonLite programme aims to refine and enhance sustainable design skills in the area in which they are currently the weakest, i.e energy performance. The new programme, which is under development and based on the German passivhaus standards, is a complete 'carbon literate' design and construction programme based around bronze, silver, gold and platinum standards. AECB members are bein encouraged to build new homes to the gold and silver standards. Work is in progress on a set of six Silver Standard construction details with more to follow in due course.

The AECB also runs courses under its SussEd (Sustainable Skills Training and Education initiative) programme, aimed at those working in all areas of the building industry. There are plans to increase the scope of the training programme with courses on a range of issues of interest to those wanting to make buildings more sustainable. Current courses reflect the AECB's current focus on energy efficient construction. The AECB can also design and run customised courses and CPD training for companies, local authorities, voluntary groups, colleges etc.

The AECB's vision is to act as a key player in the sustainable construction arena for government, the construction industry and its members. It aims to inspire, debate, raise awareness of the problems, assist with policy guidance, disseminate knowledge; produce appropriate guidance and tools. It is now a key player in lobbying and advising government and other key institutions, responding to all relevant consultations.
www.aecb.net   0845 456 9773

Building Research Establishment (BRE)

The BRE is a UK centre of excellence for the built environment with experts on environmental issues, sustainability, construction, fire and risk. Over the past 15 years the organisation has been instrumental in developing an understanding of what we need to do to design, build and manage buildings in a way that protects the environment and helps reduce carbon emissions. It has done this by undertaking extensive research in this field and then developing tools and guidance for the industry to use.

The best known is probably the BREEAM family of environmental assessment schemes. These tools set out criteria and targets for a range of issues, including energy, water, transport, pollution, materials, health and well being, ecology and land use. Designers, developers and contractors use these as a guide to aspire to, and their project is awarded a 'pass', 'good', 'very good' or 'excellent' rating depending on its achievements. There are BREEAM schemes

HOCKERTON HOUSING PROJECT TRADING LTD
The Watershed, Gables Drive, Hockerton, Southwell, Notts NG25 0QU

Tel: 01636 816902

Email: hhp@hockerton.demon.co.uk

Website: www.hockertonhousingproject.org.uk

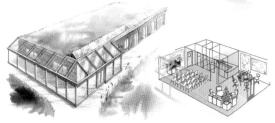

Since completion in 1998 the Hockerton Housing Project(HHP) has established itself as an exemplar of sustainable development, locally and nationally, providing a unique 'real-life' experience of living sustainably. HHP provides a range of information, services and opportunities to visit the project.

Our new learning resource centre with dedicated audio-visual room, seminar facilities and permanent exhibitions, has recently been completed to support these activities and provide a unique venue.

Guided Tours • **Workshops** • **Publications** • **Consultancy**

See the website or contact us to find out more about experiencing it yourself.

low-impact living initiative

L I L I

residential weekend courses

how to make biodiesel
natural paints & lime
straw-bale building
heating with wood
wind & solar electricity
low-impact smallholding
cob building
round wood timber framing

rammed earth building
veg oil engine conversion
self-build geodesic domes
living in communities
roofing
self-build solar hot water
sustainable water & sewage
DIY for beginners
and many more

**also: factsheets, books, home energy visits, online shop
and the best value solar hot water kit in the UK**

courses £180 / £150 / £120; includes accommodation and all meals
discounts for 'friends of LILI'; for dates, plus more information, visit our website or contact
LILI, Redfield Community (pictured), Winslow, Bucks, MK18 3LZ

01296 714184   lili@lowimpact.org   www.lowimpact.org

for many types of commercial and public buildings (offices, schools industrial, retail, prisons etc) and the EcoHomes scheme which covers housing.

EcoHomes, like all BRE's environmental assessment schemes, is updated each year. This is in response to changes to building regulations, new technology and developments in sustainability best practice. EcoHomes 2006 was launched on the same day as changes to Part L of the Building Regulations, encouraging developments to demonstrate even greater energy performance over building regulations, thus further reducing carbon dioxide emissions. Other amendments include raising energy credit thresholds, a stipulation for refrigerators, freezers and cooling systems to have A+ energy labels, rewards for low-energy lighting systems that exceed Building Regulation requirements, three new credits for renewable energy systems, and a regrading of the NOx credit that is easier for developments using small scale renewables, to achieve.

Although EcoHomes is perhaps more generally associated as the environmental hallmark for standard residential developments, the scheme can be applied to a variety of residential building types. Bespoke EcoHomes was introduced three years ago, to cater for more complex types of multi-residency housing such as student halls, sheltered housing for senior citizens, accommodation for the mentally and physically disabled and hostels for the homeless.

EcoHomes can also be used to assess homes being substantially refurbished. And this year the first assessment scheme for managed housing stock was added to the stable. EcoHomes XB guides housing associations, local authorities and other landlords through the process of improving the environmental performance of their housing stock.

Other tools and assessment schemes produced by BRE include their environmental profiling scheme which assesses the environmental impact of building materials and components and their waste management schemes.
www.bre.co.uk 01923 664500

Centre for Alternative Technology (CAT)

CAT offers practical ways to address problems such as climate change, pollution and waste, addressing every aspect of the average lifestyle. The key areas include renewable energy, environmental building, energy efficiency, organic growing and alternative sewage systems. Leading by example, there is a small community living at the centre, experimenting with different ways of living, putting cooperative and environmental ideas into action.

Visitors to the site (open 7 days a week) can look forward to seeing lots of different buildings and displays, including interactive exhibits. CAT also publishes and sells a range of books, runs a free information service (but for bigger projects, there is a consultancy service) and holds a very diverse range of residential courses - from weekend workshops to the very popular year-long MSc.
www.cat.org.uk 01654 705950

Cornwall Sustainable Building Trust (CSBT)

Cornwall Sustainable Building Trust is a charitable company committed to making building design and construction as sustainable as possible, with minimal negative impact on the environment, both locally and globally. This is achieved through the promotion of design that minimises energy consumption, and sources local and renewable materials wherever possible, CSBT aims to highlight the social, environmental and economic benefits from the provision of affordable, well-designed and healthy homes and business accommodation with low running costs, throughout Cornwall.

The Trust's aim is to raise awareness through a varied programme of events, as well as providing advice and guidance. Central to the Trust's work is the provision of training in a range of both traditional and sustainable construction techniques. In addition to a regularly revised course list, covering a wide range of topics related to sustainability and construction and filling some of the gaps existing in training provision across the regions of the county, we have been able to deliver, in conjunction with CITB Construction Skills and Cornwall College, an industry recognised qualification in traditional craft stone masonry, encouraging the application of lime in preference to cementitious mortars and renders.

Working closely with small and medium sized businesses within the construction sector in Cornwall, CSBT assists them in developing their capability to understand and respond to the expanding traditional and sustainable construction market, helping them to increase their

market potential. Also working with the micro renewables sector, CSBT's microgen project, funded by the Learning and Skills Council and the European Social Fund, will work towards develoing industry approved installer training for domestic renewable energy devices.

Changes to the planning system and increasing awareness of climate change has led to a rapidly expanding market for renewable energy installations. Solar thermal, solar PV, ground, air and water sourced heating and cooling systems, biomass and pellet carbon neutral heaters, combined heat and power boilers, heat recovery ventilation and cooling systems, numerous variations of wind power are among the many solutions currently on offer.

CSBT will work with interested installers and householders, to train new installers to the highest possible standard and prepare written

Cornwall Sustainable Building Trust

CSBT

Eden's Watering Lane Nursery Lobb's Shop St Austell Cornwall PL26 6BE

Phone: 01726 68654
Fax: 01726 67028
admin@csbt.org.uk

www.csbt.org.uk

Cornwall Sustainable Building Trust works to promote awareness within the construction industry and amongst the general public, through the provision of training in a range of both traditional and sustainable construction techniques and awareness raising seminars.

Currently CSBT is working with the Micro renewables sector to develop industry approved installer training for domestic renewable energy devices. whilst developing a valuable portfolio of Cornish property RE installations, recording best practice, customer reaction and any responsive change in attitude, and feeding this data into a wider study being carried out by Exeter University.

In addition, we offer a programme of training events covering everything from traditional timber framing, cob and rammed earth, roofing, DIY solar panel making and site waste management, amongst others.

To join CSBT, visit our website, which also includes a full listing of training events, as well as a directory of sustainable building suppliers, services and professionals.

CITB constructionskills

This project is part-financed by the European Union
Working with Objective One

one
The Objective One Partnership for Cornwall & the Isles of Scilly

Learning+Skills Council
Devon and Cornwall

defra
Department for Environment Food and Rural Affairs

Cornwall COLLEGE

reports of the chosen installations. These reports will form a valuable source of comparative data on RE installations within Cornwall and will be incorporated within a wider study currently being undertaken by Exeter University. www.csbt.org.uk 01726 67028

Hockerton Housing Project (HHP)

This organisation, a practical example, acts as a catalyst for change towards ecologically sound and sustainable ways of living. The last couple of years has seen a significant increase in interest in sustainable design and construction as evidence of climate change becomes ever more apparent. This has been fuelled by rising energy prices and growing water shortages. The Hockerton Housing Project is no longer seen as a curious oddity, but as an inspiration for others to develop solutions to these growing problems. HHP has seen a change in the attitude of visiting building professionals, from early scepticism to a desire to learn and integrate sustainable design principles into their building projects.

HHP offers both full day technical workshops and consultancy services to assist building professionals, housing providers, government officers, students and self-builders. Over the next couple of years there are plans to develop these further to meet skills gaps in delivering low carbon buildings. The HHP's community building, the Sustainable Resource Centre, can be hired as an inspirational venue for meetings, seminars or team-building activities. www.housingproject.org.uk 01636 816902

Low Impact Living Initiative (LILI)

Lili run courses for those who want to build and install their own solar hot water systems with a book due out shortly. Solar hot water has been the biggest growth area recently. An economical system can also be purchased from the group. There is an online shop. New staff are available to undertake home energy visits and to talk to people about how they can save energy and switch to renewables. It seems that interest in green alternatives is growing expo-

nentially, if web hits are anything to go by! The number of courses have increased by 50% with 4 new ones which include heating with wood. www.lowimpact.org 01296 714184.

Scottish Ecological Design Association (SEDA)

The Scottish Ecological Design Association promotes knowledge and discussion about the principles of ecological design and their application to communities, environments, projects, systems, services, materials and products, with particular reference to Scotland. This is rooted in a concern for the welfare of planetary eco-systems, and the need for man's activities to be linked to the practice of mature stewardship, which values resource conservation and protects the evolution and wellbeing of other species.

SEDA is a member-run organisation which is open to anyone with an interest in ecological design. No qualifications are required and the membership includes individuals, students, families, charities, companies of all sizes, and government organisations; there are about 200 members coming from a wide range of backgrounds, in particular the built environment. There is a considerable body of knowledge amongst the membership and so the association provides a network for the exchange of information and ideas, as well as engaging in policy decisions.

A magazine comes out three times a year, and e-mail bulletins are circulated roughly once a month. There are also regular talks, site visits and other activities, including an annual student travel award which is open to students of design who are studying in Scotland, and an informal and popular 'show and tell' get-together at Christmas.

More information about SEDA and membership details can be found on our web site. www.seda2.org 01361 840 230

© Green Building Press

THE UK CENTRE OF EXCELLENCE FOR A SUSTAINABLE BUILT ENVIRONMENT

BRE provide tools and guidance for professionals involved in construction and refurbishment

www.bre.co.uk

BUILDING A BETTER WORLD

S E D A
Scottish Ecological Design Association

Scotland's foremost voluntary forum for promoting ecological design:

- *regular events, large and small*
- *magazine three times a year*
- *e-mail bulletins*
- *research and projects*
- *opportunities for meeting like-minded people*

Membership is open to interested groups, companies and individuals.

Contact: Gill Pemberton, SEDA Membership Secretary, Abbey St. Bathans House, Duns, Berwickshire TD11 3TX. Tel. 01361 840 230

South West Sustainable Construction Network

Local organisations to promote sustainable construction and design have been set up. These local organisations are working together to share resources, expertise and lobby for stronger regional policies and promotion of sustainable building. The mission is to make sustainable building the norm by 2010. The organisations involved include:

- Somerset Trust for Sustainable Development (STSD)
- Cornwall Sustainable Building Trust
- Dorset Sustainable Building Initiative
- Devon Sustainable Building Initiative

Current projects instigated by the network include the new eco development at Great Bow Yard, the Genesis project and ongoing consultancy. The STSD organises the popular Homes for Good exhibition each year.

In addition Wiltshire RIBA and Wiltshire Agenda 21 are active in similar work and in Bristol the city council and the Create Centre do a lot to promote sustainable building.
www.sustainablehousing.org.uk
01458 259400

The Green Register

The Green Register (TGR) is an independent, self-funded organisation whose central goal is to promote sustainable building practices across all disciplines of the construction industry. This is achieved through the three main activities:

- raising awareness of sustainable building practices by running training and events across the UK. These events range from in-house CPD seminars, half-day practical workshops such as 'Delivering sustainable construction in the planning system and integrated design - the way forward', through to the two-day training course 'Sustainable building and services' (SBS)

that all TGR members have attended
- networking – TGR events provide an opportunity to exchange ideas, provide mutual support and make professional connections with other like-minded individuals
- the Green Register itself – where a list of members is placed on a web-based register, which is available to potential clients who are looking for professionals who have demonstrated a commitment to sustainable building practices.

One of TGR's core principles is to encourage cross-disciplinary debate and so TGR events and membership are open to everyone with an interest in sustainable construction.

A course which ran in October 2006 had the largest attendance to date (over 50 delegates), signalling the ground swell of interest and concern about the state of the health of the planet. TGR will continue to address this critical problem in the future by attracting more members who will, in turn, work together to reduce the impact the construction industry has on the environment we live in.
www.greenregister.org.uk 0117 377 3490

The Walter Segal Self Build Trust

The Walter Segal Self Build Trust (WSSBT) runs a one day timber frame self build theory course throughout the country. They also run occasional practical courses and will design specific courses for self build groups, local authorities and housing professionals. All the courses focus on lessening the environmental impact of the building at all stages of its life and maximise the users involvement in all aspects of the building process. Although its main focus is housing, the WSSBT also has a training programme for those planning any community building such as village halls, allotment buildings and community centres.
www.segalselfbuild.co.uk. ✆

© Green Building Press

Training and education

Green building training and education is a fast growing area. **Gavin Harper** gives us an overview on what is currently available.

Green building courses, both practical and academic, are now offered by a range of providers and at all levels. Some are introductions to the subject for the interested layman, whilst others are more academic for the professional and those wishing to make a career in green building. The internet is a great resource and low-impact way of finding out about what is available. If you do not have access to the internet many libraries can offer free access. www.hotcourses.com allows you to search for courses, from evening classes to postgraduate study. For those solely interested in university education www.ucas.co.uk is a good place to start, and for post-graduate study www.finda-masters.com

Practical training

Training courses are ideal if you are interested in acquiring a specific skill, without comprehensively covering a wide subject matter in all of its detail. Courses can be accredited (officially recognised) and non-accredited. An accredited course might be a pre-requisite if, for example, you wish to install solar panels for a living. Such accredited courses give some guarantee of quality and might be validated by an organisation such as City and Guilds, or a trade association. However, if you simply want to pursue a skill for your own development, then a non accredited course is usually the cheaper option.

The Centre for Alternative Technology (CAT) 01654 705950 www.cat.org.uk/courses is one of the longest standing providers of sustainable construction education in the UK. With an established reputation and a body of core experts in all relevant subjects, courses are available in such diverse fields as heating with wood, to alternative heating systems.

LILI www.lowimpact.org the low impact living initiative, offer a variety of practical courses suited to home owners and builders that are interested in a low impact way of life.

The Genesis Project www.genesisproject.com is a new centre opened by the Somerset College of Arts and Technology (www.somerset.ac.uk). A range of short CPD courses are available.

Amazon Nails www.strawbalefutures.org.uk run a variety of courses focused on strawbale building and working with lime.

Green Dragon Energy http://greendrag-onenergy.co.uk run a variety of courses in renewable energy technologies.

For courses relating to lime, earth, cob and other natural building products and techniques:
Mike Wye & Associates: www.mikewye.co.uk
Calch Ty-Mawr Lime: www.lime.org.uk
Lime Centre: www.thelimecentre.co.uk
The Cornish Lime: www.cornishlime.co.uk
Abey Smallcombe: www.abeysmallcombe.com
Green Wood Centre: www.greenwoodcentre.org.uk
The Dorset Centre for Rural Skills: www.dorsetruralskills.co.uk
The Permaculture Association for permaculture courses: www.permaculture.org.uk

Most of the organisations in the previous section also run practical training courses.

Higher Nationals / Foundation Degrees

For those wishing to pursue a vocationally relevant education, Higher Nationals and Foundation Degrees present an attractive alternative to a degree program. Generally these programs will have flexible study arrangements

LEEDS COLLEGE OF BUILDING LIBRARY

which permit work at the same time as study. Many employers will support learners on an HNC or Foundation Degree whilst working.

Blackburn College East Lancashire Institute Of Higher Education, offers an HNC in Sustainable Construction. They also offer a Foundation Degree in Sustainable Construction: www.elihe.ac.uk

Dewsbury College offers a Foundation Degree (FdA) in Sustainable Design: www.dewsbury.ac.uk

Cornwall College has a Foundation Degree Programme in Building Renovation and Design: www.cornwall.ac.uk

Weymouth College offers an Applied Architectural Stonework and Conservation FdSc: www.weymouth.ac.uk

Undergraduate level degree

At undergraduate level, the focus tends to be on a breadth of education in a certain subject area, for that reason, you are unlikely to find a Bachelor's degree that is specifically targeted at 'green architects' as a Bachelor's in Architecture will cover fundamental knowledge about a diverse range of architecture, rather than honing in on one specific angle.
The UCAS website www.ucas.com provides listings for all of the university level courses in the UK. You might find that an institution offers a 'green building' option as a module of a degree.

Blackburn College is the exception from the rule as it offers a BSc Sustainable Construction award: www.elihe.ac.uk

The Open University www.open.ac.uk has an established reputation for the provision of distance learning degree programs in the UK. If you are balancing study with other commitments, distance learning is a good way to extend your knowledge and work towards a qualification, whilst being able to maintain other commitments. Their course T172: 'Working

with our environment: technology for a sustainable future', provides an introduction to carbon footprinting and making an assessment of your home's ecological footprint.

Postgraduate level degree

At postgraduate level, courses become more specialised and narrow. For this reason, there are a much greater number of courses that offer 'green building' and allied subjects as a whole option. Although it would be assumed that you need a degree to start a Masters' programme, many courses offer flexible entry routes – if you have some appropriate experience, for example, you can enter as a mature student.

The University of East London and Centre for Alternative Technology run the immensely popular MSc Architecture: Advanced Environmental & Energy Studies programme. A block release course which runs in week-long units, the course provides a truly immersive learning experience which combines academic rigour with the practicalities of sustainable living in the beautiful Welsh countryside. See **www.cat.org.uk/msc** for further details. The course is recognised by the Energy Institute as counting towards Chartered Engineer status and is also about to launch a component for RIBA Part II, for those seeking professional recognition.

The University of Hudderfield www.hud.ac.uk run an MSc Sustainable Architecture, available over a year full time or two years part time.

London Metropolitan University www.londonmet.ac.uk run an MA in the Architecture of Scarce Resource, which includes a single, week-long residential week at CAT.

Oxford Brookes www.brookes.ac.uk has a good reputation for postgraduate education in sustainable building. It runs an MSc in Energy Efficient and Sustainable Building, as well as a number of research programmes.

© Green Building Press

MSc Architecture: Advanced Environmental and Energy Studies

AN INNOVATIVE POSTGRADUATE PROGRAMME OFFERED JOINTLY BETWEEN THE UNIVERSITY OF EAST LONDON AND THE CENTRE FOR ALTERNATIVE TECHNOLOGY, EUOPE'S LEADING ECO CENTRE

The programme examines the relationship between human beings and the environment and in particular offers an ecological perspective on building. The programme runs as ten five-day residential sessions every month except August and December. Students choose to complete eight of the ten sessions either by attending at CAT or by Web based study. The programme is suitable for all those with an interest in developing expertise in an area of rapidly increasing importance where skills shortages are being reported. The programme offers an opportunity for those seeking a career change and/or needing to upgrade their existing skills and welcomes those who have experienced significant breaks in their education. The programme is open to students with a wide range of experiential and educational backgrounds who are expected to have a first degree. Mature students who do not possess formal qualifications but have been engaged in activities that are relevant and/or considered likely to benefit from the programme may be accepted. The programme is accredited by the Energy Institute and selected Units are offered via the RIBA CPD providers network. An extended version of the programme to give exemption from the requirement of the RIBA part II examination is being developed.

Course materials, food and accommodation (while at CAT) are included in the programme fee

for more information visit **www.cat.org.uk/msc**
or email **m.w.thompson@uel.ac.uk** or **a.pooley@uel.ac.uk**

89

DeMontfort University www.dmu.ac.uk runs an MSc Energy and Sustainable Building Design, which is recognised by CIBSE as counting towards the requirements of Chartered Engineer status.

The University of Plymouth www.plymouth.ac.uk runs an MSc/MRes programme in Sustainable Construction.

The University of Glamorgan BSc(Hons)Architectural Innovation and Technology; Department of Art and Design; Cardiff school of creative and cultural industries; www.glam.ac.uk

On completion of your training, for work opportunities relating to work and volunteering in the environment sector:
www.environmentjob.co.uk

ATRIUM
cardiff school of creative and cultural industries
ysgol diwydiannau creadigol a diwylliannol caerdydd

BSc (Hons) Architectural Innovation and Technology

This exciting new course is about us helping you develop your creativity, advancing your technical skill and applying it to a fast moving professional environment. At its core are building design projects with real sites and real clients. In each project you will develop the brief, analyse the site and produce innovative ideas for designs. Practising architects and designers will help you develop your ideas into realisable projects, and you will be able to use the latest computer aided design software to present them to full advantage. You will be taught about both emerging, innovative technologies and established construction methods. The course will also provide you with the knowledge and understanding of the current and future planning, building, and environmental legislative framework, along with the project management skills needed for today's interdisciplinary architectural projects. Visits to key new buildings will provide inspiration and bring the teaching to life.

Designing sustainable environments and buildings to reduce climate change is embedded throughout the course. Buildings in use and in production account for around 60% of current UK carbon dioxide emissions – far more than even car or air travel – and much current architectural innovation is about reducing this. Such innovation will often generate its own 'green' aesthetic, something we will be looking for in your designs.

The course is recognised by the Chartered Institute of Architectural Technologists and our graduates obtain interesting and well paid employment; the majority of them, who achieve good honours degrees, have several job offers to choose from on graduating.

For further information on this rewarding course, please contact: Richard Penn, Dept. of Art & Design on 01443 482144 or e-mail rgpenn@glam.ac.uk

www.glam.ac.uk

Case study

MSc Architecture: Advanced Environmental and Energy Studies

Gavin Harper had previously studied with the Open University. He was interested in sustainable building, so enrolled on the MSc Architecture: Advanced Environmental & Energy Studies option at the Centre for Alternative Technology. There was a diverse mix of people on the course from a range of backgrounds but all were passionate about sustainable buildings.

The course is unusual in its format in that it runs for a week in each month at the Centre for Alternative Technology. Units are offered throughout the year, and students can pick eight separate units to complete, followed by a thesis write up which makes up a third of the total assessment. The flexible nature of the course can fit in really well with people's hectic lifestyles. The week format means that many employers are happy to support students as they work as it does not interfere too much with their working lifestyles – and there's another bonus, there is also the option to complete the course part-time over two years.

For those who could not attend for eight weeks over two years, there is also the option to study at a distance. Students can mix residential study with supported 'open' learning. This incredibly popular course only shows signs of expanding further, student number continue to increase. The course now offer exemption from the RIBA Part II examination for professionals wishing to pursue a career as an architect. For those wanting to pursue a career in engineering, the course has accreditation from the Energy Institute, as counting towards the requirements of Chartered Engineer status.

The CAT/UeL MSc course has set a precedent for educating about sustainable construction and environmentally friendly architecture. The innovative delivery method seems to appeal to full time students and those who don't want to learn full time. As the 'green building movement' grows, this course can only go from strength to strength.

© Green Building Press

LY EXTENDED

SECTION

Buildings during their construction and subsequent operation consume vast amounts of natural resources. They account for half of the UK's primary energy consumption. They demand quarrying and exploitation of forests and other natural resources to supply the materials from which they are made. In use building emissions add to global warming, damage the ozone layer and create waste disposal problems.

MSc. Sustainable Architecture

One year full time - two years part time

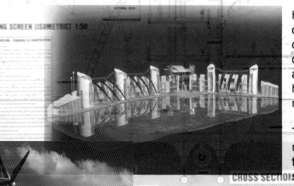

DING SCREEN (ISOMETRIC) 1:50

CROSS SECTION

OPENING ROOF PANEL DETAIL 1:20

The internal environment has been linked with ill health ranging from chronic illness caused by discomfort to life threatening illness due to the collection and concentration of pathogens and carcinogens. This course considers the tools available to alleviate these environmental and health problems such as; design methods, technologies (alternative and high tech) and legslation.

The subjects covered include: low energy design, research, management and academic methods, theglobal environment, health and contemporary sustainable architecture. The major component is a final research project or design thesis.

The course is aimed primarily at graduates in a discipline associated with the built environment (architecture, civil engineering, planning, building services etc.) but other disciplines will be considered.

This course offers graduates and practitioners the opportunity to expand their skills in an area of great concern both to clients and the public as a whole.

For further details contact:
Richard Nicholls
Tel 01484 472652, email R.Nicholls@hud.ac.uk
Department of Architecture, Huddersfield University
Queensgate, Huddersfield, HD1 3DH

University of
HUDDERSFIELD

91

3 Fundamentals

Understanding energy use

Buildings enclose a wide range of human activities. They are places of education, work, entertainment and living. Within each category there are sub divisions, for example, places of living may also be student accommodation, hostels, hotels or individual homes. **Richard Nicholls** looks at patterns of energy use in buildings and the cost implications ...

Each individual building will have a different pattern of energy consumption throughout each day of the year. To restrict this variation, for the purposes of this discussion we will concentrate on two broad categories of building to demonstrate methods for energy reduction. These are domestic buildings (houses) and non domestic buildings (commercial property). Of the 1872TWh of energy used each year in buildings, roughly 70% (1310TWh) is used in housing and 30% (526TWh) is used in commercial buildings.

Typical patterns of energy consumption in these buildings are illustrated in Figures 1, 2 and 3 which show the breakdown of the total energy consumption of a typical domestic property, a naturally ventilated office building and a mechanically cooled and ventilated office building respectively[1].

The diagrams show that space heating energy consumption, which is derived from gas, is the largest portion of the total energy consumption in all three types of building, comprising 78%, 60% and 48% of the total for the domestic, naturally ventilated office and air conditioned office respectively. It can be seen that the portion of the total energy used for space heating diminishes as the

building complexity increases. This reduction can be attributed to the additional electricity consumed to provide higher standards of lighting in office buildings and, in the air conditioned office the electricity consumption of the chillers and fans.

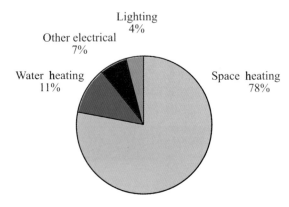

Figure 1. Breakdown of domestic energy consumption

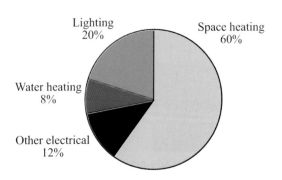

Figure 2. Breakdown of naturally ventilated office energy consumption.

© Green Building Press

The pie charts have been drawn the same size to illustrate where the energy goes and to allow a comparison between the different building types. The area does not represent the amount of energy used. If the area did represent quantities of energy used (per m²), the mechanically ventilated and air conditioned chart would have the largest area, followed by the naturally ventilated office, with the domestic chart being the smallest. This is because the total energy consumption in any building depends on climate, installed services, the building fabric, the behaviour of the occupants and the size of the buildings.

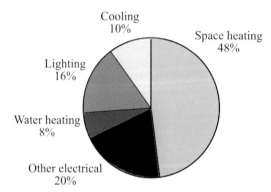

Figure 3. Breakdown of air conditioned (a/c) office energy consumption

To normalise energy consumption, for the purpose of allowing a comparison to be made between building types, it is usual to divide the total amount of energy used over a year by the building, by its treated floor area. This gives an energy consumption in kilowatt hours per square metre per year (kWh/m²/y). For our three building types, typical energy consumptions per square metre are:

Domestic	150kWh/m²/y
Naturally ventilated office	205kWh/m²/y
Mech ventilated a/c office	460kWh/m² /y

It is the aim of low energy design to reduce these values to, or below, good practice values that have been found by carrying out research into energy efficient buildings. For comparison,

the target good practice energy consumptions on this basis are:

Domestic	88kWh/m²/year
Naturally ventilated office	110kWh/m²/year
Mech ventilated a/c office	260kWh/m²/year

Why save energy?

Aside from the need to reduce CO_2 emissions and stave off global warming, there are other reasons why it is important to reduce the amount of energy consumed by buildings but the reason that engages most people's attention is cutting costs.

Another good reason is for energy security and this is also currently a hot political issue. Countries that are self sufficient in fuel are not dependent on other countries for their essential energy supplies. This is important since fuel supplied from other countries can be affected by the internal politics of that country or regional conflicts. However, whilst this is a serious topic, the politics of energy consumption will not be considered here. There are two other good reasons for saving energy:
● protecting the environment
● producing better buildings.

Both are discussed at length in other stories in this book and in the Green Building Bible, Volume 2. Here we will concentrate on fuel costs and its implications.

Cutting fuel costs

Different forms of energy have different costs per unit of energy. Table 1 shows the cost to a domestic consumer of 1kWh (1 unit) of different forms of energy. It can be seen that coal is the cheapest form of fuel, followed by gas then oil. Electricity is significantly more expensive per unit of energy than the fossil fuels. This is because the unit cost depends on both the extraction costs and any conversion costs.

This is best illustrated using electricity as an example. Electricity seems an ideal fuel. Of every 100kWh of electrical energy used by a heating appliance, 100kWh of thermal energy is released. In other words at the point of use it is 100% efficient. However, we must not forget that electricity is generated primarily from fossil fuels in power stations. Figure 4 shows the energy flows in a typical power station. It can be seen that of every 100 killowatt hours of energy input to the power station, in the form of fossil fuels, approximately 5% is lost during electrical transmission (heating up of wires whilst overcoming resistance) and 60% is lost jointly as hot flue gases and as steam in the cooling towers. This results in a conversion efficiency which varies between 31.5 and 37% depending on operating conditions. This wasteful method of production makes electricity costs high in relation to other fuels, such as gas that is simply extracted and used with little processing.

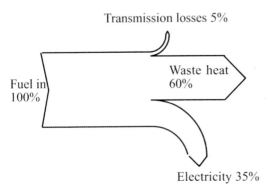

Figure 4. Energy flows in a typical power station.

Fuel Type	Cost relative to gas
Gas	1.00
Oil	1.46
Coal	0.83
Electricity	4.1 - 5.6

Table 1. Cost of 1kWh of various fuels relative to gas. Source John Willoughby's domestic fuel price guide April 06, (see Chapter 7 for full details).

Green electricity

It is possible to purchase electricity that has been generated from renewable sources such as windfarms and hydropower. This is known as green electricity because its generation releases no carbon dioxide or other products of combustion into the atmosphere.

In reality, the electricity you take from the grid may be from a local nuclear or fossil fuel power station. However, the utilities are required to prove that they are buying and supplying the same amount of renewable electricity to the grid as is supplied to customers on green electricity tariffs. A new EU green electrical markets' directive will require electricity suppliers to hold a renewable energy guarantee of origin (REGO) certificate to validate their sources. Green electricity can cost the same as standard tariffs, or slightly more, but the excess is often collected in a fund for 'green' initiatives. The websites of suppliers will give individual costs and schemes.

Commercial fuel prices

The relative unit energy costs shown in Table 1 are for domestic customers. Commercial users of energy are able to negotiate a favourable contract price for fuels from competitive suppliers due to the large quantities they consume. This tends to make unit costs lower, although there may be a complex arrangement of additional standing charges associated with patterns of energy demand throughout the year. Fuel price competition is now available to domestic customers also.

Comparative costs

The importance of energy costs in commercial buildings can only be illustrated by making a comparison with other running costs associated with buildings, such as staff costs.

Staff costs in a typical office building are approximately £2,500 per square metre per year (£/m²/year) (based on £25,000 staff cost per year and an occupancy of 1 person per 10m²), whereas total energy costs for the highest energy consuming building type, the prestige office, are a modest £25/m²/year. There are two conclusions to be drawn from this comparison. The first is that financial savings are most easily made by employing fewer staff, than saving energy. Secondly, since

© Green Building Press

the staff of a particular business are its most valuable asset, it would be unwise to risk a fall off in productivity by making the staff thermally uncomfortable during the quest to save energy. Energy savings should be made without making people thermally or visually uncomfortable.

Energy costs are of a similar size to other non-staff running costs, such as security, cleaning, water supply and maintenance. For example, typical annual costs for maintenance and cleaning are £29 and £14/m²/year respectively. This situation can mean that energy costs reductions have no greater priority to other day-to-day operating costs.

Energy conservation investments

The decision on whether or not to include an energy saving feature in a building is usually made by calculating and assessing a rate of return on the investment. The most basic way of calculating this is to use the simple payback period. This is the number of years required to recoup the initial capital cost from the value of energy savings made. The payback period is calculated from the following formula:

$$Payback\ period\ (y) = \frac{Capital\ cost\ of\ energy\ saving\ feature\ (£)}{Value\ of\ energy\ savings\ per\ year(£/y)}$$

Industry usually requires a payback period of less than 3 years for expenditure on energy saving features to be seen as worthwhile. From the payback formula it can be seen that the payback period will increase if the capital cost of the equipment increases or the value of saved fuel decreases. The biggest change in these two factors over recent years has been in fuel costs. At first these decreased due to the privatisation of the energy utilities and the introduction of price competition but most recently have increased due to global competition for diminishing supplies. This has been especially noticeable in gas prices.

The recent increases in fuel prices have two effects. Firstly, as energy costs rise people tend to use less, secondly, it shortens the payback period of energy saving investments. Both factors eventually contribute to a reduction

in energy consumption. 'Green Building Bible, Volume 2' considers this subject in more detail.

References

1. Energy Consumption Guilde 19: Energy use in Offices 1998

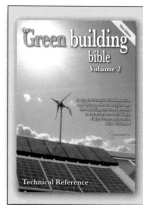

Have you got Volume 2 ?

It is the perfect companion to this book and in 244 pages delivers the techincal aspects of creating low energy buildings. Subjects covered are site layout and orientation; building form; building fabric; lighting; heating and ventilation and more.

SUBSCRIBE TO POSITIVE NEWS
5, Bicton Enterprise Centre, Clun, Shropshire, SY7 8NF
Tel: 01588 640022 • Email: office@positivenews.org.uk
Website: www.positivenews.org.uk

Design for deconstruction

The way that we design our buildings, even green buildings, can have a fundamental impact on the environment once we come to demolish them. If we were to keep an end-of-life scenario in mind, at the design stage, then we can offer those whos job it is to remove and replace them some assistance in salvaging the raw and processed materials. **Mark Gorgolewski** reports ...

Traditional demolition practices are generally destructive and usually result in damage to components, which are then only suitable for waste or recycling, but not for reuse. As the economic value and the demand for reclaimed components increases, while the cost of disposal to landfill also goes up, demolition practices may gradually change towards deconstruction. This provides more opportunity for components to be extracted undamaged, suitable for reuse, with little or no reprocessing.

Designers can make it far easier for buildings to be deconstructed if they consider how this will occur at the design stage of a building. Designers need to consider how the environmental and financial value of a building can be maximised at the end of its useful life and how it can be taken apart with the least damage to its useful components. In this way the supply of reclaimed components for reuse can be increased. "Disassembly technology is the antithesis to the technology that put the building together in the first place. Simply by reverse running the process of construction (back to the manufacturer if needs be) and looking at the building and its constituent parts we may have far reaching consequences for the transition point of building demolition." (Wyatt & Gilleard 1994).

Other industries are beginning to rethink how products are put together so that they can increase the usefulness and value of components at the end of their life. EU legislation is putting the responsibility for disposal of products at the end of their useful life on the producer - "Reversible joints, upgradeable components, and materials that can be separated are all now being incorporated into the next generation of appliances. For example, Xerox, the photocopier supplier, has adopted the DfD (design for dismantling) approach. At the end of a photocopier's life or when it is superseded, it is taken back and 'asset stripped'. This basic disassembly frees many of the existing elements enabling them to form the basis of the new model." (Fletcher, et al 1990).

Car manufacturers have been encouraged by legislation and competition to consider the end of life disposal of their products. Cars are now being designed to enable recovery of components on 'unassembly lines' and for easier replacement and reuse of worn parts. These companies have begun to realise that simpler designs, and assembly processed using less materials and components, in some cases leads to cost savings and are more suitable for disassembly. Although the nature of construction, and the timescales involved are very different to most other industries, similar approaches may soon be extended to the construction sector, requiring producers of goods to take them back at the end of their life for reuse, recycling or disposal. Such a policy is likely to lead to more interest in buildings that are designed to be deconstructed.

Deconstruction is the process of taking a building apart into its components in such a way that they can be more readily reused or recycled. It minimises the destructive aspects of the process of removing buildings, preserving components and materials, not wasting them. Designing for deconstruction means considering, at the design stage, how a building can be taken apart. Many temporary and relocatable buildings and structures around the world are already assembled using reversible processes. The same idea can be applied to new construction. Designers can increase the potential for deconstruction considerably by considering the

© Green Building Press

building as a kit of parts, that can be assembled in layers, so that each component can be removed at the end of its useful life.

To make deconstruction easier to carry out, designers should consider, at the outset, how components will be replaced in the building during its useful life, and how it will be deconstructed at the end of its life to maximise the usefulness of the components and materials. This means looking at the building systems and technologies used to ensure they can be readily and economically separated. The design team needs to think through, at the concept stage, the lifetime changes of the building. Potential problems during refurbishment and eventual dismantling should be investigated. For example, allowing site access for machinery and suitable floor loads to take demolition plant and rubble. Another key issue is the availability of relevant documentation and information about the building at the time of deconstruction. Key principles to design for deconstruction include:

- use durable components that can be reused after removal
- consider the actual process of deconstruction at the design stage and provide a deconstruction plan for the building
- consider a building as a series of layers related to different life-spans of components
- ensure that individual components can be readily removed when necessary and maintained or replaced
- use simple structural grids with clear support lines
- limit the number of parts, number of tasks, number of tools, and the time or degree of difficulty of the deconstruction tasks to reduce cost and time involved
- where possible use prefabricated components that are assembled on site and can be disassembled for reuse/recycling
- use appropriate fasteners and connections. Consider connections that can be reversed and avoid irreversible processes; reversible mechanical fixings such as bolts or screws can usually be removed, adhesives and nails are more difficult

- where possible use dry construction processes, which are more readily dismantled than wet construction processes
- Integrate services with care so that they can be easily identified, maintained, upgraded and replaced
- provide sufficient space and capacity to accommodate machinery needed for dismantling
- ensure that accurate as-built drawings and records of all changes over the life of the building are kept in a building log book
- consider who might be doing the reclaiming - the manufacturer or a third party? Do they need information or instructions such as disassembly or refurbishment plans or specifications for the qualities of the materials?

The availability of documentation that includes the information needed for safe and effective deconstruction is important. To help with this, the design team can provide a disassembly plan. Demolition is the reverse of construction, and the design team should consider this process and prepare a strategy for the dismantling of the building, similar to that developed for many temporary, relocatable buildings. Also, a log book that is kept during the life of a building should include information on the design of the original building, specifications of materials and components used in construction, details of refurbishment work carried out during the life of the building, and information relevant to dismantling, which would enable materials to be readily extracted for reuse and their specifications to be followed through their different life phases. ◐

Further reading

For more information about Design for Deconstruction see the publication from the Scottish Ecological Design Association: www.seda2.org/dfd/index.htm

Eco-minimalism – less can be more

"Things should be as simple as possible but no simpler."

Albert Einstein

If you are new to green building then please take time to digest both sides of the argument for ecobuildings. High-tech or low-tech. **Howard Liddell** puts forward a case here that 'eco-technology' paraphernalia, which has become a ubiquitous part of green specification, is overkill.

It is almost easier to persuade newcomers to green building than the old hands that the 'technical fix' icons of the green movement (wind turbines, photovoltaics, heat pumps etc) may not be as green as they seem. This is especially so when set against an alternative strategy of good housekeeping and conservation, and thoroughly convincing when they learn that it can be achieved with little or no additional cost. The fact that something can be green without being self-conscious or having to look radically different is also very attractive to a large number of people. They can be quietly green without having to seem to be a 'greenie' or have it shouted from their technology-laden rooftops.

If we are to move forward from individual eco-houses, mini eco-villages, green expos and pilot projects – towards mainstreaming ecological design as an integral part of building for the 21st century, then it is crucial that it is accessible, economic, genuinely environmentally-sound, gimmick-free and not stigmatised as a style.

Cost v/s payback

The perception that green buildings cost more is out there. Indeed, it is almost impossible to shift. Even greenies believe that they have to argue their case on reduced running costs

paying for add-ons that have payback periods of varying length and credibility. I have been involved in designing and building green buildings for over 30 years, without the benefit of being offered bigger budgets, and the contention here is that those who ask for more money for building green are using too much building technology and not enough building science.

A couple of quick examples: -

Passive design (zero heating building) - an airtight and superinsulated building does not need very much, if any, heating or fuel storage. Savings in technology can pay for increased building fabric quality. This is a straight trade off with no extra cost.

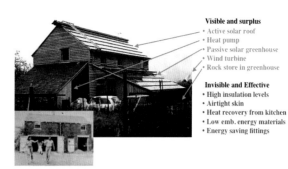

Visible and surplus
- Active solar roof
- Heat pump
- Passive solar greenhouse
- Wind turbine
- Rock store in greenhouse

Invisible and Effective
- High insulation levels
- Airtight skin
- Heat recovery from kitchen
- Low emb. energy materials
- Energy saving fittings

Granada House, Macclesfield

Dealing with humidity - hygroscopic materials, which are readily water absorptive and evaporative, (e.g. clay plaster and untreated timber - especially end grain) are up to 9 times more effective at dealing with indoor humidity levels than mechanical ventilation. The money not spent on fans, ducts, grilles and filters pays for the specification of slightly more expensive wall finishes

© Green Building Press

30 years ago I was asked to be involved in a Granada TV programme called 'House for the Future'. An early example of reality TV – it took a typical family and got them to self-build their low energy home by converting an old brick barn. The barn was gutted and wrapped up tight on the outside with 250mm insulation, and a small woodstove was installed. Whilst this was self-sufficient enough for the worst of winters, it was a little too straightforward for a series identified for 13 programmes. So new technology got layered on week by week, like Chinese dishes onto a lazy Susan. The house had passive and active solar collectors, a rock store, a heat pump, heat recovery, a wind turbine and so on and so forth, until it ended up looking like a Christmas tree. Monitoring one year later, revealed that the heat recovery from the kitchen was sufficient to run the whole house year-round. The woodstove was hardly ever used, the wind turbine and heat pump were virtually redundant, the rock store short-circuited (air in to air out by the shortest route) and the 25m² solar roof was called on for only 2% of the annual hot water demand. From here on I was a convert to doing more with less.

An approach - not a style

The term 'eco-minimalism' incorporates a combination of simple common sense with a sharp, uncluttered design. It is rooted in a passive design approach – which requires a degree of scientific understanding as to how buildings work, rather than resorting to a piece of off-the-shelf, one-size-fits-all technology. It is, however, purely and simply an approach, it is not a style. Indeed, whilst my practice may have a preference for a more modern approach to design, eco-buildings can actually be built in virtually any style.

Those who confuse the approach with the style, can be opposite ends of the spectrum. Even in conventional buildings people's level of technological sophistication tends to exceed their architectural literacy. In sustainable development this knowledge gap is possibly even wider.

Look at me - I'm eco!

In many (but not all) circumstances a number of the 'eco badge technologies' for green buildings can be shown to have somewhat suspect green credentials. Most obvious among them are solar photovoltaics, heat pumps, solar collectors, reed beds, turf roofs and even conservatories. All these need to be put under scrutiny before they are specified or used. When the numbers are crunched, the costs and benefits evaluated and the eco-footprint identified, for a specific project, they either pass muster or they don't; indeed every project is unique to either the site, client or climatic context – and often all three.

There will be circumstances (e.g. remote locations) where micro photovoltaic/ windpower combo's make cash and carbon sense. However, it is not unusual for a new client to start talking to us about a heat pump or a reed bed, before even mentioning what kind of building they want designed for them. They come with their premeditated and preferred technology first and their intended function second. Photovoltaics are experiencing a temporary trough right now and former favourites heat pumps are back in vogue. The technical jargon levels have recently raised their game, as it is not just a request for any heat pump, it is a 'ground source' heat pump or, for the nouveau technologues, a 'geothermal' heat pump, which trips off the tongue with the enthusiasm of one who has discovered the philosopher's stone.

If a heat pump is the answer
What was the question?

In a swimming pool project, many years ago, I had the sobering experience of having a heat pump switched off after only one month, in favour of simply using mains gas – because it was significantly cheaper to run the building that way. No mystery – the CoP (coefficient of performance) of the heat pump was 3:1 and the tariff difference between gas and electricity was nearly 5:1. I was moved to look into this a little further, only to discover that in using the carbon intensive UK grid (as distinct from, say, the Norwegian hydro power dominated grid) even the carbon impact of the heat pump was worse, Plans A and B below explain the logic. The initial fuel can simply be fed straight into a high efficiency boiler (up to 95%). Alternatively if a heat pump is to be used (most are electrically powered) then we need electricity and Plan B applies: - this starts with power station losses of nearly 60% in the conversion of gas to power. There are then the grid losses (8%) and eventually this very high grade energy source powers the heat pump, which then delivers a lower grade energy output at efficiencies - claimed initially to be capable of about 4:1 and usually delivered at around 3:1 or less. All that effort and expense to achieving virtually the same net output.

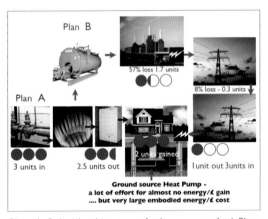

Plans A+B showing two ways of using gas as a fuel. Plan A to run a power station to create electricity which in turn would be sent to your home to run a heat pump. Or plan B, use the gas directly in the home to run an easily maintained efficient gas boiler. The final efficiency is little different.

In terms of the swimming pool project (see photo of the building in the next column) the heat pump was not the only example of redundant technology used – it turned out also that other specification was surplus to requirements, including the heat recovery unit and two boilers. In fact the outcome of a recent review - 10 years on - has demonstrated that the 33% of capital cost dedicated to the technical services could have been reduced to 25%, without any effect whatsoever on the building's efficiency. In subsequent buildings we have been able to reduce this to as little as 10%, and in a recent

school brief capped the technical element to 15% of capital cost, and had the consultants sign up to this as part of their contract.

Follow the elements

Any building project as a whole can be categorised under the four elements: fire, air, earth and water and the discussion below seeks to draw out the relative advantages of an eco-minimalist 'good housekeeping', (see right) as opposed to an eco-cliché approach, 'technical fix' at the end of this story.

Fire

The fire element is energy. The first rule in an energy strategy for a building should be to remove the need for energy consumption as far as is reasonably possible, before looking at the supply side. This may seem obvious but I have yet to see a building with a photovoltaic system on it, in the UK, which has been super-insulated and was tested for airtightness first.

Even if we were to set aside efficiency pre-requisites - proponents of photovoltaics still need to play on an even playing field with the likes of biofuels and windpower and address properly the economic questions, such as the issue of payback periods and annual degradations in equipment efficiency, which other suppliers spend a great deal of their time addressing and are booted off the pitch if they are not convincing.

© Green Building Press

Part of an energy efficiency approach would also include seeking to group buildings in terraces rather than detached form (often a social challenge) and perhaps considering community scale CHP (combined heat and power) – the Achilles heel of which is the summer hot water surplus, unless there is a hospital or swimming pool in the vicinity.

Air

The air element is used here to cover both indoor and outdoor climatic issues. It links with other elements, such as fire, through shelter belts and planting, which will give energy savings in preventing windchill losses, on the conservation side and wind power on the supply side (see also: 'Green Building Bible, Volume 2', Chapter 3). However, the social influence on what starts out as a technically sound decision can be immense and counter-productive. For example, conservatories were taken out of planning and building control permissions, in order to encourage the free use of solar gain and reduce windchill. This wishful thinking, however, has been totally undermined by the fact that over 70% of conservatories have been found to have heating systems installed in them. In terms of indoor climate issues the air element includes; designing for airtight construction and the concomitant need to deal with moisture movement and relative humidity - a link to the water element, and also to benign materials specification – the earth element.

Earth

The earth element is also an indoor / outdoor issue and linked to the other elements. Externally so much can be done to deal with the impact of buildings in a more natural way than has become the norm through the 20th century. To stop putting surface water into pipes and deal with it at source, as the rain falls, through SUDs schemes, has been one of the most economically viable, as well as positive

Good Housekeeping

Table of Eco-minimalism

Subtle Solution	Comment
Fire	
Passive Design >>	<< Fewer moving parts to maintain
Large south-facing, shaded windows >>	<< Free but controllable solar gain
Use conservation + low energy fittings >>	<< Concentrate on demand side first.
Remove phantom loads >>	<< Standby is 15% of electrical demand
Renewable tariff >>	<< Defrays effect of essential electricity.
Minimum boiler >>	<< New generation boilers 10:1 turn down
Air	
Airtightness testing >>	<< Without this superinsulation is irrelevant
Superinsulation >>	<< Often overlooked benefits hot & cold
Water	
Water conservation before treatment >>	<< Consider the total system impact
Use hard surfaces (roofs) to best effect >>	<< Rainwater - a resource best used locally
Use soft landscape where possible >>	<< Control surface water (SUDs)
Earth	
Least toxic, resource-intensive materials >>	<< Best benign material for the job
Mass wood construction >>	<< CO2 storage
Design for Recycling >>	<< Fexibility both short & long term.
Maximise biodiversity >>	<< Many benefits locally

Ballpark:- add -10% to +10%

amenity strategies of recent years. To deal with landscaping as an integral part of the energy budget of a development, whilst also respond- ing to the biodiversity needs of its inhabitants – giving them not just flora but also fauna (birds and butterflies etc). The city of Berlin adopts a 50% rule, whereby every square metre of built footprint has to have an equivalent amount of biodiverse rich landscape (soft surfaces and water).

The Earth element also covers materials choice and there are two or three eco-clichés, which need to be picked up here. The first is related to local materials. If the issue is about reusing a total building, rather than demolish- ing it, then it would make environmental, if not economic sense. In Glasgow the city council manufactures its own uPVC windows – a local product (they claim), which they defend adamantly on grounds of local employment provision. But what about other aspects of the product? There are other issues about the material (embodied toxicity for instance).

Another possible misconception relates to the generally held assumption that a material like wood is 'inherently' good. Apart from the well rehearsed issues of the source of the timber (and the cost of labelling to deal with this), it is also clear that the vast majority of timber used in the construction industry has been through at least one and probably many more processes, before reaching its destina- tion for use. A lot of construction timber has been treated by the time it reaches the builder - usually with something like CCA (copper chrome & arsenic), permethrin or a toxic stain.

The industry is awash with products that are formaldehyde rich from the glue used in them: - MDF, OSB, chipboard, plywood, blockboard, Glulam beams, and so on and so forth. Much of the wood, as used in the building industry of itself, is not inherently environmentally sound. There are also issues about the origin of many exotic timbers, as we hear almost daily about 'stolen' rainforest timber from the likes of Greenpeace.

Water

As we seek to exploit and recycle water - from rain to grey to black, the exploitation costs of alternatives to the current water and sewage infrastructure become increasingly financially onerous and sometimes even environmentally and socially dubious. Yet again, using less in the first place - 'eco-minimalism' with water saving fittings (spray taps, low-flush WCs and water- less urinals, etc) is the best starting point. I am totally mystified as to why anyone would wish to engage in installing a reed-bed system in a 'sewered' urban area, and I still await a cogent justification on any grounds. Of the options, grey water, irrigation to the gardens seems the most effective and least risky strategy in terms of both health and finance, rather than attempt- ing to recycle it. For example, in an experimental system, the diversity of the contributions of the students at Linacre College, via the showers and washhand basins feeding the college's experimental grey water recycling system, was more biologically rich than the system had been designed for!

However, dealing with water in another sense - as moisture in buildings - whether it be coming out of the sky, up from the ground or from moisture rich indoor activity, has been a battle- ground between builders and the elements as old as buildings themselves.

The concept of thermal mass is now well understood by designers. However the concept of moisture mass is new. As we seal up build- ings in the interests of energy conservation, we also seal in the moisture coming from bathrooms, kitchens and the perspiration from active pursuits, as well as overnight sleep. This has led to a growth in mechanical ventilation – which is actually not very effective in removing moisture, and just adds energy consuming fan power as a solution. This has even led to calls for full indoor climate control – including air conditioning. This is just like pressing on a balloon - press down here and it pops up over there. As long as we address single issues in hermetically sealed scientific parcels, and fail to tackle problems holistically, then we will go round in circles.

© Green Building Press

Technical Fix

Table of Eco-clichés

Technical Solution	Comment
Fire	
Photovoltaics >>	<< Payback better than 50 years?
Heat Pumps. 4:1 >>	<< versus tariffs Electricity:Gas @ 5:1
(CHP) - Combined Heat and Power >>	<< Context dependent. Summer hot water?
Active Solar Collectors >>	<< Longevity v. payback period?
Condensing Boilers >>	<< Cheap ones don't condense. Too Big?
District Heating >>	<< Specific to context, layout and form
Air	
Conservatory (semi climatic zone) >>	<< 70% have heaters in? Embodied energy?
Small Windmills >>	<< Heat churn or storage/battery system?
Water	
reed-beds >>	<< Issue of context
Grey water recycling >>	<< Expensive, - who looks after it?
Living machines >>	<< High energy costs, expensive
Earth	
Turf roofs >>	<< Heavier, plastic DPM, furtive aesthetic
Recycled materials >>	<< Strength, certif'n, embodied toxicity?
local materials >>	<< Best benign material for the job?
Timber fascia >>	<< Image? Chemically treated?

Ballpark:- add +15% to 35%

Conclusion

For those who have a simplistic view of what the sustainable building agenda comprises, the solutions have been equally simplistic and, as such, ineffective – or worse creating an equally large problem elsewhere (e.g. making a building airtight without dealing with toxic materials and humidity). On the other hand, those who have realised that the challenge is more complex, have considered the search for solutions to be complicated and daunting and involving a long list of interventions, which they have also assumed will come with a high price tag. However, after presenting the eco-minimalist approach to a wide range of people from architects and builders through to the general public and clients, it has become clear that they find this perception complex yet homogenous and therefore easier to embrace and more accessible than the quick fit and bolt on technology that is currently so popular. ☙

Howard Liddell first wrote about eco-minimalism in Building for a Future magazine in 2002 with co-author Nick Grant, before the full thrust of the current wave of wider public acceptance of the green agenda. The motivation, at the time, was that they had simultaneously become tired of the clichés in eco-building design - trotted out almost unthinkingly as technical fix or add-on solutions, whether they stood up to rigorous scrutiny or not.

Renovate before you re-develop

Too often we witness the removal of buildings just to make way for iconic glass facades with little use other than to satisfy the ego of the architect or property owner. The government's 'brownfield' strategy has done little to slow this trend. **Adrian Birch** outlines the reasons why buildings often get replaced and offers some suggestions for slowing or reversing the trend.

A renovated office building has a number of advantages over a new build. For instance, the initial embodied energy expended in construction is largely retained and less waste will be generated. Normally less energy is consumed in the process of renovation than would in replacement. The process of renovation would normally be quicker than redevelopment, reducing site overhead costs and interest charges, and permitting earlier occupation and income flow.

Planning permission and listed building consent may not be necessary and where permission is required, the planners may be more sympathetic towards extension and planning policies may be more restrictive for new-build, which would need to conform to current policies on plot ratio, parking provision, height etc. Where the building is occupied, certain works can be done with tenants remaining in place and disruption to tenants can be minimised if the work is properly planned, with noisy operations being carried out outside working hours. Overall, this can be cost-effective for both owner and occupier.

There are several levels of renovation possible. These may include fabric repairs and consequential making good. Upgrading of common parts - toilets, lift, reception. Aside from the common desire to sweep aside and start afresh and the misplaced encouragement of the government for building on brownfield land[1], the replacement of existing buildings may seem the best option if the building requires

major repairs, underpinning etc, or contain asbestos or other 'deleterious materials'. Other problems may be that existing mains services are inadequate, such as drainage systems.

Do a feasibility study

Before financial commitment is entered into, a feasibility study should be prepared by a suitably experienced person or organisation and should, ideally, encompass all or most of the following, where time and funds permit.

Only when this and other financial information has been collated can risk be assessed. Further detailed investigation of the structure and fabric may be necessary. The feasibility study should attempt to demonstrate a comparative analysis of the renovation or redevelopment options, when time and other factors are included.

Obsolescence

It is important to identify the causes of obsolescence at the outset, to ensure that the renovated building does not perpetuate the original shortcomings. If a building is to be retained and renovated, it may be necessary to look at a change of use as the only way to overcome obsolescence.

Change of use

30 years ago there was a trend to convert elegant town houses to office use. Today the trend is reversed. With the ongoing demand for new housing, offices in secondary locations may be more valuable if converted to residential use. The corresponding growth in higher education has also created a demand for student housing and it is no coincidence that in many university cities, redundant offices have been converted to student accommodation. Increased inward tourism has also generated demand for budget

© Green Building Press

hotels in many cities. Again redundant offices may be suitable for such a change of use, where strong demand exists.

The local planners should be consulted early in the process to determine their views on a change of use before following this route. There are particular issues regarding fire resistance, compartmentation and means of escape in case of fire, that must be addressed, as well as matters such as car parking, amenity space, availability of food shops etc. When assessing offices for renovation or redevelopment the change of use option must not be ignored.

cassettes to temper and recirculate the air in a space. An alternative is to use the raised access floor as a huge duct or plenum, with floor-mounted fan coils.

All these traditional approaches require heavy investment in fans, ducts and chiller plant. Where buildings can be naturally ventilated, this has to be the best option. Many renovated buildings are 'mixed mode' buildings where mechanical ventilation is used to assist the natural ventilation as required. This is cost-effective in winter if heat reclaim systems are incorporated. These do not have to be complex and many 'through the wall' fans can incorpo-

Buildings get demolished for a variety of reasons:

Excuse	Reason
Unsound structure	Physical deterioration of the structure and fabric
Not fit for purpose	The original purpose no longer exists
Obsolete	Does not perform as well as modern alternatives
Location	Often as a result of infrastructure changes
Economics	When occupation is not the cheapest alternative
Socially and legally	As a result of changes in legislation.

Design constraints

Apart from major defects to the structure or fabric, one of the main constraints upon renovating existing office buildings is the floor to ceiling height. In 60s and 70s buildings the height was usually less than 3 metres, with concrete downstand beams reducing the effective height to no more than 2.7 metres. It is virtually impossible to fit traditional ducted ventilation and air conditioning systems at ceiling level and provide an adequate raised access floor, whilst maintaining a floor to ceiling height of 2.6 metres in the occupied zone.

Some renovation schemes incorporate ducts externally or have extended floors outwards to permit ducts to be incorporated at the building's perimeter. Alternatively, localised heat pumps or fan-coil systems (fan assisted heat exchangers) can be used, relying on heated and chilled water to serve ceiling or wall-mounted

rate heat reclaim devices. Summer cooling can be a problem, but 'packaged' air conditioning systems should be avoided as they consume excessive amounts of electricity. However, they may be justifiable where there are isolated areas of internal heat gain, such as office equipment spaces.

Environmental assessment tools

An initial comparative analysis can be undertaken using software produced by the BRE (**www.bre.co.uk**). This is free to use and provides ecopoints for each strategy adopted. It is relatively simple to use and will give a relatively simple printout. For other tools see Green Buiding Bible, Volume 2.

The BRE Environmental Assessment Method, (BREEAM) has been in use for 14 years and provides a more sophisticated approach. This applies to new and renovated buildings, as well as empty offices and is divided into two main sections: 'design and procurement', and 'management and operation' (**www.breeam. org**). This provides designers with a more detailed checklist. The design will be externally assessed, and if receiving an 'excellent' rating, a renovated building may compete more favourably with a new building.

It is difficult to obtain accurate information on how many projects are assessed in this way. It was designed by BRE to help market energy efficient buildings but has yet to be universally adopted by developers and owner-occupiers. All government projects are assessed, and it may be that all non-domestic buildings exceeding 1000m^2 will require such assessment as part of the new EC Directive. ☙

References

1. The National Brownfield Land Strrategy
www.englishpartnerships.co.uk/brownfieldstrategy.htm

Further reading

'Creative re-use of buildings', two volume set by D Latham.

'The Survey and Repair of Traditional Buildings – a sustainable approach' by Richard Oxley.

'McKays Building Construction' is invaluable for traditional building techniques. This classic (originally 3 volumes)has been re-published in one book.

The above books are published by Donhead: 01747 828422 www.donhead.com

Regular discussion on the appropriate maintainance and repair of old buildings goes on on the Green Building Forum which is a free internet resource: www.greenbuildingforum.co.uk

ASSOCIATION FOR **E**NVIRONMENT **C**ONSCIOUS **B**UILDING

Established in 1989, the AECB is the leading independent environmental building organisation in the UK. At the cutting edge of sustainable building the association provides a wealth of experience across all sectors of the construction industry.

Please visit our website:
www.aecb.net
or call: **0845 4569773**

BUILDING A SUSTAINABLE FUTURE

CAMBRIAN CP PRINTERS

PRINT
EVERYTHING
GREEN

At Cambrian we've found that our environmental principles and our commercial sense are remarkably compatible. By investing in new technology to cut down **waste** and **emissions** we've also improved the quality and reliability of our colour print and finishing.

If like us you **care** about our **environment** and want to see how competitive we are for magazine or book printing **contact us on:**

☎ 01970 627111 🖨 01970 613003
or sales@cambrian-printers.co.uk

© Green Building Press

Are you doing your bit?

Look! Not wanting to be over dramatic or anything, but the sands of time are running away. We all have an obligation to act more sustainably. Here is what Kingspan Insulation has been doing.

Back in 2002 Kingspan Insulation was the first insulation manufacturer to openly publish the results of an independently certified Life Cycle Assessment. This BRE Ecoprofile shows the environmental impact that results from the manufacture of Kingspan's high performance rigid urethane insulation products.

But... things have moved on. It is no longer sufficient to while away time talking about the environmental impacts of a product's or company's performance. Impacts on Natural Resources, the Economy and Society should also be considered.

Kingspan Insulation approached renowned consultants ARUP to carry out a holistic Sustainability Appraisal of its largest manufacturing facility at Pembridge, Herefordshire. Kingspan Insulation has again openly published the results of this independent study, again being the first building products manufacturer so to do. More importantly, Kingspan Insulation has published its commitment to implement the raft of improvement actions recommended by the ARUP sustainability team, has completed many already and is working on the balance.

Kingspan Insulation has made a start – HAVE YOU? Perhaps your first decision could be to only use materials from manufacturers that can demonstrate to you what they are doing about the holistic sustainability of their products.

Copies of ARUP's Sustainability Appraisal with Kingspan Insulation's improvement action plan are available from Kingspan Insulation on:

Telephone: 0870 733 8333
email: literature.uk@insulation.kingspan.com

www.insulation.kingspan.com

Kingspan Insulation Ltd
Pembridge, Leominster, Herefordshire HR6 9LA, UK
Tel: 0870 850 8555 Fax: 0870 850 8666
email: info.uk@insulation.kingspan.com

® Kingspan and the Lion device are Registered Trademarks
of the Kingspan Group plc

Renovate sensitively

It is estimated that two thirds of the 2050 building stock exists today and that at current rates it will take 1,000 years to replace. The contribution of the existing building stock is immensely important if worthwhile reductions in carbon emissions are to be achieved. **Richard Oxley** reports ...

The lessons that can be learnt, from the field of historic building conservation, will assist in a significant percentage of the existing building stock being able to make a positive contribution to reducing carbon emissions in an appropriate and effective manner. It would be a mistake, in my opinion, to just place an importance on the thermal performance of a building.

The need to differentiate between older and modern buildings is not a peripheral requirement. Currently 20% of the existing building stock in England and Wales pre-dates 1919, most of which is of a solid wall construction, and includes some 4 million dwellings, of which it is estimated one million are listed or situated in conservation areas. Even if it was desirable the existing building stock cannot be demolished and replenished fast enough for sufficient reductions in carbon emissions to be achieved.

The only real option is to work with what we have got, in a manner that provides appropriate and effective improvements to maximise the contribution of the four million traditional dwellings, based upon an understanding of these buildings, their performance characteristics and requirements and limitations.

Distinguishing between traditional and modern

The first step is to understand the fundamental differences in construction and performance between older, traditional, and modern buildings. An older building of traditional construction is one that is of a solid wall construction, built with porous fabric that both absorbs, and readily allows, the evaporation of moisture - a breathing building if you like. This is in contrast with most modern buildings, that are constructed in impervious materials, designed to exclude moisture and that rely upon physical barriers, such as damp proof courses, membranes and cavity walls.

The significant difference in the performance between traditional and modern buildings makes it crucial that the materials and methods of construction and the intended performance of a building, together with the way in which the construction and intended performance may have been modified over time, are identified and understood.

The risks of change

The intended use of a building dictates the appropriateness, compatibility and nature of all repairs and alterations, including those already carried out and those that will be made in the future.

"In a modern building the damage or failure of one of its moisture barriers will lead to severe problems of damp penetration. In an old building prevention of the evaporation of moisture from walls will lead to similar difficulties. Hence the two building types need to be handled in completely different ways: modern buildings will be damp without a barrier to moisture because the economy of design does not provide a massive and absorbent structures, but old buildings will become damp if an impervious layer is applied to them because this prevents water within the structure from evaporating. As the moisture content of the wall increases, the likelihood of decay also increases"[1].

In the building where the traditional performance has been detrimentally changed, the levels of damp can no longer be 'controlled'. The

© Green Building Press

ability of moisture to readily evaporate has been removed. The repair with impervious materials and the changes in the manner the building is used and functions, have exacerbated the problems of dampness and potential decay for the building and will have implications for the health of the occupants.

The differences between modern and traditional buildings, and the large variations within the categorisation of traditional buildings, makes it essential that the condition of any traditional building is compared with buildings on a 'like for like' basis. Comparison with modern equivalents that have different performance characteristics is not a sound basis upon which to judge the condition and performance of a traditional building.

A failure to identify and distinguish between old and new, creates a dichotomy for older buildings, where improvements that rely on modern materials can cause physical damage, accelerate rates of decay, and lead to the loss of irreplaceable fabric, where there is an adverse change in the traditional breathing performance.

Special value and special interest

As a society we have identified a group of buildings as being culturally important, as deserving statutory protection to assist in their protection and preservation. Within the UK these buildings are protected by their status as listed buildings or by their situation in conservation areas. This formal recognition makes those three million older buildings, that do not fall within this categorisation, more vulnerable to inappropriate and damaging work, than the minority that are protected.

An older building can have a 'value' that a modern building will not have yet obtained. This 'value' can be described as the special interest of a building. Each individual building will have its own particular qualities that contribute to this interest; these may be attributable to any one or a combination of age, type, method of construction, style of the building, together with

any association with famous people, events or designing architect.

Any damage or loss of fabric will only act to devalue or detract from the interest of a building, with the loss of a building diluting the character and appeal of its surrounding environment. It is not just the economic value or the level of embodied energy, but the fact that in many instances, fabric lost can never be replicated in the same manner or to the same standard, no matter how much we try. It will never be authentic.

The workmanship, skill and knowledge of the craftsmen who constructed and repaired these buildings needs to be included in any assessment of the value of traditional buildings. Although difficult to quantify, it is an essential part of what makes old buildings special; it is an integral part of their cultural embodied value.

The investment of embodied energy of the building fabric, and the cultural embodied value of the knowledge and information contained within these buildings, provide us with a tangible link with our past. A link that, in most cases, is highly functional and that can continue in beneficial use if allowed to perform as intended and is improved, repaired and maintained in a sympathetic manner.

Many traditional buildings can provide excellent role models for new buildings that strive to be sustainable in their design and construction. Attitudes to how buildings should function are coming full-circle. The benefits of 'breathing' buildings are no longer exclusive to traditional buildings. 'Breathability' is now a high profile benefit upon which many materials and systems are marketed; for example the renaissance in lime-based mortars and the extensive use of vapour permeable roofing felts.

Reasoned and informed aproach

Acknowledging the difference and value of older buildings creates a need to act in a philosophical and rational manner, to fully consider the implications of one's decisions before acting.

The case for preservation, rather than resto-ration, was developed during the nineteenth century. With John Ruskin's Seven Lamps of Architecture laying much of the foundations of the philosophy that is in use today, both in building and environmental conservation. William Morris developed Ruskin's theme of sustainability to arrive at the tenet that we are only trustees for future generations.

Tastes and values change over time, as do the pressures for change, and for this reason great care is needed to avoid the loss or dilution of authenticity, physical loss or accelerated decay. This could prejudice the functional use and enjoyment of buildings by future genera-tions, who may come to place a greater value on them, whether for their architectural or historic merit or because they contain resources that are no longer available.

Avoid well-intentioned but damaging repairs

It is important to remember that the introduc-tion of materials, that are now being found to be inappropriate, are usually used with the intention of repairing or improving the building; very few people actually initiate repairs setting out to cause damage. The impact that a simple repair, using inappropriate materials, can have on the performance and condition of a traditional building can be illustrated where a lime-based mortar is raked out and repointed with an impervious cement mortar.

Simple everyday responses can expose a building to inappropriate repair. Not only can serviceable fabric and evidence of previous finishes be lost but also the appearance and presentation can be changed, as well as the long-term performance of the building – which will eventually affect its structural condition and the rates of decay that will be suffered.

A hard and impermeable cement-based pointing has been used to repair the wall. This simple change resulted in the accelerated deterioration of the brickwork (see below). This

degradation occurred because the ability of moisture to evaporate from the mortar joints between the bricks has been impaired. This example of a simple but inappropriate repair, illustrates there are dangers of introducing modern materials to older buildings.

The need to introduce insulation is a recent phenomenon that was initially driven by fuel prices in the 1970s, and now measures to mitigate global warming. The energy perform-ance of the existing building stock has, with justification, been targeted for improvement. The potential conflict between energy conserva-tion polices and the conservation of the historic environment is of concern and there needs to be a balance to prevent either being overtly compromised.

Introducing insulation and increasing air-tightness to traditional buildings, in particular to the levels required to make the savings needed,

Hard cement pointing to this soft brickwork has allowed water to become trapped, leading to frost blow on the brickwork

is not proven over time. We do not understand the long-term implications of introducing insulation to buildings that were constructed and designed without insulation or air-tightness in mind.

The dangers of introducing inappropriate materials to solid walled buildings have not been appreciated by those advocating the external insulation of solid walled buildings with systems incorporating cement-based renders. The use of a cement-based render will impair the ability of solid walls to breathe, and increase the levels of damp within the wall and put timbers in contact with the wall at increased risk of decay.

The external insulation of solid walled buildings based upon systems incorporating cement-based renders is a standardised solution. The experiences of those in building conservation are that the introduction of standardised insulation systems will create new problems and prejudice the future serviceability of the buildings. This is just one example of alterations to improve the performance of existing buildings that will cause problems in the long-term.

Conclusion

It is imperative that improvements made to the existing building stock, to improve their energy efficiency, are based upon an understanding of the buildings in question, if previous mistakes in the management of these buildings are not to be repeated.

To mitigate the risks associated with the introduction of insulation and increased air-tightness to buildings we must learn from past mistakes and not introduce improvements that will shorten the serviceability of the building. The lessons learnt by those in the field of building conservation have to be heeded and solutions need to be devised that are appropriate for the traditional construction and that also improve the thermal performance of these buildings.

Traditional buildings have an important role to play, as they can inform this and future generations of the development of cultures, enabling them to learn from both their successes and failures. They illustrate the importance and value of longevity and how this can be achieved with minimal cost to the environment. If we want a sustainable future, to pass something on worthwhile to our descendants, we have to work with what we have and not against it. The introduction of inappropriate materials, that have an adverse affect on the traditional performance, does not make practical, cultural, social, economic or environmental sense.

The educational value of many older buildings is also important, particularly as the process of discovering and re-learning is still continuing into why these buildings were constructed and the cultural information they contain.

Many traditional buildings that survive today have only done so because they have adapted and changed over time, to meet the demands and requirements of subsequent owners and users. This flexibility has allowed existing resources to continue in use, without creating the demand for much further investment in materials. These qualities are the very virtues of sustainability. We have a duty to pass these buildings on in a serviceable condition. ✺

References

1. 'The Need for Old Buildings to 'Breathe' by P Hughes, Information Sheet 4, The Society for the Protection of Ancient Buildings (SPAB), Spring, 1986.

Resources

Further information on how to care for traditional buildings can be found in a second story from Richard in Chapter 6.

Richard Oxley's book 'The Survey and Repair of Traditional Buildings – a sustainable approach' is published by Donhead Publishing: *www.donhead.com*

To read or participate in regular discussions on the subject of appropriate maintenance and repair of old buildings visit the Green Building Forum - a free internet resource: *www.greenbuildingforum.co.uk*

Design healthy buildings

Designing buildings to be healthy environments appears to be quite far down the scale of importance for most architects and builders. **Chris Morgan** wonders why ...

This is strange for three reasons. Firstly, whilst pollution is accepted as a major problem, at a design level, the response is conceived largely in terms of energy efficiency. Pollution happens 'out there' in the world, and we try to reduce this, but there is little grasp of the effect this pollution is having on us, personally.

Second, the awareness of health and of healthy lifestyles is quite advanced. Gyms, vitamin pills, organic food and alternative therapies all attest to a broad appreciation that our health is not all it might be, and yet the places where we spend the vast majority of our time, homes and workplaces, escape any critical analysis beyond the most immediately apparent.

Third, there have been scares. Most people now know that asbestos is dangerous, like lead in paints and pipes, and the media have picked up on concerns about electricity pylons, chemical treatments for rot and others. But like most things, these are considered isolated cases, and there is little sense of a generally, comprehensively harmful built environment. The rise in awareness of 'sick building syndrome' has made some headway in this regard, but in most people's reality, it is still not an issue.

And yet for those who investigate, it is shocking to discover the extent to which we have exposed ourselves to a wide range of untested combinations of known carcinogens, mutagens and other harmful elements, and in such close proximity to ourselves and our loved ones.

There is some resistance to such investigations. Manufacturers are understandably reticent about any possible health risks associated with their products, and it is notoriously difficult to make clear links between symptoms and the plethora of possible causes. However, a great deal is now understood about what is likely to be both good and bad for health, and it is possible to design and build homes and workplaces which are broadly free from pollutants and actively beneficial in supporting the health and comfort of occupants.

First remove the pollutants

Many pollutants have nothing to do with the building. Smoking is a significant pollutant, as are the many external fumes and particulates which can come in through open windows and air entry systems: agricultural spray drift, car and industrial process exhaust fumes, dust and pollen. Then there is electromagnetic radiation from pylons, and even radon from the ground itself in some places. Clearly there is a limit to what can be done to avoid these pollutant sources, but in some cases, the addition of 'buffer' spaces filled with plants and water, acting as conditioners for the incoming air for the rest of the building, can help.

Air

Some years ago, research in Denmark showed that the biggest source of pollutants in offices was not occupants, not smoking, not even the off-gassing of materials, but the air intake ducting and machinery itself. In other words, the equipment specifically installed to keep the air clean and healthy was the single biggest polluter. In most UK homes this should not be an issue, but it is relevant wherever there is a forced air supply.

Electropollution

The radiation effects of electrical equipment and cabling are much debated, but the links between electrical, and electro-magnetic fields and health are becoming harder to ignore, particularly at high voltage levels. Electric fields

© Green Building Press

are produced whenever there is a voltage (for example, in an electrical appliance and the cable to it, even if it is switched off), while electro-magnetic fields are only produced when current is flowing – the appliance is switched on. Both fields reduce in strength with distance away from the source, so the most common advice is simply to keep a distance, for example, between the plug, cable and electric alarm clock from your head while sleeping.

Electrical fields are quite easy to shield through the use of metal trunking or sheathing, but electro-magnetic fields are harder to avoid. The standard ring mains around a room is one source of the relatively high magnetic field in a room and one way of avoiding this is to produce a 'radial' or 'star-shaped' wiring arrangement, but this can lead to more costly wiring instal-lations. The UK is a long way behind other countries in recognising the risks attributed to electro-pollution.

Fumes
Some of the most lethal pollutants are from incomplete combustion fumes from boilers and stoves, leaky flues, or flues where there can be backdraft in the wrong wind conditions. Needless to say, these should be checked as a priority.

Paints and furniture
Decorating your home can be bad for your health! Paint stripper, and most old paint is of real concern, and conventional paints and varnishes etc. are some of the worst offenders for environmental pollution in their manufac-ture, and in terms of their effect on the health of occupants. The main concern is from the solvent fumes (the bit that dries off) but even water soluble paints may need to be avoided. Natural, non-toxic paints are available and while some are more expensive, switching to these is one of the simplest ways of reducing pollution and safeguarding your health.

A great deal of furniture and fittings now available contain toxic chemicals not only internally, but in the coatings which are applied to make them stain-free, fire-proof, 'low

maintenance' and so on. Chemicals, such as formaldehyde, benzene and phenols are found in plywood and particle boards (chipboard and 'mdf'), plastics, resins, glues, adhesives, synthetic textiles, flooring such as laminates, vinyl, insulation, carpets, curtains and furniture. Many of these chemicals 'off-gas' slowly over months and even years, and their effect can be traced in all areas of the body, particularly the nervous system.

Avoidance is the simple solution and it makes sense to keep to items which are as close to natural as you can find – linoleum not vinyl, timber not chipboard, screwed not glued, oiled or waxed not varnished and so on. Common sense – and a dash of scepticism – can take you a long way in this regard.

Timber preservatives
One of the most insidious pollutants is the chemical treatment of timber, for example, in the roof rafters, or sometimes all over in the case of some timber frame buildings. Even in old properties, such treatment is rarely neces-sary. Merely for 'peace of mind', your property has been made thoroughly toxic to human, as well as insect or fungal life. It is possible to avoid all chemical treatment of timber if the building is designed properly, and still ensure durability.

Water
Increasingly, the water that comes into our homes is likely to contain, not only beneficial minerals and other 'impurities', but also a great number of potentially harmful pollutants such as nitrates, metals, synthetic (and some volatile) organic compounds, radon and controversial additives like chlorine and fluoride. For those concerned, various types of water filtration system are available, each tending to deal better with some and not other pollutants.

Now create healthy conditions
Once you have removed the pollutants from your home or workplace, the next step is to create the ideal conditions for comfort. Even without any pollutants, it is possible (and quite

common) to design things so badly that the health of occupants will be at risk under certain conditions. The green building designer's job is to do the opposite.

Heating

The health effects of heating are the least appreciated aspect of health promoting design. A great deal is known about heating and thermal efficiency, particularly amongst the environmental design community, but, from the point of view of human health, I believe the only sensible heating system is a radiant, or largely radiant one.

Human thermal comfort is far more than having a thermostat set at 20°C. The most comfortable thermal environment for humans will be created when the surfaces of the room are a little warmer than the air, when the air is relatively still (not too many draughts, or convective currents) and there is sufficient thermal and moisture mass in the building fabric to moderate both temperature and humidity swings.

The conditions described above are almost impossible to create with a convective (warm air) system, and these systems may have a number of other disadvantages, which negatively affect the health of occupants, such as dust scorching. A low level radiant heating system, ideally at wall level, not in the ceiling, and with perhaps some 'top-up', quick-response radiant system, if needed, is the ideal.

Ventilation

At its most basic level, fresh air is needed to replenish the oxygen we use up in breathing, and to exhaust the carbon dioxide we produce. However, required ventilation rates have developed in order to account for other aspects. Air extract is needed to cope with pollutants and odours produced by people, materials and services. Extract is also needed to deal with (usually excessive) humidity and micro-organisms.

In a building with few pollutants and with humidity dealt with passively by the building fabric, the need for ventilation is much reduced. This is not recognised by the regulations yet, but the argument has been successfully submitted in Norway to reduce ventilation levels

Relative humidity plays a major role in the health quality of any building. As the chart shows, most harmful agents avoid environments where relative humidity is between 40-60%. Too dry is little better than too humid!

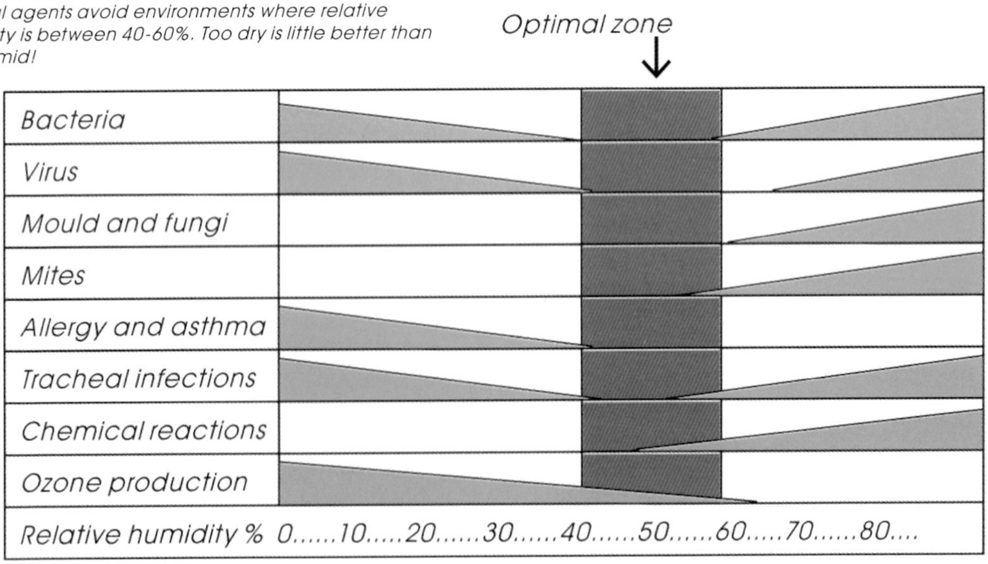

Optimal zone
↓

Bacteria			
Virus			
Mould and fungi			
Mites			
Allergy and asthma			
Tracheal infections			
Chemical reactions			
Ozone production			
Relative humidity % 0......10.....20.......30.......40.......50.......60.....70......80....			

without health risk to occupants, and to save energy, both in servicing, and in heat loss.

This brings us to another consideration of ventilation; that in extracting air, we are usually extracting warmth, hence the rise in the use of heat exchange extract fans. Given the increase in fabric insulation levels, the percentage of heat loss through ventilation has increased and so these fans perform a valuable function. However, they are effectively covert convection heating systems and, again from a health point of view, might warrant further investigation.

Humidity

The need to moderate humidity in buildings goes far beyond the risks associated with damp and mould, to well understood aspects of human health. Put simply, humans need a fairly balanced relative humidity of roughly between 40% and 65%. Beyond these, there are very close correlations with increased health risks, as clearly pictured in the previous diagram.

Air conditioning helps to moderate humidity, but like chemical preservatives, this comes with a possible health risk attached. It is possible - and preferable - to moderate humidity passively through the use of the building fabric and materials which naturally absorb and desorb moisture. These materials are known as 'hygroscopic' materials and can perform a valuable role in the design of internal air quality, helping to maintain a comfortable and healthy balance of humidity with no running costs or energy input. Clay is by far the most effective material for achieving this, but other natural materials like timber and lime also work, as long as they are not coated with impervious paints or varnishes. Another method, for those not building new, might be by the installation and use of passive vents that open automatically when there are high humidity levels.

Lighting

Natural light changes and in so doing links people back to the natural passing of time which is increasingly valuable as we now spend so much time indoors. Rooms with windows in more than one wall, and orientation, will help to

enhance this changing pattern of light.

Light surface finishes will reduce the need for supplementary lighting, and when designing artificial lighting, it is worth considering an emphasis on task lighting or mood lighting. This can be more energy efficient and likely to be more pleasant to use and control. Lighting with poor flicker should be avoided and daylight bulbs can be helpful to overcome the lack of daylight in areas where this is unavoidable.

Noise

Excessive noise is obviously to be avoided, but low level background noise, often associated with machinery, and noise from sources that cannot be controlled are considered to have the greatest potential to stress people. Many noises can be attenuated, but not all, and in many cases this can conflict with other requirements, such as the need for fresh air, so design strategies need to be considered early.

Plants

Plants use the carbon in the carbon dioxide we breathe out, and give off the oxygen we need. 'Fresh' air is largely fresh because of the activities of plants, so it is not surprising that putting plants inside a house will have some beneficial effect on the quality of the air. Beyond that, it has been found that some plants have an extraordinary capacity to absorb some of the pollutant gases which we produce as part of our modern lifestyle, so their targeted use will have benefits. Plants (and the earth in which they tend to be planted) also help to moderate humidity, so should have a more important place in our homes, beyond 'looking nice'.

Conclusion

Prioritising issues is important as it is easy to lose perspective. Everyone will have their own list, but consider the following as a starter:

- we spend a lot of time asleep, in one place. Sleep is the body's time for recuperation on a number of levels. If you can only make one place 'healthy' make it your bed and bedroom

- children, whose cells are developing quite differently from adults, are at much greater risk from the effects of toxins. They also spend more time closer to the floor than adults, so pay particular attention to floors and children's bedrooms
- arguably the worst offender for health in many people's homes can be the unassuming wall to wall carpet, not only because of the materials and treatments it contains, but its capacity to store dirt and harbour dust mites and their faeces. Beyond steam cleaning, if you are experiencing health problems and suspect carpet, replace with wooden floors, linoleum, tiling or similar. Smaller rugs which can be washed do not tend to pose the same threat
- the great majority of applications of chemicals for protection against infestation, rot, mould and so on are unnecessary. If you have a problem, consider contacting a specialist (not one trying to sell you a chemical treatment) who will probably be able to assess the situation independently and offer remedial solutions, such as better ventilation, better drainage and so on, without the need for chemicals or environmental controls.

Finally, a word or two on perspective. Wendell Berry wrote that "No place can be considered healthy until all places are healthy". This serves to remind us of the interconnectedness of these things, and of the fallacy of describing a house as 'healthy', particularly when you cannot control the way in which a building will be used.

Studying buildings and health can turn you into a sort of building-related-hypochondriac. One cough and you begin to eye the skirting boards suspiciously, whereas there may just be a virus going around at school. If you live an otherwise healthy life, it is likely that you will survive your home and workplace(!), but as with most things, why take the risk, when there is a much more comfortable and healthy way to live? ☯

Further reading

'*Ecology of Building Materials*' by Bjorn Berge

'*The Whole House Book*' by C Harris and P Borer

'*The Natural Plaster Book*' by Cedar Rose Guelberth and Dan Chiras

The above books are available from:
www.newbuilder.co.uk

'*The Toxic Consumer; how to reduce your exposure to everyday toxic chemicals*' by Karen Ashton & Elizabeth Salter Green, available from Green Shop Books: 01452 770629 *www.greenshop.co.uk*

Calch Tŷ-Mawr Lime

Manufacturers & suppliers of traditional & ecological building materials

- Lime Putty, Plaster & Mortar.
- glaster- - lime mortar/plaster with recycled glass aggregate.
- Hydraulic Lime and Dry Pre-mixed Mortars.
- Limecrete Floor Components and Advice.
- Ecological Paints and Finishing Products.

- Accredited Courses, Product Support, Site Visits, Mortar/Paint Analysis and Matching Service.
- Ecological Building Materials including Sheep's Wool Insulation, Clay Plasters, Reedboards, Reedmats, Wood Wool Boards, Pavatex Woodfibre Boards and Laths.
- Tools and Books.

glaster **limecrete**floor
www.glaster.org.uk   www.limecrete.org.uk

Tŷ-Mawr, Llangasty, Brecon, Powys LD3 7PJ
Tel: 01874 658000 Fax: 01874 658502
Email: tymawr@lime.org.uk www.lime.org.uk

© Green Building Press

green building store

product feature:
Ecoplus System
windows, doors and solar spaces

To view
Magdalene College
case study go to:
www.greenbuildingstore.co.uk/
case-ecoplus9.php

- timber and aluminium-clad windows and doors
- solar spaces and conservatories
- natural paints
- wood finishes
- boron timber preservatives
- ultra-efficient WCs and sanitaryware
- water-saving taps and fittings
- natural insulation
- steel rainwater drainage
- paint, artex and graffiti removal
- and more. . .

The new Ecoplus System range of windows, doors and solar spaces offers a new exacting level of environmental design

Using only Forest Stewardship Council (FSC) 100% certified timber – available in European oak or redwood – the new Ecoplus System systematically addresses issues of environmental impact.

FSC SUPPLIER
SA-COC-1435
© 1996 Forest Stewardship Council A.C.

FSC

Environmental features:

Engineered timber – using the latest lamination and finger-joint technology to minimise resource use and improve durability.

Super-efficient glazing – Iplus S glazing maximises thermal efficiency with a patented low-E coating and inert gas fill. Double or triple glazing is available, with centre pane U-values of 1.2 or 0.5 w/m^{2}K respectively.

Warm edge glazing technology – technically advanced Thermix warm edge glazing spacers help maximise thermal efficiency and virtually eliminate cold edge condensation.

Boron timber treatment – the Ecoplus System is treated with the inorganic borates the safest and most environmentally benign treatment available

Natural timber finishes – based on natural plant oils with no synthetic resins, biocides or other toxic ingredients.

Above: Ecoplus System at Magdalene College Cambridge

Green Building Store
11 Huddersfield Road
Meltham
Holmfirth
West Yorkshire
HD9 4NJ

www.greenbuildingstore.co.uk

01484 854898

Green Building Store is a specialist manufacturer and supplier of some of the UK's leading environmentally sensitive building products.

Make your buildings airtight!

If you live in a typical UK home, expensive, heated air is constantly escaping, giving rise to uncomfortable draughts, high energy bills and subsequently damaging the environment. **Paul Jennings** reports ...

Regardless of how much or what type of insulation you put into your building, if you fail to ensure that the fabric is airtight – i.e. free of uncontrollable draughts – your energy-saving expectations will never be fully realised. Sustainability is ultimately about reducing the carbon dioxide emissions that are causing global warming and driving climate change, giving us increasingly extreme and unstable weather conditions. As insulation levels continue to increase, an ever greater proportion of energy losses from our homes will occur through air leakage.

Draughts are uncontrolled air movement – and they make us uncomfortable. The wind blowing on our buildings can force cold air in, around windows and doors and through a wide range of other gaps and openings. Warm air rising within our homes escapes at high level, creating a suction which pulls cold air in through these same holes. Neither is satisfactory, yet at the same time we always need ventilation in our buildings to provide a healthy living environment.

We often tolerate draughts because we think they provide the necessary ventilation – wrong!! Draughts are uncontrolled currents of air, whilst ventilation is controlled and deliberately induced, using openable windows, trickle vents, extract fans etc. Most UK buildings have too much air leakage (draughts) when the wind blows and not enough ventilation on calm, still days.

Ventilation is the controlled replacement of degraded indoor air with external air and all buildings need ventilation. We need ventilation to breathe, and we need ventilation to get rid of indoor pollutants – cooking and other smells, but particularly water vapour. Minimising the buildup of moisture helps prevent condensation and mould growth, and discourages dust mites. As was pointed out in the previous story, relative humidity of between 50% and 65% will provide the most comfortable and healthy living environment. If you have open flued appliances, such as wood-burning stoves, we need more ventilation for safety, and if people smoke we need lots more ventilation.

Why minimise air leakage?

As well as allowing costly warm air to escape, air leakage gives rise to uncomfortable draughts, degrades the effectiveness of insulation by as much as two-thirds, and allows potentially damaging moisture to penetrate our walls. Air leakage is bad, ventilation is good. The slogan 'build-tight, ventilate-right' has been used for several years to encourage us to improve our buildings and reduce this shameful waste. Indeed, it has been suggested that it is impossible to build a building too airtight, although it is clearly possible to fail to design sufficient and appropriate ventilation.

As insulation levels installed in UK buildings have risen, particularly in recent years, then the waste of energy through escaping warm air has become more significant. Figure 1 illustrates how the proportion of energy lost through air leakage has increased to the point where it can be more than half of all energy losses.

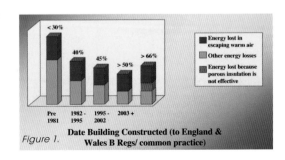

Figure 1.

This is likely to be even more significant for green designers and builders, as they tend to adopt insulation levels substantially above the minimums required by building regulations.

Airtightness testing

A 'blower door', also known as a 'door fan', is the principle tool used for measuring airtightness and identifying leakage in dwellings and other new or existing buildings. It consists of one or more calibrated fans that are mounted in an open doorway, using an adjustable door panel system. A series of steady-state pressure differences are then applied using the fan.

Once steady state conditions have been achieved, the airflow measured through the fan equals the sum of the air leaking through all the different gaps, cracks and openings in the envelope of the building or volume under test, adjusted for temperature difference.

By measuring the corresponding imposed pressure differentials, the leakage characteristics of the volume being tested can be established. Door fan testing is used to:
- provide an acceptance test for new dwellings, offices or other buildings
- identify leakage sites, provide quality control on remedial sealing works, if required
- check the performance of ventilation, extraction or mechanical ventilation and heat recovery (MVHR) systems
- establish ventilation rates in existing properties, for example to investigate the cause of condensation problems.

Leaky buildings

Our experience of testing houses and other buildings across the UK, together with test results published by various national bodies, show that the UK construction industry may well be in for a nasty shock when air leakage testing of housing becomes more commonplace.

Most UK builders have not yet grasped the nettle and learnt how to construct and finish airtight dwellings and other buildings. Sample air leakage testing of dwellings is mandatory under the revised Part L of the Building Regulations (April 2006), and eco-builders, aiming to achieve substantially lower carbon emissions than the relatively lax building regulations targets, should have testing to verify that they have achieved their target air permeability values and resulting calculated carbon emissions. Suitable targets for eco-builders are an air permeability of 3.0 (compared with the Building Regulations maximum of 10.0) in naturally ventilated dwellings, and 0.75 in dwellings with MVHR systems. These correspond to the AECB's Silver and Gold (CarbonLite) standards respectively (see page 52).

Test results published by BRE clearly show that improved airtightness in our buildings is essential – UK offices are around 2 to 4 times leakier than equivalent buildings in Scandinavia or North America, whilst industrial buildings are found to be more than 4 times as leaky. In housing, recent experience of testing supposedly airtight timber framed houses encountered many of the same problems found when testing the TRADA low energy house at Energy World in Milton Keynes nearly two decades ago!

The leakage sites to be found in dwellings and other buildings can be subdivided into two types: structural leakage and services leakage (see Figure 3 on page 120).

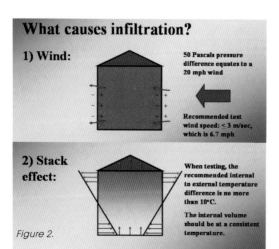

What causes infiltration?

1) **Wind:**

50 Pascals pressure difference equates to a 20 mph wind

Recommended test wind speed: ≤ 3 m/sec, which is 6.7 mph

2) **Stack effect:**

When testing, the recommended internal to external temperature difference is no more than 10°C.

The internal volume should be at a consistent temperature.

Figure 2.

Air leakage routes via the structure
(white numbered arrows)

1. A frequent and often very significant leakage site where cracks and gaps around the ends of floor joists (or hangers) connect with the floor void and thence with studwork partition walls and/or with gaps behind plasterboard on dabs. See Figure 4.

2. Cracks and gaps beneath inner window sills and around window frames. Often connect to a cavity in the wall, or may be direct to outside.

3. Leakage through windows where draughtproofing is missing or ineffective, or through hollow window frames (usually uPVC), where a continuous leakage path exists. Can include leakage through supposedly sealed double-glazed units.

4. Leakage through doors – particularly double doors - where draughtproofing is missing or ineffective.

5. Cracks and gaps beneath doors, typically through unsealed joints between the doorframe and the edge of the ground floor.

6. Cracks along the top and bottom edges of skirting boards, connecting with gaps around the edges of suspended floors.

7. Leakage between sections of suspended floors, usually timber.

8. Gaps around loft hatches. Can be particularly bad with lightweight, modern hatches.

9. Leakage paths through the eaves of a building, connecting into roof rooms directly or via unsealed service voids.

10. Major leakage frequently found around rooflights, normally where a wooden frame is not sealed to the roof timbers.

11. Another common leakage path through the eaves of a building, which connects into the top of upper rooms, through gaps behind plasterboard on dabs or hollow studwork walls.

12. Leakage through a porous masonry inner leaf. Often through poor-quality mortar joints at perpends between blocks, but can also occur directly through blockwork. Frequently connects to gaps behind drylining.

Air leakage routes via the services
(yellow numbered arrows)

13. Gaps in the inner wall where gas or electricity supplies from external meter boxes enter the building.

14. Leakage around ceiling roses and pull-switches, where unsealed cabling passes through to a roof space or cold intermediate floor. Also leakage around electrical sockets and switches mounted in hollow studwork walls that connect to a floor void or roof space.

15. Cracks and gaps around boiler flues.

16. Gaps where water and heating pipes penetrate into hollow floor voids and partition walls, frequently boxed in or hidden by kitchen or airing cupboards.

17. Gaps around waste pipes where they pass into hollow floor voids and partition walls, again often hidden by boxing.

18. Around waste pipes where they pass through the innermost layer of a wall, usually out of sight behind kitchen cupboards or beneath a bath.

19. Gaps around heating pipes into floor voids, which in turn may connect to a cavity in the external wall.

20. Gaps around and often through spotlights recessed in ceilings.

21. Around waste pipes, gas and water supplies, cables – electricity, telephone & television – which penetrate the lower floor.

22. A large hole can often be found around the top of the soil stack where it passes into a roof space.

23. Leakage through MVHR systems. More frequently, gaps around distribution or extract ductwork where it connects to a terminal mounted in a ceiling. Can also be major leaks around and through subfloor warm air heating ducts.

24. Cracks and gaps, sometimes large holes, around any or all water and heating pipes where they pass into a loft.

25. Around and through wall-mounted extract fans, also ducted vents from cooker hoods, tumble dryers and fans in internal bathrooms or other rooms.

© Green Building Press

Common air leakage routes into buildings

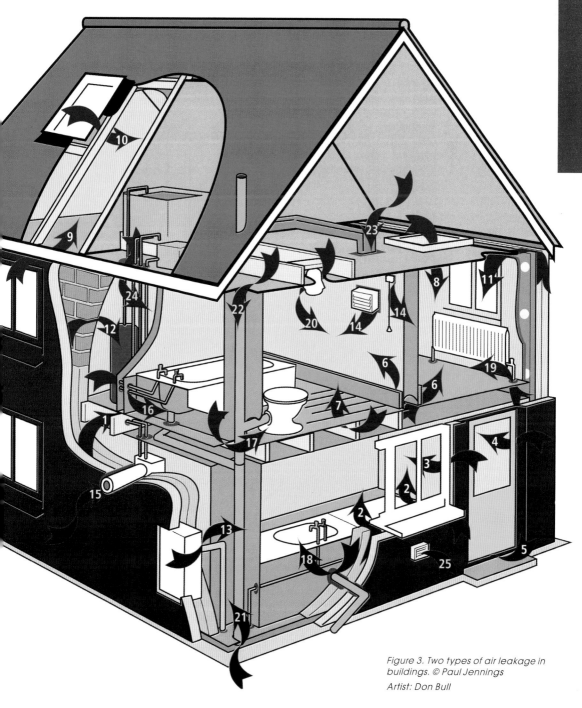

Figure 3. Two types of air leakage in buildings. © Paul Jennings

Artist: Don Bull

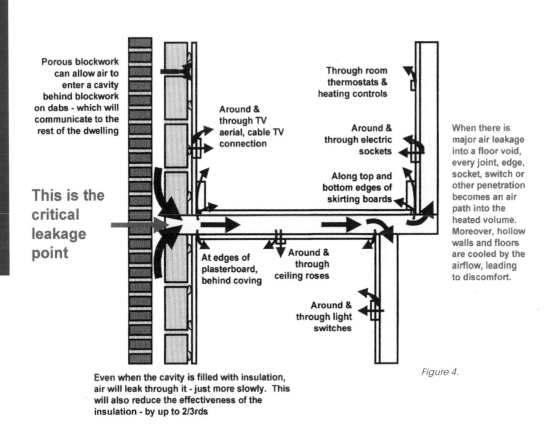

Porous blockwork can allow air to enter a cavity behind blockwork on dabs - which will communicate to the rest of the dwelling

Around & through TV aerial, cable TV connection

Through room thermostats & heating controls

Around & through electric sockets

Along top and bottom edges of skirting boards

When there is major air leakage into a floor void, every joint, edge, socket, switch or other penetration becomes an air path into the heated volume. Moreover, hollow walls and floors are cooled by the airflow, leading to discomfort.

This is the critical leakage point

At edges of plasterboard, behind coving

Around & through ceiling roses

Around & through light switches

Figure 4.

Even when the cavity is filled with insulation, air will leak through it - just more slowly. This will also reduce the effectiveness of the insulation - by up to 2/3rds

Structural leakage sites occur at joints in the building fabric and around window and door openings. Loft hatches and access openings (usually non-domestic) also fall within this category. There may also be leakage through cracks in masonry walls – poor perpends in blockwork inner leafs being the most common cause – and some diffusion through materials. These are the hardest to retrofix. Good detailing at the design stage is therefore essential. Builders also need appropriate training, so they understand how to build airtight buildings to achieve a good test result.

Service penetrations occur where pipes and cables pass into the building. These can be sewerage pipes, water pipes and heating pipes. As well as electricity cables there may also be television aerials and cable television connections. The worst problems tend to occur when these two types of leakage problems interact. (see Figure 4).

Once there is a failure of the airtight barrier where a hollow intermediate floor is supported from the external wall, a connection exists from a cavity in the external wall (which may be filled with insulation) through hollow internal partition walls to pretty much the whole of the building. Hollow floors and walls are inevitably used to run services – and just as inevitably tend not to be sealed where the services run from one element into another. The result is that electricity sockets and switches, light fittings (especially spotlights), television aerial and cable television connections, heating and plumbing pipes, waste pipes and soil stacks all become points at which air will leak into the dwelling. Even such minor items as room thermostats and heating controllers will permit air leakage around or through them. Moreover, if one such leakage site is sealed, most of the air will still escape at another site, since they tend to connect and to have a similar resistance to the movement of air through them.

© Green Building Press

Whilst it may be possible to laboriously seal all these sites and thereby cut the air leakage significantly, cold air will still get into hollow floors and walls, cooling internal surfaces and giving rise to discomfort.

Another major source of problems is the boxing-in of services, particularly water and waste pipework and soil stacks. Also riser shafts in non-domestic buildings. Once services are out of sight, it is all too easy for sealing works to be overlooked and forgotten, even if they were specified in the first place. There is no culture of airtight construction on UK sites, and until this is achieved, detailed planning and preparation, rigorous site supervision and air leakage testing will be essential to achieve satisfactory buildings. In fact, air leakage testing provides an effective, rapid and reasonably priced method to check the quality of buildings. ☙

Resources

Air testing: www.retroteceurope.co.uk

Volume, 10 No. 3 of Building for a Future magazine covered the subject of airtightness in-depth, including a number of case studies. It can be viewed free of charge at: www.buildingforafuture.co.uk/winter00/ as a downloadable pdf file.

Airtightness is also discussed in the low energy design context in the 'Green Building Bible, Volume 2'.

J.RICHARDSON
DESIGN & BUILD

EB

A Complete Environmental Timber Frame Design and Manufacture Service Under One Roof

- Innovative Designs
- Timber Frame Manufacture
- Self Build Package that includes:
    -Advice on Planning & Specifications
    -Comprehensive schedule of work
    -Complete bill of quantities
- Sustainable, energy-efficient materials

Contact: Jamie Richardson, Bryn Afal, Meifod, Powys
Tel: 01938 500899 Website: www.jrbltd.co.uk Email: info@jrbltd.co.uk

Light, sunshine and fresh air

Exploiting beneficial light and heat from the sun within buildings may be a rather obvious priority for environmentally conscious building designers. However, it is one that is often misunderstood or inadequately applied. **Stephen Lowndes** examines the issues and options ...

An appreciation of how best to manipulate nature's energy source to ensure maximum benefit of the sun's heat and light when it is available, and at the same time ensure discomfort is avoided during periods of excess, is fundamental to successful building design. Here we examine the key concepts behind effective use of daylight and solar heat, which should be adopted at the earliest stages in planning a project.

Passive solar design

Most people have, at one time or another, stood next to a brick wall on a warm summer's day and felt the radiating heat. You are feeling some of the radiant energy that the masonry has absorbed from the sun. This energy is felt more directly next to a window, the epitome being the heat one can experience, even on a cold, bright winter's day, within a greenhouse. A greenhouse is, of course, designed to maximise the capture of the sun's radiant energy and is an example of a building designed to optimise solar energy in terms of heat and light. Passive solar buildings are designed specifically to exploit this 'free' energy, making use of the sun's heat, especially in the winter, for warmth, and to mitigate the extremes of heat experienced in the summer. Usually buildings designed to maximise beneficial solar heat will simultaneously optimise daylight utilisation, although this is not always the case and the use of solar heat and daylight are not necessarily mutually inclusive. The energy utilised by the building is passive by definition, since the building has not generated the energy itself or exclusively by artificial means, rather it is effectively capturing, transferring or (in the case of heat) storing the energy from the sun.

You may be forgiven for thinking that the climate in the UK would not make passive solar design worthwhile. Studies undertaken in this country show that even conventionally designed housing, with primary glazed elevations specifically orientated towards the south, will achieve annual energy savings of the order of 3%-4%[1] and that if conventional housing layouts are planned so that most principle rooms face south, further annual energy savings of 1%-2% should be possible[2].

These savings relate to applying the first steps of passive solar design to contemporary housing without incurring any additional construction costs. Specifically designed passive solar housing schemes have demonstrated annual energy savings in excess of 8% - 10%[3]. The additional monetary costs for implementing passive solar design over and above conventional build cost can be negligible, depending on the extent of design solutions adopted and the nature of the project. These solutions will revolve primarily around the parameters of building orientation, shading, window design, thermal mass, ventilation and air-tightness.

Orientation

Imagine the ultimate passive solar house, which, rather fantastically, is constructed upon a large revolving turntable. It slowly rotates so that the primary occupied rooms are continually facing the sun throughout the day during the winter, and in the summer the house rotates so that these areas are continually in the shade. Unfortunately such a fantastic proposition is impractical and likely to be somewhat disorientating for its occupants! This shows, however, that passive solar buildings need to be designed so that rooms occupied for most of the day are exposed to optimum sun for winter warmth and daylight as well as receiving benefit from

© Green Building Press

seasonably available shade during the summer.

The maximum incident solar radiation on a vertical wall occurs for an orientation facing due south, typically 5kWh/m² in January, which drops to about 2kWh/m² if the wall faces due north[4]. Fixed room orientations up to 30° east of south, result in exposure to the sun in the morning, whereas orientation up to 30° towards the west of south achieves maximum exposure in the afternoon[5]. This diurnal variance in optimum solar exposure tends to dictate the layout of passive solar buildings. As a result it is usually recommended that living rooms and major bedrooms in dwellings achieve an exposure within 45° of south[6].

Shading

Passive solar buildings need to take optimum advantage of the different sun altitudes throughout the year. In the winter, the sun's altitude is low, which may mean adjacent buildings obscure beneficial direct solar radiation. Ideally, the building would be positioned clear of the obstructions. The reverse is true in the summer, when an adjacent obstruction is beneficial, providing shade at the start or end of the day. There are a number of ways to solve this dichotomy. For example planting deciduous trees on southerly aspects, enabling solar penetration in the winter months when the tree's branches are bereft of foliage and giving shade in the summer from a renewed green canopy.

External shading devices that are part of the building structure can be used, such as large overhanging roof eaves or deep window reveals, although care should be exercised to ensure external shading does not preclude too much daylight. These structures could also potentially provide other useful functions, such as use as a balcony or doubling up as an external light shelf to help reflect more daylight into the building, reducing reliance on artificial lighting. External shading devices offer the advantage of an increased external viewing amenity when compared to internal shading such as Venetian blinds. Internally located blinds are less effective in terms of reducing summer heat gain and can reduce the effectiveness of natural ventilation

through the window that they are covering.

Thermal mass

The effect of a shelter offering the advantages of thermal mass would have been experienced by our earliest ancestors dwelling within caves and has been utilised within vernacular architecture throughout the world. For most of the twentieth century, the use of mass produced building products, combined with modern commercial construction methodologies and timescales, has tended to favour the use of lightweight materials. Yet the ability of thermally massive materials to store or release solar heat when used as part of a building's structure for subsequent beneficial release later in the day, is recognised as a fundamental principle of passive solar building design. Buildings that make use of thermal mass tend to take longer to heat up from cold, but retain their heat for longer once warmed. This behaviour suits continuous or regular occupation patterns in the winter, enabling occupants to take advantage of available solar heat received in the day, reradiated slowly during the colder evenings, when there is greatest need for heat. In the summer the thermal mass acts as a buffer, with the same thermal storage properties helping to attenuate the peak solar gain to the space, minimising overheating.

The physical property of a material that governs its ability to store heat is its specific heat capacity. This is the amount of energy (kJ) required to raise the temperature of 1kg (or 1m³) of a material by 1°C. Materials such as soft wood have a heat capacity of about 730kJ/m³ °C and brick 1360kJ/m³ °C. These have a lower heat capacity and hence lower thermal mass than dense concrete with a heat capacity of 1760kJ/m³ °C[7]. Other more environmentally friendly thermally massive materials, such as locally sourced stone or even rammed earth and clay adobes are increasingly being used. For the thermal mass to be effective it needs to be exposed to the occupied space and not completely shrouded with light-weight finishes. This means that the proportion of exposed thermal mass should be as high as possible, which might require, for example, the exposure of areas such as floors that receive direct solar radiation, as well as areas receiving indirect solar radiation, such as ceilings. Placing an insulating layer or an air cavity in front of a heavy weight material isolates the mass from the internal environment and will reduce the material's ability to exchange heat with the surroundings. A compromise between acceptable finishes, poor acoustic environment (often a problem with excessive hard surface exposure) and adequate thermal coupling with the building mass, needs to be struck.

Windows and buffer zones

To minimise the requirement for space heating, passive solar housing designs usually incorporate reduced glazing areas on north, east and west elevations in comparison to the south. The associated reduced winter heat loss from reduced glazing on these elevations is usually greater than the potential solar gain, even when low emissivity glazing is utilised (i.e a low E coating allows the shortwave energy from the sun to enter the building, but acts as a barrier to the escape of long-wave energy from internal heat sources). Increasing the southerly aspect of the glazing using low E specification glass will usually provide a net winter day-time heat gain in most parts of the UK[8].

Conservatories, atria, entrance lobbies and porches provide a cushion or barrier between the occupant and the external environment. These so-called buffer zones act as the first line of defence against the elements and in the context of passive solar design, they make use of solar radiation to increase the temperature relative to the outside. This means that the conductive heat losses through the separating wall from the occupied space and the heat loss due to natural infiltration is reduced because of the reduced temperature difference between the inside occupied space and that of the buffer zone.

A judgement on how big windows need to be to maximise beneficial utilisation of daylight will be a function of the amount of visible or unobstructed sky potentially available, the room

depth, room height and internal finish of the room walls. Formally, the measure of acceptable daylight within a room can be expressed in terms of a daylight factor. In theorical terms this is (simplistically) the ratio of internal daylight level to external daylight level within a room, expressed as a percentage. It is possible to calculate this using formula found in most building science text books and obtain an optimum glazing area for a particular room design. Typically, living rooms should achieve minimum daylight factors of 1%, kitchens 2% and bedrooms 0.5%[9].

In practical terms, good design that aims to encourage maximum daylight penetration within a room should be pursued wherever possible:

- consider roof lights - about twice as effective as the equivalent area of window within a vertical wall (although they may lose more heat)
- allow windows that open onto conservatories and atria to be larger than normal - the heat loss is reduced by the buffer zone effect
- incorporate splayed window reveals, light-shelves and light coloured internal finishes to ceilings and walls - all help to provide increased reflective surface areas and bounce light further into a room
- provide dual aspect windows - maximise light source throughout the day, depths greater than six metres are difficult to light

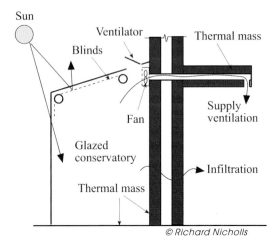

© Richard Nicholls

from one glazed elevation.

Airtightness and ventilation

As discussed in the previous two articles, there should be an emphasis on well sealed buildings that minimise uncontrolled infiltration of air. This can hopefully be achieved by careful design and well monitored site work - avoiding ill fitting windows and doors and poor building details. However this drive towards airtightness raises awareness of the importance of ensuring that the building users get the right amount of controlled ventilation to ensure a healthy, habitable environment. Passive solar design can be exploited to provide naturally powered ventilation using controlable ventilated cavities or trombe walls. In a trombe wall, an air cavity separates an internal wall from a series of glazed panels. Outside ventilation air enters the cavity at low level. Solar radiation heats both the air within the cavity, as well as the mass of the wall, which conducts heat to the adjacent space. The buoyant, heated air is displaced to the top of the cavity by cooler incoming outside air of greater density. The heated air at the top of the cavity flows into the adjacent internal space providing ventilation. Attention to detail would be essential but the method provides a natural alternative to powered fans and / or heat exchange units.

Regulations

All new and modified buildings constructed in the UK must comply with the current Part L of the Building Regulations (Part J in Scotland). Passive solar buildings should now be able to show compliance based upon the new 'carbon index' method of compliance, providing that the energy (therefore carbon) saving design strategies can be demonstrated to the satisfaction of the building control officer, since Part L now specifically takes into account schemes that incorporate passive solar heating.

In the case of dwellings, SAP ratings (often required by local authorities and housing associations to give an indication of the energy efficiency of an individual house design) have

the potential to be improved when passive solar design techniques are correctly adopted.

The weakest link

Buildings that exploit the sun's heat and light to their optimum beneficial effect have the potential to offer significant savings in energy and ultimately CO_2 emissions. It is important to understand that the concepts that drive the successful application of passive solar building design are intrinsically linked. There is no weakest link as such, since building orientation, window design, solar shading, thermal mass and building envelope are all influenced by each other. A badly orientated building, for example, affects the performance of each of the other parameters, requiring their re-optimisation to compensate. Similarly a building with optimised orientation but limited thermal mass may require other enhanced measures to help maintain comfortable temperatures during the extremes of winter and summer. In the UK we have to design to accommodate the excesses of potentially cold winters, as well as hot summers and this will always dictate how far the designer is able to pursue each particular parameter.

See 'Green Building Bible, Volume 2' for more in-depth information on the issues raised in the story.

References

1, 2, 3 Energy Efficiency Best Practice Report 27, 'Passive solar estate layout', p2, table 1, BRECSU, Building Research Establishment, Watford.

4, 5, 7 'Energy and Environment in Architecture a Technical Design Guide' by N Baker, K Steemers, (2000), pp20-24, and 36-37, E & F N Spon.

6 Good Practice Guide 79, 2001, 'Energy efficiency in new housing – a guide to achieving best practice', p8, BRECSU, Building Research Establishment, Watford.

8 Energy Efficiency Best Practice Report 27, 'Passive solar estate layout', p9, BRECSU, Building Research Establishment, Watford.

9 'The Whole House Book' by P Borer, C Harris (1998), p37-38, (new addition available from www.newbuilder.co.uk)

4 Greening the home

See also: many of the technologies featured here are discussed in detail in Chapter 7

Options for existing homes

Scientific research has recently revealed that levels of CO_2 (carbon dioxide), a greenhouse gas, are at their highest for over 650,000 years. Domestic energy use accounts for around a quarter of the total CO_2 emissions in the UK and this is projected to rise by a further 6% by 2010. **Keith and Sally Hall** outline how we can all do something to address these issues ...

More than half of all resources consumed globally are used in buildings or on their construction, and the way in which we build and use our homes dictates how much CO_2 is produced. Our comfortable, consumerist lifestyles are a primary cause of global warming, so we should all be thinking seriously about what effects our everyday lives have on the planet. Is there anything we can do to help reduce or slow-down climate change? Yes, we believe there is. We can examine our use of resources and look for compromises, which will not disrupt our lives too much and could even make our lives healthier and more fulfilled.

So, what can we do?

Heating our homes uses up the most energy. The best way of reducing CO_2 emissions is to use less energy. This will also save us money. Visit the website of the National Energy Foundation (NEF) where you can calculate how much carbon dioxide you are producing **www. nef.org.uk/energyadvice/co2calculator.htm**

Take a look at your heating system. Have you got radiator stats fitted? Try turning down the main room thermostat by one or two degrees and wear warmer clothing. Turn off lights when not in use and teach others in the family the same strategy. A single 100W bulb burning all night and every night for a year creates half a ton of CO_2[1]. Use low energy lighting where possible. Automatic sensor lights are great for lobbies and landings. These switch on and off automatically as they sense movement and can be set to suitable times, but unfortunately they should not be used with low energy bulbs which tend to blow if switched on and off repeatedly. Choose A-rated appliances which are now available from all high street retailers and clearly labelled to reveal energy and water consumption. Don't leave appliances such as TV's and radios on stand-by. 'Phantom loads' as they are known, are responsible, nationally, for hundreds of thousands of tons of CO_2 per year. Turning appliances off at the wall will also help minimise any potential health risk from electro-magnetic fields.

Your local energy efficiency advice centre (0800 512012) will provide you with free advice on how to save energy and keep your house warm. There are centres throughout the UK and these will send out free literature and can also offer free home visits. They will advise on how you can increase the insulation in your roof, walls or floors. Don't forget to insulate hot water cylinders and pipes, eliminate uncontrolled draught by adding draught proofing to doors, windows and unsealed openings, and seal all gaps around pipes and cables through ceilings and walls – the most common routes for heat

© Green Building Press

loss. If you do change or upgrade your loft insulation investigate using natural products, such as sheep's wool or cellulose fibre (recycled newsprint) insulation as these materials have a lower environmental impact and their embodied energy in production is lower, therefore offering further CO_2 savings.

Think about signing up for a green energy tariff but this action is not sufficient in isolation as the additional premium is likely to be used to investigate future renewable development, rather than actually providing you with renewable power. Most electricity companies operate green energy tariffs. You can visit **www.greene-lectricity.org** for information on the companies and their performance. Green energy tariffs should support the development of energy production from renewable or sustainable sources - from wind, sun, biomass, biogas (domestic waste) and water (hydropower).

Once you have considered all the above, you could think about some of the other options listed below to reduce your CO_2 burden even further.

High performance timber windows

There are still a significant number of UK properties with windows and doors that are single-glazed. If you have single glazing then consider, as a priority, installing high performance, double-glazed, timber windows.

Ecoplus from the Green Building Store

Double-glazing can cut heat loss through glazed areas by up to 50%, saving around £60 per annum on heating bills and up to a quarter of a tonne of CO_2 over the heating season. The optimum gap between panes is 20mm and low emissivity glass (low-e) is recommended. Argon gas filled units, with rubber edged glazing bars will give even greater savings. Timber should be from a sustainable source and FSC certified[2].
Guide cost: around £275 per window installed.

Renewable technologies

Many of the renewable technologies (if fitted by a registered installer) qualify for a grant and attract a reduction from the standard rate VAT (5% instead of 17.5%). Contact the Energy Saving Trust (EST), 0845 120 7799, **www.est.co.uk** for more information on the new Low Carbon Buildings Scheme grants. You should also contact your local planning department to check if planning consent is needed, as this may be a requirement for some wind turbines and for any visual alterations or add-ons to your property, particularly if you live in a listed building or are in a conservation area or national park.

Solar water heating

Solar water heating systems use the sun's energy to heat water and can supply around 50% of a household's annual hot water requirements. Collectors, usually on the roof, absorb heat from sunlight and transfer it, by pump or gravity, to a hot water cylinder for domestic use. In summer it can provide up to 90% of the hot

Solar water heating panels and photovoltaic (electricity) panels combined on the same roof of houses in Cambourne by Circle 33 Housing Association.

water demand, but less during the rest of the year. According to one manufacturer, its panels can save up to 250kg of CO_2 a year. Obviously a south-facing roof is optimum but systems can be designed to suit most locations from east to west facing or even ground mounted.

Guide cost: around £2500 installed.
Solar Trades Association:
www.greenenergy.org.uk/sta

System descriptions:
www.thecei.org.uk/solarheating

Photovoltaic (PV) panels

PV's convert solar energy directly into electricity. PV cells are made up of two or more thin layers of semi-conducting material, usually silicon. When this is exposed to light, electricity is generated. PV's are available as panels, roof tiles or semi opaque glazing. Their maintenance free attributes make them the darling of the renewable's industry, although they are still expensive compared with highly subsidised grid-supplied electricity. However, as they are clean, durable and low maintenance, this technology should be given serious consideration if you have money to spend. Systems can be roof, ground or even mounted on a solar tracker.

Guide cost: £7000 - £9000 per kW (installed) of energy produced. A rough estimate - 3kWh of pvs would be enough to power all the lighting and non-heating electrical loads of the average home.

*PV UK: **www.greenenergy.org.uk/pvuk2***

System design and size calculators:
www.solar-power-answers.co.uk/solar_panel.html

Condensing gas boiler

Most boilers over 10 years old are inefficient, some providing below 60% efficiency. New gas fired condensing boilers are very energy efficient (85-95%). These boilers recover latent heat from the combustion gases as they enter the flue. Although they are more expensive, the pay back period is just 3 years. In 2003 the Energy Saving Trust calculated that if everyone in the UK with gas central heating changed to a condensing boiler, CO_2 emissions would be cut by 18.6 million tonnes per year (3% of UK's emissions). Condensing boilers are by far the most efficient of all fossil-fuelled heating systems for running a radiator or under-floor

*The inside workings of a Vaillant condensing gas boiler. The EST produce a useful publication called the Little Blue Book of Boilers (0845 727 7200) which can also be accessed on the internet at **www.boilers.org.uk***

heating system. Don't be tempted to opt for an electrical heating system as the CO_2 production would be double that of a condensing boiler. If you cannot afford to replace your boiler, upgrade and insulate your existing one and ensure it is serviced regularly.

Guide cost: £100 - £300 more than a conventional boiler

*Database of gas and oil boilers, giving efficiency rating etc: **www.boilers.org.uk***

*The National Energy Foundation has a comprehensive online guide to choosing an energy efficient gas or oil boiler: **www.nef.org.uk/energyadvice/boilers.htm***

Rainwater harvesting

Climate change is likely to make rainfall less predictable but it seems we will see drier summers and wetter winters. Erratic rainfall patterns make water supply management difficult, so it makes sense to save water and re-use it where possible. If you are using mains water, such measures will also save energy at the local treatment works. Simple, low cost strategies might include using water butts to collect rainwater for gardening and general outside purposes. You can save water by fitting water saving devices in existing toilets. The more adventurous water saver could investigate an

© Green Building Press

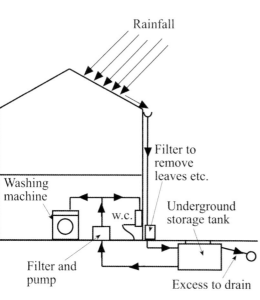

A number of rainharvesting systems are now on the market so the homeowner has plenty to choose from.

Rainfall

Filter to remove leaves etc.

Washing machine

w.c.

Underground storage tank

Filter and pump

Excess to drain

Dedicated log, pellet or woodchip boilers usually need their own boiler room and fuel store nearby. This unit is a Baxi Solo Innova log boiler.

automated rain harvesting system, which will give you a supply of water even during periods when hose pipe bans are in force. These systems collect rainwater that would otherwise have been lost into the drainage system. Large surfaces, such as roofs, are ideal for rainwater harvesting and can provide water for the garden, washing machine and to flush the toilet.

Guide cost: from £60 (rainwater butt but check with your local council as some subsidise the purchase of water butts) - £2000+ for a fully integrated and automated rain-harvesting system.

*UK Rainwater Harvesting Association: **www.ukrha.org***

Wood burners and biomass

If you have access to a source of logs, then a high performance wood burning stove or boiler would definitely be worth considering. Wood burning, providing that the timber comes from a supply in constant re-growth (coppice or regeneration) is CO_2 neutral because the carbon released from the burning of the wood equates to the carbon absorbed by the trees in re-growth. If you have your own woodland and are prepared to put some time and effort into

felling, logging, stacking and storing timber, then here is a great opportunity to keep fit at the same time as keeping your home warm. Timber growing and log burning can be the most satisfying and sustainable way to heat your home. If your home does not have a chimney, investigate installing one. There are many chimney kits available that do not involve major structural alterations to the building. The latest high performance, fanned flue log boilers are highly efficient (90 – 95% - providing dry wood is used) and only require a low draught chimney, so will perform adequately even in areas where conventional open fires might not work well. Most also have very low particulate emissions and can therefore be used in smokeless zones[3] but do check this with the supplier. These systems work best with accumulator tanks and have the added benefit of reducing refuelling to once per day.

Another biomass fuel resource is waste wood. Two million tonnes of waste timber is produced each year. This can and is beginning to be turned into biomass fuel (usually wood pellets). Pellet boilers and stoves are now available from many wood stove distributors, but at the present time all wood pellets are imported into the UK from Europe, incurring transport 'costs'. When UK pellet manufacture begins, then this will provide a low CO_2 fuel and a highly automated method of heating your home.

Guide cost: £4000+ for boiler systems or £600 or more for individual pellet-fuelled room heaters.

A useful introduction to burning wood as a heating fuel can be found at:
www.solidfuel.co.uk/main_pages/wood.htm

Biomass Task Force report and feedback on energy from biomass: **www.defra.gov.uk/farm/acu/energy/biomass-taskforce**

Wind turbines

There is a lot of hype around at the moment regarding small scale roof mounted wind turbines and certainly the media has had a good time promoting the idea. The entrepreneurs behind a couple of novel systems hope to cover our homes with as many micro wind turbines as there are satellite dishes. However, the idea and the figures promoted in the press have been criticised by many experts. There is scepticism about the predicted outputs and our own personal experience of a roof-mounted turbine is that it has needed more maintenance than anticipated due to excess wear and tear from turbulence around the building.

However, when installed in a suitable location, wind turbines can be efficient and durable. If you live on an exposed, windy site and can position a turbine away from any obstructions, this is a good option to consider.

Guide cost: from around £1800 for a 400 watt turbine and up to £20,000 for a 2.5kW turbine installed

British Wind Energy Association:
www.bwea.com/you/own.html

Micro CHP

Micro combined heat and power (mCHP) units follow the same concept as their large industrial cousins, whereby electricity is produced by a generator, driven by an engine with the by-product, heat, being captured and used for heating and hot water. With trials near completion, there are a few companies preparing to provide for the potentially enormous UK domestic housing market. The idea is not new in Europe where the market, although small, has been growing steadily for the past ten years. The attraction of CHP is that the system creates electrical and heat energy at its point of use and with the desperate inefficiency of the National Grid (less than 60% of the electricity generated actually gets used) then the concept has a lot in its favour. However, its sustainability factor will depend on the source fuel which, at the moment, is likely to be gas.

Guide cost: £3000+ installation costs. Unfortunately at the moment units are hard to obtain in the UK.

Further information: might be obtainable from the Combined Heat and Power Association: **www.chpa.co.uk** ☯

References

1. Calculated by the British Astronomical Association in 1990 (concerned about lit skies spoiling the view of the night sky).

2. Forest Stewardship Council (FSC): **www.fsc-uk.org**

3. The Clean Air Act and smoke control: www. westminster.gov.uk/environment/ pollution/airpollution/smokecontrol.cfm

© Green Building Press

Further help from GBP websites

* thousands of pages of free information
* daily green building news, chat and interaction.

Building for a Future is our main product and from the BFF homepage you can access links from the current issue and browse back issues - as far back as year 2000. Most issues over six months old can be downloaded free in PDF format. If you find a copy that you really must have in your library, then you can order a hard copy online with free delivery.
www.buildingforafuture.co.uk

A very popular service is our 'free' Green Building Newsletter which is delivered by e-mail, each month, to over 3000 readers. Back issues are also archived in the newsletter section so if you miss any you can pick them up here.
www.newbuilder.co.uk/newsletter/

The Green Building Forum is very popular. It is simple to use and doesn't make any demands on the users for e-mail addresses or passwords. It is frequented by building professionals always happy to help each other, DIY'ers and the general public with their questions.
www.greenbuildingforum.co.uk

Why is the Green Building Press so successful at what it does?
We are a small team of dedicated people with extensive knowledge of green building and sustainable living. We deliver the information, at minimal cost, right across the industry. Our funding comes only from subscriptions, targeted advertising and greenpro registrations.

GreenPro needs little introduction. No other product directory can match GreenPro for its unbiased green building content and value for money. It includes up-to date, detailed information on over 1000 products suitable for green building, as well as an extensive archive that also taps into the immense resources of Building for a Future magazine. The one-off cost is just £11.75 (including VAT) for unlimited access.
www.newbuilder.co.uk/greenpro

Our News pages are unrivalled for delivering UK green building news. We are a Google favourite with our latest news items (averaging three per day), indexed by Google within hours and going straight to top ranking positions under the relevant subject headings. We do occasionally aggregate news but much of it is first generation and unique to the newbuilder website.
www.newbuilder.co.uk/news/

We guarantee that our websites are updated daily!

Rough guide to eco-homes

Doug Stewart offers a number of simple tips and good advice for anyone wishing to build a new eco-home from scratch.

Creating a home with the correct space and specification for your requirement is like buying any bespoke, customised piece of equipment, furniture or car. Buildings can rarely be standard items and refurbishments never are. Time must be taken to get the mix right. However, where do you start?

Many people dream of finding the perfect building plot and all other thoughts are blocked until that plot is found. However, idyllic building plots are in very short supply, and if they come up, literally cost the earth. The reality is that most dream homes will be built on an 'infil' plot between two other houses and this is also the best option from an environmental sense as it can tap into nearby services, such as water gas and electricity that already supplies other homes.

Financial aspects

If you want to build a new home, then be prepared to spend at least as much money on buying a building plot as on the build itself. Money is of paramount importance to any successful project and cannot be over emphasized. It is always worth knowing what the final value of a property might be. It prevents you from overspending on fancy building products that will see no return.

Builders have traditionally used a rule of thumb guide for valuing an imaginary building on a potential plot of land; it is 1+2 =3. So, basically, if the building plot costs £100,000 then the build cost and profits need to be contained within a budget of £200,000, giving a total ballpark figure of £300,000 as the final value of the property. However, with the soaring cost of land nowadays, the equation should be adjusted to 1+1 so, theoretically, leaving you less spending

money for the actual build before you start to waste money!

Funding for any property purchase and building works can come from many sources. The rule of thumb is the more cash you have relative to eventual cost, the better deal you will get from any funding partner. The reason for this is you are lowering the risk factor of your funding partner. Whether you use a building society, a clearing bank, or a merchant bank, any lender will evaluate its client and their project for risk. Even a joint investor, such as a wealthy friend or relative, if they have any financial sense, will need to take advice on the risk factor.

Losing money does happen, and when it does it can be a spiral which goes out of control. If, however, the client and funder have both taken all steps possible to consolidate any risk factors, a successful project should follow. Sustainable and green projects are beginning to receive preferential treatment from some lenders, so bear this in mind. However, read Gideon Richard's article a little later in this chapter, on 'Smoothing the Planning Process', because sometimes overstating the environmental merits of a project can, oddly enough, work against the application in some planning departments.

A financial ceiling should be in place from the outset identifying the total of your allocated funds for the project, and how you want to spend it. Don't forget to take account of any grants available (very few at the moment). Tunnel vision can be a problem, from both client and designer/specifier, so be open, frank and discerning from the start.

The site or building you eventually acquire, to enable your vision, will form the basis of your journey into the world of construction. The impact of the choice of site should never be under-estimated, as it will have a huge influence

© Green Building Press

on design requirements, eventual cost and its fitness for purpose. An evaluation, with careful consideration of all the sites downsides and potential problems, should always be carried out, working with a suitably qualified person or practice. This will guide the client through any potential pit falls and disasters.

Remember that potential sites are in short supply. Estate agents' windows, with property photos and descriptions, often mean that the agent's close associates have already rejected the property and its possibilities. It can be a reason it is being advertised, other than achieving the best price for the seller. This may seem sceptical, but often looking outside the box or photo/description will pay dividends. The internet has many plot finder type websites, so give these a try, especially if you are looking for plots outside your home region.

Building plots usually have outline planning permission. When they do, the price reflects this. However if you can identify a 'potential' building plot before the owner has applied for outline planning permission themselves, you may be able to approach them and offer to make the application on their behalf and perhaps, if successful, get the plot at a much more reasonable price (but make sure you have first refusal in some sort of legally binding contract before you go to all that effort).

Design

Design and cost management should work hand-in-hand. If they do not, trouble could be on the horizon. Be sure that your designer and specifier (if you use one) is totally aware of your aims. If you want an energy saving, sustainable home, or your ambitions are for a zero carbon footprint, make it known at the beginning of the design process and contract negotiations. Also get references that will help to prove they know how to achieve your sustainability or low energy goals.

A well thought out building project can be one of the most satisfying processes a person can be involved with in his or her lifetime, but

if it goes wrong it can destroy businesses, marriages, a person's financial future and the credibility of all those involved. Don't leave all the knowledge gathering to the designer. If you are well informed then you can see the process unfolding and use opportunity to be involved with the decision making. Without these skills you leave yourself open to be led by the nose. Choose your professionals carefully. There are some really good eco-architects and builders out there. See the listings at the end of this book but be aware that they are not recommendations, but a useful list of professionals that claim knowledge of green building. Always seek references from previous clients and ask to see completed jobs.

The skills and resources of the professionals and practices can pay for themselves many times over if chosen carefully. Egos and personalities will come into play, so you must ensure compatibility. Like marriages, there are many potential partners available, so be sure to make the right choice. The difference in services being provided will sometimes be put forward as you do tend to get what you pay for. Make sure it is tailored to your needs and it will deliver what you want?

Sustainability issues

If you are reading this book carefully, you will by now know that there are a number of different aspects to sustainable construction, but in particular you should consider the embodied energy contained within the materials used, the energy efficiency of the fabric of the building (e.g. insulation and air permeability) and the systems utilised for power, heat and other services. A lot of emphasis is often given to the source of power, be it solar, geothermal or otherwise, but to make the best use of these technologies it is imperative that the design of the fabric of the building is given priority,

The various systems utilised within the home are numerous, and the interaction between the various technologies can lead to problems. As such you should always seek to ensure that you have a single point of responsibility for the design of the internal services, to ensure that the installation works properly and can be serviced effectively in the future.

If you are going to embark on a new building, then you really should read Volume 2 of the Green Building Bible, the companion to this book, as it looks into the technical detailed aspects of creating low energy buildings.

The build

Assumptions should be avoided at all cost, whether by consultants, client or tradesmen. Standards, regulations and applications are changing all the time, and details may not always be clear on drawings, if they are shown at all. If there is any doubt the team should not proceed without checking with the lead consultant or client. Well meaning decisions made by ill-informed workers to drive progress can lead to expensive alterations and remedial work.

Self build?

It is estimated that 20,000 'self-build' homes are constructed in the UK each year. A self-build home is generally defined as a home that is built on a single site, which is purchased and developed for occupation by the purchaser of the site. The purchaser may actually never move in, or they may move in for the rest of their life. There is no inference that the house should actually be constructed using the skills and labour of the owner!

Some self-builders may have a lead consultant, but if you have the necessary skills, knowledge, experience, nerve and confidence, then you may well play the role of lead consultant yourself. Most, however, will need to employ a construction professional, either for parts of the construction or most of it. Be it a builder, architect, project manager or designer to guide you through the maze of different materials and techniques available, and to provide the vision, expertise and solutions to ensure your project is procured and constructed successfully and the potential of your site is maximised.

Many magazines, TV shows, exhibitions, videos and books support and encourage the

Above: professionals and selfbuilders alike will both need to call in specialists at some time during the construction. Be sure to budget properly for this specialist input. In this case the specialist is installing cellulose fibre insulation and prices will have to be quoted by the supplier at an early a stage because work like this is unlikely to be included in most building pricing books. The same advice goes for most renewable power installations, uncommon insulations, etc.

self-build market. Hundreds of companies have invested millions of pounds to sell to the many dreamers and potential developers and to the small percentage of people who actually own a plot with planning permission. The media is often all too quick to promote the potential profits or possible savings that can be made through building your own home. Whilst employing a professional will have a significant initial cost, it should also significantly reduce risk and, with the right choice of expert, should also bring long term savings.

The multiplicity of options further exaggerates the risks and hurdles the often untrained and inexperienced self-builder faces, and it is essential that all construction options are considered carefully, to ensure that right decisions are made.

For major projects, a well informed, skilled working foreman, either employed by the main contractor, lead consultant or client, will pay dividends; helping to avoid delays, disputes, and ensuring attention to detail and the overall quality of the build.

A programme of works identifying the project's critical path (and thereby areas of work which will affect the overall build-time) should be in place before the project begins, and should take into account all of the lead-times for materials and fittings. Specialist contractors should be briefed on when they will be required well in advance, to avoid any delays in the programme. There is no point in having a programme if every effort is not made by the site operatives, sub-contractors and working foreman to keep to it. The client and lead consultant should monitor the programme weekly. It is also essential that services are ordered and in place before the building work

Below; the site owner is responsible for site safety. Don't cut corners on scaffolding etc. if your building is unusual and regular scaffolding is inappropriate, seek advice from a scaffolding erection specialist before the sitework begins. Also ensure that you take out adequate insurance for site visitors - even unwanted ones!

starts. Most tradesmen will require electricity and water for welfare facilities, lighting and tools.

Health and safety

Every process on a building site carries with it health and safety risks. Most of the risks require just common sense, but others, such as working from height, in the ground and with hazardous materials, plant and power tools, require more attention and care. These risks should never be underestimated, and risk assessments and method statements are now mandatory on large sites and becoming more so for small sites too, even though they do not come under the Construction Design & Management Regulations. Build safe and ignore health and safety risks at your peril.

Unplanned changes

Wherever possible, you should avoid making major changes during the construction phase of the project, as they will almost inevitably disrupt the programme, incur (usually high) additional cost, and affect morale on site. It is essential, therefore, that there is a good degree of certainty (the reward of careful research and confident decision making) before making a start with work on site. Making it up as you go along will lead to bad tempers, disputes, and even potential disasters.

Conclusion

Organisation, management, cost control, lead times, programme monitoring, quality control and health and safety are the essence of a successful project. Get it right first time is the first rule, and never allow assumptions to build a project, is the second. ☯

Further reading

'*Green Building Bible, Volume 2*':
www.newbuilder.co.uk
'*Housebuilders Bible*' *by Mark Brinkley*
'*All About Selfbuild*' *by Bob Matthews*
'*Diary of an Eco-Builder*' *by Will Anderson*
'*The Green Self Build Book*' *by Jon Broome*
The above books are available from the Green Shop:
01452 770629 **www.greenshop.co.uk**

Smoothing the planning process

For many, achieving planning consent is one of the most stressful parts of the building process. And if you are planning a green building it may well complicate the issue, or even confuse the planning officers or residents near your proposed site. There are a number of measures that you can take to ease your planning application. **Gideon Richards** discusses a few of them...

Firstly, remember that planners are not building regulation officers and, believe it or not, there may be little communication between the two offices. Planners have to work within a number of constraints and follow a standardised protocol that can sometimes appear barmy to the lay person. However, the rules have come from somewhere and the planners job is to interpret them. Remember that whilst planner's have constraints, they also have a great deal of flexibility available to them in interpreting the rules and guidelines. However, in many authorities, the final decision is in the hands of elected councillors and not the planning officer.

The level of understanding about green building, renewable energy and environmental issues and related products varies widely among planners. Like all of us, planners have very different backgrounds and interests. What is important to you may not be of such importance to them! It isn't always about logic, unfortunately! However, there are a number of simple rules that can be adopted by anyone, which may help smooth the process of making a planning application. Some of these rules may appear obvious and straightforward, however, it is a fact that planning officers often feel that many applications submitted are missing key information.

First and foremost you should understand the issues and problems you are going to face with an application. Good communication and relationships with the planners can be essential.

1. Understand the system

A bit of research, early on, will save you a lot of stress later. Find out what the local strategy for planning is based on. A good starting point is the Unitary Development Plan (UDP) and Local Planning Policies (LPP). For definitions of these please see 'glossary' at end of this article. These are usually published on the internet or can be provided by your local council. Attempting to get a consent that conflicts with these policies will immediately put your application at a disadvantage and probably set you up to fail.

Prior to completing your application form consider the information you think will benefit your application and TALK to the planners. This simple act will give you an immediate understanding of the planning officers' and the authorities' standpoint and the issues that your proposal faces and has to meet. More information, when laid out well, is better than less, if it allows for better understanding of your intentions, but please keep in mind that lots of information is no guarantee of overcoming the occasional immovable obstacles that can hinder some applications. There is no doubt that well constructed information, that allows the planners to tick their appropriate boxes against relevant criteria, can help things along.

2. Know the site and location

Do your homework. A good site appraisal will show more than where your boundaries and utilities are. It will also demonstrate that you have considered any potential impacts on the site, local community and the environment.

The planners always seek comment from other parties, including neighbours, highways, parks authorities (in National Parks) and local or parish councils. There is no real order of importance in the interested parties but,

LEDA are an award winning team of experienced architects and environmental consultants who are dedicated to creating sustainable buildings

- Fully intergrated design approach
- Client participation in design process
- Low embodied energy of materials
- Recyclability of buildings
- Minimise waste during construction
- Low energy consumption
- Incorporation of renewables
- Water conservation

Green
REGISTER
OF CONSTRUCTION PROFESSIONALS

LEDA

Architecture and Environmental Design

Micklethwaite House, 70 Cross Green Lane, Leeds LS9 0DG   Tel: 0113 2009380   Fax: 0113 2009381   E-mail:office@leda.org.uk

☐☐ Living Space
concept to completion

We like anything different, difficult, interesting and unusual...

01243 572 604
www.livingspacedesign.com

HETREED ROSS
ARCHITECTS

New Town Council Offices
in Bradford on Avon

New 6th Form Centre for
Kingswood CTC, Bristol

FRIENDLY ENVIRONMENTAL PRACTICE DESIGNING COMMUNITY, COMMERCIAL & DOMESTIC PROJECTS FOR A BETTER LIFE AND MORE SUSTAINABLE WORLD.

t: 01225 851860 f: 01225 851884
e: jh@hetreedross.com   w: www.hetreedross.com

139

suffice to say, that any single one of them can be highly influential in the outcome of your application. Strategic site access and services requirements will almost certainly need to be met or addressed. Ensure that the application takes these into consideration. For instance, vehicular access to the site could be a hazard to pedestrians and other motorists. Choose your site access proposal carefully. It may be that you don't want or cannot get vehicular access. This could be a stumbling block, but some very green minded people have successfully argued for and gained planning permission for houses where vehicles cannot access.

3. Know the neighbours

Remember it isn't only about planning officers approving the plan. There are many cases where planning officers have recommended approval but it has been overridden and rejected by the planning committee (elected representatives from the local council). The elected representatives have the final say, (except in an appeal against their decision, which is decided by a representative of the Home Secretary). Why might the planning committee go against the recommendations of the planning officer? Usually this happens if they have been influenced by strong local protest against the proposal.

The public, especially neighbours, can be powerful allies or enemies in a planning application. Do your utmost to get them on board with your ideas at an early stage. They have the right to inspect all applications and make observations. If they can understand what you are looking to achieve, and the efforts that have been made to reduce the impact on others, there should be less resistance. If there is strong local and neighbourly resistance to your application, then treat it seriously. Try to negotiate acceptable modifications with neighbours before you make your application.

4. Prepare for strategic complications

Be prepared to accept that in some circumstances rigorous restrictions may be imposed on the development. There are many national, regional and local designations that can be put on land. For instance there are various PPGs (for definition of these, see under 'glossary' at end of this article, including the Green Belt (PPG2), Green Field / Brown Field (PPS3), Landscape Designation (Locally Assigned – PPS7), Green Corridors (Predominantly Rural, Ecology routes), listed-building, conservation areas, to name but a few. The restrictions and requirements that pertain to all of these can easily be researched on the internet.

If your project is in a restricted area, such as a National Park, Area of Outstanding National Beauty (AONB), Conservation area etc, then you will need to prove exceptional circumstances for your proposal. Having established early on what the designation of the area is, or what the building's status is, a decision can be taken as to whether you give up and find somewhere else, or struggle on. If you do carry on, then building that relationship with the appropriate authorities is going to be critical.

Be prepared to negotiate and adapt your proposal. If possible have the alternatives up your sleeve prior to any meeting. As a minimum, know what your bottom line is going to be.

5. Use good communication and professionals if necessary

If your proposal is complicated or very specialised and you believe that you will struggle to explain it effectively, it is worth considering hiring an architect or agent who is familiar and comfortable dealing with your type of project. Try and choose someone who already has a good relationship with the local planning department and that you can work with. Don't be bullied into decisions. Take your time to consider all the implications and if necessary do your research.

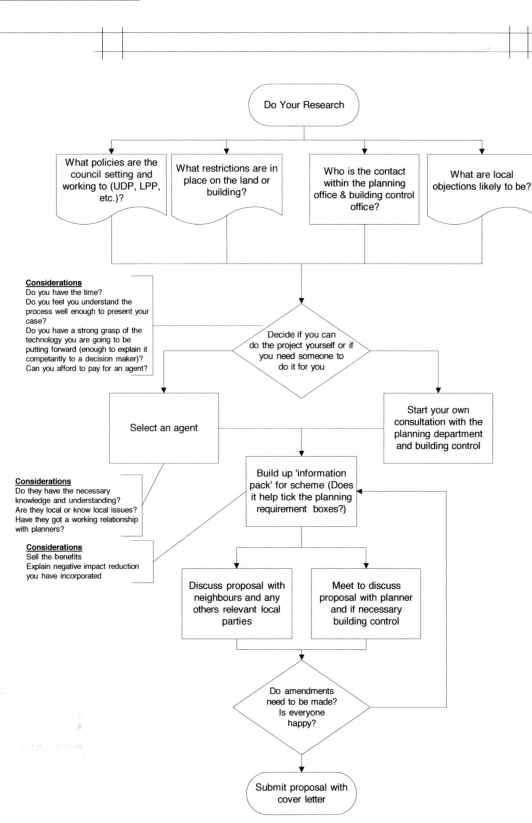

Do Your Research

What policies are the council setting and working to (UDP, LPP, etc.)?

What restrictions are in place on the land or building?

Who is the contact within the planning office & building control office?

What are local objections likely to be?

Considerations
Do you have the time?
Do you feel you understand the process well enough to present your case?
Do you have a strong grasp of the technology you are going to be putting forward (enough to explain it competantly to a decision maker)?
Can you afford to pay for an agent?

Decide if you can do the project yourself or if you need someone to do it for you

Select an agent

Start your own consultation with the planning department and building control

Build up 'information pack' for scheme (Does it help tick the planning requirement boxes?)

Considerations
Do they have the necessary knowledge and understanding?
Are they local or know local issues?
Have they got a working relationship with planners?

Considerations
Sell the benefits
Explain negative impact reduction you have incorporated

Discuss proposal with neighbours and any others relevant local parties

Meet to discuss proposal with planner and if necessary building control

Do amendments need to be made? Is everyone happy?

Submit proposal with cover letter

Remember good drawings, descriptions of schemes and support information may make the difference between 'high quality' applications and average ones, especially if you are looking to do something special or different. Be careful, however, not to over-invest in pre-approval fees. Ask for a no-approval, no fee arrangement. You may be shown the door, but if a professional is confident and likes the look of your project, then you might get a deal.

Don't drop your own research and choose your professional carefully. For instance, when selecting an architect, ask how well does he or she know the planners / development controller for your area? A good architect will have a rapport with them. A bad architect who fails to understand the local requirements/protocol, can be as good as pouring money, your money, down the drain. Ask for references from past clients, look at locally completed projects that they have designed and ask the opinion of the planning officer.

If you do choose a professional to represent your application, then consider going along to the first meeting between them and the planning officer to see how they get on. Look for any problems early on, before a lot of work has been put to paper. Put yourself in the planner's shoes and think through any possible objections and look at solutions or offer information in support of the benefits for your approach.

Explain why you have chosen the options you have. List the benefits that your project might have for the wider community. Remember, in the language of planning, 'cost is not a material planning consideration, however, impact on visual amenity and the environment are'.

6. Make clear submissions

Submit a short letter outlining your proposal. This letter should help the planner tick the boxes needed to achieve the authority's objectives. Also sell the positives, but don't ignore the negatives. If there are negatives, face them head-on and explain the measures

taken to mitigate and overcome them. If that's not possible, have alternative solutions up your sleeve early on. Putting the positives in a way that meets planning needs helps them to promote the project to the planning committee. Remember to always explain the benefits of your project in a way that the planning officer can understand and buy-into.

Planners are humans. They can have good and bad days. They are not infallible and they do make mistakes and unfathomable decisions. Remember, at the end of the day, if you really don't agree with the decision there is an appeal's process. Hopefully by taking the above steps you'll have come to an agreement well before that.

Checklist

- What local restrictions are there?
  - UDP
  - LPP
  - Listed Building
  - Conservation Area
  - Green Belt
  - Green Field / Brown Field, etc.
- Who is your planning officer (PO)?
- Who is your building control officer (BCO)?
- Build a positive rapport
- How much do PO & BCO understand about renewable and sustainable buildings and energy?
- Have regular meetings to discuss your proposals
  - With PO
  - With BCO
  - With Neighbours
- Be prepared to compromise and negotiate
- If using an agent
  - Do they have knowledge and understanding of your project?
  - Are they local or have they an understanding of local planning constraints?
  - Do they have a good working relationship with the planner?
- Provide an 'information pack' to support your case
  - Explain what you have done to minimise any negative impacts
  - Demonstrate that you have ensured the planners can tick their consent requirements
- Write a cover letter that explains the project in a way that supports planning policy (i.e. This project supports the councils requirements to reduce CO_2 emissions by X through its use of Y)

Conclusion

The planning process can be confusing and frustrating. It is important you do your research thoroughly. Keep smiling and develop a rapport with your local planning officer.

Most planners are looking to reach a balanced, fair outcome. Most minor developments (home extensions and improvements) are generally supported by the planning system. You may find a staged approach to a development appropriate and less fraught with difficulties. However, you would need to weigh up the benefits of doing the improvements all at once or carrying out the work piecemeal.

Help them to help you achieve your planning consent by giving them adequate information, including the benefits, for them to support your approval. Demonstrate that you have looked at all the scenarios and this is your preferred one. Explain why you consider your propsal is the best option. Remember that there are a number of boxes (policy, local strategy and technical) that need to be ticked for your plans to be approved - providing as many of those ticks as possible could give you a positive outcome. ☯

Glossary to this article

Unitary Development Plan – sets out a statutory framework for land-use, to ensure consistent decision making. It aims to secure the most efficient and effective use of land in the public interest.

Local Planning Policy – these are also being incorporated into other framework documents, so ensure you identify what the policies are.

PPG – these are the government's Planning Policy Guidelines , which give guidance to planning departments and the public on how the government's planning and development policies are interpreted. The revised equivalents to these are PPS Planning Policy Statements.

GREEN BUILDS

We are a small progressive housebuilding company building houses in the north Norfolk area.

Our future houses are to be super efficient in terms of insulation, energy and water usage and we would like to find potential purchasers who could be involved in the design process.

This would involve, for example, making decisions about whether to include features such as sheeps wool insulation, heat pumps, wind turbines, photovoltaics, solar panels and biomass boilers ... maybe more !

So....if you would like to be involved or you'd like to know more about our houses please call us on 020 7281 8497 or visit us at: **www.developmentinsight.co.uk**

URBANe

sustainable creative homes

Beautiful homes that don't cost the earth

- Designs provide minimum impact on the environment
- Zero defects after 12 months have been achieved
- Highly insulated in a cocooned shell using recycled materials - creating extraordinarily low heating/running costs
- Decorated with non-allergic, naturally produced low-fragrance emulsions and oils, for a healthy internal environment
- Fresh air aided and controlled with help from passive venting
- Creatively energy efficient; from low-energy light bulbs to argon gas-filled double-glazing.
- Optional heating methods include solar power panels, geo-thermal/ground-source heating, wind generation etc
- Designed and built to your own desires and requirements
- Built cost effectively with efficiency and speed

Consistently achieve top BRE, SAP and NHER ratings

ASK FOR BROCHURE and DVD

www.urbanehomes.com

urbane@urbanehomes.com   PO BOX 619 Bristol BS99 3XS
0117 955 7224/020 8659 0110

See also: insulation discussions in Chapter 7

Confusing building regulations?

From April 2006 all existing houses fall under the control of the new Approved Document L1b (ADL1b)[1]. This recent sub-division of ADL1 relates specifically to existing dwellings and now includes not only extensions but newly termed 'thermal elements'. Here **Mike George** considers the content relating to the new requirements for thermal insulation.

As with all building regulations, the Department of Communities and Local Government indicates that it is for the local authority to interpret the legislation as it sees fit. With this in mind, Barry Turner, a practising BCO was invited to express an opinion, for and on behalf of the local authority building control officers. These opinions are given on the understanding that they carry no legal standing. Here is an interpretation- of what's new.

Thermal elements

The introduction of so called 'thermal elements' mean that any roof, wall or floor falling below given U-value thresholds, must now be thermally upgraded as part of any renovation works. These improvements are triggered by works (other than decorative finishes) to more than 25% of the thermal element. Generally, if you intend to add or renovate a 'layer', such as rendering then you must upgrade the element to the specified thermal standard. There are existing construction thresholds which trigger such improvements and these, together with the enhanced U-values, are shown in Table 1, columns A and B. Before commencing work, either a 'building notice' or a 'full plans application', outlining the nature of the work, must be submitted to the BCO. This can be retrospective in the case of emergency repairs[2].

Extent of works

Using a cavity wall as an example, external work results in the whole wall attracting upgrading works. Internally, if renovating a single room, less work is necessary in that the improvements are limited to the internal boundaries of the particular cavity wall.

Limiting factors

The extent of the required works is limited to that which is 'technically or functionally feasible' and where the supplementary cost of the insulation work is recoverable within 15 years. Technical difficulties vary with specific applications and BR262[3] provides general guidance on avoiding risks. Where functional difficulties exist lesser provisions may be accepted. Examples of this, given in ADL1b, include where internal wall insulation results in the reduction of usable floor space by 5%; or where floor insulation results in difficulties with adjoining floor levels.

Historic buildings

Although no longer exempt, special considerations apply to listed buildings and more reservedly, conservation areas. Barry Turner[2] comments that the aim is to improve energy efficiency to an extent that is reasonable and practical. It would seem sensible, therefore, to liaise with the local conservation officer when considering the extent of energy efficiency improvements. Further guidance is available from English Heritage[4].

Change of Use

All thermal elements in a building, subject to 'change of use', automatically attract upgrading whether renovation works are intended or not[2].

Extensions

U-value requirements for extensions are more demanding and the most simple method for compliance is to meet the required U-values shown in Table 1, column C. Design flexibility is permissible by a more general strategy of varying U-values and window openings, using the area weighted method, and in this case values must be no worse than those in column D. In addition, a procedure similar to that used for new dwellings[5] may be used to demonstrate

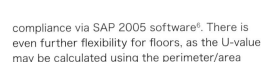

compliance via SAP 2005 software[6]. There is even further flexibility for floors, as the U-value may be calculated using the perimeter/area method for the whole enlarged dwelling.

Insulation and airtightness

Quality control of insulation installation must now be demonstrated to the BCO. This applies to both thermal elements and works to extensions; although this falls short of pressure testing. Barry Turner comments 'Initially, a statement should be made by a suitably qualified person that appropriate construction details have been adopted. Furthermore, a system of on site inspection should be in place to ensure consistency'. BRE IP 1/06[7] contains checklists for use in reports to confirm compliance on completion of the work and robust

als? How much insulation will you need? What type? This initial information must be provided by the person intending to carry out the work and subsequently verified by the BCO[2].

So what if you want to consider the effect on your fuel bills? Well, it is unclear from ADL1b how the annual energy savings should be estimated but there is some suggestion that this could also be confirmed in a report by a 'suitably qualified' person before work commences.

So do we all enrol on crash courses in surveying and measuring buildings so we know where we stand? No, it is more reasonable for some generalisations, at least in the short term, to be acceptable to the BCO. Regarding

Table 1. U-value requirements for thermal elements and extensions

	A Threshold U-value triggering improvements to thermal elements (W/m²K)	B Requirement for thermal elements worse than column A (W/m²K)	C Standard U-value requirement for extensions (W/m²K)	D Minimum acceptable U-value for extensions *** (W/m²K)
Cavity wall	0.7	0.55 *	0.3	0.7
Other wall	0.7	0.35	0.3	0.7
Floor	0.7	0.25 **	0.22 **	0.7
Roof insulation at ceiling level	0.35	0.16	0.16	0.35
Roof insulation at rafter level	0.35	0.2	0.2	0.35
Flat roof or roof with integral insulation	0.35	0.25	0.2	0.35

* walls not suitable for cavity wall insulation should be treated as 'other wall'

** a lesser standard may be acceptable if there are significant problems relating to existing floor levels

*** where alternative approaches such as SAP assessment are used

standard details are available for new build situations[8]. However the adaptation of such details to existing construction should be considered carefully.

What about DIY?

Well, as you can see, good old DIY has become somewhat more complicated. U-values, for example must now be calculated[9] and an obvious complication is the assessment of the existing construction. For example, is the solid stone wall really solid? Is it limestone, granite? What is the thermal conductivity of the materi-

this, Barry Turner[2] comments, 'it is possible that SAP data sets and relevant tables may be adopted for use'. With this in mind the 'Green Building Bible, Volume 2', provides a simplified tool for estimating U-values, energy savings and consequential payback periods[10]. All building regulations provide scope for alternative methods of compliance and it is hoped that this method will simplify the compliance process and be acceptable to building control when advocated by any member of the design team, be they DIY enthusiast, builder or architect.

>>>

References

1. DCLG. (2006). 'Conservation of fuel and power', Approved Document L1b Work in existing dwellings. The Stationery Office, Norwich, UK.

2. Turner, B (2006) Response to Part L1b questionnaire. Local Authority Building Control.

3. BRE (2001), BR 262, Thermal Insulation: avoiding risks Garston, BRE publications.

4. English Heritage (2004) Building regulations and historic buildings.

5. DCLG. (2006). Conservation of fuel and power, Approved Document L1a New dwellings. The Stationery Office, Norwich.

6. Defra (2005) The government's standard assessment procedure for energy rating of dwellings, SAP 2005 edition London. HMSO.

7. BRE (2006) IP 1/06 'Assessing the effects of thermal bridging at junctions and around openings in the external elements of buildings'. Garston, BRE publications.

8. TSO (2002) Limiting thermal bridging and air leakage: Robust construction details for dwellings and similar buildings. London. HMSO.

9. BRE (2006) BR 443, Conventions for U-value calculations Garston, BRE publications.

10. 'Green Building Bible, Volume 2' *www.newbuilder.co.uk*

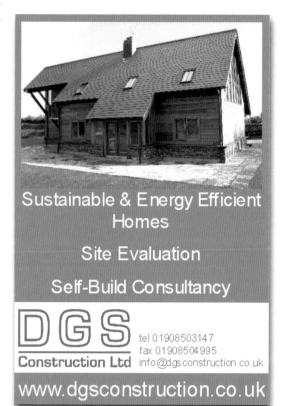

Sustainable & Energy Efficient Homes

Site Evaluation

Self-Build Consultancy

DGS Construction Ltd

tel 01908503147
fax 01908504995
info@dgsconstruction.co.uk

www.dgsconstruction.co.uk

improving the ENERGY EFFICIENCY *of traditional buildings*

OXLEY CONSERVATION
HISTORIC BUILDINGS CONSULTANCY

Oxley Conservation Limited · 8a Friday Street · Henley on Thames · Oxon · RG9 1AH
Tel: 01491 414191 · Fax: 01491 414198 · email: info@oxleyconservation.co.uk · www.oxleyconservation.co.uk

146

Heraklith®

Heradesign®

SKANDA
National Distributors of Roofing and Insulation Products

Heraklith magnesite bound wood wool panels – sustainable natural products for acoustic ceilings and timber buildings.

Innovative Dialogue between ecology and design

The unique combination of wood and magnesite is a convincing solution for architects, designers and installers alike , offering outstanding value when it comes to heat insulation, building biology and sound absorption.

Advantages:

- Recognised for organic building design
- Heat Store Ability
- Diffusion permeable
- Easy to work with
- Compatible with all normal construction materials
- Ideal for rendering

Heraflax

The natural insulation material made of flax fibres for high living comfort.

Advantages:

- Thermal and sound insulation
- Compensates humidity changes
- Recycleable
- Recognised for organic building

SKANDA

Skanda (UK) Limited.
64-65 Clywedog Road North
Wrexham Industrial Estate.
Wrexham. LL1 3 9XN
Tel: 01978 664 255
Fax: 01978 661 427
E-mail: info@skanda-uk.com

147

It's not easy being green! Part 1

How difficult is it to find out about green building and is any of the information available really helping in the decision making process. We invited three families to write up their experiences and thoughts on the subject. Each of the families have, over the last five years, 'downshifted'. First up, housewife and mother **Kerry Hughes,** who used the internet as a vehicle for finding out the hard facts about how green her family is and what more could be done ...

It's everywhere, after decades of apathy; you cannot escape tales of global warming. At some point you have to consider whether you are going to keep your head firmly fixed in the sand and hope that the problem will somehow go away. OR acknowledge that you and your household can make a difference. But can I personally, one individual in a nation of 60 million, make a difference?

I have to say that my head is not continuously buried in the sand. My family, one overworked husband, three energy draining sons and I moved to West Wales from the Midlands to get away from the high levels of pollution there. We are aware of environmental issues; I am a member of both Friends of the Earth and Greenpeace, we recycle, we have low energy light bulbs and yes, I do turn off the tap when I'm brushing my teeth! But there has to be more we can do. I confess to being a bit of a material girl and I do like my home comforts, but what future is there for our children and future generations if we all continue to consume in the way we do?

So step one to the new me. On went the computer and I hit the internet. I decided the first thing to do was to check out my carbon footprint. I put 'carbon footprint' into the search engine and got 153,000 results! I'm obviously alone in my ignorance of this subject! On **www.carbonfootprint.com** I calculated my personal primary footprint which was terrifyingly

17,125kg CO_2. With a UK average of 5,013kg and a recommended level of 2,500kg, that put me way above average, so what am I doing wrong? The site did not acknowledge that I live in a household of five people, so to ease my conscience, I could divide that figure!

One of the questions asked on the site was whether we have a green electricity supplier. We didn't! Before changing supplier I had to check with my money guru on **www.money-savingexpert.com** whether now was a good time to do it, in the middle of this period of price rises. Apparently 'yes' and two sites were recommended where I could check out the best deal – **www.energyhelpline.com**. Both sites offered the option of making your choice based on 'price', 'service' or 'green energy'. So although I was tempted by the predicted saving of over £200 a year on the 'price' selection, I ignored that and headed for the green section. I promptly changed my supplier to Scottish Power H_2O which promises 100% renewable energy from hydroelectric power stations in Scotland, and to save me £64 a year.

Both sites offered incentives to switch with them; the first offered £12.50 and the second a free bottle of champagne. Naturally I opted

© Green Building Press

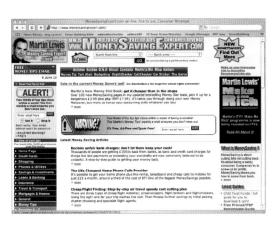

have kept the house warm by lighting the wood burning stoves in the living room and kitchen using wood collected on walks on the beach. We've felt good about this but boy has bedtime been cold!

- unplug your mobile phone when charging is complete. Whoops, I'll do this from now on

for the champagne so now we have a green electricity supplier, £64 in my wallet and a bottle of Piper Heidsieck - result. I re-entered my information to calculate my carbon foot-print, including my new green energy supplier and my footprint was down to 13,615kg. This is definitely a good start in my quest. However, I still have concerns. Does this now mean that I can use huge amounts of electricity without a thought for the environment? And if every household in the UK decided to change their electricity supplier to one that promised 100% renewable energy, is there enough renewable energy out there?

So what next? Other recommendations on the carbon footprint site were:
- switch off electrical items when not in use. I already do this and nag the children to do the same
- turn down the central heating. We haven't used the central heating this winter, we

- do your weekly shopping in one go. Living 20 miles from the nearest supermarket means that this is a necessity. In our previous existence, living in a city, I was at the local supermarket almost daily, so not only has our move been better for the environment, it has been better for my wallet
- fit energy saving light bulbs. We have these, thanks to our previous electricity supplier who provided us with the first four
- install cavity wall insulation. We have 75cm thick stone walls, so this is not an option.
- Insulate the loft - I poked my head through the loft hatch to discover that it is fairly well insulated already with that horrid pink glass fibre, not to mention a layer of dead flies!
- replace your old boiler with an energy efficient condensing boiler. We changed the boiler from coal fired to oil fired three years ago but I'm beginning to think that wasn't one of our wisest moves!

Naturally we were moving to our Welsh dream home and it had to be accompanied by the heat spewing 'Aga' in the corner, very rural! So we now have our central heating and hot water supplied by an oil fired 'Rayburn' and I have the delightful view of an enormous green plastic oil tank through my kitchen window! This, of course, is accompanied by soaring oil prices and tales of oil eventually running out! So what are the other options? Do we consider producing our own energy? If so, how do we do it and can our wallet cope with the changes needed?

Back to the internet then, to look at what alternatives are out there. I typed 'alternative energy' into the search engine and got 10,100,000 results – now that could take some time! Maybe there is something or someone locally that could give me the information I'm looking for. I decided to check out the local free papers. Perhaps one of those numerous small ads would be informative. Sadly not – but it's amazing what people do advertise! Next came a hunt for the telephone directory, which I eventually located, in a dusty corner. If dust and cobwebs are good insulation then we are well away! Nothing under alternative energy but

there under 'energy' was the West Wales Eco Centre offering 'free advice on energy saving and renewable energy' – yes! But what questions do I ask them? Do I show my complete ignorance and display my lack of knowledge publicly or should I check out their website? The coward in me headed for **www.ecocentre.org. uk** - don't forget the UK bit or you'll end up on a tasteful French site!

The site has a number of fact sheets about the various renewables available, but for a

novice like me they were way too complicated and took me back to those physics lessons of many years ago complete with the associated headache. I'm a bit confused between my ac's and my dc's and do I need an inverter to convert or a converter to invert? A number of the fact sheets had a link onto **www.est.org. uk** and here I found more simple explanations of the alternatives. Now at least I feel that I have some idea of what options are out there. The next step is to find out the logistics and, most importantly, the prices of the alternatives available.

So what are my options?

Ground source heat pumps – I'm assuming this is not an option for us, as this system is most efficient supplying underfloor heating and we have wooden floors and an enormous basement. And don't you need electricity for the compressor and the pump, so doesn't it kind of defeat the object? Trawling around a few suppliers on the internet I found estimates ranging from £4,000 - £10,000 for an 8kW system. Pricey.

Small Scale Hydro (water power) – I thought I had found a straightforward explanation of how this system works on **www.british-hydro.org** until I found the following equation $P = h\,r\,g\,Q\,H$. Do I really need to know that? The most positive

© Green Building Press

factor about small-scale hydro is its high efficiency, quoted as being 70-90%, by far the best of all the alternatives. Unfortunately, this is not an option for us as our house is half way up a hill and a distance from the river. There is a fast flowing river going through the village so I do wonder why its energy is not being sourced at least for the residents whose houses back onto it.

Small scale wind power - my image of wind power is the large turbines sited together on the hills around and about. I have found it difficult to find information on smaller scale turbines for domestic use. There is an interesting briefing sheet on **www.bwea.com**. I'm assuming that due to the siting of our house, a wind turbine may not be a viable option. We are on the leeward side of the hill and have a number of buildings fairly close behind us, including the church. As the church tower is the focal point of the village, how popular would we be if we were to obliterate the view with a wind

turbine the size of a telegraph pole in front of it? Out of interest I asked the opinion of some neighbours to gauge their reaction if we were to erect a turbine. Our immediate neighbour thought it was an excellent idea and was keen to join us in such a venture. But I was surprised at the negativity of others, in particular those who have just erected a upvc conservatory which gazes directly into our garden! The only site I could find that gave details of wind turbine packages available for domestic use was **www. provenenergy.co.uk**. For a grid-connected system, which should power the average 3 bed house, they quote £11,000 and a battery charging system would set us back £15,800.

Solar PV (photovoltaics) There is an excellent downloadable homeowner's fact sheet on **www.est.org.uk/myhome/generating/types/ solarpv**. The one downside to the EST website is that I have found it difficult to navigate and I've struggled to re-find information previously viewed. It also has a fact sheet telling you why MP Peter Hain has solar PV, if anyone is remotely interested! There were 291,000 results when I entered 'solar pv' into the search engine. Of the initial few I looked at, the sales pitch seemed to be 'free electricity'. So it was refreshing to see on **www.imaginationsolar. com** that, even with a government grant it would take 50 years to achieve payback. They also made it clear that solar PV would only produce 30-50% of the average household requirements. The average price quoted was £9,000 per kWp. I would be interested to get a quote from a supplier but I think our three-storey, hill house would be daunting to anyone needing to get on the roof! Also we have huge chimneys which cast a lot of shadow across the roof, so I'm not sure how achievable this option is.

Solar (thermal) for water heating – Again this one is more straightforward to understand and there were useful fact sheets on the EST website (mentioned earlier) and on **www.very-efficientheating.co.uk**. I preferred the prices for this one, with an average between £2,500 - £4,000. But the same issues exist as for solar PV – hard to access roof and chimney shadows.

I'm beginning to think that alternative energy is not for us, for a number of reasons. There are drawbacks to each of the systems I have looked at, some of which may be unique to us, but others would probably be relevant to anyone in

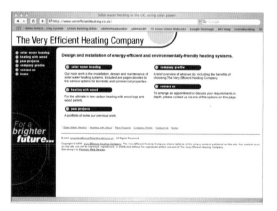

the average house. I know that we don't have £9,000+ to spare and I'm not sure I'm too keen to take out a loan to cover the costs. At **www. est.org.uk** (yes I have spent hours on this site!) you can enter your postcode to see if there are grants available. Information can be requested on cavity wall insulation, loft insulation, heating, appliances, energy saving light bulbs, renewables or radiator panels. I entered renewables and found information about the Low Carbon Buildings Programme. These grants have minimum requirements, including 270mm of loft insulation and using energy saving light bulbs. To get full details of what is available, you need to fill in a home energy check. This I would

do if it were a little more anonymous, I am not keen on giving out my personal details over the Internet. The information on the previous Clear Skies grant programme seemed much more straightforward to access!

But I think there may be a light at the end of my seemingly never-ending alternative energy tunnel. The final option I have looked at is biomass, otherwise known as bioenergy or biofuels - that is using organic matter of recent origin such as logs or woodchips. Now I may be simplifying this one too much, but isn't that what we've been doing by installing wood burners and collecting wood from the beach? This option appears to be so much more within the average household's grasp.

I looked at **www.stovesareus.co.uk** and for an extra £150 we could fit a boiler to our existing wood burner to provide all our hot water. Being on a fairly low budget we have paid under £400 for the stove itself. This is a much more achievable price tag than the £2,000+ for the solar water heating option and way more attractive than the £15,000 for a wind turbine. I assume that we are fortunate not to be in a smokeless zone and maybe this isn't an option for everyone. But if you are in a smokeless zone you just need to ensure that you have sufficient storage space for the fuel, and you need to check with your local planning department before fitting a flue, if you live in an area of outstanding beauty. One concern I do have is that to supply sufficient wood to warm our homes and heat our water in this fashion there

© Green Building Press

will need to be large plantations of fast growing trees. By planting row after row of such fast growing trees, for example, willow, will that not affect the biodiversity of the woodland? Would we then put certain species at risk? The cultivation of a single species over large areas clearly does not sustain normal or healthy biodiversity.

So I am now on my way to my new electricity supplier, I am poised to order a boiler for my wood burner and I should be feeling jolly self-righteous. But boy has it been a trial. The suppliers and those hoping to enlighten the world of the green alternatives, need to make the information easier to access and much easier to understand. When I was purchasing my 'Rayburn' as a new cooker and boiler, I didn't need to know the inner workings and the mathematical equation that was needed to heat the oil to the appropriate temperature to ensure my meringues were perfectly crisp and not burned. I just needed to know about efficiency and approximately how much oil we would need annually, how much the system and the ongoing running of it would cost, and that it could maintain a low enough temperature to ensure the perfect meringues! But it has been the basic information I have struggled to find. Most of the websites out there are keen to blind you with the science of the systems available. Is this to impress? Is it to inform? Or just to make the whole thing hard for the general public to access and achieve? And shouldn't it be the opposite of that? Shouldn't everyone have easy access to alternative energy?

For all of the options available, except biomass, I feel I would need to get an expert in to advise me right from the start and of course this generally means paying out right from the start! I'm not a great lover of paying consultants, I like to do the groundwork myself. And I would like to know that any 'experts' that I consult would have straightforward answers. But maybe the answer isn't to produce your own energy; it's just to do the best you can with what you've got. So maybe I should get back up the loft and see if those dead flies need some extra assistance in insulating my roof space. And maybe a few old-fashioned draft excluders wouldn't go amiss at my ill-fitting doors.

Of course there is another option open to me - 'carbon offsets'. Now what is that about? Is that about reducing the damage to the environment or is it about quelling our conscience? If I had remained on **www.carbonfootprint. com**, I could have calculated that, to offset my personal carbon emissions, all I would need to do was to send them the money to plant 11 trees. At £10 per tree this is a much cheaper option than any of the energy alternatives I have looked at. If I include £1.75 p&p I'll also receive a certificate endorsed by Bill Oddie! So with my £110 cheque in the post and my framed certificate on the wall I can, with a clear conscience, stick my head firmly back in the sand and like the majority of the population, hope that the global warming issue will just go away! I think not ... ❧

Register once
access forever!

Find the best green building products for your job using the UK's only comprehensive green product directory. Registered GreenPro users now benefit from unlimited lifetime access - we just charge a one-time set-up fee of £10.00 (£11.75 incl VAT)to set up your personal account.

Register for GreenPro right now. Go online to www.newbuilder.co.uk and follow the links to GreenPro where you can pay your set up fee and get access (within 24 hours). Alternatively send a cheque for £11.75 to GBP, PO Box 32, Llandysul, SA44 5ZA. Please remember to include a valid e-mail address.

(Make cheques payable to 'Green Building Press')

It's not easy being green! Part 2

Our second 'not easy being green' story comes from **Becky Gillham**, a single mother of three who believes that being really green is more of a philosophical state of mind, rather than a life changing experience. She believes that financial stability plays the greatest part in influencing our society ...

If I was giving up smoking I'd do it slowly not all at one time. For me going green is the same - it's happening slowly. I believe that climate change has always happened and mankind won't make a lot of difference, nature always wins. I'm following my own rules - keep it small, keep it simple and definitely recycle.

We, as a family (single mum, 3 kids aged 3-11), want to lessen our environmental impact because we love nature. We have a vision of not being reliant forever on supermarkets and the high street multinationals - that vision alone just feels better! However, we're not panicking just because of this latest eco craze. For me it's got to be sustainable; emotionally as well as physically, not about guilt but about living comfortably and having respect for the planet. It's important we don't ostracize our friends and family, so by going green slowly, it is less of a shock.

We live in a small semi-detached house. Our neighbours have a warm house - I believe that their heat helps insulate our house. When choosing this house I took a compass and made sure it was south facing with large windows (already recently double glazed) on the south side. Changes to the house have been slow because I want to have fun, not feel that the children are missing out and we certainly don't want to be 'hippies' or elitist greenies. It struck us the other day, when dropping hints to a friend how very 'bad' dishwashers are, (i.e. lots of electric and water) that we had no right to judge anyone for any reason, as such an attitude must surely put new greenies off, so we're just doing our (little) bit.

If I had met some of the friends I have now five years ago, and seen their level of self sufficiency and ability to do without many of the usual trappings of socity, I would have run quickly in the opposite direction with feelings of failure and wonderment. The area of West Wales, where I now live, has a lot of eco types. Now I'm amongst them and a sea of greenness is washing towards me in waves. I really can see the possibility of being in up to my neck sometime in the (not too distant) future.

The positives:
- we have many supportive friends and family, and the potential of a better income as I have just returned to part time work
- we have more and more easily accessible information (phone, friends, library) and combined with our keenness, the future is looking good
- government initiatives to promote grants for sustainable energy also look good for the future.

The negatives:
- many 'green' technologies and commodities are not as yet mainstream, they can be expensive and certainly too expensive for us at the moment
- some of our friends/family are sceptical (many may not find others' opinions matter but they do to us)
- our society's increasing reliance on computers (along with TVs, i-pods, DVD players and credit cards) concerns me. People who have got them assume life is un-livable without. In the move to be less reliant on anyone or anything why be a slave to all these 'trappings'.

I'm totally happy not to have instant e-mail and internet access. However, obtaining information on anything green would have been quicker/easier if I had a computer (I used my mum's researching for this story). Even when talking to local companies they often refer to

© Green Building Press

their web site! But we refuse to buckle under just because of assumptions. Computer-less people may be few and far between but the computer-less are a strong force. It's not just the electrical exposure that's worrying, but the whole concept of something else to eat up time - rather than actually 'living' and being part of the wide world and all its natural glory.

Achievements to date

Lighting

I have changed the lighting to low energy. All the major retailers often have discounts on low energy bulbs so I wait until they're on special offer. The next step is to try and get the children not to leave lights on. I am trying to get them to understand how the energy we use to run the lights has to come from somewhgere - or kids grow up thinking it is just 'there'. Removing the stair light was easy. It's not needed and got 'accidentally' turned on nearly every day. It wasn't dangerous as the hall and upstairs light make it safe. In another house we'd considered installing movement sensor lights but we've cracked it pretty well here and we really don't want to buy things that aren't needed. We use candles sometimes too.

Heating

The oil boiler was on a timer to heat the water and radiators - I now control it manually as we found the times that we were in the house and used the water varied so much - a manually controlled system proved better for our lifestyle. The insulation jacket around the hot water tank seems to be very thick so no changes needed there. We use our wood burning stove a lot, and the kids have fun collecting firewood from local woods and the beach. Our biggest saving on heating though, has been the introduction of a couple of snuggly blankets on the sofa and we love snuggling up, while chatting or watching telly. For some reason the children would risk pneumonia, rather than wear extra jumpers! I have changed our oil company to one that checks the efficiency of our boiler for free and advises us on the best boiler for our needs. They say our

best option would be a condensing boiler, which re-utilises the waste heat energy that normally goes up the flue. However, they cost about £1300 and need to be professionally fitted, so I have to keep our existing boiler (about 8 years old) for now.

Insulation and furnishings

The house has attic rooms - it's quite difficult to check the insulation but, after filling out a questionnaire at a recent eco fair, I found that it is likely to be 4" thick, which is far from adequate. The house has good fitting, modern windows and I have put thick curtains over the windows and doors. We do tend to prefer it a bit colder and airier as one of the children has asthma. Hot, sweaty rooms can encourage mould and bacteria to multiply faster; dust mites and bed bugs thrive too. See the healthy building stories elsewhere in this book for more information on this subject.

We have no fitted carpets as I believe it's healthier to have scatter rugs (made of cotton or wool). These can be shaken outside everyday and washed in the summer and allowed to dry naturally. No energy to hoover, no cleaning products and minimal water once or twice a year to clean. This, combined with cotton bedding, removable cotton sofa covers and keeping soft toys clean and to a minimum has definitely helped eliminate the need to pump asthma chemicals into my daughter.

Our curtains are gradually being changed to cotton - the dining room curtains are dust sheets dyed and decorated by the children. They are easily available from most building merchants, but you can get them from most DIY shops. Dust sheets are cotton, so create less static (static attracts dust). They are also huge, so ours are double thickness and three times the width of the window - cosy, warm and easily cleaned.

Electricity

I have switched our electricity to n-power (juice). Supposedly this means that for every watt of electricity we use, n-power has earmarked that amount in green energy (usually wind powered, but in future this could be hydro electric). Each unit costs the same, but supposedly it registers the level of interest of the general public.

Water

We've recently had a new bathroom suite. The new one is plastic and stays hot for ages. It also uses less hot water (the old metal one got cold very quickly). We've also put insulation under the bath (old jumpers) and around the hot pipes. We've put a brick in the toilet cistern to use less water. I used to have a hot deep bath every day to relax in more than anything. The children would also have baths most days. Now if we've been out swimmimg in the sea (which is most days in the summer) we rarely bath. When we do, and in the winter, we mostly use the same water or go in together. Now we can bath in about 5 inches for a quick dip and feel clean (but not relaxed!). If we go swimming in a local pool we won't wash chlorine off when we get back but we have a quick shower after our swim using the pool facilities! Now we also save washing up for a whole day, rather than do a bit at a time.

We have no water butts, so we have put three buckets in strategic places around the building and now have plenty of free water for rabbits, chickens and plants. The buckets didn't involve cutting any pipes, just placing them strategically under drips. Some councils sell cheap waterbutts to encourage people to save water, but ours doesn't.

Shopping

I hate, with a vengeance, the amount of waste involved doing our weekly shop. Where possible we buy loose items to lessen packaging and we take our bags back to use again. Our main store has promised biodegradable bags at any time now, and I can't wait! I know that organic food is better because less pesticides are used. Unfortunately we can't afford to buy everything organic, so we buy organic root crops and staple foods, like rice and pasta, which we bulk-buy as part of a local whoefood co-operative. We actively search for local foods or at least foods from nearby countries to lessen air miles.

It has taken me three children to get good at saying the word 'no'. Very rarely the kids will ask for something plastic and ultimately useless (apart from short term play value) and even more rarely we'll buy (usually from a charity shop), as I sincerely believe children who are repeatedly turned down can become mean and un-generous, or at worse rebellious. Also I feel that children who are not in some way the same as their peers can be ostracised. However, my kids certainly don't follow every fad, like wearing designer trainers or having mobile phones. Our compromise is that we get nice clothes, and sometimes other items, from second hand shops, and this is topped up with gifts from family and friends.

Present buying

Gifts are difficult because we come from a family culture of generous Xmas and birthday present giving. This will have to stop! For 5 years we've made our own cards (we have card making sessions). Now we're making presents (dream catchers, cakes, glass painted wine-glasses, knitted toys etc.). In recent years we've bought presents only for grandparents or children. In the future we will be considering alternative gifts, such as buying woodland in the name of a person, Alternative Technology Centre gift vouchers, or sponsoring animals or children in deprived areas. Many charities operate such gifts, such as the Woodland Trust, Action Aid etc. So this year we'll save on even more packaging, consumables and do some good. Father Christmas is becoming better at choosing toys too, choosing those made of timber from sustainable woodlands (FSC mark), for example.

Products

Some people might buy shampoo, soap and hair products from organic health shops or the Body Shop, but our instinct is to buy 'value' brands at big supermarkets because they do huge bottles (cheaply) which cuts down on packaging. Our cheap washing up liquid hardly bubbles so we presume it's very watered down. Often the thicker the product, the harsher the chemicals. In the washing machine we use nothing for a moderately dirty wash (full load of course). Occasionally we use wash balls (from Kleeneze) but rarely any detergent.

Five years ago I wouldn't have been seen dead without make-up, now I buy none - and it's okay! I've managed to keep my self esteem, and find other ways to feel good about myself (keeping fit, cheerful and positive, for example). We use bicarbonate of soda for most cleaning jobs (a teaspoon dissolved in warm water, with a squeeze of lemon to smell fresh, to wipe down surfaces, for example). This is something my gran used to do. We have a bottle of cheap, thin cleaner which we use on the surfaces in the kitchen, toilet and bathroom occasionally - we'll use it neat on a rag (old socks usually).

The children have pets and it would be better to buy pet food in bulk - but the dog and cat won't eat it, and at 15 years old they deserve what they want. We'd like to shop at the Co-op as it is much more eco-friendly, but the nearest one is 20 miles away. I'm changing our bank to them though because they have an encouraging ethical policy.

The car
I've just gone back to work and am now using the car a lot more, unfortunately. I have had an ancient Koa Pride 1.3 for about 18 months and my instinct says keep it going at this stage because I know that all the bits and pieces bought for it and the services it's had must; (a) make it financially worth keeping and (b) make it more eco as the regular services should make it run more efficiently.

Holidays, education and entertainment
We really can't justify foreign holidays, although the children will nag me until we go at least once, perhaps to France to help them speak French. When we do go away, we go either with someone who was going anyway, and we can cadge a lift, or we holiday locally. This year we're going camping twice locally and once with my parents to Cornwall (the Eden project), who were going anyway. The children are educated at home, so we don't do the school run. We try and keep things as local as possible and often we'll car share with a friend. The children are

encouraged to do things like dancing, riding and guides (as opposed to travel, computers and motorboats, for example).

Gardening and DIY
These are my favourite hobbies and I don't use any chemicals. For gardening I use peat free compost and make my own compost out of kitchen waste, shredded paper, chicken and rabbit droppings. Our garden is quite wild looking and we leave big areas for the birds and bugs. We have recently bought 2 ducks which certainly help with slug control and they, plus our chickens, also keep us in eggs. For spot weeding on the drive, if we can't get a weed out, I pour boiling water on it. For the children, we've built a willow dome and make things from willow (no impact, fun and free). We have also put up a climbing frame using timber from a local woodland, given to us by friend.

We, as a family, feel that gardening is very important. It teaches children the value and beauty of nature and how we can change nature (or harness it) in a good way. Also hopefully they'll grow up with a respect for nature, because of it being part of their early lives, and realise why it's so important to try to live in harmony with it.

The future
I am in the process of sourcing thicker loft insulation. A water butt has been ordered and this may be the year that we can afford to move to a bigger home.

We would like to move house, to a small property but detached so no neighbours to complain (although at present they do help to keep us warm in winter). I would like a windmill (or two), our own water supply and drainage, solar water heating, maybe PV panels, and rainwater harvesting. I would also like an electric car that could be run from our renewables! Our ideal would be to make any house we live in as eco as possible. We've read so many books and listened to so many TV and radio programmes and spoken to friends and local companies from the yellow pages, I've got a picture in my head of what I want. Ten years down the line, we can see things will be more mainstream, but now its tough unless one is pretty solvent.

Grants

I have looked into the government's Low Carbon Buildings Programme (which replaces two previous renewable power grant schemes), and they have promised £80 million to promote a more holistic approach to reducing carbon dioxide by encouraging householders to consider energy efficiency and micro genera-tion (mini power generators in the home such as wind turbines, special boilers that make heat and electricity and solar panels etc). Apparently, if you install any sustainable fuel/ energy system (from an approved list) using a specially registered company the government will provide 30-50% of the cost (maximums differ).

The only thing I would consider in our present house would be solar panels (for hot water). A local company has quoted about £1400 (not installed) so I think I won't bother until we've moved home. The Eco Centre in Newport, Pembrokeshire in Wales was very helpful. They have lists giving information on the estimated power consumption for certain items, for example, hoovers. They also give hints on how to save energy and other useful tips. ☙

Useful links
Obtained using my mothers' computer!
www.lowcarbonbuildings.org.uk
(grant info)
www.est.org.uk/myhome/gid/
(grant info)
www.est.org.uk/myhome/whatcan/hec/
(Home Energy Check)
www.saveenergy.co.uk/renewables
(Energy Saving Trust Information)

JUNO

A magazine for parents with an ethos based on natural parenting, sustainability, social justice and spirituality. Contains interviews, reviews, personal stories, crafts and celebrations.

Available from Borders, selected organic and health food shops, green baby shops, on-line and direct.

"Juno has a level of serousness, combined with warmth and joy which is hard to achieve", Sally Jenkinson

1 issue for £3, 4 issues for £12 and 8 issues for £23

For sample articles and to subscribe on-line visit:

www.junomagazine.com

Juno, PO Box 592, East Grinstead, West Sussex RH19 3AQ

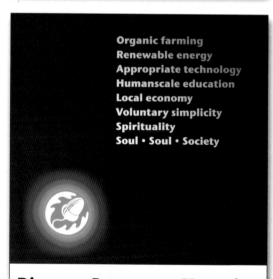

Organic farming
Renewable energy
Appropriate technology
Humanscale education
Local economy
Voluntary simplicity
Spirituality
Soul • Soul • Society

Discover *Resurgence* Magazine

Every issue contains a rich diversity of articles, with front-line news on environmental and social issues from around the world. It brings together leading writers to present topics of vital importance to our world.

Subscribe or find out more: 01208 841824, **www.resurgence.org**

 Resurgence

It's not easy being green! Part 3

Yes, you've guessed it. It was the title of a recent BBC programme. This programme followed the journey of a family from a pleasant residential area in Cheltenham to a 3.5 acre smallholding in Cornwall, where they proceeded to 'go green'. Well **Trevor Davies** moved from Oxford to Carmarthenshire, with his partner and two children. Here are his opinions on energy in the home ...

There were many useful topics covered in the TV programme, much of which, however, could be gleaned in greater depth from John Seymour's book, 'The complete book of self sufficiency'.

As a family we have always been aware of our impact on the planet and have tried to live a more environmentally friendly lifestyle where possible. One, of probably many, things we don't do is produce our own energy. Global warming is a reality and unless the individual starts to take some responsibility, the effects will only worsen.

One thing from the BBC programme really interested me, micro-generation, using a wind turbine to produce your own power. Fortunately I had videoed this episode so was able to freeze the frame and saw 'Windsave' on the turbine. Excellent I thought and got onto the internet there and then. A quick google and I was there **www.windsave.com**. The blurb sounded fantastic, a 33% reduction in electric bills (based on national average consumption), 5 year pay back, 10 year lifespan. Not only would I be more green, but it's going to put money in my pocket. At this point alarm bells started to ring. If it sounds to good to be true, then it probably is.

Okay, let's look at the figures. Windsave quotes the national average domestic electricity consumption at 3200kWh per year. Now we as a household of 4 use an average of 4800kWh per year. I was somewhat surprised at the

difference as all our appliances are 'A' rated and we try not to overuse electricity. A further googleing brought me to the DTI website **www. dti.gov.uk/energy/statistics/regional/ index.html** where you can download files of electricity consumption both 2003 & 2004. These government supplied figures suggest an average annual domestic consumption of 4600kWh per household. So we're not as bad as I first thought, but Windsave seems to be over egging the pudding somewhat. A further problem with this type of generator is that is has no energy storage capability. 'Batteries are expensive', says Windsave. So basically it's a use it or loose it system. Also it transpires that if the grid goes off, then so does the turbine, so no power - hardly what I'd call self sufficient.

What about the 5 year pay back? The turbine, fully installed, costs £1595 plus VAT, giving a total of £1874. The Low Carbon Buildings Programme grant, would give you 30% of the cost of this turbine i.e £562. This leaves you with £1312 to find out of your own pocket. Over 5 years this equates to roughly £262 per year. The Windsave website info says, "The Windsave system on average will produce sufficient electricity to claim one ROC (Renewable Obligations Certificate)". 1 ROC is currently worth £56. This then leaves a require-ment to produce £206 worth of electricity per year. £206 of electricity at about 10.3p/kWh (Oct 2006 prices) requires the turbine to produce 2000kWh of electricity per year, and the end user to use all of it. For this size turbine to produce that much energy would mean living in some of the windiest places in Britain. The idea of this turbine is starting to look less favourable than I first thought.

Still never mind it's not the only turbine out there. I recently received some green energy info from our electricity supplier and a quick look through the paper work found it. The Swift rooftop wind energy system. So, back to the computer, and a quick search found it at **www.**

renewabledevices.com/swift/index.htm. This is a slightly bigger turbine at 2.1m diameter and the info indicates that it can produce 2000-3000kWh of electricity per year, dependant on siting and wind conditions, although there is no mention of which wind conditions produce this much power. Further searching found a reference at www.ashdenawards.org/winners/swift which gives this turbine's output as 4000kWh per year at an annual mean wind speed of 8m/s. The British Wind Energy Association (BWEA) have a map of UK annual mean wind speeds at www.bwea.com/images/misc/noabl_c.gif and this shows 8m/s to be well in excess of what is normal for most areas. In fact using the BWEA website www.bwea.com/noabl/index.html it is possible to ascertain the wind speeds for any UK location, and for our location we get 4.7m/s at 10m above ground level, which would equate to an approximate output from the Swift turbine of 800kWh per year, somewhat below the 2000-3000 claimed. Furthermore, this turbine is also a grid connect system, so if the grid's off then no power, no matter how hard the wind blows. This turbine is, similarly, looking less favourable that it first appeared.

This did get me thinking though. If all of our electric appliances are 'A' rated then why are we only average in our electricity consumption. Admittedly we do live a fairly normal life with its luxuries; cooker, automatic washing machine, dishwasher, fridge, freezer, TV, Hi-Fi, computer but NO tumble dryer. Then it occurred to me that the one thing we use all the time, which is not energy efficient is lighting. A quick back of the envelope calculation showed that as a household we use about 1000kWh of electricity per year, just on lighting, that's 22% of our electric usage, I couldn't believe it, but further reading showed that 20% would not be unreasonable. Some 10 years ago I did invest in a couple of low energy bulbs, expensive though they were, about £10 each I seem to recall. But they seemed to take an age to warm up, the light was poor and at the end of the day didn't appear to last any longer than a normal bulb, so I dropped the idea. Technology has moved on since then. So, bearing in mind how much

lighting energy we use, I have now installed low energy bulbs throughout most of the house and am currently happy with their performance. I estimate that this will save, annually, approximately 800kWh, of electricity or about £70, which is over double what I've spent on new bulbs. Put another way, this saving is about the same as I'd expect from installing a small wind turbine.

We're definitely not ruling out micro-generation but rather than jumping in at this moment we need to do more research first and identify what our total energy usage is, and what areas to aim our resources at, to get the best net benefit in terms of reducing greenhouse gas emissions as a household. ☻

Note: the grant for wind turbines gives £1000 per kW installed, to a maximum of £5000, with an overall limit of 30% of the installed costs. However, to quality for the grant, an approved installer has to be used: www.lowcarbonbuildings.org.uk

Have you read RENEW yet!

RENEW- the UK's long running bimonthly update on renewable energy developments. Packed full of information, contacts and analysis, Renew is an indispensible and high-value way to keep in touch with the technologies and policies shaping our sustainable future. Produced for NATTA, the National Network for Alternative Technology and Technology Assessment by the Energy and Environment Research Unit at the Open University.

"A fantastic source of knowledge and critical comment regarding UK energy supplies and the renewables sector"
Keith Hall - editor, Building for a Future magazine

Subscription is £18 per annum, or £12 if you are unwaged. Send a cheque made out to the 'Open University' with your name and address to:

NATTA, EERU, The Open University, Milton Keynes MK7 6AA. Indicate if you want a paper copy or the PDF file version - and, if the latter, provide an email address.

More info at http://eeru.open.ac.uk/natta/rol.html

© Green Building Press

There are four simple ways to make your buildings greener ...

Subscribe to Building for a Future magazine for a year

and we will send you one of them every three months!

Just £20 per annum

Subscribe now online at **www.newbuilder.co.uk**

or telephone 01559 370798

Green Building Press ...

promoting energy efficient, healthy and sustainable buildings

See also: painting and decorating discussions in Chapter 7

Don't get homesick!

On average we spend up to 85% of our time inside buildings. Therefore we need to ensure that the buildings that we occupy are safe inside. **Anita Bradley** reports on the issues involved.

Our buildings have changed over the last 30 years. We have increased their energy efficiency and airtightness a little but more dramatically, the majority of us have, through a multitude of products and consumables, introduced a wide cocktail of chemicals into our homes.

The way we build, the materials used, the installations needed, and the way we maintain our homes and offices has given rise to the incidence of 'sick building syndrome' (SBS), officially recognised as an illness by the World Health Organisation since 1986. If we are to continue making our houses even more energy efficient and less 'leaky' (draughty) then we will need to be much more thoughtful about what products we build and decorate with.

'Sick building syndrome' is a general malaise of multiple symptoms of an unknown or unclearly recognised aetiology. It should not be confused with 'building related illness' (BRI) in which both the disease and its cause is known – such as legionella, asbestosis, or humidifier fever. Although the two share common features, the former is more difficult to pin down and rectify. Difficulty in identifying SBS lies in the vast array of conditions presented, the subjective nature of the complaints and the lack of solid evidence as to causes. People can react very differently to specific conditions and symptoms vary with time and location.

Symptoms associated with SBS include:
- headache
- loss of concentration
- nasal irritation
- dry or watery eyes
- lethargy
- skin irritation
- throat problems
- possibly more acute conditions and diseases.

SBS is a chemical, biological and mental/psychological phenomenon which, if ignored, can lead to expensive remedial action, absenteeism, lower productivity, and loss of well-being.

It has been estimated (WHO) that up to 30% of refurbished, and a significant number of new buildings, suffer from SBS. Any aspect and any type of use of a building can produce SBS, with several possible causes having been identified:
- contaminated land
- radon and other gases
- asbestos and lead
- contaminated water
- volatile organic compounds (VOCs)
- electromagnetic fields
- moulds, dust and other allergens
- micro-organisms and body matter
- lighting
- heating, ventilation and air conditioning (HVAC)
- poor architectural, engineering design and specification
- inadequate facilities management
- negative ion depletion
- psychosocial factors.

© Green Building Press

Indoor air quality

The Building Research Establishment (BRE) found that air inside buildings could be up to 10 times more polluted than the air outside. In the late 20th Century, industry and commerce has produced around 70,000 new synthetic materials and chemicals. Of these, less than 2% have been tested for safety to humans and up to 70% have not been tested at all. Around 1,000 new chemicals and materials are marketed each year, without the full cost to human or ecological wellbeing being considered. We take in this chemical cocktail via breath, skin, water and food.

Indoor air contains microscopic particulates – perfumes, bacteria, viruses, animal dander, dust mites, respiration particles, pollen, mould; combustion products – carbon monoxide, nitrogen dioxide, sulphur dioxide, hydrocarbons; and volatile organic compounds (VOCs) – benzene, formaldehyde, chlorine, synthetic fibres, PVC and other chemical products. Pollution comes from paints, preservatives, insulation, adhesives, carpets, soft furnishings, furniture, cleaners and air fresheners. Other sources include timbers, ply, particle board and such like, which may have been treated with preservatives, glues, paints and varnishes. Fire retardant chemicals add to this burden.

Due to increasing a building's energy efficiency, newer construction techniques and materials have meant that buildings have become virtually air tight. In such buildings the external walls have been designed to minimise leakage of air conditioned air to the outside but have also stopped fresh air permeating to the inside. Sealed windows and artificial air conditioning plants (heating, ventilation and air conditioning – HVAC) are thus needed to maintain warmth or coolness within. However, this trend seems to be allowing a build up of noxious air. HVAC plant have recently been identified as a potent cause of SBS and thus there are strict fitting and maintenance guidelines to keep them working at an optimal level for efficiency and health. Microbes and bacteria were found in ducts and filters. An article in the prestigious British medical journal 'The Lancet'

reported the trial of using UV light to kill bacteria within HVAC plants with a high degree of success.

Building techniques that allow the building fabric to 'breathe' are best but not always the desire of the building financier. The notion of the building as a 'third skin' is ideal wherever possible. (This is an idea from the 'Building Biology' movement: the first skin is that stretchy stuff that protects the body; clothes form the second protective skin; and the building fabric is thus seen as the third protective skin.)

Another factor that may help reduce the effects of SBS is that of 'Indoor Surface Pollution' (ISP). This is presented in a BRE paper addressing the importance of ISP in building management and suggests ways of reducing it. The method involves defining ISP by a 'Fleece Factor' (the area of carpet, curtains and other fabric, divided by the volume of the space) and the 'Shelf Factor' (the length of open shelving or filing space divided by the volume of the room). Above all, the recommendations in this paper stress the need for good hygiene. The need for extra, or specialist, cleaning is reduced or made easier by careful design, furniture selection and office/space layout. (*G.J.Raw: 'The Importance of Indoor Surface Pollution in Sick Building Syndrome', BRE Information Paper IP 3/94. Feb 1994.*)

Two factors that are widely thought to contribute to sick building syndrome come from electrical installations (the wiring layout) and appliances left plugged in on standby mode.

Electromagnetic field pollution (EMF's)

Electromagnetic fields occur both in nature and the man-made environment. In nature these fields are very low and occur due to climate, terrestrial factors, cosmic radiation and from the body's own electrical activity. Such fields are generally very low in strength and frequency and are usually beneficial or essential to health. Man-made electrical fields (EMFs) are part of a controversy regarding their effects on the health of people exposed to them. The fields in question are non-ionising in their action and are produced whenever there is a flow of electricity. An EMF is made up of an electric field component (measured in volts per metre – V/m) and a magnetic field component (measured in Teslas – T). Electric fields form wherever there is a voltage and its strength is dependent on the magnitude of the voltage. A magnetic field arises whenever there is a current flowing. Both components reduce with distance from source. The frequency, shape and strength of these fields are important factors in determining the effect they have on health. Sources of manufactured EMFs are power lines, electrical wiring in buildings and appliances

Studies have been carried out into EMFs since the possibility of health problems started in the 1960s. These first studies were on occupational exposure. The first study of general exposure began in the late 70s when two American researchers found a suggestive link between power line EMFs and childhood leukaemia. Since then many more and varied studies have been conducted to ascertain if there are health risks arising from exposure to a myriad of EMF sources. Studies have suggested links with cancers and leukaemia, depression and suicide, immune disorders, and allergy.

Over half the elevated levels in buildings come from wiring configurations and appliances. The wiring regulations do not specifically concern themselves with EMFs, but, according to Powerwatch, in following their implementation, the fields produced would be minimised. Large commercial buildings can have very low fields because the wires are housed in appropriate metal trunking; but some buildings can have high fields because currents flow along 'earthed' pipework. Electric fields can still be high if a metal conduit is not used. The use of 'ring' circuits give off high magnetic fields and therefore 'radial' wiring is the preferred method. Electric fields can be shielded quite cheaply, but the magnetic field is extremely difficult to eliminate, therefore this is best designed out or shielded wherever they are generated.

Britain has been well behind other countries in acknowledging the risks, especially for the magnetic field component. The Radiation Protection Division of the Health Protection Agency (formerly the National Radiological Protection Board) sets maximum exposure levels as $1,600\mu T$. For comparison, Switzerland $1uT$; Sweden $0.2\mu T$; and parts of Italy 0.2-$0.5\mu T$. The magnetic field levels at which certain diseases have been shown to occur at are:

Miscarriage	$1.6\mu T$
Childhood leukaemia	$0.3/0.4\mu T$
Adult brain cancer	0.2-$0.6\mu T$
Depression	$0.2\mu T$
Suicide	$0.2\mu T$

(Source: 'Health effects of EMFs – evidence and mechanisms', Professor DL Henshaw. HH Wills Physics Laboratory. University of Bristol)

Hard floors are the darling of the anti dust mite brigade and can certainly play a major role in the reduction of possible toxins from carpets in the home. There is plenty of evidence to be found that blames carpets for not only containing chemicals, but also harbouring dust etc (foot traffic). The British love of carpet, though, is not without reason. They make our feet feel warm and give a cosier feel to the room. So the choice is yours!

© Green Building Press

However, in 2004 the National Radiological Protection Board (NRPB) recommended the adoption of reduced level of exposure to the magnetic field component of EMFs in the frequency range 0-300GHz. This is for general public exposure. The limit recommended is $100\mu T$ (down from the previous $1600\mu T$) and is the level adopted by the International Commission on Non-Ionising Radiation Protection (ICNIRP). The frequencies covered include TV and radio broadcasting, mobile telecommunications and the electical supply. Whilst this reduction may seem large it is not so low as to prevent illness as supported by many researchers and scientific papers. Professor Henshaw of Bristol University (an expert in this subject) states that these proposals should go much further. "The proposals to limit public exposure to magnetic fields to $100\mu T$, 250 times higher than the $0.4\mu T$ where doubling of the risk of childhood leukaemia is acknowledged, looks ridiculous when viewed alongside the well established practice for chemical carcinogens where levels are set at least 1000 times below the level where evidence of harmful effects have been found."

According to Powerwatch the ideal magnetic field level should be less than $0.01\mu T$ and the electric field should be less than 5V/m. Levels of exposure of $0.03\mu T$ and 10V/m can be reasonably achieved. The average exposure is $0.04-0.05\mu T$ for exposure from both outdoor and indoor sources. Several organisations offer testing and advice on EMFs, including Powerwatch.

Noise

Noise is not always considered in studies of SBS, but it can contribute to the condition and cause suffering or disturbance for the building occupant. Sources of noise in buildings are air-conditioning plants, outdoor noise filtering indoors, office equipment and 'people' noise. Air conditioning systems can be disturbing if they are functioning badly, poorly maintained and ill designed. Air rushing through vents is a source of noise but the vent size can be increased for the same output, which will lessen levels. Ductwork can carry noise around a building,

so insulation and good design are essential. However, noise control is not just about lowering levels as a space that is too quiet can also be troublesome. Continuous soft noise is another factor to be avoided. CIBSE state an upper limit for office work of 46dBA (where decibels 'A' refers to the particular decibel scale on sound level meter). Many offices exceed this level.

Lighting

The links between lighting and sick building syndrome are well known. Glare, flicker, lack of contrast, inadequate illumination and unsuitable spot lighting can all add to a users burden. Many offices or developments are of deep plan design and therefore are unable to be illuminated by daylight to the interior. The use of fluorescent lighting is commonplace and therefore a common problem. Their use can give rise to eye strain and headaches among other symptoms. ('Fluorescent Lighting: A Health Hazard Overhead', London Hazard Centre). If these lights cannot be avoided then regular maintenance or the use of full spectrum fluorescent is preferable.

Another aspect of lighting design in relation to sick building syndrome is the ability of the occupant to alter their exposure to meet personal comfort. Different tasks require different lighting. CIBSE recommends 500 lux for general office work and 750 lux for deep plan offices or where close work takes place (such as at a drawing board or reading).

Tinted glass is not recommended as we need light levels to maintain our physiology such as the endocrine system. Deprived of lighting cues our body to change to a 25 hour cycle rather than the 24 hour cycle. Lack of light (essentially bright sunlight) can cause depression, anxiety, fatigue and the modern diagnosis of Seasonal Affective Disorder (SAD). Adjustable and well-designed shading devices are the most desirable solution to both lighting problems and to reduce glare and heat gain.

Ions

Ions are essential to life and health. They are

atoms that can be either negatively (-) or positively (+) charged. Negative ions are the benefices of health and are shown to reduce headache, nausea and dizziness. They also make a person more comfortable and alert. Lack of negative ions (i.e. an abundance of '+' ions), are associated with depression, lethargy and anxiety. Many buildings can give rise to a shortage of beneficial ions through materials and equipment; metal ducts for HVAC plant attracts the ions as they pass through, static electricity attracts these ions as does tobacco smoke and dust particles. Static can be reduced by the avoidance of synthetic materials, 'earthing' of all electrical equipment, and good building hygiene. A high density of people can also alter the ratio of negative to positive ions. There are fewer negative ions when the indoor temperature is greater than 22°C, and where there is a high relative humidity. Typical office air contains only 50 negative ions per millilitre whereas clean outdoor air can carry as many as 1000.

Useful contacts

Powerwatch: www.powerwatch.org.uk

The Health Protection Agency: www.hpa.org.uk

Environmental Protection Agency USA: www.epa.gov

Human Radiation Effects: www.electric-fields.bris.ac.uk

Women's Environmental Network: www.wen.org.uk

Healthy Flooring Network: www.healthyflooring.org

Building Research Establishment: www.bre.co.uk

London Hazards Centre: www.lhc.org.uk

Further reading

'The Healthy House' by S & J Baggs

'Cross Currents: The Startling Effects of Electromagnetic Radiation on Your Health' by R Becker

'Killing Fields in the Home' A & J Philips

'Electromagnetic Man: Health Hazard in the Electrical Environment' by Smith CW & Best S. The Bath Press 1989 (A classic which is currently out of print but is essential reading if you can find it).

'Water, Electricity and Health -protecting yourself from electrostress at home and work' by Alan Hall

The Toxic Consumer; how to reduce your exposure to everyday toxic chemicals' by Karen Ashton & Elizabeth Salter Green

Most of the above books are available from the Green Shop: 01452 770629 www.greenshop.co.uk

BOOKS FOR INSPIRATION AND SUSTAINABILITY

the **Green** shop

PRODUCTS FOR A SUSTAINABLE FUTURE

Diary of an Eco-Builder - Will Anderson shares his vision of building a highly energy efficient, beautiful and sustainable home and how he brought it into reality. **£14.95**

Oxford Dictionary of Architecture and Landscape Architecture - 6000 entries of architectural terms and styles. Fascinating, useful and comprehensive. **£10.99**

Building with Cob - All that's needed to be known about building and restoring with cob. Beautiful book. **£25.00**

The Water Book - Rainwater harvesting, grey water and the general use of water. **£12.00**

How to make Biodiesel - All the information required to start making your own. **£8.95**

Rubbish! - Should be read by all, including Cabinet Ministers and Local Authorities. **£7.99**

Your Brick Oven - Build your own wood-fired brick oven and then enjoy delicious food. **£10.99**

FOR A FULL RANGE OF ALL OUR PRODUCTS AND BOOKS FOR EVERY NEED, VISIT WWW.GREENSHOP.CO.UK OR PHONE 01452 770629 FOR A GENERAL CATALOGUE

GreenPRO

product directory

Register once access forever!

Find the best green building products for your job using the UK's only comprehensive green product directory. Registered GreenPro users now benefit from unlimited lifetime access - we just charge a one-time set-up fee of £10.00 (£11.75 incl VAT) to set up your personal account.

Register for GreenPro right now. Go online to www.newbuilder.co.uk and follow the links to GreenPro where you can pay your set up fee and get access (within 24 hours). Alternatively send a cheque for £11.75 to GBP, PO Box 32, Llandysul, SA44 5ZA. Please remember to include a valid e-mail address.

(Make cheques payable to 'Green Building Press')

© Green Building Press

1. Floors

Minimise the areas of carpeting in the building. Consider other types of floor finish such as linoleum, rubber or even cork. Slate and wood floors are back in fashion but some proprietary laminated floorboard systems are not always real timber so watch out for that.

2. Ventilation

Try to design your buildings with adequate natural ventilation. This is not always easy on large commercial buildings but if considered early enough in the design stage then it may be possible to reduce the dependency on heating and ventilating plant to some degree or even eliminate its need.

3. Light and access

Make sure that your buildings are light and airy and the immediate outdoor vicinity is attractive, (fragrant flowers, grass and trees) natural and safe for children. The building user will want to open doors and windows and enjoy the fragrances of the natural environment.

4. Treatments and preservatives

Minimise or eliminate the use of preservatives on timber used within the building. This is a big problem as many builders still believe that by using treated timber they are providing their customers with a higher quality product. They are not!

Eight simple steps to reduce sick building syndrome

5. Materials

Reduce the use of 'composite' materials in the designed fabric of the building by as much as practically possible. Remember the building user will add plenty of their own in the form of furniture, furnishings, white goods and electronics. This, of course, is out of the control of the building designer but remember, large quantities of composites can cause toxic overload in poorly ventilated inner spaces.

6. Services

Minimise on excessive electrical cable provision. If necessary design in future-proofing access for adding or removing cabling as needs arise. Also keep cable runs along predetermined routes and avoid the creation of electrical 'fields' which can inadvertently be produced by poor layout design.

7. Finishes

Reduce the use of paints and other coatings to an absolute minimum. Decorating for good health means following a 'less is more' scenario. Consider specifying or using self colour materials such as clay plasters or high quality plasterboard systems that need little or no decoration. Use durable species of timbers to reduce the need for excessive painting. Even consider using unfinished (durable) timber for windows and doors.

8. Aesthetics

Avoid 'glue on' character. Use the style and structure of the building to achieve character rather than adding fake layers. Natural and minimalist is in vogue at the moment so there are few excuses.

Energy and water saving advice

Fuel poverty is on the rise. In 1996 the figure of homes in fuel poverty was a huge 35%. This dropped significantly to 13% in 2002. However the figure is going up again, and the latest figures show fuel poverty at 14.5%. Water is another issue, with summer droughts in many areas causing problems. We asked **Ben Bamber** to look for opportunities to green the home that those on low incomes could tap into.

Households are said to be in fuel poverty when more than 10% of their income is needed to pay fuel bills. One energy company said that 60,000 of its customers in the lower income brackets were benefiting from special help to pay bills. Fuel debt is proportionately more prevalent with prepayment customers. 26% of households in the UK are classified as fuel poor, that's 20 million households. There is therefore a huge drive to motivate householders to save energy and for local councils and power companies to promote energy saving with incentives, grants and publicity campaigns. Water is also becoming a major player as drought continues in the south east and costs rise because of aging infrastructure. There are a number of ways energy and water can be saved, meaning that when energy and water usage is being driven down, more households would be taken out of fuel and water poverty status, which is good for government figures, good for households and good for the environment. The following is therefore a summary of the best energy and water saving devices, grants and schemes offered by a variety of different government and non-government organisations and businesses.

Grants and trusts

The government is offering a wide variety of grants for home insulation, heating and energy saving solutions. In Scotland homeowners can qualify for grants worth up to 30% of the cost of installing a renewable technology system, up to a maximum of £4,000. The Energy Saving Trust (EST) says on its website that 'a household can qualify for up to two grants'. This scheme is only available in Scotland, via the Scottish Community and Householder Renewables Initiative.

There are also a number of different initiatives the Scottish grants will cover. Household grants that are available through SCHRI can cover: biomass, ground source heat pumps, small scale hydro turbines, solar water heating, solar space heating and wind turbines. The Scottish Community and Householder Renewables initiative also offers funding to community groups. More information can be found at **www.est.org.uk** (The Energy Saving Trust).

The government's Low Carbon Buildings Programme, launched in April 2006, provides grants for solar PV and other renewable technologies. 0800 298 3978.

Eaga Partnership Charitable Trust

The Eaga Partnership Charitable Trust are running a campaign to assist people who suffer from fuel poverty, and as a key part of the campaign, along with financial help they, will be providing energy saving advice and solutions. The objectives of the Trust are 'the relief of fuel poverty and the preservation and protection of health by the promotion of the efficient use of energy'. There is no minimum or maximum amount that individuals and groups can apply for, as each application is judged on its own merits. Eligibility criteria are available on its website: **www.eaga.co.uk** or call 0800 316 2808. Eaga also offers free central heating to the over 60's. You can get more information on 0800 316 1653.

If you want to search for a suitable grant for yourself or your organisation a grants database and search engine is available at **www.est.org. uk/myhome**. And if you're struggling to pay your water bills, most water companies have a charitable trust attached to their company which in certain circumstances may cover your bill and bring it up-to-date. This is done on a case by case basis.

The Carbon Trust

The Carbon Trust **www.thecarbontrust.co.uk** offers a range of energy saving advice, and on their website there is information to help you reduce your energy bills. This includes, cleaning light fittings annually, keeping the thermostat at 19°C - costs rise by 8% for every 1°C increase, not heating unused space, storerooms, corridors and areas where there's heavy physical work. Reduce heating during holidays and weekends and keep radiators clear of furniture - it reduces efficiency and output. Check that thermostats are sited out of draughts and away from either cold or hot spots. Keep windows closed in cold weather. If you are too warm, turn the heating down instead. The Carbon Trust also says, 'If you can't measure it, you can't manage it'. Check regularly on your consumption of electricity, gas and oil, and check that your bills relate to what you actually use, rather than an estimate. .

Warm Front

Defra runs a grant scheme for insulation and heating costs for people on low incomes and state benefits, called Warm Front, which is administered by the local councils. Grants for £2,700 and £4,000 for oil central heating are available to eligible applicants. Most borough councils will have a department to field enquiries for the scheme, so contact your local council for details.

Warm Front provides funding for insulation measures including: loft insulation, draught proofing, cavity-wall insulation, hot-water-tank insulation; heating systems including central heating, gas room heaters with thermostat controls, electric storage heaters, converting a solid-fuel open fire to a modern glass-fronted fire, time controls for electric space water and water heaters, heating repairs and replacements. Other measures include energy advice, two free low-energy light-bulbs, and a hot water tank jacket. This is the local government's main

grant making programme aimed at local people without their own money to invest in energy saving measures. However, there are also schemes aimed at encouraging higher earners, by providing a proportion of the costs of larger installations. Again your local council will have all the details.

Cavity wall insulation grants

The major power companies have been partly funded and partly compelled to offer a range of discounted and subsidised schemes to home owners and tenants. These companies offer discounts on cavity wall insulation and loft insulation. A discount of 50% or 100%, depending on whether you are in receipt of state benefits, and which type of benefit also makes a difference. People on Income Support will be considered for 100% grant, in most cases. Contact any of the following companies on the numbers below; although some of them are restricted to particular regions, most are nationwide.

- Npower: 0800 022 220 **www.npower.com**
- Powergen: 0500 201 000 **www.powergen.co.uk**
- Scottish Power: 0845 601 7836 **www.theenergypeople.com**
- Home energy and British Gas: 0845 971 7731
- Scottish Hydro Electric: 0845 777 6633
- HEAT Cymru Project (Wales): 0800 093 40 50 **www.heatproject.co.uk**

General energy saving tips

There are now a number of products and services on the market which will save energy use and help clean up the environment. In the following section, we've listed some of these that can be bought on line, supplied by a utility company or on the high street.

Insulation

Draught excluders are a cheap and effective way of making your home more energy efficient. Much of the wasted energy is lost through gaps in doors and windows, key holes, letter boxes and gaps in loft hatches. Sometimes the most obvious things can be missed, and it is these aspects of energy saving devices which are the most available, and easiest to fix. A roll of draft proofing tape for windows will cost £6, (10m) and is available from any good DIY shop. A letter box cover can cost as little as £4, and a draft excluder for external doors, (and internal if necessary), can be picked up at about £6 each. A hot water cylinder jacket, costs about £12, depending on the size of the cylinder. It is also possible to insulate exposed hot water pipes. The basic tasks outlined above will cost about £60 in total, and could save up to £25 in fuel bills, yearly.

Secondary glazing is more expensive, and as far as I know there are no government schemes to cover the costs. A basic pack for an average sized un-openable window will cost £65. Although the cheaper option, secondary glazing can still be expensive, and may not be all that accessible if you're on a low income.

If everything you can do is being done, you can expect to save up to £165 from your yearly electric and gas bills. It never ceases to amaze me, just how much energy is being wasted from simple and easily fixed problems. All of the above can be achieved within a budget of £500 - £800 and therefore it is possible to have repaid your investment within 3 to 5 years.

Radiator panels are also a good idea if you have central heating in your home. A good deal of the heat coming from your radiator is wasted out the back of the radiator and through the walls of your house. A radiator panel is available from **www.proeco.co.uk** for £24.99 for six, or £29.99 for eight. These panels can save a large proportion of the energy used to run the radiators. These are also available from other retailers, including the Kent Energy Centre for £20 for ten. They are easy to install, and so there are no installation charges.

Lighting

Low energy light-bulbs are coming down in price as demand increases. Although Powergen offer 2 x 20W low energy light bulbs, at a discounted rate for their scheme, it is more expensive than some high street shops. Wilkinsons, a high street shop, offers light bulbs at £1.99 each across the range. Some of the discounted offers by other energy companies are also more expensive than high street prices, so shop around. Your local council may offer two free bulbs as part of their energy saving schemes.

Water saving

Water use is also very wasteful in the average home. Given recent droughts, there are a number of things you can do to reduce water consumption, especially relevant if you're on a water meter. If your loo flushes 9 litres (80% of houses still use this size cistern) then fit the Interflush retrofit kit to your existing toilet siphon to save water. See **www.interflush. co.uk**. Once fitted, the average household of 2.4 people could save 27,000 litres per year which equates to a 47% water saving. The costs of the system are £19.90 which you can buy online. You can also add a bag of water into your cistern, below the fill capacity, which could reduce the flush amount by up to 20%. You can buy manufactured clip on bags as well, from **www.h2obuildingservices.co.uk**. Their bag could save you up to 2 litres per flush. They also offer a service to make your property as water efficient as possible, and promise your investment will have paid for itself within 9 to 12 months. The website does not contain any price

Low energy light bulbs and grants for insulation are available to pensioners and those on low incomes.

© Green Building Press

information, so ring 0113 2820 820 for details.

Thames Water offer a free water usage online calculator, as well as advice and information about water saving devices for people in the Thames area. See **www.waterwise. fortune-cookie.com/home**

Eco balls for clothes washing

If you're worried about the environmental impact of detergents and cannot afford the higher priced eco alternatives, you might want to try an eco ball. They use the oxygen in the water to lift dirt and clear away bacteria. They also have hypoallergenic properties. One ball will do 1000 washes, which works out at 3p per wash. They soften clothes and the rinse cycle can be shortened, saving on water use as well. They cost £34.99, and come in a set of three. You use all three in your wash and they are available from a range of eco-specialists, includ-

ing ProEco, and **www.ecoballsdirect.co.uk**. Both companies charge the same price.

Logmakers

Another great toy is the logmaker. You take your waste paper, stuff it into the logmaker and it produces burnable fuel for a fire or stove. It costs £19.95 and is available online at **www.proeco.co.uk** 🐾

Subscribe to the UK's leading sustainability magazine

resource
A NEW PERSPECTIVE ON WASTE · SEP-OCT 2006 · NUMBER 31

Watching the detectives
The MET's arresting strategy

Island recycling

Toxic-free fashion

Taking stock
Building for the future

PLUS: Indian summer · Weapons of Sound · Electrical processes ·

Call us now on
0117 9077245
to receive a free sample copy
or email marketing@resource.uk.com

Greening the kitchen

What should we consider when we are designing a kitchen refit? Choices about appliances, lighting, materials for the cupboards and worktops, and even the colour can have a bearing on the environmental impact of the finished design. **Jerry Clark** takes us through the process, using his own kitchen as an example...

To illustrate the type of considerations you might be faced with, I will begin with a description of the kitchen we inherited when we bought our current house in 2004. The units were a dark mahogany colour, and the walls were tiled in bottle green - the room is north facing, and even with two windows it was dark.

The kitchen is 5.5 x 4.4m, not small by any means, but the layout was so poor that the room seemed cluttered. A tall oven unit dominated one wall, there was a peninsular unit with a large built in table attached to the back, and there was a free standing island unit

in the middle of the floor - in all far too many units for the size of the room. There was not even enough free space to fit in our fridge and freezer. Also, the hot water took a long time to get to the tap for reasons which became apparent later.

Change the kitchen or adapt it?

Our first thoughts were whether we could use the existing units and rearrange the kitchen to suit our requirements. We ruled this out for several reasons - we would have needed one or two more base units, and although the kitchen was only installed six years before, it was no longer available. Also, this would not have addressed the darkness problem (although this could have been resolved by painting the units a pale colour). However, we had to remove the built in table immediately in order to install our fridge and freezer – this left an unsightly mess on the back of the peninsular unit.

Before

© Green Building Press

Another important consideration was our decision about heating the house. Although only built in 1999, and a fairly large house, it was heated entirely by electric night storage heaters. We wanted to find a way of heating with renewables - in this case wood. The solution we preferred was a wood burning Rayburn in the kitchen, plumbed to heat radiators in the other rooms, and doubling up as a cooker in winter. This entailed removal/rearrangement of a considerable number of kitchen units. In the end we decided to replace the entire kitchen with something more robust and to our taste.

Light and bright

Having decided on a suitable layout, the next consideration was how to make it a brighter place to work in - with the mahogany kitchen cupboards we were having to use electric lighting even on fairly bright days. We decided to go for an off white silk eco-paint on the cupboard doors, and a matt version of the same colour on the walls. We changed the splashbacks to light cream tiles. We wanted something reflective for the worktops to

After

bounce light back up into the room. Another consideration was a very high Cyprus hedge about 8m from the windows. After cutting over a metre off the height (it is still 2.5m high), we found that light was bounced back to us from the pale south wall of the neighbours house about 15m away. We retained the existing electric lighting configuration, but we changed all the bulbs to low energy, reducing the power consumption to 88W from the original 700W.

Materials

We wanted to avoid the usual laminated chipboard carcasses, as, particularly when new, these off-gas copious quantities of formaldehyde, which is not good for the environment or your health. We decided to make a strong (50mm x 75mm section) FSC softwood frame with zero formaldehyde MDF for the panels. All joinery was morticed and tennoned and drawers were dovetailed for extra strength and long life. Bespoke joinery from kitchen specialists can be expensive, but I used to do this sort of thing for a living. However, it is possible to save a considerable amount of money by having the basic units made up by a joiner to your design, rather than using a kitchen company with all their overheads and profits to maintain. We deliberately placed the oven below the worktop, and kept wall units to a minimum to open out the space.

The old chipboard and laminate worktops were already beginning to peel, so we decided to fit something that will last forever, solid 40mm thick granite, cut and polished at a local quarry. Again, though expensive, a lot can be saved by going direct to the quarry and using whatever material they have to offer - slate is another possibility. Worktops away from hot and/or wet areas were made of solid beech and oiled.

The sink

The existing sink was reused, it was good quality and in good condition, but we replaced the broken mixer tap. The new one has a second spout connected to a filter for drinking water, which has saved a lot of arguments about who last used the filter jug and didn't refill it!

Rearranging the kitchen gave us the opportunity to re-route the plumbing for the hot and cold water. To hide the pipes, the previous owner had routed them behind a tall oven unit, adding at least 8 feet to each pipe run.

Appliances

Our existing fridge and freezer were very efficient 'A' rated appliances. When looking at these goods, don't just look for 'A' rating – there is a second figure which tells you which 'A' rated appliances use the least electricity – that is the kWh/year figure. Our fridge was rated at 120kWh/year, but other similar sized fridges had much higher figures and were still 'A' rated. We also obtained an 'A' rated oven, and the most efficient electric hob we could afford (quick reacting halogen). Apparently an induction hob would have been more efficient, but you need special pans, and there may be issues with electromagnetic fields - the fact you can't use one if you have a pace-maker gives a hint!

Floors

If you can live with your existing floor, especially if it is cemented in place as ours is, then it would save a lot of work. If you have vinyl cushion floor or similar, then changing to something like ceramic tiles or wood could be an option. Our floor is of mid to dark slate patterned ceramic tiles, darker than we would like, but we decided to live with it to save the work and upheaval. It would be worth changing if it was in poor condition, or if underfloor heating was to be installed.

Alternatives

If cost is a major consideration, you can do quite well buying second hand units, and these will have off-gassed most of their original formaldehyde. We took out our old units as carefully as we could, and sold them quite easily through the local papers. In fact, our units found a home in two smaller kitchens, and we have heard that the new owners are delighted with them – they did have better natural light than we did!

The finished kitchen feels spacious, light and airy - a far cry from what we started with. ☯

© Green Building Press

"Only magazine I've read from cover to cover in years"

WIN A LUXURIOUS FAMILY HOLIDAY

The **Green Parent**

JUNE/JULY 2006 £2.95

RAISING KIDS WITH CONSCIENCE

Summer Fun for Kids
Fab free ideas for families
Guide to green London

TIE THE KNOT
Guide to green weddings
Organic dresses
to fair trade diamonds

Go green
15 pages of
ORGANIC & ETHICAL SHOPPING
from baby food to wine and more

HOW TO:
Achieve good
work/life balance
Give birth naturally
Find the perfect jeans

CASTLES & HARRY POTTER
Family holidays in
Northumbria

THE UK'S LEADING GREEN LIFESTYLE MAGAZINE

FREE INSIDE EVERY ISSUE: Magazine for children with nature activities

Find out what everyone is talking about,
www.thegreenparent.co.uk

LEEDS COLLEGE OF BUILDING
LIBRARY

See also: heating and solar discussions in Chapter 7

Keeping warm without fossil fuels

The choice of alternative ways to heat your building using non-fossil fuels has never been greater. With conventional grid-supplied electricity and natural gas prices currently on the rise, maybe the time has now arrived for serious consideration of the alternatives. But just how easy is it to adopt non-fossil fuelled heating within our building projects? **Stephen Lowndes** looks at the options available.

Whether you are considering a cosy log burner in your renovated country retreat or a wood pellet boiler to run your office heating system, the first line of enquiry will usually start with an understanding of the required performance from your heating system. This will usually entail an assessment of your heating load – the amount of heat you need to maintain your building at a comfortable temperature, during the coldest period of the year. The overall heat demand may very well encompass the load associated with heating your hot water for washing and cooking and your space heating demand. Whether or not you choose a non-fossil fuel heating system the priority should be to minimise the heating load as far as possible, in order to conserve fuel and optimise financial payback. Good standards of thermal insulation, glazing specification, air-tightness and ventilation should be adopted. Whilst this may be easier to implement for new build projects the importance of upgrading existing buildings should be integral to any change or upgrade of a space heating system. Other issues relating to heating controls are also important and will depend very much on the actual system used to heat the building.

Fuel choice

The choice of fuel will be influenced by a number of considerations. All fuels need to be able to satisfy an end-user's requirement in terms of environmental impact, affordable cost, availability, whether specialised equipment or facilities are needed, whether it is 'user friendly' and whether it needs to meet both heating and cooking needs.

Solid fuel

Non-fossil solid fuels include hard and soft wood and timber derivatives, such as processed timber bricks. Pellets and chips may also be classed as a solid fuel, although due to their own specialist development over recent years these fuels are considered separately. Basic non-fossil solid fuel is predominately derived from logs, timber processing and forestry thinnings, commonly used for small scale applications, such as firewood in individual homes. The ability to burn a solid fuel like wood may be very limited if you live in an area classed as a smoke free zone. Under the Clean Air Act, you may have to apply to your local authority for an 'exemption licence', to burn any type of wood fuel. However, there are now many wood burners that burn efficiently enough to be used in a smokeless zone. Ensure you check with the supplier.

Logs

If you are lucky enough to live near to forest or woodland you may find you are close to a conveniently sourced supply of timber. Of course permission to cut trees, unless they are on your own land, cannot be assumed and even when trees are on your own property, there may be local covenants and restrictions in place preventing you from doing so. To put this into perspective, the amount of timber a typical home, operating entirely on solid fuel timber for all space heating, hot water and cooking needs is likely to be in excess of five tonnes a year. If you have plenty of land, the option to grow and harvest timber on a coppicing basis might be an alternative. This sort of enterprise, even on a small scale, planting densely, high-yielding varieties such as willow or poplar, is likely to require at least 1 hectare for self-sufficiency[1].

Timber fuel must be available to burn in as dry a state as possible. You should avoid

burning green, damp and unseasoned wood on the grounds, not only of reduced combustion efficiency, but because it can also cause a harmful build up of resinous deposits in the chimney, preventing it from functioning safely. Any building that incorporates solid fuel heating using timber will therefore require spatial allocation to ensure dry storage of the fuel.

Small-scale domestic solid fuel is usually burnt within wood-burners, which heat the space they are in directly. Their primary means of control, is governed by manual adjustment of combustion air intake by the user. The wood burner, which could be a cooking range located in the kitchen, or a box stove in the living room, may be connected to a hot water storage vessel for domestic hot water use and can also incorporate a pumped hot water circuit to remote radiators to heat the rest of the house. Prices range from around £350 for a 3kW box stove to well over £1000 for a solid fuel boiler. Flues may utilise existing chimneys, although, depending upon their condition, internal liners may be required. New flues are usually stainless steel and are required to comply with UK Building Regulations Part J (Part F in Scotland).

Logs and all wood fuels need to be as dry as possible. Wet wood releases tars and pollutants to the atmosphere, creates greater risk of chimney fires and reduces efficiency drastically. Dry wood from sustainable sources (reforested or coppiced) is hard to beat ecologically and can help create local employment too.

Wood chip

Chipped wood is commonly available from timber processing and tree surgery waste. Timber can be chipped on site using machines, where it should also be possible to dry the chippings. Until quite recently wood chip heating was predominantly restricted to large-scale non-domestic applications. In recent years smaller wood chip boilers have become commercially available down to about 25kW output, making them suitable for large domestic or small-scale commercial use. A wood chip boiler can connect to conventional pumped hot water heating circuits and hot water storage cylinders.

Modern woodchip boilers keep a small core of the fire-bed continuously alight, allowing the boiler to respond to periodic drops in heating load. Unlike conventional gas fired boilers, they cannot respond instantaneously to changes in heating demand. To accommodate periods

when there is no heat demand, a heat accumulator is recommended, to store the heat produced during peak burn for use later, either for space heating or domestic hot water.

A dry storage facility for the wood chip fuel is necessary and this needs to be adjacent to the boiler location so that the chips can be fed automatically to the boiler. Combustion efficiency will be dependant upon moisture content. Wood chips are typically supplied pre-dried at 20-25% moisture content. It may be possible to obtain chips with higher moisture content at a lower price than dryer fuel, but it is difficult to dry-out in bulk before use on a small-scale and the lower calorific value could make what seemed like a bargain at the time a false economy.

Wood pellets

Wood pellets are a type of reconstituted wood-fuel and originate from the by-products of the timber processing industry, utilising sawdust and shavings extruded into small cylindrical pellets. They are of consistent quality and size, have low moisture content (5 to 10%), are relatively clean to use and produce less smoke and ash, compared with unrefined forms of wood fuel.

Pellets can be used in a wide range of stove and boiler equipment, making it a convenient choice for heating domestic properties and small buildings. Wood pellets are usually gravity or screw fed into the appliance automatically, at a rate that is varied, depending upon the desired heat output from the appliance. Larger wood pellet boiler models are usually installed within designated boiler rooms or utility spaces and are screw fed from covered fuel stores located outside of the building. As with all solid wood fuel the pellets must be kept dry.

Prices start at around £1000 for an 8kW (max) pellet burner that has a combined hopper feed. Grant funding is available under the UK Low Carbon Buildings' programme. As a private householder you may be eligible for a grant to cover a good proportion of an installation and if you are undertaking a community project up to 50% of capital and installation costs (up to a maximum limit) may be available. These grants are unlikely to be awarded to DIY installations, as the funding is meant to encourage development of an accredited installer network.

Although supply sources are improving, wood pellet fuel can be difficult to source and is one of the reasons why pellets can be a more expensive fuel when compared with wood chip or seasoned logs. Price will also be dependant upon whether you buy in bulk or in bags. Recent comparisons published by British Biogen place bulk purchased wood pellets as being slightly more expensive than natural gas in terms of pence per kilowatt hour, with bagged pellets about 60% more expensive and seasoned logs being slightly less than natural gas[2]. Of course natural gas prices are currently on the rise, so the comparison is heading more in favour of wood fuels.

Bio gas

Bio gas is produced primarily from anaerobic digestion, a process involving the digestion of organic wastes by bacteria in the absence of air. The process occurs in an anaerobic digester enabling the conversion of organic waste from livestock farming and food processing into methane. The waste from the digestion process is reduced to slurry and is suitable as a fertiliser. Bio gas requires cleaning before being used in conventional gas boilers. Although it is possible to operate a conventional heating boiler from bio gas it is unlikely that you will have easy access to a bio gas source due to the limited avenues currently available.

Bio gas cannot be liquefied like LPG, which means that it requires large volume storage even when pressurised and has attendant safety issues, due to its high combustibility. This coupled with the ability to produce enough fuel for self sufficiency on an individual cost effective domestic scale has limited development in the UK. Nevertheless as the technology becomes more cost effective, there is an increasing potential for small scale bio gas operations run by farmers using their own animal waste feedstock, recycling the residue as fertiliser and using the bio gas for heating farm buildings. Larger scale centralised operations have also been established that involve feedstock from multiple sources including both livestock farming and commercial food processing waste.

Bio-gas can also be produced from both gasification and pyrolysis of wood and organic matter. Although possible at small scale, gasification and pyrolysis development has tended to focus on larger scale operations that enable the use of solid bio fuel to run engines to generate electricity and heat (combined heat and power).

Solar heating

Up until now we have concentrated upon heating that involves the direct or indirect combustion of bio fuels. Using the sun's energy directly in the form of solar heat to heat buildings and hot water is a way of offsetting the fossil fuel that would have otherwise been used by conventional heating plant. Even with our UK climate, the application of passive solar design within our buildings can be worthwhile, helping to minimise space heating load and the installation of solar panels effective at contributing to reduced operation of boilers to service hot water demand. Passive solar design is discussed in detail elsewhere in this publication, so a brief look at solar hot water heating is covered here.

Solar hot water heating is an established technology and whilst ideally optimised when drawing up plans for a new build project, systems can also be incorporated fairly easily into existing buildings and often without the need to throw away your existing hot water installation. Solar panels are able to utilise the sun's heat even on cloudy days, with a typical system capable of providing enough heat to satisfy up to 50% of the average annual household hot water demand.

There are various types of solar panel, ranging in efficiency from fairly basic flat plate designs that are often available as DIY kits and comprise black aluminium fins fixed to a copper piping grid, enclosed in a thermally insulated box with a glazed top facing the sky. More efficient and more expensive designs consist of factory made arrays of evacuated tubes each enclosing a heat pipe, connected to a water manifold. Hot water is either circulated via thermosyphon effect or pumped through a solar panel and used to indirectly heat water in a hot water storage cylinder. Usually the solar heated water is stored separately from the hot water generated by a conventional boiler and connected so that the solar hot water preheats the conventional cylinder, reducing the need for the boiler to operate. Solar panels are usually roof mounted, although they don't have to be and thermosyphon systems require the panel to be below the hot water storage cylinder, making roof mounting impossible on some buildings. For optimum effect panels should be located on an aspect within 45° of south. A typical solar hot water system employed on a house would require spatial allocation of about 4m² for the panel.

Domestic scale solar hot water systems currently cost in the range of £1500 to £3000 to supply and install, and with typical annual savings on conventional hot water heating bills between £50 and £100, financial paybacks are long[3]. As mentioned earlier, it maybe that your project is eligible for funding under the Low Carbon Buildings' programme.

Electric heating from renewables

You may be considering the use of electricity, generated from a renewable non fossil fuel source. The ability to plug in electric heaters anywhere within your building might appear an attractive and convenient form of heating, but how can you ensure the electricity used is fossil fuel free? Well, the only sure way is to ensure you generate enough electrical power on site to service all your electrical consumption for space heating and hot water. In most cases it is unlikely that you would achieve 100% self sufficiency in electricity, even when incorporating a mixed bag of renewable generation including photovoltaic and wind power, so most of us will need to consider import of additional electrical power from the national grid. If you have no intention of generating any of your own power at all you will of course be totally reliant on the national grid to power your heating.

The use of grid supplied electricity that is sourced solely and directly from a renewable basis is not feasible at the present time (see story on page 312). This is because the National Grid is a UK wide network of power distribution taken from a number of different generation sources, of which renewables account for only a tiny proportion in comparison to contributions from gas and coal fired power generation. Your commitment to purchase electricity using a green tariff scheme may on the face of it be a way of ensuring you contribute to investment in renewable power on the basis of the amount of electrical power that you use. But not all is at it seems on the face of it. There is only one power company in the UK that guarantees 100% investment in new renewables generation - most others are just trading in existing output. However, a green tariff does make a positive contribution to increasing the use of

© Green Building Press

renewable generation only if it increases the amount of renewable sourced power that a supply company has to buy over and above their minimum statutory obligation. There are only a limited number of green tariffs currently available that do this and these are based upon ensuring the supply company surrenders their surplus Renewable Obligation Certificates (ROC), rather than selling them on to supply companies that have not met their renewable supply. This creates a higher demand for renewable generated power than is already created by the government's legal obligation on suppliers to source a percentage of their total supply from renewables.

Conclusion

The reality is that for most domestic and small scale building projects aiming to totally avoid the use of fossil fuels for heating, a number of different solutions will need to be encompassed. Any non fossil fuel scheme should have at its foundation a thermally efficient building envelope and encompass the principles of passive solar design in order to minimise the heating requirement in the first place. Wood based fuels such as log or pellet are likely to be the most appropriate choice for many domestic scale projects, backed up with solar hot water generation and utilisation of woodchip fuelled boilers on larger projects. Other projects may rely more on a mixture of building integrated renewable power generation and purchase of green tariff electricity to achieve the fossil fuel free goal. ☙

Other heating systems such as CHP GSHP etc are covered in the chapter on heating later in this book and in Volume 2 of the Green Building Bible.

References

1. 'The Whole House Book' by P Borer, C Harris (1998) (new edition available from www.newbuilder.co.uk

2. 'Wood as a fuel': www.r-p-a.org.uk

3. Energy Saving Trust web site: www.est.org.uk

Sources of further information

Information on all aspects of wood heating (British Biogen has recently merged with the Renewable Energy Association); www.r-p-a.org.uk

The government website for grant funding information for biofuel heating and building integrated renewable

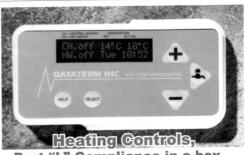

Heating Controls,
Part "L" Compliance in a box...

Dataterm IHC is a fully programable Energy Management System disguised as a normal day to day programable room thermostat. It complies with Part "L" of the building regulations, Saves Fuel, is Energy Conscious and it is kind to the planet by reducing CO_2 emissions. It is simple to use and very cost effective. **Dataterm will reduce the emissions of an average family by 1 Ton per year without any loss of comfort or control.** Programming Dataterm is flexible & easy with 8 time and temperature set-points per day with room for 3 personal and 30 built in plans to choose from. So if comfort and control with no fuss sounds good to you fit Dataterm Today! Features include illuminated display, optimum start / stop, close temperature control and an **average 25% savings in fuel spend per annum...Dataterm is recognised by the Energy Saving Trust in recognition of its ability to save fuel and help the planet.**

WARM WORLD
THE INTELLIGENT HEATING DECISION

Tel: 0117 949 8800
www.warmworld.co.uk

energy saving recommended

The Ceramic Stove Company

continues to offer a diverse selection of woodfired, retained heat stoves, many containing a high percentage of recycled material, from suppliers who care about style and the environment in equal measure.

The Ceramic Stove Company, 4 Earl Street, Oxford, OX2 0JA
Tel/fax: +44(0)1865 245077   email: info@ceramicstove.com
web: www.ceramicstove.com

5 Greening commercial

Does green building pay?

Green buildings can be frugal in their consumption of resources, with fantastic payback, but, if incorrectly managed by occupants, they can easily turn into small scale energy disasters. **Gavin Harper** looks at the options ...

When assessing whether a green building pays, you first need to truly know what you value - is payback purely financial?

There are a number of ways of attacking this question. In terms of satisfaction - most definitely! You have constructed your building in the knowledge that you have done everything possible to minimise its impact on the environment, and where environmental impact is unavoidable, you have done everything that you can to mitigate that impact – what could be more satisfying. But satisfaction doesn't pay the bills.

It is not inevitable that building green will cost more; sometimes building green is simply about being an informed consumer – two products with a similar price tag but differing environmental credentials.

Whilst it would be easy to be optimistic and say, 'Yes, green building always pays', looking at conventional economics, it can sometimes be hard to justify the cost of a green building. Payback periods can be long on some renewable energy sources, and investment in energy saving measures does not always present an instant return.

In the defence of economical green building, the US Green Building Council asserts that a silver rated LEED building does not have to cost more than a conventional construction.

Equally, it is an urban myth that building green is like throwing money into a bottomless pit - living in a society that is increasingly aware of environmental issues, you can consider adding green measures as adding asset value to your building. Green doesn't have to mean expensive – this is a common misconception, green can also mean 'resource efficient', efficient in construction, efficient in use.

It is important when designing a green building for cost, that the design is considered holistically. With green building, it makes no sense to 'value engineer' every item for cost, as a little investment in, say, better insulating windows, can mean a saving elsewhere, for example, reduced demand for heating plant in the winter.

But to keep costs down, it is important that all members of the design team are aware of the desire to build green, from the earliest possible opportunity in the project. That way, it becomes easier to work together as a team; efficiency increases and costs stay low.

By considering the whole building as a system and by facilitating teamwork between members of the design and build team early in the project, value can be engineered into the project as a result of the synergies that arise when all members of the team work to a common goal.

Cost savings
When looking at cost savings there are a number of tangibles which become immediately apparent, a green building can save in:
- energy costs
- plant costs
- maintenance costs

© Green Building Press

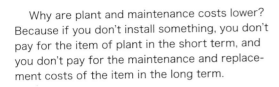

Why are plant and maintenance costs lower? Because if you don't install something, you don't pay for the item of plant in the short term, and you don't pay for the maintenance and replacement costs of the item in the long term.

Air conditioning has become a mainstay of the commercial world. Though completely unnecessary to keep your employees cocooned in a tundra-like atmosphere, in many instances, it has become accepted as a norm.

> Remember – a business does not always have to absorb the full cost of green measures added to a building – if it is your own building then investment in energy efficiency and green technologies can be considered as an 'added asset value' on the property – it could allow you to charge a premium if you sell the property or lease it in the future.

There are a number of benefits that are not immediately tangible on the balance sheet, but which can be justifying factors for green building. Employees feel more comfortable in the working environments and hence are more productive. Discerning consumers will be influenced by a company with eco-credentials.

Companies are fast realising that energy is not in endless supply, and in the years to come, it is wholly likely that we will be paying more for our energy than ever before.

A further incentive to build green, is that if any of the schemes mooted for 'carbon credits' or 'carbon rationing' were ever introduced, the companies in the strongest economic position would be those with the smallest carbon footprint.

> It is important to set the question 'does green building pay' against a rapidly changing economic landscape, where energy futures are uncertain to say the least. What seems uneconomical today, could well prove an attractive investment for tomorrow.

'Business continuity planning' is a tool widely used to ensure a businesses longevity and continued operation in onerous circumstances.

If energy prices rise significantly in the future, the businesses that will struggle the least are those that have invested in energy saving measures.

However, there is a case in point that a green building for your company should be as part of a concerted effort to make your company's activities as sustainable as possible rather than a shallow 'green washing' exercise, as this is quickly seen through.

Consumers vote with their wallets

It is not simply enough to 'build green'. The building is not green by design, it is green by use. The energy consumption, and hence ongoing costs of your building, is influenced by the way that your occupants use the building – the building will only be a green building if the ethos implemented in design and construction is carried forward by the users.

There are many spectacular examples of buildings in the public and private sector that have been 'built green', but whether through ignorance or inappropriate, use are not green in action.

> It is no good building 'green' passive architecture if your users dont know how to operate the building correctly. A building with good energy payback could quickly turn into a disaster if your occupants bring in portable electric heaters, for example, to keep them warm in the winter

Historically, it has always been much easier for owner occupiers of buildings to justify any additional costs than for developers. However, with environmental assessment methods, such as BREEAM in the UK and LEED (see page 51) in the US, coming to the fore for energy rating buildings, it has become easier than ever for developers or landlords to sell or let a building.

A developer in the marketplace who delivers commercial buildings with green credentials, and all of the benefits these entail, gives themselves a unique selling point which sets them above the others vying for their business. As an aside for developers looking at buildings as a commercial investment – the saying 'the more you do it, the easier (cheaper) it gets', is true for green buildings.

There is an initial cost involved with getting the expertise and resources required to build green, but as you become more familiar with the process, the easier and cheaper it gets. As with anything, there are economies of scale as you increase levels of production.

When assessing 'does green building pay?', it is essential to keep in mind that conventional economics does not keep in perspective the real costs of product, in terms of the impact it has on our environment. To summarise the above in a sentence – green building can cost more, but it doesn't have to. ☯

Further reading

'Green Building: Does it Pay?' Plumbing Systems and Design 2006; Vol. 5: No. 2 by Ham, Paul L. The American Society of Plumbing Engineers

'Does Green Building Have Better Market Value?': *www.abetterearth.org/subcategory.php/221.html*

'Why Build Green?' - Rocky Mountain Institute / ENSAR built environment team.

'Green Building: Project Planning & Cost Estimating', edited By: R.S. Means

'Green Buildings Pay' by E Edwards, can be ordered from the Green Shop: 01452 770629 *www.greenshop.co.uk*

Case study
The NMB Bank

© Green Building Press

The NMB Bank building on the outskirts of Amsterdam was one of the first major green building projects in Europe, and was completed in 1987.

The architect was Anton Alberts – his vision was a series of 7 towers linked by walkways, each seven to eight stories high. With daylight flooding in from an atrium above, and natural ventilation accomplished with large amounts of opening windows, the building did away with energy sapping air-conditioning by using thermally massive, internal eighteen inch walls to provide night cooling of the space.

The green building theme was continued in the landscaping of the buildings – outside Alberts created a beautiful park space with formal and informal gardens, waterfalls and all manner of curiosities to delight the buildings inhabitants. Wetlands and ponds created nice spaces for employees and users of the building to seek inner calm, whilst also providing a habitat for fauna.

The NMB bank building in Amsterdam is widely praised for its natural aesthetic and green building credentials. When commissioning the building, the bank set down two objectives to be met. The first was that the design would be organic, natural and epitomise green architecture. The second mandate was that the building should cost not even a single guilder more than a similar function building built using traditional methods. Both objectives were met and the building exceeded first expectations.

Why in this instance did green building pay?

The project was the product of a design team that were heavily integrated from the start, it resulted in a construction that utilised daylighting to good effect, passive solar architecture and rainwater harvesting.

Was the investment justified?

Yes, the building was a resounding success. The energy saving features in the building paid back within the first three months of use. The bank saw 92% energy savings, compared with a similar sized facility, furthermore the bank made

an estimated $2.9 million savings, per annum, compared with a building of conventional construction.

Back to the 'intangibles' mentioned earlier – absenteeism dropped by 15%, with workers reporting an increase in productivity and an increased enjoyment of their internal and external office environment. However, there is a twist in the tale – with the takeover of NMB by ING, along came a new corporate ethic. According to Coldham Architects. The new ethic meant that spending time relaxing in the grounds was an indication of a *'lack of ambition'* and was discouraged. The new politics of the new organisation meant that there was then a change in the way that the occupants interacted with their building. Coldham go on to say "*the significant accumulation of slime on the walkways, stepping stones, pathways, etc, to the point that some are now dangerous to walk along, is evidence of their almost complete lack of use.*"

This is an interesting case in point as this celebrated building demonstrates how it is not simply enough to 'design a green building', but in order to reap the rewards of good building design, you must also design a 'green ethic' for your business, that embraces the concepts embodied within the architecture and extends it to company policy and the way in which employees interact with each other and their environment. ◑

References

www.coldhamarchitects.com/greenbuilding/ greengrandtour/SW_NMB/nmb_ing_desc.htm

www.rmi.org/sitepages/pid208.php

www.architectureweek.com/2002/1023/ environment_2-2.html

www.facilitiesnet.com/bom/Nov02/ Nov02environment.shtml

www.epa.gov/ne/greenbuildings/pdfs/ gb_casestudies.pdf

www.rmi.org/images/other/GDS/ D92-21_NMBBankHQ.pdf

Is there a market for green offices?

Due to difficulties of oversupply in the early 1990s and the bankruptcies and redundancies that followed, developers, fund managers and commercial agents in the UK are risk-averse. Whilst many will appear to be supportive of energy efficiency measures, they tend to only include green measures if it has no effect on the initial costs and can be seen to be simple to install and easy to operate.

There have been a number of post occupancy evaluations of 'green' office buildings constructed within the last 5 years (See the PROBE reports at www.usablebuildings.co.uk and in following stories in this section). These have identified a number of successful buildings as well as a few problem areas. Most of the buildings assessed were owner-occupied, where the client was supportive of energy efficiency measures, as they had control over both initial and operating costs. Nevertheless, it was apparent that even in these buildings, unless the designers' intentions had been properly conveyed to the occupiers, there was a risk of the buildings underperforming. This was mainly due to lack of awareness by facility managers and others, complex building management systems and inadequate commissioning.

There have been very few speculative 'green' office developments, as developers are worried about lettability, and the perceived lack of commitment by an unknown tenant to engage with the building and share the objectives of the original design team.

The Sherwood Energy Village is an example of one of the few speculative 'green' office developments in the UK. 38 of its 91 acres are allocated for industry and include offices. The hub of the project is the E-Centre, shown right. More information about this building is given in the next section. ❧

© Green Building Press

Image courtesy of Sherwood Energy Village (see next page for story)

Case study Sherwood Energy Village

Sherwood Energy Village (SEV) is a unique development in the heart of Robin Hood country. SEV is the trading name of Sherwood Environmental Village Ltd, an organisation founded in 1996 when it purchased a former colliery site from British Coal. **Sally Hall** tells us how the project came about ...

The organisation is an Industrial and Provident Society; a full trading company, with its profits ploughed back into the project. It now has a subsidiary consultancy company, SEV Solutions, which offers advice on setting up similar projects across the UK and abroad. The profits from this company go to SEV.

The SEV project is unique as it evolved from direct action by the local community who, back in the '90s, were concerned about the future of the two main industries (mining and hosiery) that provided the bulk of employment in the small village. A group of determined members of the community took the SEV project forward when the decision to close the colliery was made, and the group managed to do this with no direct involvement from any local authority or government agencies. The colliery site was purchased; 36 hectares (91 acres). The local

people wanted jobs with good housing and leisure facilities.

From the outset the main aim was to create a mix of industry (38 acres), housing (11 acreas) and leisure/amenity space (42 acres). Strong eco-credentials, including energy efficiency, renewables and biodiversity were introduced into the proposals early on. SEV is now in year twelve of the regeneration of this former mining community, with the wider surrounding area also benefiting from the project. Unlike other similar regeneration projects that have failed, SEV's voluntary directors have worked hard to ensure the project has stayed true to its original aims and objectives and not merely been used by short term profiteers.

All buildings are being constructed to a high environmental standard. The E-Centre, completed in 2006, is also the new HQs of the SEV, which occupies the top floor. It is an unusual crescent-shaped building with green roofs, rainwater harvesting and renewables. Ground source heat pumps provide heating in the winter and cooling in the summer. There is also a full height winter garden acting as the 'lungs' of the building, capturing light,

heat and passive ventilation. It includes 'transitional work points' for small businesses / self employed that need minimal office space and can benefit from the shared office facilities (photocopying, telephone services etc). Other industrial units and offices completed to date have been rented out to different businesses, which benefit greatly from the low energy builds.

Images courtesy of Sherwood Energy Village Ltd.

© Green Building Press

In addition to the commercial area, the 11 acres allocated to housing are being developed by the SEV. The building work commenced August 2006. A total of 196 dwellings are planned, ranging from single dwelling bungalows and apartments through to terraced, semi detached and detached houses. There are even 4 earth-sheltered houses proposed. All will be sold freehold and designed to achieve a minimum EcoHomes 'excellent' rating. SEV believes the challenge for Britain is to provide housing types that people want, and which perform well in environmental terms, including:

- reduced energy costs
- water efficiency
- well-built, architect-designed dwellings
- sense of space, community spirit
- safe, secure environment
- walking distance from shops and services
- a nice place to live, work and play and which people can buy to occupy.

Much of the external works are now complete. Off-grid renewable powered lamp-posts illuminate the landscaped grounds. Water conservation and management is an important integral part of the village and it has the UK's largest application of engineered SUDs (sustainable urban drainage), with all surface water being managed on site. To help alleviate flooding, swales have been installed. The successful scheme adds to the biodiversity of the site, mitigates flooding and looks attractive. SUDs deals with surface water run off from the roads and other hard paved areas. The water gently permeates or evaporates creating green corridors through the site and stopping any risk of flash flooding. The colliery tips are now restored and provide local amenity space with community woodlands, golf courses, heathland habitats, lakes and nature trails. There is an arena of 6.46 hectares (16 acres) forming a natural amphitheatre, with mature trees bounding the area. The clay-lined swales have formed a wetlands area with the arena designated for the development of sporting and recreational pursuits. ☾

Post occupancy evaluation

If we claim that our buildings are green, ecological, sustainable, carbon neutral, or energy efficient, we need to ensure (more than ever!) that we know how well they perform once they are in use, and how closely this relates to our design intentions. Here, **Isabel Carmona, Bill Bordass and Adrian Leaman** outline a few techniques available for different types of buildings and suggest what post occupancy evaluation (POE) should cover ...

There continues to be a discrepancy between design input and outcome in the construction industry as whole. Examples of buildings that have been monitored, green or not, show that, normally, the results are not as good as the design expectations (Ni Riain et al, 2000; PROBE team, 1995-2002). But knowing what caused the problems and why can be a positive thing, if you learn and share your findings with others. The aim is to create virtuous circles of continuous improvement (Bordass et al 2001).

Buildings are active systems, with users and owners in constant interaction. Occupants just use the building features to suit their needs – and their behaviour may not accord with your design intentions – which may not be clear to them intuitively, and about which they may never have been told.

We have to decide what we would like to know about our buildings in use and find out the best way of obtaining that information.

Collecting feedback

As part of a Partners in Innovation project, the Usable Buildings Trust (UBT) collected available feedback techniques into a multi-dimensional matrix (Figure 1). The matrix can be viewed by sector, the stage of development of the technique (e.g. is it new or well-established), and where to use in the life cycle of a building or a construction project[1]. The portfolio is currently being expanded from ten general-purpose techniques, to include a number which are specific to a particular sector (e.g. schools).

Figure 1. As part of a Partners in Innovation project, the Usable Buildings Trust (UBT) collected available feedback techniques into a multi-dimensional matrix.

Key:
H = high relevance
M = medium relevance
L = low relevance
Prepare = preparation stage

UBT Feedback Portfolio: Techniques

	Prepare		Design		Implement		Finish		Use	
	Verify need	Strategic brief	Option appraisal	Develop design	Prepare to implement	Implement	Complete	Initial operation	Routine operation	Change
AMA Workware Toolkit	H	H	M	H				H	M	H
ASTM Standards	H	H	H	M						
BCO POE Method										
BRE Design Quality Method										
BRE Toolkit										
BREEAM	H	H	H	H						M
BREEAM Schools	H	H	H	H						M
BUS Occupant Survey	M	M						H	H	H
CIBSE TM22 energy survey		M	M	M	M	M	M	H	H	
CIC DQIs	M	M	H	H				M	H	H
DEEP										
DQI for Schools										
Healthcare Design Quality	H	H	M							H

© Usable Building Trust

© Green Building Press

Feedback collection techniques

Techniques currently fall into six main groups, as outlined below:

Facilitated discussions: where team members discuss and share their experiences in a positive non confrontational manner.

Packages of techniques: where more than one technique is used as a set to provide an all around POE assessment. PROBE (Post-Occupancy Review of Buildings and their Engineering), for instance, includes a preliminary questionnaire, a Building Use Studies occupant survey, CIBSE TM22 Energy assessment and reporting methodology, and sometimes, a building envelope pressure test to CIBSE TM 23. This combination of soft and hard issues was used for the PROBE studies series, published in the Building Services Journal between 1995 and 2002[2].

Process improvement: where special arrangements improve the design and construction process, in particular to learn more from existing buildings and the experiences of the client, project and management teams, to facilitate a smooth transition between handover and occupation, and to improve performance in use.

Questionnaires and interviews: these include paper and web administered questionnaires, and one to one interviews. For example, the Building Use Studies (BUS) occupant survey and benchmarking method covers 44 variables, including a self-assessment of health and productivity. Design Quality Indicators (DQI) has 100 questions organised on three sections: Functionality, Build Quality and Impact.

Technical assessments: these methods help define how well design requirements match achieved outcomes with regards function and performance. For instance, Medical Architecture Research Unit (MARU) Evaluation Studies provides a range of techniques for health buildings.

Sustainability: these techniques look at the impact of the buildings in their surroundings.

Of these, BREEAM stands amongst the best known in the UK, but at present it is mostly design-focused and provides an overall rating with little information on specific achievements. CIBSE TM22 focuses on energy use; it can be used to report design expectations, actual energy use and predicted savings from changes (Figure 2).

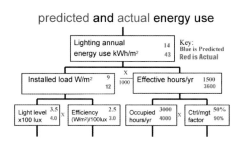

Figure 2. Comparisons of elements of predicted and actual energy use.

Type of buildings: The portfolio includes techniques suitable for defence, education, health, office, leisure, housing and other buildings (Figure 3). Some techniques such as BREEAM, BUS Occupant Survey, CIBSE TM22 and 'learning from experience' are suitable for most building types. Others, like AMA Toolkit (offices and similar workspaces), NEAT (health), MARU (health), DEEP (defence), are suitable for specific building types.

A user group of designers and clients tested some of these techniques on case studies of their choice, in the course of a UK research project that ran between 2001 and 2004 (Bordass, Leaman, 2005).

What to test for?

We are getting used to claims that buildings (or whole developments) are green, energy efficient, or even carbon neutral. Those claims need to be substantiated by some independent assessment in order to prove their success. POE has shown that expectations tend to be more optimistic than the results. There are often valid reasons for some of the differences, but they need to be understood if we are to produce better designs in the future, which take

Figure 3. The POE portfolio includes techniques suitable for defence, education, health, office, leisure, housing and other buildings.

Note: Y & N (yes or no) indicate whether the technique exists in a version that can be used for the building type.

UBT Feedback Portfolio: Techniques

	Defence	Education		Health	Offices		Leisure	Housing	Other
	Defence	Higher education	Schools	Health	Public sector	Private sector	Sports	Housing	Other
AMA Workware Toolkit					Y	Y			
ASTM Standards									Generic
BCO POE Method									
BRE Design Quality Method	To some extent	To some extent	Y	Y	Y			To some extent	
BRE Toolkit									
BREEAM	Possible	Y	Y	Partial	Y	Y	Y	Y	Y
BREEAM Schools			Y						
BUS Occupant Survey	Partial	Y	Y	Partial	Y	Y	N	Partial	Possible
CIBSE TM22 energy survey	N	Y	Y	Y	Y	Y			
CIC DQIs	Partial	Y	Y		Y	Y			
DEEP	Y								
DQI for Schools			Y						
Healthcare Design Quality				Y				Possibly ...	

© Usable Building Trust

proper account of what really happens. As a minimum we suggest that you aim to go back and check two things.

1. Natural resource use (energy and water)

Energy use, where it is not provided by renewable sources, is the main source of CO_2 emissions. We suggest you collect data on a monthly basis and analyse usage on a yearly basis, keeping electricity separate from other fuels. Translate energy use into CO_2 emissions.

Benchmark your emissions against similar buildings, if data exists, or collect your own to compare your year on year progress. If you use renewable sources of energy, measure their contribution and establish how much you are reducing emissions. You can analyse the data further to know which uses are the greatest (e.g. lighting, office equipment, catering...). More data on truly green buildings should encourage improvements beyond the current good practice standards, which sadly are often not reached. Useful techniques available include:
- National Energy Foundation CO_2 calculator[3]
- CIBSE TM22 Energy assessment and reporting methodology.

Water is, increasingly, a scarce resource. Meter and monitor your water use, analyse what it is used for, and communicate results. Benchmark your water use against similar buildings. Useful techniques available include the Envirowise water account tool[4.]

2. Occupant satisfaction

To be successful, "green" buildings must provide a comfortable environment for occupants. Sadly, this is not always so. Designers normally do not occupy the buildings they design, their clients or tenants do! The challenge is to make buildings easy to operate and live with, not over complicated, with effective controls (that give feedback of what they do!), and have sensible default conditions, which provide safe conditions with minimum energy use[5].

Occupant satisfaction is often considered a 'soft' issue, supposedly difficult to measure and quantify. However, there are well-established ways of recording and evaluating occupants' opinions and needs, such as questionnaire surveys, formal discussion groups and accompanied building visits and interviews.

As a minimum, return to the building once it has been occupied for a while, after all the initial tuning faults have been resolved, and have a frank discussion with the users. Match your methods to the building type – a bulky questionnaire might not be appropriate for a single dwelling. Record the responses to provide a reference if you decide to go back further down the line. Ideally, share your findings so that others may benefit from the lessons learnt.

Important questions are:
- are basic needs, like space and comfort requirements, being properly met?
- do people feel healthy?
- does the building affect productivity?
- what are the good features?
- what are the annoying features?
- what can be improved tomorrow?

Useful techniques available include the Building Use Studies (BUS) occupant survey (widely used in the UK and internationally, with benchmarks available).

Conclusion

POE studies provide lessons that we can learn from - some general, some specific[6]. For major effect, those lessons from case studies need to be communicated to a wide audience. Public exposure of green buildings will help promote their features, intelligent critiques will facilitate their acceptance and greater realism about their intended and achieved performance will improve future implementations.

References

1. You can access the UBT Feedback Portfolio at www.usablebuildings.co.uk/fp/index.html

2. The full list of the 23 Probe studies is available from UBT's website: www.usablebuildings.co.uk under PROBE

3. www.nef.org.uk/energyadvice/co2calculator.htm

4. You can find information on monitoring and submit your data for benchmarking on Envirowise's website: www.envirowise.gov.uk/page.aspx?o=wateraccount

5. Read more on usability in the Quick Intro section of UBT's website, see 1, above

6. Building Research and Information, Vol. 29, No2, March-April 2001 gives a strategic review of POE.

Further reading

'Assessing building performance in use 5: conclusions and implications' by W Bordass, A Leaman and P Ruyssevelt (2001), Building Research and Information, 2001, vol 29, no 2, 144-157

'Making feedback and post-occupancy evaluation routine 3: Case studies of the use of techniques in the feedback portfolio' by W Bordass, A Leaman, (2005), Building Research and Information, 2005, vol 33, no 4, 361-375

'BRE's Environmental Building: Energy Performance in Use' by C Ni Riain, J Fisher, F MacKenzie, J Littler, (2000), CIBSE Conference papers

'When Rivers Run Dry: Water: the defining crisis of the twenty-first century' (2006), Eden Project Books

PROBE team, 1995-2002, Post-Occupancy Review of Buildings and their Engineering, PROBE 1- 23, Building Services Journal, 1995-2002.

'Closing the Loop: Benchmark for sustainable buildings' by S Roaf (2004) RIBA

L cate architects

30/3 high street portobello
edinburgh eh15 1dd

tel: 0131 620 0530
fax: 0131 620 0697
e: mail@chrismorgan.fsnet.co.uk
w: www.locatearchitects.co.uk

Specialists in Contemporary Ecological Design and Sustainable Development

very low energy – renewable supply – passive design
healthy interiors – chemical free - natural materials
low impact construction - local sourcing – site specific solutions
commercial – domestic - community - £50k to £5m
top images: design: north woods construction & locate architects

Case study

Refurbished offices
West End House, Hills Place, London

Reid Architecture chose refurbishment over new development for their London headquarters in 2001. Despite their proximity to the buzz of Oxford Circus, they rejected the traditional approach of sealing the building, ducting in fresh air and air conditioning, and opted for a natural ventilation strategy, with external shading to prevent overheating and chilled beam cooling for extreme summer conditions. Since they moved to their new premises, they have monitored energy and water use and carried out an occupant survey to reveal how successful they have been and where they can make improvements.

The project

In 2001, Reid Architecture (RA) chose to refurbish a 1958 office building as their new headquarters, merging their workforce into a single office. The entrance space at ground floor was very limited, so they added a lift tower (that doubles as a ventilation stack) to take you to the reception/gallery on the 4th floor, see Figure 1.

Figure 1. West End House before and after.

© Green Building Press

There are three narrow floors of office accommodation, which made natural ventilation a viable option. Existing single glazed windows were replaced by double glazed opening windows, incorporating natural ventilation grilles underneath to allow air to enter the building as shown in Figure 2.

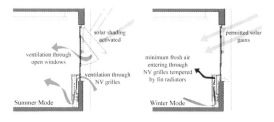

Figure 2. Window section.

The grilles are controlled through a building energy management system (BEMS) and open when free cooling is available. The air exits via two separate stacks, as the result of stack pressure differentials, see Figure 3. A night time ventilation strategy is also incorporated into the BEMS operation. Due to the fixed orientation of the building and likely internal gains (resulting from occupant density), a chilled beam cooling system was installed. This was the lowest energy in use option, as the installation of displacement ventilation was not possible and because its use is robust enough not to be unbalanced by occupants opening windows. External fabric awnings were installed to control solar gain. They come down automatically when it is sunny, operated by photocells linked to the BEMS. Manual overrides are also provided to allow occupants some adaptive control, as all floors are activated simultaneously and the lower floors might not need the shading, see Figure 4.

RA specified a number of healthier finishes such as natural paints and linoleum flooring for the washrooms, neither of which contained organic volatile compounds. Secure cycle storage within the building and staff showers was also provided to encourage staff to cycle into work. They also installed waterless urinals,

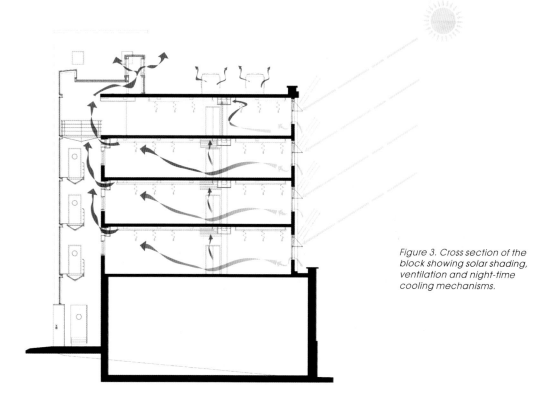

Figure 3. Cross section of the block showing solar shading, ventilation and night-time cooling mechanisms.

Figure 4. *External fabric awnings were installed to control solar gain. They come down automatically when it is sunny, operated by photocells linked to the BEMS.*

dual flush toilets. Self-closing taps were also specified to try to reduce water use.

Lessons learned from monitoring energy and water use

Hills Place was a case study in the Feedback User Group run by Usable Building Trust in 2003 (Bordass, Leaman 2005b). The exercise included analysis of energy use from utility bills to EARM[1] Stages 2 & 3.(Figures 5 & 6). This gave a very good comprehension of the break-down per use and highlighted a few issues.

Gas consumption for the survey year (adjusted for weather and occupancy) was 150kWh/m^2 (28.5kgCO$_2$/m^2), which is 9% below typical consumption of a mixed mode building. Air leakage, heating and hot water settings and accessibility of controls were reasons for a less efficient performance than expected.

Electricity use analysis took into considera-tion three special uses: large computer server room, vending areas and plotting and repro-graphics facilities on all office floors. Without the special uses, the electricity use appears 1% above good practice (Figure 5), but more detailed analysis points out that the electricity for all four lighting, computer suite, office equip-ment and catering/vending facilities are above the good practice values (Figure 6).

Manual overrides are also provided (above), to allow occupants some adaptive control as all floors are activated simultaneously and the lower floors might not need the shading.

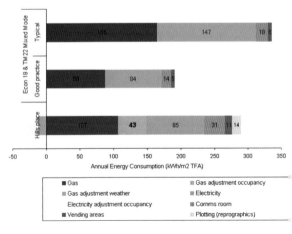

Figure 5. *The general electricity use appears to be 1% above good practice.*

© Green Building Press

Especially disappointing is the high use of artificial light within a shallow floor plan that allows plenty of daylight into the building. Unfortunately, the perimeter of the building has not got a separate circuit and gets switched on with the middle bay. The feedback report recommendations included education of staff, clear labelling of switches, switching off monitors when not in use and consider replacing monitors and vending machines with efficient models.

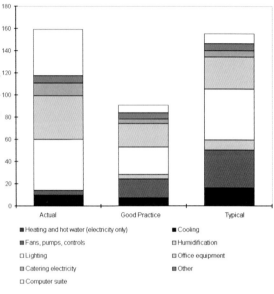

Figure 6. More detailed analysis points out that lighting, computer suite, office equipment and catering/vending facilities electricity are above the good practice values.

Water use: RA water consumption in 2005 was 516m³, which is equivalent to 6.1m³/person year. This looks good against the suggested target of 6.8 m³/person year for offices over 1000m², without catering[2]. Excluding shower use, estimated at approximately 40m³/year, this consumption equates to approximately 24 litres/per person, per day. RA installed dual-flush unisex toilets on the 1st to 3rd floors and waterless urinals in 4th floor men's toilets, used mainly by visitors. The urinals work on a gel cartridge system that requires replacement. Instead of basins, there is a wash shelf with a couple of self closing taps.

There is, however, some room for improvement here. The greatest water use is still the WCs with an estimated 54% (Figure 7). Perhaps, a move to promote a greater use of the waterless urinals by the male employees could reduce water use further. RA report that they would specify waterless urinals again, although they would investigate the option of using the Airflush urinal system to avoid the use of chemicals.

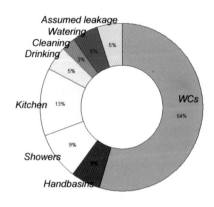

Figure 7. The greatest water use is still the WCs, with an estimated 54%.

Occupant satisfaction

As part of the feedback user group study, Reid Architecture carried out a building use studies' (BUS) questionnaire survey to assess user satisfaction. The survey had a very high response rate of 91%, with a very positive

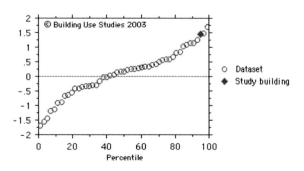

Figure 8. The survey had a very high response rate of 91%, with a very positive result: Hills Place stands amongst the best 5% of BUS UK50 dataset (Graph 4)[3].

result: Hills Place stands amongst the best 5% of BUS UK50 dataset (Figure 8)[3]. Only 3 out of 44 variables appear worse than the benchmark, control over cooling, control over heating and noise overall. This perceived lack of control over heating and cooling stresses the need for understanding (and communicating) the way systems work.

29 variables appeared better than the benchmark, including a perceived productivity increase of 9.4%. This result is important to communicate to managers the benefit of the change to the new premises. Before they moved premises, RA carried out a simple survey, which compared with BUS shows the improvement achieved in the environmental conditions of the offices, (Figure 9).

Feedback on materials specified

Regarding the materials used in the refurbishment, RA report that many of the areas painted with the original natural white emulsion paint have been redecorated with Keim Ecosil paint, due to the original paint discolouring. The linoleum flooring in the toilet areas has worn well and the self-closing taps over the wash

shelf have been found to be very effective. The external fabric awnings have worked well, although they are now due for some maintenance.

Conclusions

It is very positive to see an office refurbishment in the middle of London that has not adopted many standard commercial preconceptions. It is doubly important as new buildings account for only 1% of the building stock.

The energy results show once more that care with air infiltration is important for reducing heating loads. Detailed analysis of electricity use is beneficial, even if the overall figures seem positive, to realise where there is room for improvement.

This quick study has spurred RA to try to monitor more closely their consumption at regular intervals, as they realise that a single study, though positive, looks at a frozen situation, whereas, the use of energy and water does vary greatly with patterns of use.

Results for the comfort study were very positive. This success might spring from the

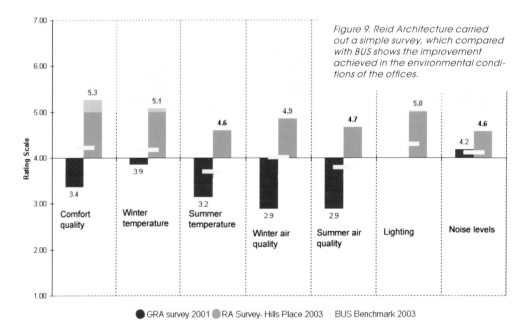

Figure 9. Reid Architecture carried out a simple survey, which compared with BUS shows the improvement achieved in the environmental conditions of the offices.

● GRA survey 2001 ● RA Survey- Hills Place 2003   BUS Benchmark 2003

© Green Building Press

involvement of the practice in the refurbishment, the excitement in merging the workforce into a single site, and the improved conditions from former premises.

It would be very interesting to repeat the exercise as there has also been a flux of people, as well as changes in office layout, and about 43% of the present staff did not participate in the 2001 study. Recent studies, within the building, have suggested that adaptive opportunities (such as opening windows, and manual control of the external awning) are positively contributing towards occupants' comfort (Barlow & Fiala 2006)

The study shows that we need to know, not only that our intentions work, but also learn how they evolve with time and use, and whether they represent robust solutions, easily adaptable to change. ☙

CONSULTING WITH A PURPOSE
work with people towards making a safer, more energy effective environment.

CWAP
advise organisations and individuals on their environmental obligations and how to capitalise on the latest environmental developments.

CONTACT:

Gideon Richards
45 New Laithe Hill, Newsome, Huddersfield
HD4 6RF
T: 01924 261341
E: gideon@cwap.co.uk

References

1. EARM is the Energy Assessment and Reporting Methodology published in CIBSE Technical Manual 22.

2. Targets as appear on websites by Friends of the Earth (Scotland) and Thames Water in June 2006. These seem slightly more tailored than the more general target of 7.7m³/personyear found in Envirowise and DEFRA websites.

3. For more information on Building User Studies occupant survey see www.usablebuildings.co.uk

Many of the technological solutions covered in this case study are discussed in more detail in the 'Green Building Bible, Volume 2' : www.newbuilder.co.uk

Further reading

'How adaptive comfort theories might influence future low energy office refurbishment strategies' by S Barlow and D Fiala (2006), proceedings of 'Comfort & Energy Use in Buildings: Getting it Right Conference', Windsor, UK: http://nceub.org.uk/uploads/Barlow_Fiala.pdf

'Making feedback and post-occupancy evaluation routine 1: A portfolio of feedback techniques. Building Research and Information' by W Bordass, A Leaman (2005), vol. 33, no. 4, pp 347-352.
See www.usablebuildings.co.uk/fp/index.html for information on feedback techniques.

'Making feedback and post-occupancy evaluation routine 3: Case studies of the use of techniques in the feedback portfolio' by W Bordass and A Leaman (2005), Building Research and Information, Vol 33, No 4, 361-375.

CA Sustainable Architecture

we design comfortable buildings to your individual needs with a minimum impact on the Earth's environment,

ca-sa offers:
Full architect's service:
Brief writing and feasibility
Planning and Building Control Applications
Detail design, specification
Production Information and Construction Phase
Post Occupancy Evaluations
Sustainability reports

Contact:
Isabel Carmona
Tel: 01635 48363
e-mail: enquiries@ca-sa.co.uk
web: www.ca-sa.co.uk

EcoHomes
EcoHomes and BREEAM
are trademarks of BRE

Eco-renovation

Before looking in detail at renovation strategies it may be helpful to consider the market for new and renovated commercial and industrial buildings and the context in which decisions are made. **Adrian Birch** explores the concept...

The last 30 years has seen the ongoing decline of manufacturing and a move to service industries, with the workforce becoming more office-bound. Coupled with this has been the IT revolution, the desktop computer at every workspace, and the consequential development of the out of town business park near to motorway connections.

The growth of car ownership, lack of investment in infrastructure and public transport and inner-city congestion has fuelled this migration of offices from the traditional business districts to the suburbs. This has left a residue of unloved crumbling concrete monuments to the first post-war office boom becoming hard-to-let and neglected, and thus offering potential for those developers and others, with the requisite nerve and funds, to renovate or redevelop.

Because of the buoyancy of the housing market many obsolescent city-centre office buildings have often been converted to residential use, student accommodation or budget hotel use. Local authorities have generally welcomed this, as it can serve to revitalise city centres, which in turn increases demand for leisure and other facilities, gyms, restaurants etc.

Many industrial estates, established in the post–war period, are in inner city and inner suburban areas. Most buildings are of steel or concrete portal-frame construction and many are clad with asbestos cement or steel profiled sheet claddings, with minimal insulation. There was little provision made for offices, car parks and landscaping and many estates are looking run-down by comparison with more recent developments nearer to motorway junctions.

Industrial buildings are less reliant on location than offices but easy access to the motorway network and to the available labour force is desirable. Inner city industrial sites may be incompatible with the residential use surrounding them. Because industrial buildings were often constructed as short-life buildings, there is less incentive to renovate them, and redevelopment may be more attractive. Planners have to strike a balance between retaining manufacturing employment and improvement of the environment.

The participants

The commercial property market in the UK is one of the most sophisticated in the developed world, with battalions of pinstripe-suited property professionals offering a wide range of property investment advice to the unwary, for a fee. Commercial and industrial property, more than any other, is treated as a commodity to be traded in a market where the property agent sets the ground rules.

Major commercial and industrial developments are normally owned by pension funds and other financial institutions, which expect property they invest in to meet certain 'institutionally-acceptable' criteria. These organisations are generally risk-averse and will normally only purchase a completed development from a developer when it is fully-tenanted and is providing a regular flow of income in the form of rents and service charges.

The 'risk' is taken by the property development companies who purchase sites for redevelopment in locations they think will maximise their returns in the relatively short term. They will normally manage the development process from inception through to the final sale to the financial institution, and may engage external project managers, architects, surveyors and engineers to provide advice and to share the design risk.

© Green Building Press

The commercial and industrial agent is the professional go-between providing market sector advice to developers and investors and procuring tenants for projected or completed developments. Developers will try and manage their risk by ensuring that a suitable tenant or tenants are signed up in a 'pre-let', and that the pension fund or other institution is willing to take on the completed development, before the developer commits funds to the development.

In order to appeal to the widest range of tenants, the property has to be 'lettable'. Most office agents will say that for the building to be lettable it needs to be sufficiently flexible to accommodate different space-plan configurations, and air-conditioned to accommodate variable occupational densities. They can also charge a higher rent if the building is air-conditioned, as this 'adds value' in their terms. This of course 'adds value' to their fees, which are based on the rent achieved. They don't add that air-conditioning adds significantly to operating and maintenance costs, as well as consuming substantial amounts of electricity, and if poorly maintained can lead to humidifier fever and other respiratory infections, such as legionella.

Tenants will normally base their property decisions on a number of different criteria, with location, parking provision and space flexibility being high on their list. Operating and maintenance costs are of less consequence, as they will argue that these form a minimal part of their overhead, maybe as little as 5%, and any reduction will have minimal effect on the bottom line. It is perhaps not surprising, therefore, that there is little incentive for tenants to save energy, and property agents will argue that the market is tenant-driven. The government has set an ambitious energy-reduction target and has introduced the Climate Change Levy in an attempt to raise awareness of the issues by hitting the bottom line. Responses to this have been mixed. Forthcoming EC legislation will require commercial buildings offered for sale or lease to have an 'energy label' to inform prospective tenants of the building's energy consumption, in an attempt to encourage developers and agents to improve energy efficiency.

Approaching the renovation

For environmental design an holistic approach is essential, whether for a new-build or renovation. The external fabric of the building acts as a climatic filter, allowing light, air and solar gain in, and allowing polluted air out. Openings, such as windows and vents, provide fine control of the airflow.

When assessing an existing building, various strategies need to be considered both individually and collectively in order to reach an optimum environmental solution. This then, has to be tested alongside other criteria such as initial and lifecycle costs, time, buildability, risk etc.

Insulation

In the UK climate, the type and location of insulation can have a major effect on the demand for energy and the performance of the building.

External insulation utilises the thermal mass of the structure and fabric and can offer some heat storage capacity, but needs to be protected from the weather and from impact damage. Only certain types of insulation are suitable for external application, and most organically derived insulants may be unsuitable if wetted. Openings require attention to detail.

Internal insulation is less costly to fit but can cause disruption and will reduce room sizes. It can also cause 'interstitial' condensation affecting the performance of the external fabric, which will remain cold in the winter months.

Cavity insulation is often seen as the best of both worlds, particularly if retro-fitted to existing claddings such as cavity brickwork. However, problems can occur if water subsequently penetrates to the inner skin of the wall. It should only be undertaken where the site is relatively sheltered and the building is low to medium rise. The quality of the external skin should be assessed as it will be subject to greater fluctuations of temperature than before, and if porous could suffer from frost damage.　　　　　　　>>>

Cladding and roofs

Many older buildings leak - most often from defects to flat roofs, at junctions with windows, or if constructed of prefabricated cladding panels, around joints. Wall and roof junctions are particularly vulnerable. There are several possible repair options, depending upon the form of construction. One way to deal with this is to remove the cladding (if possible) and start again. This is usually quite costly and usually requires the building to be empty. An alternative is over-cladding, where a lightweight rainscreen cladding system of steel, aluminium, or fibre cement is fitted to a metal sub-frame over the existing cladding. These systems are designed to shed the water, either by 'drainage and back ventilation' or by 'pressure equalisation'.

If cladding is replaced then insulation can normally be incorporated behind it. It has the added advantage of being capable of being fitted whilst tenants remain in occupation. The disadvantage is that it will increase the load on the structure and foundations and, if fitted to a prefabricated panel system, will increase the load on the original panel fixings. If the original cladding is concrete, tests of the concrete are necessary to ensure it has not 'carbonated' to an extent where it could fail within the lifetime of the over-cladding system. Fire stopping will also be required to the cavity.

Openings

If windows and other components are poorly fitted in openings then heat losses will occur due to cold bridging or air leakage. The more complex the construction, the greater the probability of leakage. Building Regulations L2 give guidance on what is required.

Lighting

By increasing the availability of natural lighting it should be possible to minimise demand for artificial lighting and its associated heat gains. The difficulty, of course, is that natural light is variable and sunlight is directional, and problems can arise with glare when the sun is at a low altitude. The orientation of the building is critical. A lighting strategy must take all these elements into account. Sensors and switching should be designed to provide close control of artificial lighting components, if energy is to be saved and heat gain minimised.

Glare can normally be controlled by specialist glass or Venetian blinds. Electrically operated internal and external blinds have a poor track record and can cause maintenance problems. Certain inter-pane blinds are to be avoided as they reduce the amount of natural light. Manually operated systems are the least troublesome but tend to be less liked by occupiers, who have to get up from their desk and operate them! There can be problems with poorly selected windows fouling blind systems. Cleaning can also be a problem.

Solar heat gain can be controlled by specialist glass or externally located shades or blinds above windows. Solar reflective glass can present problems, as there is a loss of daylight, resulting in the need for artificial lighting and consequential internal heat gains. Specialist films can be applied to existing windows, but are prone to delamination if incorrectly applied.

Ventilation

The occupational density of offices can vary considerably depending upon the nature of the activity taking place. Meeting rooms and call centres with 24-hour occupancy have different environmental and ventilation requirements from an executive's office that is partially occupied. Where occupational density is high there may be a requirement for mechanical ventilation and cooling, for all others natural ventilation may be possible and for health reasons, desirable.

Natural ventilation

Air flows from high pressure to low pressure and for buildings this normally means from windward to leeward (to borrow a nautical expression!). The greater the pressure drop the greater the potential air speed. As a rule of thumb, single-sided ventilation (i.e. to cellular offices), works optimally where the depth does not exceed 2.5 times the clear height. For cross-ventilation (to open plan offices) the rule of thumb is 5 times the clear height. As floor

© Green Building Press

to ceiling heights in many older office buildings are in the region of 3m, the maximum window-to-window distance across the building should not exceed 15 metres for natural ventilation to operate. Luckily many 60s buildings are quite narrow and would be suitable for cross ventilation, all things being equal. In many city locations air and noise pollution may prevent effective natural ventilation, unless the building is 20m or so from the roadway or shielded from traffic by other buildings or trees.

One particular benefit is night ventilation. If windows remain open overnight in summer, the cooler night air will cool the building down, particularly if the concrete ceilings are exposed and act as heat exchangers. The building can be pre-cooled for the following day using sensors and meteorological data. There are obviously security considerations, together with motor-ised control of night vents to be considered in the design of such a window system. Low velocity extract fans are normally incorporated, so as to purge the building of stale warm air.

Another way of benefiting from natural venti-lation is by harnessing the natural buoyancy of heated air (the stack effect) by the creation of vertical ducts within the building drawing warmed polluted air up and out, to be replaced by cooler fresher air at lower levels. Atria fulfil this function. With existing buildings, the scope for providing a glazed atrium may be limited, nevertheless there are several proprietary stack ventilation systems that can be retro-fitted into existing buildings, incorporating fans if neces-sary and/or 'light pipes' to duct natural light to dark interiors.

One of the simplest forms of natural ventilation is the provision of trickle vents to windows. These are are normally manually controlled but can be motorised in more sophisticated systems (OK until the motor breaks). Alternatively 'through the wall' vents can be retrofitted, with sensor-controlled or fan assisted variants available, as well as a heat reclaim capability.

Mechanical ventilation and cooling

One of the main problems in recent years with both new and renovated offices has been internal heat gain generated by people, lights, computers and other business equipment. This has been resolved to some extent by develop-ments in technology, with new generations of lighting and computers giving off far less heat. Servers and other office equipment will require cooling and these can usually be located away from the occupied zone and can be locally air-conditioned, if necessary.

Fans, chiller plant and the like consume large amounts of electrical energy and if a building has been properly designed their use should be minimised. Nevertheless, with existing build-ings, such decisions are often dictated by the location, form and intended use of the building and perhaps the client's desire to compete with new buildings nearby. The problems of retro-fitting air conditioning have been discussed above. The optimum approach is to minimise internal and external heat gains, to naturally ventilate occupied spaces and to provide extract ventilation and cooling, if necessary, to equipment rooms. Air quality is an important matter, particularly in equipment rooms, and filtration must be adequately maintained, which-ever mechanical ventilation systems are fitted.

Operational strategy

Underlying all the above strategies is how the user engages with the building and its systems. Complex systems are unlikely to be understood by most users unless facilities management staff initiate a proper induction process. Building management systems have their place but often produce disappointing outcomes, particularly if building users have no personal control over their internal environment or little faith in the management system adopted. ❧

Many of the above strategies are discussed in greater detail in 'Green Building Bible , Volume 2': (www.newbuilder.co.uk)

BRE's sustainable refurbishment/redevelopment decision support tool, Office Scorer, enables users to systematically compare and test the environmen-tal and economic impacts of different office design concepts, using BRE's Ecopoints system: www.officescorer.info

6 Building styles & systems

Caring for old buildings!

In these dynamic times we must increasingly be aware of the dangers posed by traditional buildings having to meet new and improved standards of performance. The fabric can be put at risk from replacement, alteration and adaptation or decay, particularly where standard solutions are adopted to improve thermal performance. **Richard Oxley** explains ...

I would like to outline an introductory approach that will improve the understanding of the building and the likelihood of providing successful improvements. All buildings of a traditional construction need to be approached in a manner that reflects their specific perform-ance characteristics, not those of a modern building, if they are to benefit from appropriate improvements that are in the building's, and environment's, long-term interest.

The construction of a traditional building, therefore, should be considered as a whole and treated in a holistic way. Its structure, materials and methods of construction and patterns of air and moisture movement should be properly understood. To be in a position to make appro-priate and effective improvements you have to first understand the building. This is a basic requirement within the field of historic building conservation, and one that could be applied to great effect when improvements are being planned for existing buildings.

The materials and detailing of construction will influence the appropriateness and prac-ticability of improvements that can be made. For example, if a building is constructed with soft stone or earth walls, it will be imperative to maintain, or reinstate, a good eave's overhang to protect the walls from the weather.

Understanding the building
Understanding how a building has been repaired and maintained will provide an insight into problem areas and where inappropri-ate impermeable materials have been used. An understanding of how older buildings have developed is crucial to making successful alterations, improvements and repairs. Even in a Victorian terrace, a typical dwelling can be subject to a whole range of alterations; removal of internal walls, the removal of chimney breasts, the replacement of timber floors with solid floors, the provision of a rear extension etc.

Cultural significance
It is important to understand what makes a building of interest. It could be a 19th century social housing project that forms an important part of our collective memory and culture.

Protected status
It is crucial to determine if a building is listed or in a conservation area, as protection will influ-ence the extent and nature of work that can be carried out. It is important to appreciate that it is a criminal offence to carry out unauthorised works and as such works should only proceed once approval has been gained from the local planning authority.

Performance
Once the intended performance is understood, it is important to assess what changes have been made from that performance and ask whether the changes are having an adverse influence on the condition of the building. Unfortunately too few older buildings have escaped the introduction of inappropriate mate-rials. Where this is a problem for the condition

© Green Building Press

CHALK HILL
LIME PRODUCTS LIMITED

A marriage of modern manufacturing and traditional methods bring to you the perfect solution for your TRADITIONAL BUILDING MATERIALS.

Chalk Hill Lime PUTTY - slaked from ground quicklime which produces the finest and smoothest putty suitable for running moulds as well as all mortars.

Chalk Hill Lime PLASTERS - smooth enough for a half millimetre skim, typical of the average Victorian homes.

Chalk Hill Lime MORTARS - made using a wide range of aggregates chosen for your specific requirements.

Natural Hydraulic Lime - The only remaining British hydraulic lime, in NHL 2 NHL 3.5. Also NHL 5 From France.

ALL IN STOCK AND PRICED TO GO
Call for more info on: 01653648112

Chalk Hill Lime Products Limited, Terrington, York.
YO60 6QB
BUY ON LINE www.chalkhill-lime.co.uk
Email:robertperkins@talktalk.net

The alternative treatment for dry rot, wet rot and woodworm...

ProBor™ wood preservatives are based on Boron, a naturally occurring mineral. They are water-based and offer exceptional protection against wood-destroying organisms.

ProBor™ timber preservatives have a deep penetrating action that gives a distinct performance advantage over conventional preservatives.

Call **01403** 210204 to talk to one of our technical advisors or visit our website for further information, including case studies and our **FREE** GUIDES to dry rot and woodworm control.

DB120150
PRESERVATIVE RANGE

Wood preservatives for professionals.

Safeguard Europe Limited . Redkiln Close . Redkiln Way . Horsham . West Sussex . RH13 5QL
T +44 (0) 1403 210204 F +44 (0) 1403 217529 E info@safeguardeurope.com www.safeguardeurope.com

CA Sustainable Architecture

we can help you achieve more sustainable outcomes

ca-sa offers:

Sustainability consultancy:
Advice on site layout.
Energy Efficiency.
Renewable energy options.
Sustainability assessments: EcoHomes licensed.
Environmental simulations and calculations (SAP,SBEM).

Research:
Post Occupancy Evaluations including:
   Energy Use studies,
   Occupant satisfaction surveys.
Briefing for sustainability.
Sustainabilty assessment tools in use.

Contact:
Isabel Carmona
Tel: 01635 48363
e-mail: enquiries@ca-sa.co.uk
web: www.ca-sa.co.uk

EcoHomes
EcoHomes and BREEAM
are trademarks of BRE

Natural Building & Decorating Products
Better for you, your home and the environment

Natural Paint Products
Casein paint, natural emulsions, primers, undercoats glosses, eggshells, pigments, colourwashes, silicate masonry paint, paint stripper, citrus thinners, oils, waxes, varnishes.

Lime Products
Lime putty, lime mortars, lime plasters, limewash, hydraulic lime, pozzolans

Insulation Products
Thermafleece Sheepswool, Warmcell cellulose fibre, Light expanded clay aggregate (LECA), woodfibre boards.

Earth Products
Clay boards, reed boards, reed mats, cob blocks, earth plasters.

Practical Repair Course using Traditional Lime Mortar
£70 including lunch & VAT

Associated Products
Chestnut, oak and larch laths, oak lintels, waterproofing, handmade ironmongery and a large range of tools

Venetian Marble Polished Plastering Practical Course
£117.50 including lunch & VAT

Mike Wye & Associates
01409 281644
visit our website www.mikewye.co.uk
for unbeatable prices, guide sheets technical specifications & much more besides

of the building, the intended performance will need to be reinstated. This usually means that inappropriate materials have to be removed, where this can be achieved without causing more damage than if they are left in place. Once the inappropriate materials are removed, repairs to the exposed fabric of the building are usually required.

One of the most overlooked areas of performance is how a building performs when in use. Simple assessments can be made but in many cases the input of a specialist is required. The methods of assessing the performance of a building include the following areas.

Data logging: a means of obtaining information on the performance of the building before, during and after improvement. The information collected typically includes the external temperature and internal temperature and relative humidity within selected rooms and roof spaces. Without this information it is not possible to assess if the improvements made have had a positive affect.

Fuel bills: a simple means of measuring the success of improvements that can be presented in monetary terms for ease of understanding by lay-people, in effect a real-life SAP calculation!

Fan pressurisation tests: these are important diagnostic tools in understanding how the building performs, they are more than just a means of providing measurements. Areas of excessive air infiltration (draughts) can be positively identified and resources targeted at actual, rather than perceived, problems.

Thermal imaging: a diagnostic tool that improves the understanding of the performance in use of the building and assists in the identification of problem areas such as cold bridges.

Dampness diagnosis: if improvements are to be made, it is important that inherent problems, such as damp, are fully understood and that remedial measures are carried out to address the causes of the damp (and this does not

mean going to a specialist damp and timber contractor!). In most cases this means fixing rainwater gutters and downpipes, reducing high external ground levels and the careful removal of impermeable cement pointing and render.

Occupant feedback: the occupants and users play an important role in achieving a good understanding of the building. They usually know which rooms are coldest and where problems of condensation occur. This information is not only important before the improvements are made, but also afterwards, to ascertain if comfort levels have actually been improved.

Continued assessment: monitoring during the project when repairs and improvements are being made will maximise the success of the improvements and avoid progressing so far with the works that they cannot be effectively addressed before scaffold access is removed. These, and other, assessments assist in achieving a true understanding of the performance in use of a building. Only when the building is understood, can appropriate improvements be devised that are appropriate for that particular building and its individual circumstances.

Targets

There will be desire or pressure for existing buildings to meet targets in performance. It is important to understand what the building is realistically capable of achieving and what is desirable for the long-term use and preservation of the building.

Targets, and how they have been calculated and set, are largely based on arbitrary assessments and assumptions that do not take into account the actual construction of the building, the real life performance and use or location. They are largely developed with the design of new build in mind. In many cases these targets cannot be met by existing buildings, or where targets are achieved. This may create problems for the building and/or the occupants. Applying targets that have been designed for new build is not guaranteed to be successful for the existing building stock.

© Green Building Press

The need to be flexible when applying targets to existing buildings is important when improving air-tightness. Ventilation rates are calculated for the general removal of odour and moisture, with 8 litres/second/person, or 0.4 ac/hr (air changes per hour) being considered what is safe for normal domestic occupancies. Typically modern airtight homes can reach 0.4 ac/hr.

In solid walled buildings an adjustment needs to be made to allow for the walls to breathe, over and above the requirement to remove odour and moisture. Adjusting the target for solid walled dwellings to 0.8 ac/hr would allow the same amount of air for the building as the occupants. This is an arbitrary figure and would need to be monitored to determine if the requirements of each building and its individual circumstances have been satisfied.

We currently do not know what the correct level of adjustment needs to be, but we can be certain that it would need to be adjusted to suit the individual circumstances of each building to reflect construction, location, exposure and intensity of use.

If there is an over adjustment, where the air changes are reduced too much, this could lead to mould growth, associated health problems for the occupants and the conditions for fungal decay and insect attack of the building timbers.

As it can be seen, there are risks associated with strictly adhering to, or striving to reach, modern standards and targets as they can compromise the building's performance and create new problems.

Informed improvements

There are significant dangers in adopting standard solutions. Time invested in designing bespoke solutions, that reflect potential areas of conflict and weakness, such as wall and roof junctions, will enhance the chances of providing an appropriate and effective improvement. It is important that the materials used to improve the energy efficiency of existing buildings are selected carefully; they must have similar performance characteristics to the building fabric. In most cases this means avoiding vapour barriers and checks and looking at traditional materials and modern materials similar in character and performance, which will minimise the creation of problems.

"Faulty judgements arise from ignorance of the availability of crafts and materials, the desire to find cheap and easy solutions and the belief that modern methods are, in any case, superior to traditional materials"[1].

Solutions have to be devised for each circumstance encountered, to move away from a reliance upon standard solutions and those who advocate and profit from them. This principle is reiterated, ironically, in British Standard BS 7913.

British Standards and other specifications and codes of practice should not be applied unthinkingly in the context of building conservation. While the application of particular specifications, structural design codes and calculations can be appropriate in many circumstances, there can be other circumstances where it will be necessary to follow professional judgement, on the basis of what has been proved to work.

It is inevitable that modern materials will need to be used to repair or to make alterations to traditional buildings. We do not live in an ideal world where we have access to the full palette, of materials or the necessary knowledge and skills, that was available when many of these buildings were being constructed, even as late as the Victorian or Edwardian period.

In building conservation there is a presumption in favour of the use of traditional materials and methods that are proven to be compatible with the performance of the building. One of the principal benefits of using proven materials and methods is that you can have confidence in the performance of the repair, whereas it is unwise to experiment with untried materials and techniques, as you can never be confident about the results.

Traditionally there was an in-depth knowledge and understanding of the characteristics and performance of the materials used to construct and repair buildings. This was primarily due to the passing down of empirical knowledge over the years, if not centuries, by the craftsman to his apprentice. The number of materials available was relatively limited, primarily masonry, mortars, plasters and timber, and would be tried and tested and used with confidence.

Today there are thousands of products on the market that can be used in the construction and repair of buildings, with new products continually coming onto the market and being actively promoted. The difficulty with using these materials in the repair and improvement of traditional buildings is that, although they most likely will meet some form of standard in their production or short-term performance, their long-term performance and compatibility is unproven.

Conclusion

The existing building stock has to make a significant contribution to the reduction of carbon emissions. We have one opportunity to get it right and it cannot be wasted.

We must avoid repeating the well-intentioned, but damaging improvements of the past with a reliance on standard solutions. We cannot allow inappropriate improvements to blight these buildings that could ultimately provide justification for their demolition. This would be a case of gross mismanagement of a valuable resource.

Any improvements to the existing building stock needs to be made on an informed basis. An understanding of the building will enable targeted and effective remedial works to be implemented, rather than a best guess hit and miss approach.

The knowledge and experience gained from practical building conservation should be used to ensure that changes are well managed and truly sustainable, so that short-term solutions that pass problems on to future generations are avoided. This can be achieved by:

- maintaining and reinstating the intended breathing performance, that is proven over time to prolong the serviceable life of older buildings
- maximising the retention of existing fabric
- making improvements and alterations with reversibility in mind, so that we do not prejudice future generations with irreversible 'solutions'

Before renovating an older building it is important to stop and ask: do I understand this building? Listening to what the building has to tell us will enable appropriate and effective improvements to be made that will result in long-term solutions for this and future generations. There is a need to ensure that a significant percentage of the existing building stock is improved and repaired in a manner that is compatible, cost effective and also effective at reducing carbon emissions. This would enable these buildings to be cared for in a truly sustainable manner. ✆

Reference

1. 'Building Conservation Philosophy' by J Earl, third edition, Donhead Publishing.

Resources

'The Survey and Repair of Traditional Buildings – a sustainable approach' by Richard Oxley: www.donhead.com

'McKays Building Construction' is invaluable for traditional building techniques. This classic (originally 3 volumes)has been re-published in one book. www.donhead.com

Regular discussion on the appropriate maintainance and repair of old buildings goes on on the Green Building Forum which is a free internet resource: www.greenbuildingforum.co.uk

© Green Building Press

The *green* way to treat damp

- Non toxic – so no harmful fumes.
- Can be used on most types of walls e.g. solid, cavity, brick, stone.
- Used by councils and housing associations.
- Accepted by mortgage companies and building societies.
- Offices in Cheshire, Bristol and London.
- 2005 winner of business of the year award.
- Dutch National prize winning invention in 1988.
- Has been installed in over 25,000 buildings across the UK and Europe.

A green system to rid the home from damp is being used by thousands of home owners across the UK.

Holland Damp Proofing UK Ltd. use an environmentally friendly damp proofing system, proven for more than 29 years in Holland where more than half of the country lies below sea level.

The system comprises of humidity regulating bricks which are fitted in specially prepared niches in the outside walls. Due to their special shape, outside air is allowed to flow into the 2 air chambers of the bricks and then out again. On its way through the inside of the wall this airflow causes moisture to evaporate, therefore drying out the walls and allowing them to 'breathe'.

The environmentally friendly technique works without the use of chemicals and can be used to treat damp problems such as rising and penetrating damp, condensation and mould. It is often much cheaper than other methods with treatment of an average mid-terraced house being around £1,200 - including VAT. Results are guaranteed and work, carried out by our own engineers, is usually complete within 1-2 days.

The product is a permanent solution unlike chemical damp proof courses and coatings which tend to break down over the years. All work is carried out externally because there is usually no need for messy re-plastering.

Since 1997, the system has been available in the UK and has been installed in thousands of properties ranging from barn conversions and terraces to major commercial properties and manor houses.

Diagram of the system

Humid Air

Humid Air

Humid Air

Humid Air

Dry Air Enters Chamber 1

Humid Air from Chamber 2 Transport Outside

Stone Element Inserted into Brickwork

The system looks attractive and has little impact on the appearance of the building.

Customer Quotes

Marita Grace, a property developer from Merseyside tried the system after discovering her house was riddled with damp.

Marita said: "I called for quotes and found that the chemical injection method was expensive and the results couldn't be guaranteed. The Holland Damp Proof System® was absolutely superb. There was no mess or fuss. It has been two years now, and I have no sign of damp. Plus the system has a lifetime guarantee."

Kenneth and Ivy Burt, from Highridge in Bristol had the system installed five months ago.

He said: "When you think about it, the system is a very logical way to treat damp using airflow to dry out the house. I have been in the building trade for over 40 years and I've seen a lot of different damp solutions, so I was pleased to find a treatment that really works well."

Ivy added: "The installer was very pleasant, punctual and efficient. They were hardworking, clean and tidy. I would certainly recommend the system to other people."

For more information please call FREEPHONE 0808 155 2571.
or visit our website at w w w . d a m p p r o o f i n g . com

209

Low impact construction

The term 'low impact construction' describes a methdology of construction which seeks to cause minimal disruption to the local and global environment. These are the 'deep green' buildings and can often have a quite different approach to 'conventional' construction. **Chris Morgan** introduces us to the low impact building arena.

Although the term describes a wide range of techniques, many of the principles, or characteristics of these buildings are shared and many can have distinctive characteristics of a region or even country.

One characteristic shared by most low impact projects is that they tend to be practised at small scale and usually in rural areas. This often diminishes their perceived value and relevance, so it is worth stressing that there are few technical reasons why most of the construction types discussed here could not be employed on both a large scale, and in urban situations.

It is likely that the small scale and rural aspect to most low impact buildings is one reason why clients and builders feel able to experiment. As a result many of the most valuable innovations and developments, which may pervade more mainstream construction in the future, are probably being tried out even now in sheds, extensions and small homes up and down the country!

Low impact buildings almost always have very low embodied energy in their fabric, where the use of natural materials is often the starting point for clients and designers alike. Because of this, such buildings can, by their structural make-up, be very energy efficient and this is another of their great advantages.

For many who undertake low impact buildings, it is part of a much wider approach to life in general. However, this is not strictly neces-sary, as the advantages can be appreciated on their own merits. Unfortunately, it is usually only those already disposed toward this sort of thing, and who make the leap of faith which is often required, who are able to experience the advantages.

The myth of maintenance free!

Maintenance has become a dirty word for some, and much talk is made of 'maintenance free' construction and products. However, in cheating the natural cycles of decay, many man-made products invariably contain toxins and alien materials in their composition, which are environmentally damaging and in most cases, can only prolong the inevitable for a certain time. Due to this, the culture of 'regular maintenance' has been abandoned and when something does go wrong, even when only a

Plastering a 'low impact 'straw-bale wall - labour intensive and local. These are key aspects of Low impact building.

© Green Building Press

Low impact construction harks back to primeval man, when homes were built from the raw materials that could be found locally. From an ecological perspective this may be one of the best ways forward for mankind. We can employ our ingenuity, resourcefulness and the technical skills that we have learnt over generations, to create beautiful and desirable buildings. Below is one example - the Brighton earthship.

Roger Bamber

Michael Reynolds

small part is broken, most 'maintenance free' products are removed, discarded and replaced

In contrast, an environmental approach – and the approach of all low impact construction – is to accept an element of maintenance and to design this into the process of co-habitation with your building. Maintenance is regular, but simple, and in the process, the building and its elements are able to be kept in good order far longer – and therefore far more cheaply in the long run – than their maintenance-free counterparts.

Types of low impact construction

Low impact buildings can theoretically be constructed from any appropriate material that is found in reasonable abundance in the locality of the site where the building is to be built. Most traditional (vernacular) buildings are low impact due to the fact that our predecessors had few opportunities to transport materials very long distances. For instance, many stone farmhouses across the UK usually boast a small quarry somewhere on the farm. This is where the raw materials for the walls will have come from. Excavated by hand, or with simple machines and transported the short distance to the building site by horse and cart. Nowadays, however, stone is not really classified as low impact, as developers often choose stone from distant quarries and even from distant continents. Not so eco now!

Types of construction that might be included under the term 'low impact construction' could include:
- earth construction: cob, rammed, adobe and light earth
- hemp
- straw bale
- other crops
- timber (though many timber eco-buildings are quite high-tech, the underlying philosophy would still be low impact)
- re-used or recycled materials, old tyres for instance, known as earthships.

Materials

Most of the natural materials associated with low impact construction are hygroscopic, which means that they breath - absorbing and releasing moisture, rather than trying to just expel it (which often results in trapped moisture). Clay, in particular, absorbs and desorbs moisture freely and as such can act as a moderator of the humidity in the air, though ventilation remains the key tool for this. This function of balancing the relative humidity in the room is particularly valuable for occupant health, since many of the health problems associated with modern buildings can be exacerbated by extremes of relative humidity.

The same is true regarding heating, and the

Rammed earth walling at the Centre for Alternative Technology, a low tech material being employed in a rather high tech way. Great skill and highly accurate shuttering systems are required for rammed earth. Nice, but highly time consuming and ultimately the most expensive way of employing earth walls in a building.

CAT

© Green Building Press

concept of thermal mass is well understood. With both thermal mass, and moisture mass, some understanding of the issues is required, but it is possible to actually design the internal climate of a building so as to most benefit the health of occupants without the use of moving parts and the associated maintenance problems.

Sourcing materials can be problematic. Simply finding the raw material can be difficult, particularly if you intend to build in an urban area. In addition, materials are rarely standard, nor have any recognised performance criteria (in a conventional sense). This puts the onus onto someone involved in the construction to be sufficiently expert in the field to be confident when it comes to sourcing the right material.

In addition there is often no commonly recognised framework for cost, so it can be difficult not only to budget, but to know if you are getting a good deal. And the issue of cost is complicated by transport, storage and by the seasons.

Whilst the material cost of low impact constructions tends to be low (providing too much transport is not needed), these savings are usually well offset by higher costs associated with labour and time. This often means that the anticipated lower costs of low impact buildings are not realised. Many self builders get involved in building in order to offset some of the labour costs associated with builders and many also run training or volunteer days to draw in labour.

Material types
Earth - cob, rammed earth and adobe
Earth construction is still the most widespread construction method used by mankind and one third of humanity still live in earthen buildings. The material even gave its name to the entire planet – or was it the other way around - but in any event it comes with significant pedigree.

Vernacular forms of earth construction survive in many parts of the world and remain instructive on the most efficient way to produce earthen buildings, even today. There are a number of techniques but broadly they can be divided into three. The first involves stacking and compressing earth to form a monolithic wall – examples are 'cob' and rammed earth using shuttering (very specialist), adobe pre-formed and dried into blocks and then laid in the same fashion as normal blocks. Both of these techniques employ earth as the principal load-bearing material. The principal advantage of the latter is that it avoids most of the problems associated with shrinkage, whilst the disadvantage is that it entails double handling.

The third alternative is to mix earth with some filler material like straw and apply it to a framework which takes the structural loads. This was more common traditionally where timber supplies were plentiful.

A common disadvantage of all earth constructions nowadays is that it can be difficult to attain the thermal insulation values required by the building regulations within the thickness of the wall itself.

Light earth - One way around the above problem of poor insulation value is to add an insulating filler to the earth itself. This has been found to 'help' the wall comply with modern requirements for thermal performance. The main techniques employed is by adding straw to the earth before it is applied, usually as an infil to a timber frame structure, as the addition of

Amazon Nails

Straw bales being fitted between a timber frame at Suffolk Clow Beck Centre in Sussex.

large quantities of straw reduces the loadbearing properties of the earth.

Hemp construction - lime and hemp, is similar to the above, where hemp stalks are mixed with lime to form a solid, non-loadbearing, fairly well insulating mass wall.

Both of the above techniques require drying out times and are vary labour intensive, though mechanisation can be employed, such as mixing and placing with excavators, though this is a small compromise of the low impact ethos. Most of the earth construction can be self finished or plastered/rendered over. Large roof overhangs are usually employed to help keep off driving rain.

Straw bale construction - normally involves

placing rectangular bales, exactly as bricks are placed, to form a wide, hairy wall which can be either load bearing or infill to a structural frame, and which is normally plastered on both sides with a clay or lime-based render.

Straw bale construction has a number of advantages over earth and insulated earth construction types. It is a dry system and so has none of the (admittedly minor) problems associated with drying out and shrinkage. It is also a very good insulation material which, when combined with the sensible placement of thermal mass, makes a lot of sense overall in the UK.

Straw buildings are also quite quick to construct, but possibly more involved than the other techniques to adequately finish. There is

Above: a simple, but very effective, small scale gridshell roof construction at Pishwanton in Scotland, which was built on site and moved into place by volunteers. Gridshells can use a very small amount of timber to form a substantial span. The gridshell is braced by the overlayers of timber boarding.
www.buildingforafuture.co.uk/winter02/index.php

Below: in stark contrast, the huge gridshell roof at the Weald and Downland museum was more akin to army manouvres but proves that low impact construction can be engineered to suit mainstream construction and can compete with more energy intensive materials, such as steel.

no doubt, however, that straw bale construction is relatively quick, cheap and easy to do, and increasingly easy to get through the legislative and financial hurdles which often bedevil low impact projects.

Other crops - a number of crop-based materials have found their way into the building material supply chain, though these are mostly imported into the UK. Among these are hemp, flax, and sheeps' wool, all used for insulation, while flax is also used in the manufacture of linoleum. Sisal, coir and jute are used in carpet manufacture, and reeds are becoming a little more common, not only for traditional thatching, but bound and used as backings to plasters and renders.

Timber - use is so widespread it is easily overlooked but timber forms the mainstay of much conventional, very high impact construction. It also has the capacity to be an integral part of very low impact construction if used wisely.

If sourced from local (at least, not imported) and certified forests, and if used efficiently and without chemical treatment, and if detailed well so as to be durable, timber represents a low impact material choice. Types of timber construction include the following.

Timber frame - a method of building which uses dimensioned timber to build frames that are then raised into place and bolted or screwed together. One, quite well known method of simple timber frame construction, is the Walter Segal method[1], which uses timber very efficiently and is simple enough for self-builders and novices.

Not everyone is happy with our use of timber in buildings as the native indians of Sarawak and many other tropical regions would attest! Remember timber is only a low impact and renewable resource if it is sourced locally and from re-afforested areas. Unless you personally know of the extraction location of the timber that you use, then it would be wise to request FSC certified.

Greenpeace

Above: novel use of masonry - crushed aggregate from demoltiion waste was used at the Earth Centre, near Doncaster. The downside was that it leaked air like a sieve.

Timber and brick construction - is commonly used by developers, whereby the internal, load-bearing frame of a building is timber, usually pre-fabricated offsite, with an external cladding of masonry. This is not a low impact method of construction but mentioned here to avoid confusion.

Traditional stone and brick construction, using lime and clay mortars probably counts as 'lowish' impact as discussed earlier. Brick manu-facture can use large quantities of energy but in their favour, stone and brick are extremely durable materials so the 'embodied energy' reduces with age. With this in mind, reclaimed masonry and roof/floor tiles and slates are low impact (providing they are sourced locally). On the downside reclaimed masonry and slates are in great demand and can be very expensive, which tends to negate one of the attractions of low impact construction.

Roundpole construction - as the name suggests, employs poles which can be either direct logs or dimensioned poles (dimensioned poles, however, would take the method out of the low impact construction arena somewhat). The idea of round pole construction reduces the machining of timber, while retaining all of its strength. Log buildings are an example of round pole construction.

Gridshell construction - enables very efficient use of small amounts of timber, yet can create very large span structures. Gridshells again straddle the low tech/high tech arenas because, for large span buildings, a great deal of struc-tural calculations need to be employed.

Green timber building - (using timber that is freshly felled and not dried) - the use of 'green' timber also avoids the energy needed for kiln drying and there are a number of ways in which timber can be used. The most common examples in the UK are green oak frame build-ings, such as seen in many of our historic towns and cities.

Below: a breathing wall, timber frame holiday home, on a croft in Scotland. All natural finishes and native timber (except the floors where the client wanted engi-neered timber over the underfloor heating).
North Woods Construction and Locate Architects.

Interestingly there has been use, in some parts of England, of traditional rubble footings employing stone and lime (rather than poured concrete) in what may be termed low impact foundations.

People are becoming more familiar with the use of lime, and increasingly, clay, for mortars and plasters. Perhaps the main advantage of these materials for mortars is that the bricks or blocks can more readily be re-used at the end of the building's lifetime, as they clean easily, not like cement mortar which tends to adhere like glue.

Re-used and recycled materials

A few constructional techniques have been developed to deal directly with some of the waste arisings from industry. One of the most enduring has been the common tyre. Rammed full of earth and tied together, these have become symbols, especially in the US, of ecological design through the re-use of waste (Earthships). Drinks cans and bottles, short logs and many other unlikely materials have been similarly employed to create walls.

The principal of using waste materials is a sound one, and be it tyres or recycled paper insulation, there is no doubt the impact of development is reduced.

Permaculture

Are all low impact buildings a form of permaculture? Possibly, but not necesarily. Some low impact buildings and many that will be built in the future do not encompass or take advantage of local eco-systems that a permaculture approach might suggest. What is permaculture? It is a way of life; a philosophy that anyone can adopt which has grown to encompass the design of sustainable human habitats – in short it is an ecological approach to providing for all our basic needs (food, building, finance and social structure). It is now practiced as a philosophy (not a religion) world-wide. It is a design system that is based on working with nature rather than against it and caring for the Earth. It embraces many ideas and skills but is closely modelled on natural ecosystems.

The permaculture vision is based on three ethics; care for the earth, care for people, and living within limits; creating sustainable human habitats by following nature's patterns. It is a complete process of looking at an area holistically and taking matters into our own hands, thinking before we act, making changes in our own lifestyles rather than demanding that others do it for us. It can deliver productive landscapes and biodiversity with humans as an integral part of the same system. It gives us the fundamental desire to do what we believe to be right, thereby making us feel part of the solution, rather than part of the problem. It uses ideas from traditional building methods and farming practices, as well as modern science and technology, encouraging us to work with what we already have. We can preserve what is best, enhance existing systems and introduce new elements. The resulting solution will therefore differ from one area to another and every project will be unique.

Permaculture is not a set of rules; it is a process of design based around principles found in the natural world, of co-operation and mutually beneficial relationships, and translating these principles into actions. This action can range from choosing what you eat, how you travel, the type of work you do, and where you live, to working with others, making decisions that relate to all your other decisions. It means thinking about your life or project as a whole system - working out the most effective way to do things that involves the least effort and the least damage to others, and looking for ways to make relationships more beneficial.

Permaculture values the house itself as an important energy system. The sun's energy is vital and utilised by passive solar design. It can encompass any of the technologies addressed within this book. A key feature is 'zoning'; placing things appropriately in relation to each other, working on the principle that those things which require frequent attention are placed closest to the home. It is about using time, energy and resources wisely. There are many books on the subjects and regular courses are run throughout the UK.

The term 'permaculture' originated in the 1970's from Australian academic Bill Mollison, and his associate, David Holmgren. They used it to describe "harmonious integration of land-scape and people providing their food, shelter, and other material and non-material needs in a sustainable way. Permaculture is also the conscious design and maintenance of agri-culturally productive ecosystems which have the diversity, stability and resilience of natural ecosystems".

References

1. Walter Segal method of timber frame construction see: www.segalselfbuild.co.uk

Further reading

'The Ecology of Building Materials' by B Berge available from www.newbuilder.co.uk

'The Green Self Build Book' by Jon Broome (out April 2007)

'Low Impact Development: Planning and People in a Sustainable Countryside' by S Fairlie.

'Building Green; a complete guide to alternative methods' by C Snell & T Callahan.

'Building with Hemp' by S Allin.

'The Natural Plaster Book' by Cedar Rose Guelberth and Dan Chiras available from www.newbuilder.co.uk

Earth Construction

'Building with Earth in Scotland Innovative Design and Sustainability' by B Little & T Morton.

'Earth Construction Handbook, Earth in Modern Construction' by G Minke.

'Rammed Earth; design and construction guidelines' by P Walker, R Keeble, J Martin & V Maniatidis.

'Building with Cob; a step-by-step guide' by Adam Weismann & K Bryce, available from www.newbuilder.co.uk

'Light Earth Construction' by C Morgan, DTI Research Report 2002 available from Gaia Architects: www.gaiagroup.org.uk

Straw Bale Construction

'The Straw Bale House' by A & B T Steen.

'Building With Straw Bales: A Practical Guide for the UK and Ireland' by B Jones, Download pdf format www.strawbalefutures.org.uk

'Build It With Bales' by M Myrhman & S MacDonald.

Timber

'Out of the Woods: Ecological Designs for Timber Frame Houses' by P Borer & C Harris.

'Oak-framed Buildings' by Rupert Newman, available from www.newbuilder.co.uk

'The Woodland House' by Ben Law, available from www.newbuilder.co.uk

Waste

Recycled Materials for Housing, Scottish Homes (now Communities Scotland) 1993 by H Liddell www.gaiagroup.org.uk

Permaculture

Permaculture Association Britain 0845 4581805 www.permaculture.org.uk

Permaculture magazine 01730 823311 www.permaculture.co.uk

'The Earth Care Manual; A Permaculture Handbook For Britain & Other Temperate Climates' by Patrick Whitefield.

'Permaculture in a Nutshell' by Patrick Whitefield.

'The Earth User's Guide to Permaculture, 2nd edition, a designer's manual' by NB Mollison.

Most of the above books are available from the Green Shop, 01452 770629 www.greenshop.co.uk

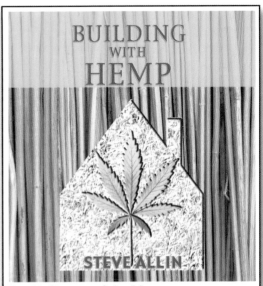

Building with Hemp

Written by hemp building consultant Steve Allin. All aspects of the revolutionary system of building with hemp explained for the first time. Illustrated with many colour photos.

price £ 20 +postage   purchase on line

www.hempbuilding.com

   hemp building courses - designs - materials

© Green Building Press

Tradical Hemcrete® combats climate change.

More than 9 million* tonnes of CO_2 may be saved in the UK every year !

Applications
> Insulating solid walls
> Roof insulation
> Insulating & acoustic renders & plasters
> Insulating & acoustic floor slabs & screeds

Benefits
> Healthy living environment
> Saves energy, saves cost
> Sustainable technology
> Durable, high quality buildings
> Simple, quick construction
> Adaptable for architectural diversity

Tradical®
Building lime innovation

Call 0845 634 0254 or 0845 603 1143
www.tradical.co.uk
uksales@lhoist.com

*based on calculated CO_2 (carbon dioxide) sequestration
and saving emissions from high energy materials.

Cob building

Cob building is seen by many as a synergy of vernacular building traditions and the modern natural building movement. Now freed from the shackles of being the 'poor man's building material', **Adam Wiseman** and **Katy Bryce** explain why ...

Cob is now being recognised as a fully modern, chic, yet earthy, grounded and accessible building method. It is also no longer confined to being only the chosen method of the 'alternative' self-builder, but is being used in the public realm to create new schools, community centres and modern housing developments. This is because, while not producing a panacea for all building solutions, it has many excellent attributes as one of the most 'green' building materials on the planet.

A new generation is now emerging, of people who are engaged in a global search for alternatives and solutions to the state we find ourselves in; and these solutions are not proving hard to find. Some of these solutions can be seen in the buildings of the past, the structures of the still-existing rural tribes and communities around the world. They are in the very ground beneath our feet, and the grasses blowing in the wind, the sun that warms us, and the hands and feet that we are born with.

Sometimes, the simplest solutions can be the hardest to fathom.

Earth building, along with other natural building techniques, is once again being noticed and valued as a practical and life-enhancing solution to the state we find ourselves in. Clay is a healer on all levels. It can heal physical trauma as a receiver of toxins, and can address all levels of society – the academic can analyse it, the scientist and engineer can test it, the poet can lyricise about it, and the child, woman and man can hold it in their hands and build their own home together, to suit their needs, to enjoy for a lifetime.

Imagine a building material that can be dug from or near the site; needs only the addition of locally grown straw, locally sourced aggregate and water; can be mixed with your feet and built with your hands. And when the building is no longer needed, it can fall to the ground, ready to be re-used by the next generation of natural builders. This is cob.

Cob is a simple, low-tech material, being composed of the cheap, accessible ingredients of clay sub-soil, straw, aggregate and water. The materials can generally be sourced on-site or locally, which means that no transport is needed to import foreign materials.

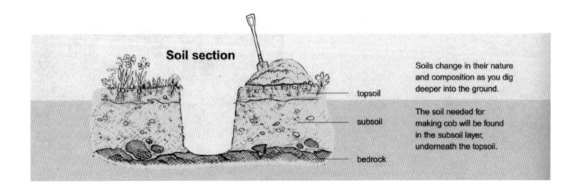

Soil section

topsoil

subsoil

bedrock

Soils change in their nature and composition as you dig deeper into the ground.

The soil needed for making cob will be found in the subsoil layer, underneath the topsoil.

© Green Building Press

These ingredients can be mixed with feet and hands and built onto a stone or brick plinth, using simple tools such as spades, garden forks and wooden mallets

Building with cob is something that is easy to learn, and can be executed by all genders, age groups and levels of ability. All of the materials are 100% biodegradable and recyclable – when the building is no longer needed, or is left to disintegrate, they will simply return to the earth leaving no trace, or can be re-mixed and used to construct a new building

Though earth construction does not provide the best insulation, when constructed as part of a passive solar design, cob can be used to great advantage as a huge heat store. Due to its high thermal mass, when oriented towards the south (in the northern hemisphere) it can absorb the heat from the sun and then release it back into the building when the temperatures decrease at night. It will also provide passive cooling in the hot summer months.

Sourcing material to make cob

Cob is made from the simple soil beneath our feet - but not the topsoil from your garden, which is full of organic matter. It is made from the subsoil layer underneath the topsoil, which may or may not contain in varying proportions the essential ingredient in cob: clay. The essence of cob building has always been to source the materials as locally as possible, to produce a structure that is literally in and of the immediate environment.

Clay subsoils are present in many areas of the UK. Nature gives us clues as to where we may find these clay deposits: look to areas where water comes to the surface, or where water sits for a long time after a rain storm; also the areas in your garden which are notoriously hard to dig, and where the ground cracks when dry.

The ideal scenario is to source the subsoil from your own back garden or the plot on which you hope to build. If this is not possible,

there are many other places where clay can be found locally: old quarries, a neighbour who is digging a pond, a farmer's field (farmers are good people to talk to as they work the land the daily); and our favuorite option is to utilise clay subsoil dug up to make way for the foundations of a housing development or road works. This 'waste product' of the building industry is carried off to a landfill and dumped at a cost.

There are many simple tests which can be done to identify the suitability of your subsoil, but the simplest way of identifying the presence of clay is by its colour: from golden browns, oranges, deep reds, pinks, greys and mauve, and also how it feels between your fingers - take a small sample and make it into a paste with water. If it is sticky and smooth there is a good chance it has a high clay content.

How to make a cob mix

There are many different ways to mix up cob. From the very basic low-tech, low-impact, where the only pieces of equipment you will need are your feet, hands and a tarpaulin, to the more high-tech, high-impact method of using a JCB or tractor as shown below.

To make a good cob mix you must have good ingredients. Your four basic ingredients (see picture at bottom of page) are:

- **a suitable clay subsoil** - this acts as a sticky binder to hold the aggregate particles together.
- **aggregate/sand** - this stabilizes the clay subsoil, and minimises shrinkage and cracking in the cob
- **fibre** - this gives tensile and sheer strength to the cob wall, and prevents major cracking from taking place once the cob is dry
- **water** - this enables all the dry ingredients to be mixed into a homogenous, sticky batch of cob.

To mix cob on a tarpaulin you simply need a large tarpaulin (laid flat on the ground), onto which proportions of dry clay and aggregate/sand are placed. The tarpaulin is folded from side to side to mix these together. Water is then added, and the material is stomped on with your feet to mix it all together. The straw is then added in small increments, stomped in, and the tarpaulin rolled back and forth numerous times until all the ingredients are formed into a homogenous cob mix.

Building with cob

The tools you will need for building with cob are refreshingly simple and low-tech. You can find most of what you need on your body, and after a quick rummage through your garden shed. The two most important tools are your very own hands and feet. Other than that, you will need the following items: a sturdy garden fork for lifting cob up onto the wall, a flat spade for trimming the walls, and a large wooden mallet for compressing the cob from the side.

Cob must always be built onto a stone, brick or block plinth, which is at least 600 mm off the ground. This prevents water from seeping into the base of the cob and causing it to disintegrate (see diagram right).

A cob wall is built up by compressing fork-

Clay subsoil and fresh long, strong straw

Aggregate / sand and water

© Green Building Press

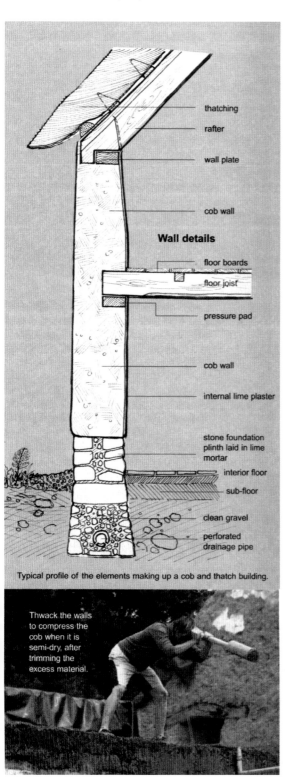

Wall details

- thatching
- rafter
- wall plate
- cob wall
- floor boards
- floor joist
- pressure pad
- cob wall
- internal lime plaster
- stone foundation plinth laid in lime mortar
- interior floor
- sub-floor
- clean gravel
- perforated drainage pipe

Typical profile of the elements making up a cob and thatch building.

Thwack the walls to compress the cob when it is semi-dry, after trimming the excess material.

fulls of cob onto the plinth, which are then trimmed from the side to create a plumb line. The walls are built in a series of 'lifts', or layers, which comprise roughly 300-500mm lifts of material built in one session. Building too much in one go will cause the wall to bulge and potentially collapse under the weight of too much wet material. It is necessary to allow the 'lifts' to dry for at least three days in between building sessions. It is essential to keep the walls trimmed as you build up, using a flat spade, so that a straight wall is maintained at all times. The standard thickness for cob walls is 600mm, although walls in Devon are sometimes built up to 900mm thick.

Cob is the perfect material for creating organically shaped structures, as it is easy to mould and shape into curvilinear forms.

Suitable finishes for cob walls

Cob walls can be left un-rendered as long as they do not receive driving rain or experience prolonged freezing conditions. A render or plaster, specifically applied to any sort of earthen wall, must serve the purpose of allowing the cob to breathe, and must therefore be made of a porous material. Lime and earth are the preferred materials of choice, as they are soft, breathable and flexible, and will truly enhance the forms and curves inherent in the cob.

The principal breathable finishes that we recommend for cob walls are lime plasters/ renders, earth plasters, lime wash, natural breathable paints based on plant materials, also clay paints and casein paints. ☙

The pictures and illustrations for this story were taken, with permission, from a recent highly illustrated and practical guide to building with cob written by the authors of this story: Building with Cob: ISBN 1-903998-72-7. £25.00

This book, along with a few other selected books, are available from the Green Building Press website: **www.newbuilder.co.uk/books**

Case study
Cob home in Devon

Kevin McCabe has always had a passion for cob. He was brought up in a cob house in Devon and lived with his family in one for many years. Now he has built one. Until Kevin built this house, no new cob homes had been built in the UK since the 1930s. **Clive Frewins** visited and tells us about the project ...

Its rich red rough walls, built from clay extracted from an adjoining field, mixed with straw and sand, stand exposed. Kevin McCabe and his wife, Rose, love the colour and the exterior texture so much that they are having serious difficulty convincing themselves that they should follow the accepted practice of limewashing it.

It is cob with a difference. The materials and method of construction are strictly traditional, but the unusual shape of the house - it faces into the sun and is shaped like a kidney - is an attempt to prove that cob and modern living

are not, contrary to what some people might think, mutually exclusive. The interior of the house is largely open plan downstairs and by the judicious use of the southern orientation and the many windows McCabe has managed to encourage a great deal of light through the south-facing frontage.

After having lived there since July 2002 McCabe is as convinced as ever that cob can produce houses that compete in every way with the best of modern materials. He is hardly surprised by this, because his previous cob and thatched family home 10 miles away, which he built on the footprint of an old barn, proved to be a successful test bed. "I have always been convinced of the thermal efficiency potential of cob, although the Building Regulation's U-value requirements for walls will create quite a challenge in the future," said McCabe.

The couple designed most of the new house

© Green Building Press

themselves and Kevin built the house, together with his two assistants, David Joyce and James Strong.

There is hardly a straight wall in the three storey 340m² house. Inside the walls have been decorated with a thick earth plaster. "I find the transmission of humidity between the rooms and walls much better with earth plaster than with lime," McCabe says. "I learned this from a German earth building specialist, Professor Germont Minke, whom I met at the Terra 2000 conference in Torquay three years ago. However, we have given it a 4mm skim using a lime putty-based plaster to give the internal walls a finer finish and make them easier to paint with limewash."

Apart from being painted in delightful colours, the walls all have the most wonderful rounded feel - an advantage of having designed the house in a curved shape facing into the sun. Rose said, "everyone who comes here says it is bright and modern - and yet it is built with solid walls 750mm thick in this wonderful ecological material. Friends love the way it flows - the human form of it. There are no nasty sharp edges. The interior has a sculptural quality

that can only come with a natural material like cob." The south-facing elevation is punctuated by a series of tall windows, made from sweet chestnut, that allow light into the solid cob spiral staircase.

While the ample size of the many double-glazed windows mean the house is full of light, they did not make the task of achieving the thermal requirements of the building regulations any easier. "Officials at our local authority (East Devon) were quite positive throughout about this issue," McCabe said. "To achieve the current 0.25 U-value requirement in cob you would need walls six feet thick. Fortunately the walls were completed when the requirement was still 0.35."

All the above ground structure is solid cob - McCabe reckons he and his team mixed a total of 350 tonnes using soil from a neighbouring field. The below ground and floor structure used cement in the aircrete blockwork and the concrete slab. "Although I am an earth building devotee, I have no qualms about using cement in the appropriate places," McCabe says.

The plinth has local stone set against

a 100mm aircrete backing block, a 50mm cavity, then 300mm polystyrene insulation and a 150mm inner block. The concrete slab has 100mm of insulation beneath the screed which contains the underfloor heating. There is no heating upstairs and McCabe has built 30 tonnes of solid cob thermal mass into the feature he is most proud of - the solid cob winding staircase that leads from the first floor to the second. The other staircase, also spiral, that leads from the front door up to the first

floor, is also of solid cob.

To add further interest, and also to reflect the surrounding Devon landscape, the house is built on a series of levels. This means the whole house is stepped, and there are interesting short flights in the cob staircases.

Although this created a great deal more work, it has meant that by carefully juggling the levels, Kevin and architect, David Highett,

All photos ©Clive Frewins

were able to ensure the overall height from the highest internal floor level to the lowest external ground level is less than 4.5m. This was very important to McCabe and Rose because it has meant they have not had to install fire doors on the winding semi circular cob staircase that leads to the second floor. "We think fire doors would have completely ruined the effect of the house," McCabe said.

Even so the top floor, which measures 110m², is only half living space, the upper level being designated storage, something that is badly needed as the ceiling is a cathedral one, designed to make a feature of the massive curved oak purlins and tie beams that McCabe constructed entirely himself.

The lower level of the top floor is used for a second sitting room. The winding cob staircase up to this room is wrapped around the main chimney. "This building will perform much better than a similar-sized new-build with cavity walls, which possess the same thermal resistance figures, because of its massive central thermal storage capacity," McCabe says. "The huge mass of cob in the centre means the building heats up and cools down very slowly, which makes it very warm in winter and keeps it cool in the summer.

Cob also has health advantages according to McCabe. "I am convinced that, because they have slightly higher internal humidity levels than most modern houses, cob houses are healthier to live in," he says. "Living here the children seem to get far fewer sore throats and colds than their friends."

The couple's only disappointment in the build is the temperature in the vast 'room in the roof', with its eyebrow windows under the thatch, looking out at the surrounding countryside from all sides.

"Despite the good insulation qualities of thatch we have found the second floor colder than we expected," McCabe said. "This is a very exposed site and I think this problem is largely caused by the cavity between the thatch and

the fire barrier beneath. To cope with cold, windy days we have decided to run a loop off the underfloor heating system to power a large radiator up there.

"Nonetheless we have shown that you can build an imaginative modern house in cob. It is a labour-intensive but very cheap material. It is also not as slow a method of building as some think," McCabe says. "There was three months solid cob work in this house which we spread over five months. The total build time was 15 months. Unless they are of timber frame very few self-builds of this size and finish are completed in less than this time." Once it is built, if it is anything like McCabe's, a new cob house should be highly thermally efficient. "Obtaining our SAP rating of 100 was a complicated process but at least it shows that if you build in cob and have a condensing boiler you can run the house on low energy costs," McCabe said. ☯

Reforesting Scotland
restoring the land and the people

Will you help us restore woodlands and forest culture to Scotland?

Our vision involves the creation of a well-forested and productive Scottish landscape and a culture which values and uses its woodland resource.

During 15 influential years, Reforesting Scotland has helped bring about a transformation in the way we view Scotland's forests and the level to which communities are involved in forest management and

use. Reforesting Scotland also makes links between buildings, energy, food and all aspects of sustainable development.

Join us and receive our widely acclaimed, twice-yearly Journal, our members' newsletters and information on local events. You can join from our website or call Mandy to request a **free** back-issue and membership form.

*Reforesting Scotland
62 – 66 Newhaven Road,
Edinburgh EH6 5QB
Tel: 0131 554 4321
www.reforestingscotland.org*

Hemp building

Hemp builder and author, **Steve Allin**, introduces us to this natural and sustainable building material. Hemp buildings breathe, are airtight, lightweight and strong, with good insulating and heat storing properties - impressive green credentials.

France has a long history of hemp use in industry and so the evolution of it's use in building was perhaps inevitable. A large number of architects and builders there have developed a broad understanding of how to use natural materials, so being a hemp growing region hemp was a 'natural candidate'. As a result of many years of use and experiment there, hemp - as a building product, is now ready to make its entrance into the wider building arena.

The hemp plant (cannabis; sativa L)

One of the earliest plants husbanded by man, hemp materials have seen a revival in interest in the last twenty years, due to world wide demand for commodities produced in a sustainable manner, and the grant aided support within the EU for it's production.

Hemp could be said to have the highest 'green credentials' of all agricultural crops. Although there are some other plants such as flax and jute that provide similar materials of fibres and wood chips, few produce the variety of materials (fibre, wood, and seeds) that have the climatic range or broad scope of uses that can be ascribed to hemp. Few oil crops produce the biomass level attainable with hemp, and if they do, as in the case of sunflowers, there is not the added production of fibre. Many biomass crops only produce combustible materials and do not have the added advantage of being able to provide the energy conscious farmer with an ideal rotation crop. Due to its weed suppressing capabilities, the dense canopy of hemp leaves will reduce the need for other chemical or mechanical treatments, and so is eminently suited to the organic producer.

Two elements of the hemp plant are used

Wet spraying of hemp/lime mix into a modern timber from construction.

to produce building material, the fibres of the stem (which are used in insulation matting, usually mixed with polypropylene), and the woody core of the stem, which is an agricultural waste product, produced in a chip form (called hurds). The 'hurds' have in the past been used coated with bitumen or silicates as a dampproof loose fill insulation, but it is the mixing of these chips with cements and limes to form breathing lightweight "hempcrete" that has proved to be the most revolutionary.

Hempcrete is a term used to describe a mixture of hemp fibres, from the stalk of the plant, with lime. The resulting mix has properties that work well across a range of different thermic values; conductivity, capacity and effusity, and in tests, it has been proved that a combination of these values, results in levels of comfort and reduced energy above and beyond what would normally be expected.

Why mix with lime

Lime has more ecological credentials than other binders or cements used in building by comparison of the embodied energy levels. This is certainly one of the reasons why lime is preferred to cement as an ingredient in the hempcrete mix, but more important is the way lime works with moisture mechanically in the structure of the medium. The most common of modern building lime materials is the hydrated

© Green Building Press

Hemp and lime as an insulating fill for timber framed buildings has been used for centuries in France.

builder or designer with a material that has a wide range of applications. With variations in the proportions of the mix it can be used to insulate roof spaces, between or beneath floors, or to build walls. When mixed with a greater proportion of lime it can also be used as an insulating plastercoat. When used to build walls it is normally cast around a timber frame.

Post and beam frames are particularly suited to hempcrete use but all types of framing systems are suitable for encasing with this seamless uniform layer of insulating and heat storing material. A lighter weight variation (more hemp less lime) of hempcrete mix can be cast between the roofing rafters so that a continuous envelope can be achieved. The advantages are that none of the gaps, which may occur when using batts of fibre insulation, are present. It is also possible, in the same way, to produce a thermal and acoustic barrier between floors.

The technique of using hempcrete as ground floor insulation is to many modern architects and engineers the most unorthodox of uses, as it does not require the inclusion of a damp proof membrane. The only point in the structure that utilises a dpm in hempcrete homes is at the base of the walls, between the timber frame and hempcrete and the foundation of the wall where there is a likelihood of rising damp. In the UK, hempcrete has very definite potential for use in conservation as an infil to the many old oak frame buildings, and as a fireproofing layer beneath thatch roofs. It also can provide the ecologically conscious newbuilder with a natural and simple material.

There is a division in the green building world at present, between those that are devising building systems that rely heavily on layers of industrially produced materials and those that wish to utilise natural or traditional materials in a more sophisticated manner. Hemp building would fall into the latter, but once in use can be used by the homeowner as an ordinary dwelling. ☯

or white lime sold by builders merchants, which is usually mixed with portland cement to increase plasticity, when being applied, and flexibility to the structure. To be able to mix uniformly with the hemp, the lime has to be in powder form as opposed to putty. The lime 'community' usually regards this material with scorn, as being inferior to lime putty as it might have started to carbonate by exposure to air in storage. However, I have found through my use of it in hempcrete, that, provided it is manufactured correctly, it can be used quite successfully with small quantities of hydraulic lime binder to achieve the initial set, even as external render mixed with only sand and water.

Natural hydraulic lime offers the structural porosity that gives lime its breathability, but can give the added characteristic of setting much faster. So a combination of these attributes is used to produce a binder for the hemp particles. The lime element of hempcrete needs to both bind the hemp wood particles together throughout the mass and allow the moisture to migrate through and out of the resulting structure. The setting time of hempcrete is also important, as it needs to acquire a certain hardness and set to be able to apply the material in an economic and practical timeframe.

Modern uses for hempcrete

Hempcrete provides the ecological house

Further reading

'Building with Hemp' by S Allin: ***www.hempbuilding.com***

Earthship building

Imagine a building with no utility bills, free from rising fuel prices and dwindling supplies of water. Earthships enjoy the weather, whatever the weather. If it's raining they catch free water, if it's windy they generate free power and if it's sunny they capture free heat and electricity. **Mischa Hewitt** tells us more.

Water conservation and energy efficiency measures ensure that the rainwater and renewable energy harvested goes as far as possible. Built from waste materials, earthships combine many elements of sustainable construction; creating a building with outstanding green credentials. There are now two earthships in the UK and the movement is growing.

Earthships are 'living' green buildings, constructed using waste car tyres and other recycled materials. They use the planet's natural systems to provide utilities - using the sun's energy and rain to provide heat, power and water. In essence, they are buildings that heat and cool themselves, harvest their own water and use plants to treat their sewage.

Earthships have evolved from 35 years of work by the environmental pioneer Mike Reynolds[1]. In New Mexico, Reynolds has built, and helped others to build, hundreds of earthships in three autonomous communities called the Greater World, Star and Reach.

The key to the earthship approach is using the land and resources that are all around, which means that their day-to-day running has a very low environmental impact.

There are currently two earthships in the United Kingdom, one in Fife[2] and the other in Brighton[3]. Earthship Brighton is a community centre for Stanmer Organics set in Stanmer Park, Brighton. Both projects can be visited and Earthship Brighton offers tours on the first and third Sunday of every month. A recent visitor on a hot summer's day commented: "It's an amazing building, not what I expected all. I like the idea that it's nice and bright and warm out there and really cool inside here."

The basic structure

Earthships are 'earth sheltered', timber framed buildings which can be built on any south-facing land, whether flat or a hillside. On a hillside, the site for the earthship is excavated and the soil is piled in front of the building. This is the material that will later be used to fill the tyres, which keeps transportation of heavy materials for the walls down, as only the tyres need bringing to the site. Next the damp-proof membrane and insulation for the thermal wrap are installed and then the tyre work begins.

The tyres are effectively used to replace masonry and are rammed a course at a time, up to 10 or 14 courses high. Tyres can also be used for a variety of other structural or non-structural applications, such as the footing for the front two glass faces. Potentially, any wall could be replaced with a rammed tyre wall.

The tyres are lined with cardboard and filled with earth, each tyre taking 2 to 3 wheelbarrows loads. The earth is compacted using a sledgehammer, until fully 'inflated' and level. Each tyre takes between 20 to 45 minutes to ram and any type of earth can be used, from chalk to clay as well as hardcore and other building rubble. The rammed tyres are laid like bricks and when finished form virtually indestructible steel belted rubber walls. As the tyres are round, they lend themselves to building undulating curves and other organic shapes. Between the tyre wall and thermal wrap (insulation) up to 1.5m of earth is compacted to create extra thermal mass and to earth shelter the building[4].

After the tyre work, the timber frame part

© Green Building Press

of the building goes up. From here onwards all of the techniques are standard and follow the pattern of a conventional build. Once the front timber frames, roof trusses and structure go up and the windows are fitted, the basic shell is completed and interior decoration can begin. The power and water systems should be installed as early as possible, which means the building site itself can run on rainwater and renewable energy[5].

In total an earthship should take between 4 to 6 months to complete for a team of five or six builders, a handful of volunteers and a few specialist sub-contractors. The earthship approach readily lends itself to self-build and throughout the Earthship Brighton project

Earthship Brighton. One of only two earthships in the UK so far. these buildings ar designed to be self sufficient and not dependant on the national grid. That is why they are called earthships.

hundreds of people have gained hands-on experience of green building techniques, from tyre ramming, mixing and plastering with adobe, to installing renewable power and rainwater systems. The approach of using volunteers for low skill work is a fantastic way of easily transferring building skills to communities.

Earthship Brighton

The Earthship Brighton project began 6 years ago with the creation of the Low Carbon Network. The Low Carbon Network was formed to highlight the connection of building and global warming through innovative demonstration projects. Earthship Brighton was the Low Carbon Network's first initiative and will be a community centre for Stanmer Organics, a local organic co-operative, set in a 17 acre site in the beautiful Stanmer Park, near Brighton.

It took two years to locate some land, get

Misca Hewitt

planning permission, resolve building control issues, raise funds and, with the help of Mike Reynolds, adapt the Earthship design to be suitable to the English climate.

Construction began in 2003 and Reynolds came over to help build the hut module and train people. The shell of the earthship was completed by that winter and since then; the Low Carbon Network has been raising money to finish the project. The earthship was completed in 2006 and is now open to the public and as a community centre. Renewable power systems have been installed and the Low Carbon Network, responsible for the project, won the South East Renewable Energy Awards 2005 in the category of Innovation.

The future

With the price of utilities increasing and climate change looming there has never been a more pressing need for environmentally sound buildings that consume no fossil fuel during

The conservatory in Brighton Earthship. Passive solar heating through carefully positioned glazing with thermal heat storage in the structure (floor and walls) is the main heating system in earthships.

What would you do with 1000 old tyres and a heap of bottles?

The Earthship concept uses a variety of 'waste' materials from reclaimed timber and masonry to recycled glass bottles and used car tyres. The UK throws away 48 million car and van tyres a year. The Landfill Directive that came into full force in July 2006 has completely banned them from landfill[7]. Reynolds comments, "We don't desperately need tyres, but they're growing as fast as trees, if not faster." Rammed tyres are a very versatile building material and can be used in various ways, including foundations for straw bale buildings, and retaining walls. A 130m² earthship would typically use 1,000 or 10 tonnes of used car tyres. Other materials include recycled glass bottles, reclaimed timber, salvaged masonry and lots of other discarded materials from the local area, from skips and building sites.

---

day-to-day running.

The next step will be to replicate the Brighton project elsewhere in the UK and empower communities with the skills to build with waste materials and have the confidence to deliver beautiful environmentally sound buildings. This has recently happened with projects in Oxford and Bristol. There are plans to build several other community centres following the Brighton model, as well as plans to develop small communities of earthships throughout the UK, the first of which could be realised in another part of Brighton. A planning applica-

© Green Building Press

tion has been submitted to Brighton and Hove council by Earthship Biotecture to develop an 'armada' of 16 earthships in a range of 1, 2 and 3 bedroom options; 6 of which will be available as affordable social housing.

A recent market survey demonstrated how many people like the idea of earthships and would like to live in one, so the blueprint for the Brighton project could be the first of many. Every detail of how the Earthship Brighton project has progressed and developed has been captured and a new book about earthships in the UK will be published in spring 2007 to add to the range of earthship books already available.

The rammed tyre walls of the earthship are earth sheltered with up to 1.5m of rammed earth as a backfill berm. Behind the earth-shelter is a 'thermal wrap' of rigid insulation which surrounds the building and makes the thermal mass of rammed tyres and earth act as a storage heater. Just like a stone wall on a hot day, the rammed tyre walls retain heat and release it again when the building cools. The thick walls, coupled with lots of insulation, enable the earthship to maintain a comfortable temperature in any season - the building remains hot in winter and cool in summer. Increasingly a stable in-doors temperature makes a property far more comfortable, given that 9 of the 10 hottest years on record have been in the last decade[6].

The University of Brighton's School of the Built Environment has buried 32 temperature

The solar collectors on top of Earthship Brighton, which uses four renewable technologies; photovoltaic panels, a wind turbine, solar thermal panels and a wood pellet stove as a backup boiler.

Mischa Hewitt

probes in the walls and floor of Earthship Brighton and is currently undertaking a three-year thermographic study of the building's performance[8]. In this climate the addition of a front greenhouse acts as a buffer zone and further increases the thermal stability.

Renewable power

The earthship has no connection to the national grid and no fossil fuel is used for electricity generation or water-heating. Earthship Brighton uses four renewable technologies; photo-voltaic panels, a wind turbine, solar thermal panels and a wood pellet stove as a backup boiler. All of these technologies are discussed in more detail in a later chapter of this book and in Volume 2 of the Green Building Bible. Earthship Fife uses some of these as well and has a micro-hydro turbine. The electricity is stored in a battery bank. The biggest energy demand in residential buildings is heat for space heating and as the earthship deals with this through thermal mass coupled with super-insulation it is easy to generate any electricity needed from renewable sources.

Rainwater harvesting

The earthship has no connection to the water mains[9]. The roof collects water and channels it through two filters before storing it in underground tanks. The storage capacity tends to be larger than most domestic rainwater harvesting systems, because there is no mains back-up for dry periods. As the water collected is consumed, the choice of roofing material needs to be carefully made. The roof membrane used at Earthship Brighton was a TPO membrane, which has potable water certification. The water then flows to the 'water organising module', which further filters the water to a potable standard by removing any bacteria. Earthship Brighton can harvest over 70,000 litres of water per year, which coupled with water conservation methods and grey-water recycling, is more than enough for the needs of the community centre. With high levels of rainfall in the UK, most buildings are very well placed to collect and use rainwater on site and thus have a lower reliance on a centralised water main.

Using plants to treat waste-water

In an earthship, grey and black water are dealt with separately and all water is treated on site. Grey water is treated with indoor planters or 'living machines', located next to the south facing windows. The plants thrive in the sunlight and nutrient rich water, and clean the water through natural processes, such as transpiration and oxygenation by roots. All plants work well in the planters, but some 'hardier' species are good to start with; including bananas, avocados, geraniums and aloe vera. After being cleaned, the 'recycled' water is then stored in a sump, which is then fed to the toilet cistern for flushing. All black water leaves the earthship to settle in a septic tank before over-flowing to a reed-bed for treatment. Greywater and wastewater treatment is covered in more detail in a later chapter in this book. ☙

References

1. www.earthship.org

2. For Earthship Fife see www.sci-scotland.org.uk

3. For Earthship Brighton see www.lowcarbon.co.uk

4. Tyre pounding techniques are covered in depth in Earthship Volume 1: How to Build Your Own - see below under 'Further Reading'.

5. For a more in depth discussion on this subject, see Earthship Volume 3: Evolution Beyond Economics.

6. www.met-office.gov.uk/research/hadleycentre/index.html

7. For more details see www.tyredisposal.co.uk

8. See www.durabuild.org

9. For more information about the earthship water systems see the book 'Water from the Sky', see below.

Further reading

'Earthship' Volumes 1, 2 and 3 by M Reynolds.

'Water from the Sky' by M Reynolds.

The above books are available from Green Shop Books 01452 770629 www.greenshop.co.uk

© Green Building Press

Finally the world makes sense!

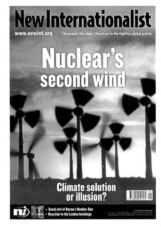

New Internationalist

Essential reading! Each month New Internationalist magazine explores one important issue, breaking the subject down into easy to understand articles, factspreads, charts and stunning photography.

Subscribe today at a special introductory rate... and get a free world map!
Phone us: 01858 438 896
or visit: www.newint.org

FLAGON TPO ROOF SAVES WATER AT EARTHSHIP   Advertisement

Flagon EP/PR TPO roofing membranes from Flag UK has been donated to support a unique community centre in Sussex and enable 73,000 litres of rainwater to be collected and harvested every year.

Earthship Brighton has no mains water connection so the rainwater flows from the roof through two filters and is stored in 4 underground tanks. It is then gravity fed to a series of filters where it is purified to drinking standard and then distributed to sinks and showers.

Project Manager for Earthship Brighton Mischa Hewitt said, "The choice of materials was crucial as the rainwater we harvest needs to be free from chemicals and other contaminants. Flagon EP/PR membrane with its WRAS potable certification was the perfect choice."

Flagon EP/PR TPO membranes have a positive environmental impact which starts during production and ends with a recyclable product that has a life expectancy in excess of 25 years. TPO's are inherently flexible remaining heat weldable through their serviceable life, resistant to weathering and ultraviolet rays and do not contain harmful chlorines, bromine or halogens.

- **TPO Membranes**
- **Green Roofing Systems**

Flag UK,
Marlborough House,
Beacon Hill Road,
Hindhead,
Surrey GU26 6QL.

Tel: 01428 604500
email: info@flaguk.co.uk
www.flaguk.co.uk

Straw bale building

Straw bale building began over a hundred years ago in Nebraska, USA, just when the baling machine had been invented and farmers were looking for a way to build some cheap, easy and temporary housing. A few of these buildings still exist today and have again, in more recent years, spurred a renewed enthusiasm for this natural, reliable, fun and sustainable way to build. **Rachel Shiamh Whitehead** explains ...

The health aspects of a straw bale home are immediately apparent. With a wall coating of lime or clay plaster, not only can the walls breathe, but one has the comfort of knowing that there are no chemicals or toxic glues.

At between £1.50 to £2.50 a bale, both material costs and labour - a bale wall can be raised in less than a week during a group wall raising session - the cost of building a straw bale house is way below the cost of building a conventional concrete block house, which brings us to the spirit of straw bale build ...

Everyone can participate in straw bale building. As Barbara Jones of Amazon Nails, a pioneer in straw bale building in Britain and Ireland, reminded us during a workshop whilst building our straw bale house, "Everyone can help to some degree, if you can make bread or bake a cake, then you know how to mix plaster" (and there's a lot of that). Everyone, from children, women, to the elderly can contribute their own skills, whether it may be snipping or retying bales, hand plastering the walls, or even making tea (most important). All these contribute in equal ways to the success of the whole project, and to the construction of a well-spirited home.

A straw bale home is a sustainable one; meaning, that it doesn't take from the earth's resources more than is necessary and can return, to the earth, its organic material if ever taken down. It can have much less impact on the environment than conventional housing.

With a typically thick wall of 450mm, the U-value of a straw wall is about two to three times lower than most conventional buildings, being around 0.13, which is a good score in terms of the present building regulations. This also reduces any heating bills considerably. In terms of sound insulation, straw offers good sound-proofing. Also, the acoustics created within a straw bale room offer a warm ambience, a feature which has prompted a wave of music studio building using the method.

Although straw bale houses can be built and plastered to look like a conventional house, the gift of straw bale design is that it offers so many opportunities to sculpt and curve a struc-ture with an ease and authenticity that brings

Earth plastering of straw bale walls at the author's own straw bale home in Cardigan, Wales.

© Green Building Press

Two views of the award winning Ecology Building Society meeting room. It is attached, via a walkway, to the Society's new headquarters at Keighley in West Yorkshire. The straw building was built by volunteers.

beauty to an environment, which has all but lost such gentle aesthetics in building.

Building methods

Straw must be protected from adverse weather conditions. It must therefore have 'a good sized hat and pair of boots' (B. Jones). Whatever the design, it is important that, especially in British climates, the roof has a good 500mm overhang. Also important is that the straw has a good 450mm plinth wall below it to prevent any splashback from rain. Given that, let us look at some of the most common design approaches that can be used:

Loadbearing / Nebraska and hybrid

The load bearing method means that the straw bales are bearing the weight of the roof, without the use of timber framing for support. This approach, although used in the US, Australia and Canada, has only in more recent years become a more tried and popular method for house building in Europe. The first two storey load bearing straw bale house in Europe was

built in Ireland by a self builder and the Amazon Nails team. We built the first two storey load bearing straw bale house in the UK with Amazon Nails during 2003-06 in Pembrokeshire.

The benefit of this kind of a build is the reduction in the amount of timber used, which saves time and expenditure. It is a recommended approach for self-builders, as the wall raising is a simple process and lessens the need for complex carpentry skills. There is also more flexibility in the design shape; it is easier to create curves and circles and enhance its aesthetic appeal.

Rain on the side of the bales is not a great problem, but if the rain gets in and down the inside of a bale wall, then it cannot dry and will rot and need to be replaced. This can be remedied by using some large, strong tarpaulins to cover over the walls during the build, or if budget permits, by building a temporary roof covering over the site.

© Green Building Press

Infill / post and frame / timberframe

This method requires the use of a framework, usually timber, to carry the weight of the roof. The straw bales are then used as an infill material between the framework.

Probably the most well known of this style of straw bale house in the UK is Ben Law's, which was featured as a beautiful example of self-build and sustainability on the TV programme, Grand Designs. The benefits of this method are that the framework and roof can be built first, reducing the risk of any straw damage through rain. Disadvantages can be the extra expenditure on carpentry and design, and the requirement of those skills, plus the higher environmental impact.

Left and below: two views of the author's own straw bale home, under construction, showing how openings are formed and footing details.

Detailing
Foundations

Foundations for straw bale houses offer many more choices in both materials and depth, as the overall weight and distribution of the walls is far less than a conventional brick, stone or concrete block house. One example is the recently built straw bale load bearing meeting room building at the Ecology Building Society, West Yorkshire, constructed with the help of Amazon Nails. Its groundbreaking design is believed to be the first UK building with shallow foundations to be granted building regulations, although historically, it was the practice to have shallower foundations as this minimises ground impact and gives the building the flexibility to move with the earth, rather than being a rigid structure.

Choices of foundations for straw bale buildings can be: local stone, concrete blocks, pier foundations using timber post, blocks or bricks, rammed earth, (or) tyres. Tyres, although not biodegradable, are a waste product and can stand the test of time for thousands of years!

In order to benefit from the high insulation properties of the straw bale walls, it is essential that the plinth walls and the floor are well insulated to avoid any cold bridges into the house.

Roof

With a good overhang of about 500mm, the roof can be constructed using the same materials as used for most conventional houses. It is important to remember, with load bearing walls, to spread the weight of the roof evenly over the walls to ensure even compression.

Natural slates can be used. We used cedar shingles, which look particularly attractive with straw bale and are sustainable, as is a thatched roof. Shallower roofs can accommodate turf or sedum.

Finishes and services

Once the walls are up, the roof on and, with a load bearing house, the walls compressed (allow about 6 weeks), then it is time for plastering the straw walls. The ideal plaster for a UK climate externally is lime plaster. It breathes and works incredibly well with any moisture in the air. It holds moisture to itself and then releases it back into the atmosphere. This is ideal for a breathable straw wall. In warmer climates, clay is more commonly used as a plaster, with a limewash finish. In the wetter climates, clay can be used inside.

Plumbing and running electric cables in a straw bale house are very similar to a conventional house. However, electric cables should be encased in plastic conduit to protect from any potential heat generated from cables. Plumbing pipes should also run inside a larger plastic pipe to avoid any potential leakage into the straw.

In conclusion, straw bale building offers a simple and rewarding construction method, whether it is through a self-build project, or with the expertise of the growing teams of skilled 'strawbalers' in this country.

Straw bale walls can be trimmed and shaped before the render coats are applied. This allows the interior surfaces to be worked into interesting shapes, where often alcoves and secret corners are added.

Further reading

'Building with Straw Bales' - by Barbara Jones.

'The Beauty of Straw Bale Homes' by A & Bill Steen.

'The Straw Bale House' by A & B Steen.

The above titles are available from Green Shop Books, 01452 770629 www.greenshop.co.uk

'The Woodland House' by Ben Law, available from www.newbuilder.co.uk/books

© Green Building Press

Case study

House in Wales

This house was built by the owners, Rachel and Ravi, with the help of a few paid workers and many volunteers and straw bale building course attendees. The style of the build is a nebraska hybrid system. One of the most striking aspects of this home is that two of the ground floor walls are glass, which required timber framing, whereas the rest of the building did not.

The straw bale walls were built on a ladder styled wall plate, which sits on a 450mm lime mortared stone wall. The bales were staked with hazel stakes after the 4th course, then 6th and 7th. Another wall plate then sat on top of the straw bale wall and joists for the next floor were fixed to the wall plate. The next floor was then built in the same way with a wall plate, straw bales raised like bricks and a roof plate hazel staked into the bale wall so that the rafters could be fixed.

Once the roof had been built, they then allowed for about 3 inches compression of the bales. It is important to use compact bales for building. This paticular job could have been more compacted and in the end they had nearly 5 inches of compression. Tie downs were then taken over the roof plate and down under the wall plate to secure the roof further. As the design was hybrid downstairs, they had to place 3 inch wedges between the posts and beam. As the building compressed, the wedges were knocked out to allow for an even compression.

The one disadvantage they came across with this method was in trying to keep the whole building dry before the roof was put on. With a large two storey house, it is advisable to begin the build in the spring and aim to have the roof on before the autumn rains come.

They chose to use lime plaster outside, with a natural pigmented limewash (see below). The inside was plastered with clay. 'If the earth in your garden is low in clay, as ours was, a tonne of dry clay from a brickworks is very cheap at around £15 a tonne', said Rachel.

The plastering stage can be quite laborious. Plaster is lovingly applied with rubber-gloved hands. It is possible to spray the lime plaster on which speeds up the process. However, the clay used on the interior walls of this project; a mixture of clay, sand and finely chopped straw,

View of the house, right. and above: straw bale chopping for mixing with the earth render.

setting in woodland. The house we built was a natural home, a common sense one; simplistic and beautiful in its nature. I also knew that if we were going to get the house we wished for, I was going to have to project manage the build, with the support of Amazon Nails."

was all hand and foot mixed (above right) which took time, despite the assistance of many volunteers.

When Rachel first set out to build a house she recollects that, "time was spent reflecting on the land and site, which was a rural, quiet

It quickly became apparent that not all trained builders and carpenters were appropriate for the build, unless they were willing to re-programme and re-tune their approach to the ways of straw bale building. What she found was that with such a build, the right workers seemed eventually to turn up, as did volunteers who came and developed new skills. The courses were run to teach and empower people to work in straw bale building and created a sense of community long lost in building. ☯

karmacolour
the natural painting company

commercial:domestic:interior:exterior:VOC free
we use 100% natural paint and varnish

tel: 077 255 15 158
email: info@karmacolour.co.uk
web: www.karmacolour.co.uk

Timber-straw frame building

If the first little pig had owned a baler, the story of the three pigs would have ended there. He would have built his house with straw bales; it would have been sound, solid, well-insulated and fully sustainable. Instead of reinforcing the great British tradition of building with bricks, the moral of the story would be to build with readily available natural materials – responsibly and sustainably. **Tom MacKeown** tells us about the development of the timber-straw frame concept.

Straw has been used in construction for many years: as thatch; mixed with mud to make mud bricks; as a support for lime plasters in roofs and stud-work; Stramit developed and made cementitious straw panels for use as walls and partitions and, of course, straw bales have been used as building blocks. As a building material, straw is probably the most sustainable; its insulation properties are exceptional; it is an agricultural waste product and is therefore inexpensive. Lastly, the environmental footprint left by straw-bale construction is perhaps the smallest of all building materials.

There are many fine examples of straw bale buildings in the British Isles (the previous article is testament to this) as well as an increasing number of straw bale builders. Straw bales are laid in place in much the same way as bricks and are then all pinned together with hazel sticks. The pins create rigidity and afford protection against racking stresses from the wind. The whole lot is then compressed to form a resilient, solid wall that is then capable of bearing the stresses of a second storey and a roof, together with the forces that nature will throw at it over the lifetime of the building. It is common, if not traditional, to leave an area of straw open – or at least visible behind a 'cupboard door' or truth window – so that visitors can see that the building really is of straw!

Limitations

Every material has its limitations, and straw is no exception. For all its excellence, straw bale buildings must be built in the dry. The British climate is not known for reliability and so straw bale building can often be frustrated by our variable weather. For most self-builders, this is not a problem - just wait for the weather to improve! However, this is one factor that has limited straw to the small or self-build market. The other is the lack of precision. Each bale is slightly different from the next so that no two straw-bale buildings can be identical. Again for the most part, the self-builder and small scale developer will enjoy this quirkiness. However for straw to become a viable product for use in large projects, ways of introducing uniformity and weather resistance must be incorporated to allow for ease of erection on site from 'pre-engineered' panels.

Straw-timber panels

Straw-timber panels are, very simply, a wooden frame (see photo next page) enclosing straw bales which are protected from the weather by an OSB (oriented strand board) sheath on at least one side – the other may be rendered. The whole assembly is then lifted into position and secured in much the same way as a timber frame structure is assembled on site from components that are pre-engineered off-site. For the first time straw is now appropriate for use in large projects. The pre-engineered panels conform to large development requirements and far exceed current Building Regulations' minimum requirements as far as insulation for both heat and sound are concerned. At last there is a sustainable building material that has earned a rightful place in large developments!

Such panels have been used in the construction of several buildings in recent years, the most well-known being the new 'EcoDepot' in York. EcoDepot will be the largest building of

electricity generated on site will provide 12% of current use – a figure set to increase as the EcoDepot (below) will use less energy, thus further enhancing the sustainability of the project.

Other projects, using similar technology to that of Modcell, include the construction of four dwellings – local houses for local people – near King's Lynn in Norfolk. At the time of writing these are the first dwellings to use the straw panel idea. They will also offer the opportunity of self-build.

its type in Europe. Designed by 'White Design' the EcoDepot is built of straw panels. These are made by AgriFibre Technologies. Known as Modcell, the panels are manufactured off-site in a 'mobile factory' as it were – at Easingwold near York – and are transported to site ready to be placed into position complete with lime-rendering and rain-screen thus minimizing the risk of damage from exposure to the elements.

The predicted benefits include a massive 76% reduction in energy requirements to heat the new depot. The EcoDepot will also feature rainwater harvesting, grey-water recycling;

The advantages of timber-straw panels are:
- speed of erection on site
- quality assured: off-site manufacture ensures consistency of quality
- weather-proof
- straw is kept off site until needed
- no waste on site: significantly reduces risk of fire from loose straw
- full sustainability can be achieved even on large projects
- plentiful supply of material: a new crop is harvested every year!
- affordable housing can mean just that, not only to the pocket, but also more importantly, to the environment. ☯

Useful links
www.york.gov.uk/ecodepot
www.agriboard.com

© Green Building Press

Timber building

Timber can be one of the most sustainable materials in our green building palette. However, on one hand it is the epitome of environmental design, and on the other, the indiscriminate use of timber is responsible for some of the worst excesses of environmental degradation on the planet. Timber is renewable, unlike most other modern building material components, but this implies only a potential advantage. To realise this potential, we, the users have a bit of detective work to do. **Chris Morgan** explains ...

Around half of the world's original forest cover has been destroyed, largely during the latter half of the 20th Century. Unfortunately, the forest industry is heavily linked with this forest destruction, even though a large proportion of the clearance is for other purposes, including subsistence agriculture and beef ranching. Globally, around 1.6 billion cubic metres of timber are currently harvested annually, and realistic estimates expect this to rise to 2.5 billion cubic metres by 2050. Can

this level of extraction be sustained? Well, perhaps surprisingly, current research suggests that with responsible forest management, a major crisis can be averted.

To attain any semblance of 'sustainability', the use of timber on a building must compare favourably with four criteria. These are:
- source
- transport
- treatment
- detailing.

If any one of these four criteria cannot be met, then the term 'sustainable' should not be applied.

Sustainable supplies

A sustainable source is one where the growing, management, harvesting and re-planting of trees is socially, environmentally and economically sustainable. The bottom line is that the

Northwood Construction & Locate architects

forestry work (timber extraction) must be profitable enough to sustain communities, who can afford to stay, raise families, manage and re-plant appropriately, maintain and even enhance soil conditions, avoid erosion and nutrient loss and generally improve the conditions of the local area.

Experience all over the world, and throughout history, suggests that this is not easy to achieve. De-forestation, due to lack of replanting, soil erosion, fires (and firewood collection), conversion to agriculture, lack of management and a host of other reasons, along with subsequent de-population of rural areas, is often the norm.

Certification schemes have developed to try to account for these many variables because of widespread global concern about the damage being caused, and there is no doubt that great advances, not least in understand-

Sourcing local timber

In many building projects, timber is normally sourced by the contractor from established connections with builder's merchants and suppliers. More often than not this timber will have come from far off places way outside the UK. However, most contractors will show scepticism when you suggest local timber and will probably be reluctant to deviate from their normal suppliers. Your builder will, of course, be concerned with reliability, durability, cost and so on, so bear in mind there are a number of technical problems to sort out, as well as your ethical and eco concerns! If you do manage to convince him/her, phone a few timber suppliers (see later) to find out what is available locally. It might be worth contacting the Forestry Commission and perhaps estate managers of local landed estates.

With homegrown timber, there will be other issues raised, such as an understanding of the species and durability etc, so one of you (you or your builder) may need to bone up on the subject a bit – there are also fewer universal guarantees to protect you from warped, knotty, late, damp or just plain wrong timber. Remember too that the industry, despite talk of integration and joined up thinking, is not at all joined up yet. You will quickly come to appreciate that, but it will make it all the more rewarding once your wood is safely installed in your project!

There does not seem to be a single voice for local timber merchants in England so look in your yellow pages under 'timber merchants'. Wales and Scotland seem to be more organised.

Useful contacts

Coed Cymru for Wales: www.coedcymru.org.uk
Welsh Timber Forum: www.welshtimberforum.co.uk
Woodlots: www.woodnet.org.uk
Forestry Comission: www.forestry.gov.uk
ASHS for Scotland: www.ashs.co.uk

NOR-BUILD

TIMBER FABRICATION & FINE CARPENTRY LTD.

TREE TO HOUSE

Manufacturers & Suppliers of
Scottish Timber &
Ecological Building
Materials & Products

Marcassie Farm, Rafford, Forres IV36 2RH, Scotland
Telephone/Fax: (01309) 676865
E-mail: norbuild@marcassie.fsnet.co.uk

Members of Association of Scottish Hardwood Sawmillers, www.ashs.co.uk

© Green Building Press

Structural Carpentry

Timber Routes produces quality jointed timber frames. Engineered using sustainably sourced douglas fir & oak.

We build traditional & modern houses, extensions, roofs & barns, including cost effective solutions for selfbuilders. Free initial consultation & estimate.

Timber Routes.
42 Armoury Square,
Easton, Bristol, BS5 0PT.
T:01179522585
E:paul@timber-routes.co.uk

www.timber-routes.co.uk

RAWNSLEY WOODLAND PRODUCTS

FSC
FSC SUPPLIER
SGS-COC-0975 RWP

Producers of
Home Grown Western Red Cedar
Shingles and cladding
also
Solar Kiln Dried
Local Hardwoods

RAWNSLEY WOODLAND PRODUCTS
WAVERLEY · BURLAWN · WADEBRIDGE
CORNWALL · PL27 7LD

TEL: 01208 813490 · MOBILE: 07817 450009

EMAIL: INFO@CORNISHWOODLAND.CO.UK
WEB: WWW.CORNISHWOODLAND.CO.UK

Responsibly sourced Native and European Timber

P ALL THINGS OAK PROJECT OAK

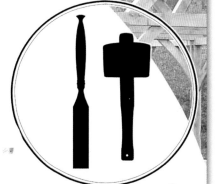

Fresh Sawn, Air Dried, Joinery Timber. Trusses, Worktops, Doors, Hardwood Fencing, Flooring, Sleepers, Cladding, Mouldings. Architectural Ironmongery, Gates, Green Oak Construction, Installation Services, Bridges. etc, etc.

Area Distributor for
Treatex
eco-friendly finishes

PROJECT OAK Cwmcafan Fawr, Felin Fach, Lampeter Ceredigion, SA48 8PJ
Mobile: 07866 670 285 Phone: 01570 470 701 Fax: 01570 470 150 Email: allthingsoak@aol.com
www.projectoak.co.uk

VAT REG. No. 841032862

ing of the issues, have been achieved. None of the schemes claim to be 100% water-tight, and there is still a very long way to go.

Independent certification

WWF and many others believe independent certification is the answer to recognising good forest management and extending good practises to a greater area of forest. For this purpose they were instrumental in setting up the Forest Stewardship Council (FSC), providing a framework for standard setting and auditing to be applied worldwide. Most operators who have had to modify forest practises to achieve certification have since reaped social and economic benefits.

Studies show that the scale of the challenge of extending certification is manageable given appropriate leadership from industry and the green movement. The biggest producers and users have been identified, and many of these are already making moves in the right direction. There are now many hundreds of companies in the Global Forest and Trade Network committed to producing, trading or purchasing forest products certified as sustainably produced. This applies pressure to the remaining slightly more reticent companies to clean up their act or lose out as consumers spend elsewhere. If a proportion of the largest companies are brought on board, either producing or using only certified timber, then a critical mass will be created for the uptake of certification.

Finding a credible forest certification system

Certification is a process by which an independent third party gives written assurances that a product, process or service conforms to specified requirements. To be effective, forest certification must be based on:

- objective, comprehensive, independent and measurable performance-based standards - both environmental and social
- equal and balanced participation of a broad range of stake holders
- a labelling system that includes a credible chain of custody
- reliable and independent third party assessments that include annual field audits

- full transparency - to the parties involved and the public.

It must also:
- take place at the forest management unit level (and not at country or regional level)
- be cost effective and voluntary
- positively demonstrate commitment from the forest owner/manager towards improving forest management
- be applicable globally and to all sorts of tenure systems, to avoid discrimination and distortion in the market place.

Who to believe?

The Forests & European Resource Network (FERN) still believe that only the FSC delivers on every important component of a credible forest management certification system. Consequently, FERN consider the FSC to be the only available framework that meets the basic expectations outlined above. The FSC is therefore the forest certification system that can be recommended to consumers or promoted among forest managers, policy makers and the public.

The Forest Stewardship Council (FSC) (01686 413916 www.fsc-uk.org) set up by representatives from environmental groups and the timber industry was formed to provide an independent, international and credible labelling scheme for timber and timber products. This scheme takes into account how forests should be managed in a way which is environmentally appropriate and respects the interests of local and indigenous people, but at the same time is economically viable. The actual inspection and evaluation of the forests is carried out by independent certification bodies, such as the Soil Association. Once approved, all wood and wood products from that forest are endorsed by the FSC and can bear its logo.

As previously stated, certified forests now exist in a growing number of countries, including the UK. To be successful the scheme needs support. You can help by asking for timber and wood products that bear the FSC logo. Most wood supplied by builders and timber

© Green Building Press

Natural Cork Flooring From Osmo

Topos Cork Toploc with the new Topos hard wax oil surface from Osmo UK is the alternative and easy to fit flooring solution for everyone who doesn't want to refrain from anything.

- Made from natural cork, highly durable and scratch resistant

- Unique double tongue and groove joints (see below) to achieve a sleek, smooth finish

- As comfortable as carpet and as easy to look after as a tiled floor

- Joint sparingly elastic, step-quiet and wonderfully warm for feet

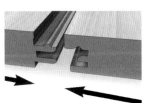

osmo

Osmo UK Ltd
Osmo House
Pembroke Road,
Stocklade Industrial Estate
Aylesbury HP20 1DB
Tel: 01296 481 220
Fax: 01296 424 090
www.osmouk.com
info@osmouk.com

CEFNLLWYN TIMBER

Beams, Lintels, Boards, Cladding, in naturally durable timbers.

Oak, Western Red Cedar, Larch & Douglas Fir Fresh sawn, air and kiln dried, Machined to your requirements

-----

Native Hardwoods Cleft Chestnut Fencing Oak & Cedar Gates Home grown Cedar Shingles

-----

01974 831560 www.cefnllwyntimber.co.uk mail@cefnllwyntimber.co.uk

FSC

Association of Scottish Hardwood Sawmillers

Bringing Scottish Wood to Life

21 sawmills across Scotland specialising in homegrown hardwood

For all your hardwood needs:

Cladding
Shingles
Flooring
Decking
Interiors
Beams
Structural timber
Indoor Furniture
Garden Furniture

Kitchen worktops
Kiln dried timber
Fresh sawn timber
Waney-edged boards
Craft products

For more information see our website:

WWW.ASHS.CO.UK

249

merchants has been imported into Britain from elsewhere.

Source of supplies

Transportation of timber is an issue largely because of the pollution associated with it, but also because of the failure to realise the potential of revitalising local economies, which is inherent in the worldwide trade in bulk timber.

The scale of the pollution associated with transported timber is often under-estimated. In other words there is more pollution associated with imported timber than there is with other, supposedly 'less green' materials. And so, it makes sense to look at the use of UK sourced timber because only then can it be said, with confidence, that the timber is anything like sustainable. In doing so, a number of other advantages become clear. Using homegrown timber:

- stimulates UK forestry and related rural industries
- creates and/or maintains employment in rural areas, and promotes good woodland management in the UK, which also benefits the local ecology.

Such considerations rarely show up on 'green building' checklists and assessment schemes, but these aspects are important, and the potential capacity of the construction industry to engage with, and benefit local forest industries, is vast. There is no doubt that homegrown timber is the 'greenest' choice for UK construc-

tion, but there is a snag...

There is no way in which the UK construction industry (let alone the paper, fencing, pallet and other industries) could source all its timber requirements from within the UK. Annually, the UK consumes around 50 million cubic metres of timber. In the same period, it produces only 7.5 million cubic metres of timber. In other words, we produce only 15% of what we consume, and we import the remainder at an annual cost to the nation of around £7 billion (not to mention the environmental cost in CO_2).

This may seem a lost cause, but there are reasons to be positive about the future. First, the amount of timber produced in the UK is set to increase from 7.5 million to 16 million cubic metres by 2020. The challenge is to create a larger market share for this timber in the construction industry.

Under 15% of the total wood and wood products consumed in Britain each year come from British woodland. Most of this goes into agriculture and fencing, yet much of it is highly suitable for use in buildings but is simply overlooked by merchants because supplies can be erratic and involve more legwork on their part to ensure throughput.

Most of the timber used in construction (by volume), does not need to be particularly good quality. Studs, joists and rafters, battens and so on, could all be readily sourced from homegrown softwood, though designers may need to alter their practices to account for weaker

Energy requirement for manufacturing and or producing selected building materials (source: Whole House Book).

Material	KWh/tonne	KWh/cu.m
Timber-local air dried	200	110
Timber-local green oak	200	220
Timber-imported softwood	1,450	754
Non-fletton bricks	860	1,462
Lightweight blocks	500	600
Steel	13,200	103,000

© Green Building Press

timber, by specifying lower strength classes, closing up on spacings, increasing section sizes and so on. Choosing to use C16 grade timber at 450mm centres rather than C24 timber at 600mm centres, for example, is a small price to pay for being able to cut all the pollution associated with importation, and benefit our own forestry industry.

Some have already started to look at initiatives to realise the potential of this extra timber, and various investigations are underway, such as high-tec jointing, gluing, de-knotting, heat treatment and so on. These initiatives will doubtless benefit the industry, but there is far greater potential simply by adjusting our expectations and design practice to suit the material we have to hand.

One excellent technique, particularly suited to the UK timber supply, is solid wood panel construction. Pioneered on the continent where it is usually known as 'Brettstapel' construction. One London practice specialises in the technique, but the potential to produce very strong, insulating, structural panels with excellent environmental credentials is huge.

Insulation can be made direct from timber – one product on the market now is timber based and imported from Finland,[1] even the binder is timber based. Woodchip and sawdust can be combined with clay and lime to produce insulating wall mass, as described in the article on low impact construction elsewhere in this book. Locally supplied woodchip can also be used for fuel. Insofar as this normally replaces fossil fuel alternatives, it is one of the most significantly beneficial uses of timber now available in the UK. Almost all wood pellet fuel is currently imported. With only 12% of the land in the UK under forest, just one third of the EU average, we could always plant more trees...

Treatment

The chemical treatment of timber makes it unsustainable for two reasons. First, these chemicals can be harmful to human, as well as other biological life. Second, treatment takes a

completely natural, biodegradable material (one of the few available to the modern designer), and turns it into toxic waste which at the end of its useful life will have to be disposed of at approved sites. The UK has a huge waste disposal problem, which is becoming worse, and timber treatment adds to it.

Supporters for the treatment of timber will argue that this is all very unfortunate but sadly unavoidable. Others claim that treatment makes timber more durable – so fewer trees have to be cut down – and people like me ought to be very grateful for it! The answer to both these points is that, with a few exceptions, the treatment of timber is avoidable, and once you know how to avoid it, the continued use of it all around you appears unforgivable.

BRE Digest 464, Part 1 gives an indication of the chemicals to be found in all that innocent looking, 'environment friendly' treated timber.

The possible emission of VOCs and formaldehyde should be an important consideration during selection of a building product. Timber studs, frames, and beam supports are usually treated and can contain organic solvents in the timber fibres as preservatives. High VOC emissions can be released from the treated timber and from other coatings.

There are locations and uses where timber is unavoidably at risk and chemical treatment is one answer. Choosing another material which is not liable to decay is also possible, and often preferable. However, the majority of situations can be designed so that timber may be used safely without treatment. There are three main tactics to avoid treatment and these are covered in the next section, which deals with good practice in detailing more generally.

Detailing

Good detailing and specification are critical. If the timber installed only lasts a few years because of poor detailing, most of the effort (and money) has been wasted, and the whole affair can hardly claim to be sustainable.

There are three main tactics worth following to avoid timber treatment and still ensure good durability of timber, all of which need to be considered at the design stage, though of course some of the following is applicable for existing buildings.

The first, and by far the most important, is good design detailing and specification. The second is moisture transfusive construction. The third is species choice. This is in some ways part of the first, but is worth mentioning separately.

Good detailing for durability is well covered by organisations such as TRADA, BRE and others. Many specialist publications offer guidance, as well as magazines, trade literature from manufacturers, conference proceedings and other sources of advice. The references list, at the end of this article, gives some of these sources.

The key to good detailing in general is to

avoid any build-up of moisture, which cannot escape. It doesn't matter too much if timber gets wet, but it matters very much if it stays wet. Stopping it getting wet is normal, but making sure that once wet, it can easily and quickly dry out again, can be more important. One of the most common ways timber stays wet is because it is touching, or within about 4mm of another material. Where this happens capilliary action can keep moisture in, and so this sort of detail needs to be avoided, wherever possible. Since timber usually has to be fixed to something, it is clear that different forms of detailing start to emerge.

It is also important to allow for movement

This gridshell roofed Woodland Enterprise centre at Flimwell was built from small section coppice chestnut timber from woodlands surrounding the site. The building used 12.5 tonnes of prepared chestnut derived from 40 tonnes of coppiced wood - equivalent of 5 hectares of land and can be regrown within 5 years. Architect: Feilden Clegg

© Green Building Press

of timber, as it responds to varying ambient humidity levels. Grooves can help reduce shrinkage cracks, which externally, at least, can be a significant cause of decay. Leaving at least 6 or 7mm between boards externally, will overcome capilliary action (even allowing for board expansion), and sawn faces tend to evaporate moisture more readily than planed finishes, so may be used with advantage on external boards and cladding.

The important thing about timber coatings in external situations is that they are vapour permeable and allow the timber to move without peeling off. Some coatings achieve this by being somewhat elastic. Others, like oil and wax based coatings, do not form a skin in the same way and so are not vulnerable to movement. Light, opaque coatings protect timber better (from UV and thermal movement) than darker and more translucent coatings.

Moisture transfusive construction – well known as the 'breathing wall' is a useful tactic, not only in controlling moisture movement, but in so doing, protecting the timber used from decay. Because moisture in a 'breathing' wall, floor or ceiling will tend toward the outside and safely evaporate, there will be no build-up of moisture which could lead to decay, and so timber studs and so on may be safely left untreated.

Species choice can have a significant effect on the durability of timber elements, and in many cases the cost difference is negligible, since most of the cost is in the machining of elements. Oak and European larch heartwood, for example, are quite durable externally and may be used without preservative treatment for decking, cladding and so on. Softwood external joinery normally needs to be treated but some hardwoods do not, though bottom beads on windows are best protected, or replaced with aluminium. Cills, which are more prone to the destructive effect of UV radiation, need extra protection.

Conclusion

Perhaps the defining aspect of the environmental design movement, at present, is how it manages to remain true to its ideals whilst acknowledging the need to mainstream and influence the majority. The use of timber in buildings, particularly the use of homegrown timber, is a useful gauge of this process, but the movement must also develop and deepen its understanding of the issues. At present there is a great deal of timber used unwisely and unsustainably. We still have a lot to learn on the subject.

One interesting development, which could have huge repercussions for the forest and timber industry in construction and elsewhere, is the idea of timber use as a carbon store. Initial work in Norway and Scotland suggests that using mass timber, and indeed timber

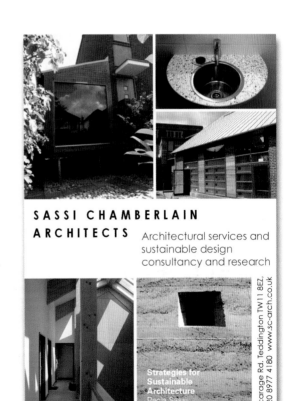

SASSI CHAMBERLAIN ARCHITECTS   Architectural services and sustainable design consultancy and research

Strategies for Sustainable Architecture
Paola Sassi

14 Vicarage Rd. Teddington TW11 8EZ.
Tel. 020 8977 4180 www.sc-arch.co.uk

generally, contributes more than you might imagine to storing carbon in the medium term, more even than installing pv cells on your roof, for example. This notion may have some currency in the wider carbon sequestration debate. Of course, it depends where it comes from...! ☙

References

1. 'Timber based insulation "Vital" is available from Construction Resources: *www.constructionresources.com*

Timber certification

Some of the above information is extracted from 'Behind the Logo'. The full report is availabe at *www.fern.org* (follow links from campaigns/FSC).

Forest Stewardship Council: *www.fsc-uk.org*
PEFC: *www.pefc.org/internet/html*

Other useful websites

If you are interested in purchasing timber from local woodlands contact Beacon Forestry: 01721 724788 *www.ecolots.co.uk* (contacts for FSC timber and locally grown timber throughout the UK).

Forestry Commission: *www.forestry.gov.uk*
UK Forest Products Association: *www.ukfpa.co.uk*
TRADA: *www.trada.co.uk*
British Biogen (now merged with the Renewable Power Association): *www.r-p-a.org.uk*

Further reading

'New Wood Architecture in Scandinavia' by C Affentranger.

'Out of the Woods: Ecological Designs for Timber Frame Houses ' by P Borer & C Harris from the Green Shop: 01452 770629 *www.greenshop.co.uk*

'Timber: Its Nature and Behaviour' by J M Dinwoodie, Spon, ISBN 0 419 23580 9.

'Forests Forever Responsible Timber Purchasing', Forests Forever, (2001) 0207 839 1891.

'Forests Forever Timber in Buildings: The Environmental Choice', contact above.

'Building in Wood: Construction and Details' by G Gutdeutsch, Birkhäuser, ISBN 3 7643 5277.

'External Timber Cladding' by P J Hislop & TRADA, TRADA Technology Ltd., 2000 ISBN 1 900510 30 8.

'Timber Decay in Buildings: The Conservation Approach to Treatment' by B Rideout, E & FN Spon, ISBN 0 419 18820 7.

'The New Wood Architecture' by N Stungo,

Laurence King, (1998).

'TRADA British Grown Hardwoods: The Designers' Manual', TRADA Technology Ltd., (1996) ISBN 1 900510 02 2.

TRADA Timber Frame Construction TRADA Technology, 2001 ISBN 1 900510 32 4.

'Building the Wooden House: Technique and Design' by K Wachsmann, Birkhäuser, ISBN 3 7643 5134 9.

Two very contrasting low impact timber buildings that were built mainly of local timber were discussaed at length in Building for a Future magazine, Volume 13, No. 4, Spring 2004.

The full magazine can be downloaded free from: *www.buildingforafuture.co.uk/spring04/*

Free information:

Back issues of Building for a Future magazine (six months after publication) are available to download free of charge from: *www.buildingforafuture.co.uk/catalogue/*

The Walter Segal Self Build Trust

helping people to build their own homes

www.segalselfbuild.co.uk

© Green Building Press

Join Centre for Alternative Technology

Europe's leading eco-centre

Discover tomorrow's green solutions today

Support CAT's work and get our quarterly magazine *Clean Slate*, 1st Issue free. Annual membership from £15.

Join by direct debit and receive CAT *Green Living Tipsheets* free

Visit CAT's website **www.cat.org.uk/membership** or phone 0845 330 4593

Please quote Green Building Bible in your reply

1st issue FREE

Advertising Policy of the *Green Building Press*

Advertising space will only be offered to companies whose products or services (in our opinion) offer clear environmental advantages over similarly available products for the same purpose.
In particular we will not accept adverts for products that:
* include ozone destroying gasses
* are wasteful of energy or are high energy consumers
* contain components that are considered harmful to human health, either by passive or active exposure
* are racist or sexist in nature

The product selection criteria used for our GreenPro database forms the basis of our advertiser selection process.

Green Building Press

Bespoke Oakwrights

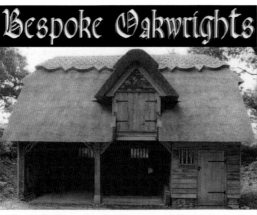

Specialist Oak Frame Carpenters

Design & Construction of Standard & Bespoke Oak Framed Buildings

Specialist Oak Joinery – i.e. Trussed Roofs

Restoration & Renovation Carpenters

See our website for full details:
http://www.bespokeoakwrights.co.uk

T: 0800 – 234 3627
M: 07944 – 086306
E: bryan.kinnear@virgin.net

Subscribe to a Better World

Permaculture Magazine is published quarterly for enquiring minds and original thinkers everywhere. Each issue brings you practical, thought provoking articles on permaculture, organics, eco-architecture, food, farming, earth medicine and lots more...

A years subscription costs just £12.50, a saving of 20% on the cover price. Subscribe today and get a FREE extra back issue, plus a copy of our Earth Repair Catalogue.
Permaculture Magazine BGB, The Sustainability Centre, East Meon, Hampshire GU32 1HR. Tel: 0845 458 4150
Email: info@permaculture.co.uk Web: www.permaculture.co.uk

permaculture *magazine*
SOLUTIONS FOR SUSTAINABLE LIVING

Passive house building

The 'passivhaus' system

The 'passivhaus' system, (passive house) originating in Germany, is considered by many to be
the world's leading design standard in energy
efficient construction. The term 'passivhaus'
refers to specific construction standards for
residential buildings, which have excellent
comfort levels in both winter and summer.
Sally Hall explains the basic premise of the
concept...

A passive house relies on an airtight
structure with superior thermal insulation and
mechanical ventilation. A mechanical system is
necessary as this will work in all climates and
in an airtight house, the heating and cooling
energy required will be sufficiently less. The
passive house should achieve heating savings
of at least 80%, compared to conventional
standards. The energy requirement for heating
is lower than 10 to 20kWh/(m²a) (depending
on climate). The running costs of such a house
will be exceptionally low and the houses are
comfortable, healthy and sustainable.

Basic principles

A dwelling built to passive house standards
would need to include:

- very good levels of insulation with minimal
  thermal bridging
- good solar and internal gains
- excellent levels of airtightness
- good indoor air quality, using an efficient,
  whole house mechanical ventilation, with
  highly efficient heat recovery system.

Providing the above are strictly adhered to
(and quality control procedures are essential
to avoid on-site problems, which may prevent
appropriate air tightness and thermal values),
these features should ensure the design heat
load is limited to the load that can be transported by the minimum required air. The house
should therefore not need a traditional heating
or air conditioning system and yet still remain
comfortable throughout the year. However, at
times some additional heating may be required.

Any new building can be built to the passive
house standard and theoretically does not need
any particularly different construction method,
and neither should it change the character of
the building. However, it is essential to get the
detailing right. The procedure is a series of
improvements in the detail of the construction,
i.e. more insulation and higher performance
windows (double glazed, low-e coating and insulated frame) and a heat recovery system from
exhausted air, for example. Excellent air tightness is vital and the building must be pressure
tested on completion. The build cost will be
higher but this will be offset by lower running
costs and benefits in terms of carbon emission
savings. It is claimed that a passive house
reduces energy consumption to less than one
seventh of a home built under current normal
practice.

Putting theory into practice

To quote the Passivhaus Institute's material,
passive houses "are buildings in which the
space heat requirement is reduced by means of
passive measures to the point at which there is
no longer any need for a conventional heating
system; an air supply system essentially suffices
to circulate the heat that is generated". This
heat is only generated by people living in the
building, equipment such as lights, TV's etc, and
of course passive solar energy from the sun.
The same air supply system will expel excess
heat when necessary and or return heat from
waste air via a heat exchanger to the incom-
ming fresh air." The standard measuring stick

Birth of the passivhaus

Dr. Wolfgang Feist founded the Passivhaus Institute in 1996 in order to further the propagation of highly efficient house buildings. It also functions as a certification Institute, testing the various technologies inherent to passive houses.

The passive house was developed in cooperation with Professor Bo Adamson of Lund University (Sweden). Their motivation was to find a solution that was at the same time comfortable, energy efficient and cost effective. The low energy prices at the time (late eighties, early nineties) meant that the saved energy costs could never cover the additional investments required. Therefore, the key idea was to reduce the energy demand so much that the necessary HVAC technology would be dramatically simplified. This results in a reduction of the investment costs.

Comfort was a main motivator, for the simple fact that people do not wish to live in uncomfortable houses. Cost effectiveness was also an important factor; no one wants to pay more. Finally, energy efficiency was obviously important to the concept, even if the majority of the people haven't accepted or understood this yet. However, now that the energy prices have so clearly increased, and threaten to go even higher, it is gradually becoming clear why we must use energy more efficiently. The fact that energy resource scarcity can be a source of conflicts is also clear. In addition, as Tony Blair himself has made very clear lately, a reduction in our use of fossil fuels as a source of energy is important if we want to limit 'global warming'.

The development of the passive house standard was based upon a variety of experiences and theories. There was already the experience of the successful construction of low energy houses (publications from Adamson in Sweden, Feist in Germany). These houses were used to validate the calculation and simulation methods. They simulated the first houses completely on the computer before building them. There was also an extensive pre-construction research project, financed by the Hessian Ministry of the Economy.

Although few people claim to have yet built a true passive house in Britain, the 'BedZED' houses by the architect Bill Dunster are, in principle, passive houses – even if he doesn't name them as such. The passive house is not protected, everybody can build

passive houses, it's a group designation people can use freely.

The construction of passive houses has expanded very gradually after the first pilot buildings: Darmstadt in 1991, Stuttgart in 1993, Naumburg, Wiesbaden, and Cologne in 1997, the first houses in Austria in 2000, Sweden in 2001. First projects in Italy (southern Tyrol) in 2002, the first house in the US in 2003, Ireland in 2005,

The knowledge and experience gathered so far must be passed on, and the know-how must be learned. The expansion, therefore, requires a certain period of time – largely because almost everyone is convinced that such a building, a) simply cannot function, b) probably leads to 'frozen' inhabitants, and c) when a + b don't occur, it's all certainly far too expensive. This was also the general opinion in Germany, until proved the opposite. Interestingly, this is experienced everywhere. It requires a lot of stamina in order to render such an innovation reality.

Further reading and internet links

CEPHEUS: Living Comfort without Heating. Ed. Helmut Krapmeier, Eckart Droessler. Vienna: Springer, 2001

CEPHEUS-Project Information No. 36: Final Technical Report. Dr. Wolfgang Feist et al. Hannover: enercity, 2001

Passive House Institute (a selection of pages in English): **www.passiv.de**

'Wohnen & Arbeiten' (a few pages in English): **www.passivhaus-vauban.de**

Dr. Wolfgang Feist

for a passive house energy consumption is 15kWh per square metre of floor area of the building per annum (this would essentially be the running cost of the air handling unit). This is a factor ten improvement on the 'average' home in Germany, and an 80% improvement on the 1995 German Thermal Insulation Ordinance for new homes. Numbers aside, a passive house also represents a marked improvement in the level of comfort experienced by homeowners

THE VELOX FACTOR 10+ passivhaus houses

* Future-oriented living without wasting energy
* Light-flooded rooms
* Ecologically sensible construction using wood and concrete
* In the Velox Factor 10+ House, regional raw materials are turned into local building materials
* Scientifically simulated thermal properties
* Lowest possible material input - perfectly ecological
* The energy needed to produce heat insulation is already saved in half a heating period
* The massive structure creates a balanced room climate, even without shading the façade facing south
* LEK = 24 (thermal leakage) LEKeq = 4
* HWB = 8 kWh/m²a (energy needed for heating a building)

This page shows example buildings from a company that builds only passivhaus homes, Velox Factor 10+ houses.
*Builder: Dieter Tscharf: **tscharfd@aon.at***

© Green Building Press

and a dramatic reduction in their energy bills.

Building to the passive house standard means optimising two key components of a house: the building envelope and the windows. These key components are detailed and insulated to a point where their combined efficiency of reducing heat loss cancel the need for a conventional heating system. The extra costs of detailing and building such a structure are claimed to be compensated by the fact that an oil, gas or electrical heating system is no longer necessary, giving two savings: the installation and maintainance cost of the equipment and the running costs over the lifetime of the building.

This said, the building envelope design must be exceptionally good, eliminating all thermal bridges and air leakages. In addition, insulation must reach certain minimum requirements. The term passive is a bit of a misnomer however as there needs to be, as mentioned earlier, an automatic ventilation system to provide a continuous, but precisely regulated, supply of fresh air. To warm the incoming fresh air, a high efficiency heat exchanger transfers the heat from the extracted indoor air (usually coming from the kitchen and bathrooms). These airflows are not mixed, and a small heating element is used for those rare cold days when additional heat is necessary.

Passive houses are essentially solar houses. With the windows being carefully dimensioned to provide the necessary daylight, the incoming solar energy covers roughly a third of the passive house's heat demand. Triple-glazed and super-insulated windows are therefore necessary, as they allow in more solar heat than they lose. The main glazing should be south facing in order to maximise the passive solar benefits.

The passivehaus design tool

The Passive House Planning Package (PHPP) is a tool for passive houses, developed and used for the first time in 1998. It is a clearly structured design tool that can be used by designers and builders constructing to passive house standards. It has been used for many years on a number of different projects. In Europe over 4,000 dwellings, with a wide variety of designs, have been built according to passive house principles. The PHPP includes tools for:

- calculating U-values
- calculating energy balances
- designing comfort ventilation
- calculating the heat load (no heat load climate data contained yet for locations outside Germany)
- evaluating summer comfort calculations
- other useful tools for the reliable design of passive houses.

The package includes worksheets for heating energy balances (heating period or monthly techniques), heat distribution and supply, electricity demand and primary energy demand. The package is continually updated and new design modules have been added over the years, e.g. calculation of window parameters, shading, heating load and summer performance. The PHPP is continuously re-evaluated and refined, based on measurements. As part of accompanying scientific research studies, more than 300 projects have so far been compared with calculation results. The PHPP energy balance module was shown to be able to describe the thermal building characteristics of passive houses surprisingly accurately. This applies particularly to the new technique for calculating the heating load, which was developed specifically for passive houses.

Further information

Passive House (The new UK arm of the passivHaus movement): **www.passivhaus.org.uk**

Useful UK site: **www.passivehouse.co.uk**

Promotion of passive houses in Europe: **www.europeanpassivehouses.org**

10th International Conference on Passive Houses 2006: **www.passivehaustagung.de**

Passive house design tools for calculating energy balances: **www.passiv.de/07_eng/phpp/PHPP2004_F.htm**

The AECB (the sustainable building association) **www.aecb.net** *has been creating a proposed set of building standards for use in the UK, based on the passivHaus model, for incorporation into its own CarbonLite programme. See Chapter 2, 'Trends and direction.'.*

Offsite construction

Offsite construction (OSC), involves the partial or complete manufacture of buildings in factories and it has received increasing attention since the Construction Task Force's report, 'Rethinking Construction', in 1998 (otherwise known as the Egan Report). At the time OSC, though applicable to building types from housing to hospitals, was seen as having the potential for improving quality, increasing productivity and profitability and addressing the construction skills shortage. **Paola Sassi** explains the advantages and pitfalls.

Today, OSC is promoted as one of the modern methods of construction (MMC), through government funded initiatives such as Constructing Excellence in the Built Environment. There are several types of different OSC systems and materials, and while OSC has the potential for making the construction process and the constructed buildings more sustainable, OSC and sustainability cannot be considered synonymous.

The uptake of OSC and MMC has been slow, with only 10% of house builders in 2004 using MMC and currently only 4% (£3billion) of the total spending in the construction industry going towards OSC. The reasons for its slow uptake include a lack of understanding, confidence, track record, an absence of agreed product and process standards, a perception of OSC being high cost, and not least the association to its historic precedents of prefabrication with its reputation of poor quality building and poor design. In respect of housing, there has also been incidences where mortgage applications for OSC housing have been turned down by mortgage lenders. This reluctance to embrace OSC is a missed business opportunity according to Dennis Lenard, Chief Executive of Constructing Excellence in the Built Environment, (formed by a merger of the DTI funded Constructing Excellence and supply

chain body Be). Lenard believes OSC can offer a number of business advantages by potentially reducing construction time by 30%, freeing the construction process from weather constraints and contributing to achieving a high quality built product.

There are also some environmental benefits associated with the use of OSC. Working in a controlled and weather tight environment improves working conditions and reduces health and safety risks. Pollution and waste production can be controlled and minimised more easily. Water can be recycled in a factory situation. The higher quality of finishes not only affects aesthetics, but can also improve building performance by, for example, creating more airtight structures. The reduced period on site reduces the local impacts, such as noise and dust.

Claims that OSC is inherently more energy efficient are, however, simply incorrect. OSC is about the building process and while some OSC technologies facilitate the achievement of highly energy efficient structures, others do not. Furthermore some forms of OSC have high embodied energy, and some of the lightweight construction systems may, in a future of elevated average temperatures, fail to provide comfortable environments by passive means.

Types of OSC

The concept of manufacturing building elements in an environment designed for their production, and by people specialised in the field of work is, of course, not new. The prefabrication of building elements, such as doors or stairs in workshops away from the site has a long history. In contemporary construction the use of bathroom pods in hotels or student accommodation is common practice. What is perhaps different about contemporary OSC

© Green Building Press

© URBANe

© URBANe

Offsite construction has been used by eco-builders for some time, but the mainstream industry has been slow to catch on. Above, left and below: URBANe, in 2004, erected a highly energy efficient eco-home to a watertight stage, using a system called 'Tradis, in just 24 hours.

© URBANe

is the potential scale of the prefabricated elements. There are four categories of OSC that range from smaller 'traditional' OSC to virtually complete buildings. These are: sub-assemblies, panellised, volumetric and hybrids.

Sub-assemblies are the most 'traditional' and widely used system of prefabrication. Prefabricated sub-assemblies can include elements of a variety of materials. Concrete is used for beam and block floors and foundations. Prefabricated foundation systems, consisting of precast post-tensioned concrete beams, that can be used in conjunction with geotechnical support, including piles, vibro or grouting that can result in reduced impact on the ground and reduced material use. Other sub-assembly units include glass reinforced plastic (GRP) chimneys, steel for curtain walling and timber stairs. Relatively large sub-assembly units include bathroom pods, which can be made in timber, steel or concrete and have a long history of use in hotels and other repetitive serviced structures.

Panellised. These can be open, closed, composite or solid panels made in timber, steel and concrete.

Open panels include small section timber and steel framed panels. These are connected to form a structure that is then finished in traditional manner.

Closed panels incorporate insulation and can include factory-applied finishes. Timber and steel versions are available. Timber versions may include service voids.

Composite panels combine two materials to form a rigid panel. These include SIPs (structural insulated panels), comprising two layers of OSB with a rigid polyurethane insulation core. Relatively new to the UK, they are extensively used in the US and Canada. Bonded polystyrene cores are also used, but produce panels of lesser strength. SIP panels are used for walls and roofs and openings are pre-cut in the factory. The panels vary in thickness from 100mm to over 200mm and are glued together.

Solid panels are available in timber and in concrete. Concrete wall, floor and roof panels have been used since the 1960s, but the contemporary systems have overcome the structural problems experienced then. Concrete panels can be mechanically fixed, grouted together or bonded using in-situ concrete joints. Some comprise two layers of concrete, used as sacrificial shuttering. Waterproofed concrete basement walls are of interest in terms of a potential increase in basement construction in the UK, as land prices continue to rise. While most timber open, closed or composite panels are lightweight structures, solid timber panels, such as those used in Carlisle Lane housing by architects, Pringle Richards Sharratt, provide some thermal mass. Compared to concrete solid timber panels constitute a more sustainable material choice, being manufactured from forestry waste material and small section timbers.

Volumetric units are three-dimensional units, often framed steel structures, but can also be concrete, that can stand alone or be stacked one on top of the other to form a multi-storey structure. The interior finishes are often factory-applied and the services factory-installed. In certain cases the exterior finishes are also factory-applied. Volumetric systems are commonly used for building hospitals, schools, fast food restaurants. A standalone restaurant may take as little as 24 hours to assemble on site. Volumetric has successfully been used by architects Alford Hall Monaghan Morris and Cartwright Pickard, for housing developments.

Hybrid OSC involves a combination of the previous examples.

Environmental considerations
Material choice and insulation
OSC systems comprise a selection of materials and some, such as concrete or polyurethane, are associated with significant CO_2 emissions and pollution, others make use of sustainable timber supplies. Some systems, such as SIP systems, can achieve high levels of insula-

© Green Building Press

tion and airtightness relatively easily. Others are being used to provide nothing more than Building Regulation compliant structures. The fact that a building is constructed offsite does not mean it is necessarily energy efficient or sustainable in its material makeup. It is still up to the building designer to ensure this.

Thermal mass

As part of a one year DTI funded project (ARUP & Bill Dunster Architects, 2004), Chris Twinn of Arups investigated the current and future performance of lightweight and heavyweight housing constructions and concluded that, based on current global warming predictions, light weight buildings, including many of the OSC buildings, would prove uncomfortably hot in as little as 20 years time. Bill Dunster attempted to address this issue in the design of his RuralZED (see seperate story later in this chapter), where precast eco-concrete wall panels, made of a China clay waste product, provide thermal mass. Dupont has also invested

in research to address this issue and are developing a thermal mass board, less than 10mm thick, that can easily be integrated within lightweight structures. Sassi Chamberlain Architects will be testing the board in a zero heating housing development in Cardiff and monitoring its effect on indoor air temperatures.

Design for disassembly

OSC may offer opportunities for reducing waste during manufacture and the recycling of any manufacturing waste produced. However, OSC does not necessarily mean the buildings are also demountable, or for that matter, particularly flexible. Some of the volumetric systems offer the opportunity to relocate the units as

Below and inset: Kingspan Insulation were not slow off the mark in launching their range of Tek houses a few years ago, and have now secured a strong position in offsite manufacture, with a wide range of homes that homeowners can choose from a catalogue.

Kingspan

required. This facility has been integrated in a number of buildings, including housing by PCKO (see opposite) and classroom buildings by Cole Thompson, using four 13 x 3.3 fully fitted out units.

Cost

The study for the Joseph Rowntree Foundation 'Planning Gain and Affordable Housing' (T Crook, et al. 2002), identified a deficit of 30,000 and 45,000 affordable housing units being built each year. Addressing this issue is a priority for sustainable development and OSC is thought to be well-placed to help alleviating this deficit. Yet the National Audit Office issued a report in 2005 that stated that while MMC can produce four times as many homes as traditional building technologies, using the same amount of on-site labour, it also acknowledged that MMC are still more expensive than traditional ones. A greater uptake of OSC is likely to bring prices down, but for now its contribution to affordable housing is still unclear. There are, however, examples of cost-effective OSC. PCKO designed and coordinated the procurement of eight flats for key workers within a four storey block in Barling Court, London for Hyde Housing. The volumetric steel framed system, which has a 60 year lifespan, was manufactured in Poland. The volumetric units have been designed so they can be disassembled and relocated elsewhere. The installation of the modules took only four days and at £1260/m² it is equivalent to a 12% reduction on traditional construction methods and 20-30% reduction on other prefabricated methods.

Transport

In addition to Polish companies, a number of German companies are marketing high quality prefabricated housing systems in the UK. Some systems are highly insulated and incorporate PVs and solar hot water panels. For an overall assessment of the sustainability of using OSC, the question of the embodied transport-related energy has to be asked. Even when not imported from abroad, OSC may also involve double transport, i.e from the material manufacturer to the OSC manufacturer and from there to the site.

OSC in the future

The infrastructure to support OSC is increasing with initiatives such as LPS2020 (Loss Prevention Standard for Innovative Dwellings) addressing the Council of Mortgage Lenders' and the Association of Building Insurers' concerns regarding the longevity, buildability and performance of OSC. Increased uptake of OSC should reduce costs, in particular, if standardisation of prefabricated modules is encouraged.

Standardisation is, however, associated with concerns from the architectural community believing that it equates to loss of design freedom and individuality. Architects, Cartwright Pickard, have tried to address this issue by developing Optima Homes in collaboration with Pace Timber. Their aim was to provide a system that would allow architects to design almost any housing form for up to five storey apartments, but would benefit from standard components. If this truly succeeds then one of the barriers to adopting OSC is removed.

If standardisation does take off, then it would be of paramount importance that energy efficiency standards are set at suitably high levels from the start. Setting up manufacturing facilities and supply chains, involves significant effort and investment and manufacturers would understandably be reluctant to upgrade these in the near future. Government pressure should be for OSC to be synonymous with the AECB's Silver and Gold standard, not just compliance with Building Regulations.

Finally it is worth keeping in mind that new build occupies, particularly within the housing industry, only a part of the building industry. As reported in Hyde Housing Association's 'The Hyde Commission: Principles and Practice' (2004): the fact is that 50-60% of construction in the housing sector is remedial work. Will we in future see OSC applied to this area of work as well? ✆

>>>

© Green Building Press

Barling Court housing development by PCKO for Hyde Housing was built on a site that was made available for a limited amount of time and was therefore designed to be relocatable to a new site in future. The development constitutes 5 rows of volumetric elements, stacked one on top of the other four storeys high. All finishes and services were installed in the factory and the balconies were installed on site.

Links

URBANe: www.urban-e.com

Tradis: www.excelfibre.com

Kingspan Tek: www. tek.kingspan.com

Peabody Trust: www.peabody.org.uk

Further information

Books

'The Prefabricated Home' by C Davies, Reaktion Books Ltd, London: 2005.

'Prefabs: a history of the UK temporary housing' by B Vale, E & FN Spon(1995).

'Off-Site Fabrication: Prefabrication, Pre-assembly and Modularization' by A G F Gibb, , Caithness: Whittles Publishing (1999).

Reports, guides, information papers

'Off site construction: an introduction, Good Building Guide' (leaflet), Building Research Establishment, Watford: 2003.

'Off-site produced housing: a briefing guide for housing associations' by M Gorgolewski (SCI), M Milner (TRADA), K Ross (BRE), Building Research Establishment, Watford (2002).

IP 16/01 - Information Paper 16/01 is in three parts: Parts 1 and 2 describe two case studies and Part 3 summarises the research into best practice in flexible and modular residential construction.

'Prefabricated housing in the UK: a case study - Murray Grove, Hackney' by C Bågenholm, A Yates and I McAllister, Building Research Establishment, Watford (2001).

'Prefabricated housing in the UK, a case study: CASPAR II, Leeds' by C Bågenholm, A Yates and I McAllister , Building Research Establishment, Watford (2001).

'Prefabricated housing in the UK: a summary paper' by C Bågenholm, A Yates and I McAllister, Building Research Establishment, Watford (2001).

UK Housing and Climate Change. Heavyweight vs. Lightweight Construction. London: ARUP Research & Development and Bill Dunster Architects, (2004) can be downloaded at: www.zedstandards.com

'Modern methods of house construction: a surveyors guide', Building Research Establishment, Watford: 2005

Design and Modern Methods of Construction, CABE, 2004, funded by Housing Corporation and can be downloaded at www.housingcorp.gov.uk/server/show/conWeb-Doc.3306

Journals:

OSC Offsite Construction Magazine Mcclelland Publishing

Building for a Future magazine - Green Building Press

Useful websites

Industry-wide organisations promoting OSC, includes publications and downloads www.buildoffsite.com

Constructing Excellence www.constructingexcellence.org.uk

The Concrete Centre www.concretecentre.com/mmc

Timber Frame Association www.timber-frame.org/index.php?page=129

Above and right: the Peabody Trust's Murray Grove in Hackney, was a volumetric housing development of 30 flats which demonstrated that considerable time savings are possible with the use of volumentric units. The units were assembled on site in only 10 days and saved an estimated 18 weeks in the overall construction time for the scheme.

The locality around the site is disrupted for a shorter period, reducing noise, pollution emissions and local traffic disruption. Furthermore, the lightweight nature of the construction can offer potential for smaller foundations and therefore less groundworks, also reducing local disruption from moving spoil away from the site, and bringing concrete into use in the foundations. Conversely, the large deliveries of volumetric or panel units to site can be disruptive to the area and need careful management to avoid problems.

© Green Building Press

The Architects Journal created a supplement called 'Prefab Sprouts' which documents the Peabody Trust prefabricated buildings at Murry Grove in Hackney, including design detailing and costings. *www.ajplus.co.uk*

Cartwright Pickard's Peabody pods
English Heritage's new chief
PLUS: aj interiors ● architech
aj the architects' journal

Prefab sprouts

Zero energy developments

So what's it going to be like in the UK towards the middle of this century – when severe rationing of fossil fuels seems inevitable? How are we going to keep our computers and trains running on the limited stocks of renewable energy available within our national boundaries? Will we have enough green electricity to power all the heat pumps and air conditioning needed? **Keith Hall** reports (with thanks to **Bill Dunster** for his input).

Whatever the improvements in technical efficiency in buildings and the renewable energy sector, we are going to fall far short of our requirements. The first luxuries to go will have to be unnecessary air travel, followed by a reduction in food miles (food from outside our national boundaries) and far more people will have to live within walking or cycling distance

of their jobs. Tough times ahead. With half the current UK carbon emissions coming from buildings, and the other from our collective lifestyles, it is essential that we plan an overhaul of our urban fabric. We need to stay within the limited stocks of renewable energy and biomass resources that are within our own national boundaries. We need to set benchmarks limiting, and perhaps rationing, the consumption of these resources as soon as possible. Scary stuff!

For business, it is now no longer enough to buy the 'green' energy for your London office-block from a company operating a wind turbine in Wales and thinking that you've done your bit - unless the offices have already adopted all possible load reduction measures. Similarly it is not acceptable to make claims that a new

*Dunster's flagship BedZED is the prototype for his proposed step-change to ZEDstandards.
Photo: Marcus Lyon*

© Green Building Press

residential community in the Thames Gateway, powered by the waste from another London borough, is carbon neutral, as, sometime in the future, that borough will need to utilise its own local 'waste to energy' scheme to maintain it's own public services. I would be more impressed if Thames Gateway generated its own renewable energy on site. This would minimise the drain on the national grid, be it gas, or electricity. Surely, this is what decentralised power is all about; local generation for local needs!

There is much debate about how 'green' the construction industry needs to become, and how fast. The BRE's 'EcoHomes' highest standard, 'excellent', only produces a 35% carbon saving over the Building Regulations minimum. However, the volume housebuilders have been slow to adopt even the lowest EcoHomes standards, making it difficult to introduce higher standards when they don't seem to be wanted. Even the World Wildlife Fund (WWF), with its 'million sustainable homes' campaign, has found itself supporting low environmental performance standards in an effort to maximise take up of its campaign. The sad fact is that even if millions of new homes were built to the EcoHomes 'very good' standards, then national carbon emissions will continue to rise steadily.

Unfortunately this British advocacy of gradual incremental change isn't going to keep the lights on in thirty to fifty year's time, without resorting to the abominable nuclear energy scenario – and our politicians know it. That is why the government is considering nuclear, even though it is unpopular with the public.

Step-change

The answer would be to limit national demand of energy by encouraging a step change reduction in our built environment's demand for heat, power and cooling. Step-change, zero fossil energy developments are only expensive because hardly anybody is building them – every small scale project, so far, has been a prototype.

Where to begin

The government's sustainable community programme plans to build an additional 180,000 homes a year, for the foreseeable future, to reduce, they hope, property values in the south east – many of these homes will be built on land already owned by the government agency, English Partnerships. Renowned and controversial architect, Bill Dunster, has created a company called ZEDfactory. Research has shown that it would only take somewhere in the region of 2000 and 5000 new homes a year, built to 'zero energy' (ZEDstandards), for economies of scale to cut in and make them affordable, i.e no additional premium over and above what we build now.

If the government could somehow agree to adopt this step-change initiative proposed in Dunster's ZEDstandards, (which is similar to the German passivhaus, see story earlier), then Dunster believes that a buyer's club could be formed, enabling even the smallest projects anywhere in the UK, to take advantage of centrally negotiated volume discounts on a wide range of renewable technologies and low impact, low energy building products.

Then, as these economies of scale snowballed, there would be no additional cost premium for a ZED step change specification, and the conventional industry lobby (who seem engrossed in cost and the bottom line) who always resist change, will have no further grounds to complain. Dunster believes that a public promotion of the health and quality of life benefits of such an environmental approach would create considerable demand for this new style of building, a style that requires low or zero imported energy. At last check, ZEDfactory had a database of over 1000 people wanting a ZEDhome like those built at BedZED, and with only a handful of units being built a year, they have no problem demonstrating that demand exceeds supply by a healthy margin.

We are no longer a nation with our own secure fuel supplies. North Sea oil and gas are likely to be exhausted within ten years. Energy security is now a political hot potato and energy prices are rising monthly. "If we want our children to stay at home when other nations are fighting over dwindling oil supplies, and we want to avoid leukaemia clusters around nuclear plants" says Dunster, "this sort of initiative may be a constructive way forward".

RuralZED

Out of the ZEDfactory stable comes the RuralZED home. It is a self build kit which has attracted many plaudits. Built from materials that include recycled and local products, the house features foundations made from reclaimed concrete railway sleepers, micro wind turbines, a heat exchanging system using the now famous ZED-cowl (see picture previous page), and a green roof which can be covered with local plantlife. The design boasts ultra modern energy technologies which means, as you would expect from a zero energy home, that the house produces most of its own electricity, and needs no extra heating, apart from possibly during the very coldest weeks of the year. Consequently the running costs will be very low. The plan with RuralZED is that, wherever possible, local resources and suppliers can provide products for the building. Being designed to be self-built, they can also be affordable and help to create local employment.

Prototype and competition winner

A prototype RuralZED home was built inside a disused factory building in Cornwall. This was a great opportunity to prove that it really could be built by a semi-skilled workforce and utilise local materials. The RuralZED design was among others proposed as a response to a competition developed by a group called the 'Cornwall Sustainable Building Trust' (CSBT) to find 'a novel sustainable affordable solution' to Cornwall's housing problem. The competition required designers entering the competition to focus on a potential development of 5 houses for a specific site, which was approximately half an acre in size and adjacent to existing local authority housing. The competition looked for three particular aspects that RuralZED fitted perfectly.

Novel: e.g. materials, natural systems, micro-climates, new partnering/ownership arrangements, creativity etc.

Sustainable: the winning design needed to achieve some form of measurable sustainability. The Building Research Establishment's (BRE) EcoHomes 'excellent' rating was chosen as the target - no problem for a ZED home.

Affordable: the competition pre-requisite called for the design to achieve a unit cost that those on an average 'local' wage (in this instance Cornwall - £390 a week or less) could obtain a mortgage for. Given that the average cost of a Cornish house at that time was about £188,000 - the RuralZED actually cost just £85,000 to build. Considering the zero energy standards built in, this is one affordable eco-home.

The next step was to build the prototype. An undercover location was preferred, but not easy to find, as it needed to be large and high enough to build a house in. A local company,

RuralZED specification

The building is a timber, lightweight frame with pre-cast concrete sections used internally for thermal mass. The precast concrete infill sections are eco-concrete, made from a mix of ground granulated blast slag, small amounts of cement, reclaimed aggregate, Cornish china clay and local sand. This has only 1/3 of the cement content of normal concrete, but it is more expensive. In general production, RuralZED units will use normal concrete mixes. The total amount of concrete used on a RuralZED home is less than that used by a conventional timber frame home with mass concrete foundations. This is because the concrete is used carefully in a 40mm thick lining to the inside of walls (see picture below), ceilings and floors to maximise thermal mass potential. Dunster predicts that RuralZED homes will be 4 to 5^{0}C cooler than conventional timber frame homes for most of the UK summer. In the future, Dunster and others predict that in hot, dry summers owners of lightweight homes will be forced to use loads of energy running home air conditioning in an attempt to stay comfortable. Affordable coolth will become as important an issue as affordable warmth. ☯

CPR Regeneration, agreed to let CSBT use the disused factory as a workspace.

The philosophy behind RuralZED

Bill Dunster describes the philosophy behind the project as exactly the same approach as Ikea (who have also produced a flat pack house); "What we are trying to do is demystify the construction process and people's fear of the future by showing them how to live high quality lives with integrated conservation techniques and preventing the use of fossil fuels".

Paul Bright of CSBT said, on completion of the project, "The objective was to show that we can make house building completely sustainable. There should be no need to release emissions by using poured concrete, or wasting energy by importing raw materials from the other side of the world, or transporting skilled labour from the rest of Britain or Europe."

Further information

ZEDStandards: **www.zedstandards.com**

RuralZED: 020 8404 1380 **www.zedfactory.com**

Two reports on Dunster's developments at BedZED are available from: **www.newbuilder.co.uk/books**

CSBT: 01726 68654 **www.csbt.org.uk**

7 **Products and materials**

General material selection

Many building materials use large amounts of energy and produce toxic wastes during manufacture. Some are not healthy to use or to live with, and many are difficult to dispose of safely, as well as having adverse effects on the environment when land-filled or incinerated. **Mark Gorgolewski** proposes some guidelines for selecting materials.

The choice of materials and components for improved environmental specification is complex, and requires the balancing of many issues which often conflict. It is important to consider the environmental impact of a material over its full life, including: manufacture, construction, operation, maintenance, demolition, and disposal. In each phase, it is important to take into account the energy used, resources consumed, waste generated, potential for reuse or recycling and pollution emissions generated. In addition, materials need to be durable and perform well throughout their life to limit the environmental impact of their maintenance and replacement.

General guidelines

It is not practical to rank materials, as their environmental impact is linked to the purpose they are used for in the building, and how they are integrated. However, it is important that environmental performance is one of the main aspects that designers consider when choosing materials for a project. The following are a set of general guidelines that can be used.

Use materials efficiently - try to minimise the volume of materials used and avoid wasteful specification. Using less material can reduce the overall environmental impact of the building,

and using standard sizes reduces off-cuts.

Choose durable materials - replacement of a component during the life of a building adds life-cycle environmental impact. So durable components that have a long-life are often beneficial.

Choose low maintenance materials - maintenance, such as painting, and even cleaning, can be very environmentally damaging over the life of the building, and once the building is complete the designer usually has little control over this. It is therefore beneficial to minimise the need for regular maintenance, such as painting and replacement of floor coverings, by using appropriate materials.

Use materials from renewable sources where possible - to avoid depleting stocks of non-renewable materials, it is often preferable to use renewable materials. These are materials that will re-grow or regenerate at a rate which at least replaces what is taken, or harvested.

Choose reused or recycled materials where appropriate - reuse and recycling can save on primary non-renewable resources, but care must be taken, as in some cases, the energy used in transport and reprocessing of recycled materials can be high, and negates the benefits (see recycled materials web sites at end of this article).

Use materials close to their natural state - materials closer to their natural state will tend to have had less processing, which often means less energy use, less waste and less pollution.

Use local materials - using local materials can

© Green Building Press

reduce the need for transport and benefits the local economy and community. However, it is important to consider other factors and ensure that the materials have not been moved around the country for processing, before being returned to their starting point for delivery to site.

Minimise transport impacts - about 30% of UK road freight is due to movement of construction materials, which contributes significantly to climate change and local environmental problems. Any project should set out a strategy for minimising the impact of transport through: using locally sourced materials wherever possible, batching deliveries to site to ensure full loads are used, wherever possible using local labour on site, providing shared transport for labour to site, providing transport links to the building during the in use phase.

Source from manufacturers who have a proven environmental management record - some manufacturers have developed materials and products that are aimed at reducing environmental impact. Others have ISO 14001 environmental management systems in place to control their environmental impact. These manufacturers deserve support.

Source from manufacturers who readily provide environmental data - some manufacturers take environmental control of their processes seriously and will be able to provide appropriate environmental information on their products in their literature. However, be aware of green-wash, as some manufacturers are making very general or unsubstantiated environmental claims.

Minimise waste through co-ordinated design and site practices - much waste occurs through poor co-ordination of sizes etc. during design. Consider how to co-ordinate dimensions to reduce material use, and minimise waste.

Avoid uPVC - the campaign for reducing PVC use continues and various alternatives for windows, guttering, underground drainage pipes, flooring, and cladding are increasingly

available. See the Greenpeace web site for alternatives.

Use low emissions paints and finishes wherever possible - this is a complex area and general guidance is difficult. However, where possible low emission paints should be used, and preferably water based and mineral based. Good timber stains, based on oils and waxes, are available. Look for paints with the EU eco-label (see the website contact at end of this article).

Ensure that all timber comes from well managed sources - timber has a vital role to play in green building, yet the timber industry is still having a huge effect on the environment. The available information can be confusing and contradictory, making it difficult to take an informed stance. Certified timber by the Forestry Stewardship Council (FSC) is still the preferred option. Alternatives include locally grown timber or Pan European Forest Council (PEFC) timber.

Encourage reuse or recycling of materials at the end of their life - appropriate design and construction practices can help components be easily extracted at the end of their useful life, in such a way that they can be reused or recycled.

Avoid hazardous materials - materials can have various impacts on health. Hazardous materials, such as lead should be avoided. Also, materials that are significant sources of VOCs (volatile organic compounds) in the indoor environment should be avoided. These include: carpets, particularly man made (PVC) backing materials and man made fibres, vinyl flooring and wall covering materials, many adhesives, many wood based boards such as chipboard, melamine faced chipboard (kitchen units), plywood, MDF and OSB, solvents used in timber treatment, many paints, and polyurethane coatings for timber.

Avoid ozone depleting materials - only zero ozone depleting insulation products should be used. This rules out products blown using CFC or HCFC gases. Many manufacturers of polyurethane and extruded polystyrene foams now produce zero ozone depleting insulation boards.

Avoid packaging waste - a significant amount of site waste is from discarded packaging. A strategy is required to maximise recycling of packaging waste, in particular pallets, other timber, cardboard, plastic containers and sheets and polypropylene bags. There will often be conflicts and trade-offs between the various principles listed above and the decision about each material or component will have to be considered independently. The specifier must use their judgement to make an appropriate choice for each particular case. ☙

Further information

GreenPro, the on-line eco-building product database at www.newbuilder.co.uk contains listings of over 1000 building products available in the UK that have ecological merits.

'Green Building Handbook' by T Woolley, S Kimmins, P Harrison & R Harrison

'Ecology of Building Materials' by Bjorn Berge available from www.newbuilder.co.uk

'BRE Green Guide to Specification' - available from the Building Research Establishment: www.bre.co.uk

'Handbook of Sustainable Building' by D Anink, C. Boonstra & J Mak, James and James, 1996.

Greenpeace web site for PVC alternatives: http://archive.greenpeace.org/~toxics/pvcdatabase

'BRE Environmental profiles of the principal construction materials': www.bre.co.uk

'Environmental handbook for building and civil engineering projects', Vol 1 and 2, from CIRIA: www.ciria.org.uk

List of EU eco-label products including some construction products: www.eco-label.com

London Hazards Centre for information about emissions from paints and other products: www.lhc.org.uk

Forestry Stewardship Council: www.fsc-uk

Pan European Forest Council: www.pefc.org

UK Woodland Assurance Scheme: www.forestry.gov.uk

Healthy Flooring Network: www.healthyflooring.org

Certified Forest Products Council: www.certifiedwood.org

ISO 14001: www.iso14000.com

Hockerton Housing Project: www.hockertonhousingproject.org.uk

Green Product Information, Literature and Books

Independent information and **free** product literature is available for collection on sustainable building products for domestic and commercial projects.

Contained within the reference library there is a comprehensive range of green products that can be accessed by visiting The Building Centre's Information Services.

The Green Building Guide is available for £7.95 published by The Building Centre. Consists of ideas, products and contacts for building the ecologically friendly way -everything from recycled materials to natural energy products.

The bookshop also stocks the widest range of sustainability titles for all building projects.

Access green building product information

www.specifinder.com

Eco-Zone Gallery

A dedicated exhibition area within The Building Centre, devoted to sustainable building materials that preserve the natural environment within the built environment. The gallery showcases a selection of products and materials from manufacturers who have adopted environmental management policies. Literature is also available for each product featured.

The Building Centre
information and inspiration

26 Store Street, London, WC1E 7BT
Tel: 020 7692 4000. All visitors welcome

Choosing the right materials

The construction of buildings and their infrastructure are major causes of environmental degradation, pollution, climate change and energy use. A building's design and the choice of materials and processes can minimise the ecological impact during construction and in use, or can influence and cause a (possibly unforeseen) chain-reaction of damage. **John Shore** reports.

Green design aims to achieve a sustainable balance between human and environmental requirements. This balance is not just a matter of science and technology - following your intuition may be equally valuable and essential. History shows us that techniques and technologies once considered as wonderful improvements sometimes prove to do more harm than good. We also need to create healthy environments – are materials which incorporate potentially toxic waste products the best thing to embed into our homes, offices and schools? People have very individual approaches as to how we should live and build. Some are drawn to living closer to nature and building with biodegradable materials, while others are much more risk-averse and argue fervently for long-lasting concrete and foam-plastic insulation. Through careful design we can avoid the need for many of the less eco-friendly materials.

Choice of materials

Green building is now firmly set in the public consciousness. This popularity has encouraged a confusion of claims for green credentials, which sometimes are unrealistic or even inaccurate. Many manufacturers argue that green equals energy saving, while drawing a veil over the environmental and social costs of materials extraction, processing, toxicity issues and the manner of production or the costs of sales and distribution. Care needs to be taken, since similar products from different sources may vary greatly in their eco-properties and impacts.

While it is often true that material embodied-energy is relatively insignificant, compared to the energy-saving potential a material offers in the long term, we should always aim to find and use materials which deliver on all aspects of long-term environmental sustainability.

Apart from the clear distinction between natural and synthetic building materials, it is useful to consider five main groupings:
- renewable (timber, wool, etc) - from photosynthesis / biology
- extracted (earth, sand and gravel) - minimal processing
- extracted and processed (lime, plaster, slate, stone, brick)
- extracted/highly processed (cement, steel, glass and plastics)
- recycled (re-used timber, brick, aggregate, steel, glass, insulation).

Many green designers and builders want to work mainly with renewable, extracted and recycled materials and by doing so, help the building industry evolve and develop along this more natural path. Understanding and choosing materials on environmental grounds is a complex task and the work done by the Centre for Sustainable Construction at BRE is an invaluable resource. To date only a few products have been profiled[1], and some are products not normally associated with the concept and ethos of green building - while many of the greenest product suppliers are unable to afford inclusion!

Material properties

The tables on the following pages for conductivity, embodied energy and thermal capacity, graphically illustrate important material properties. Be aware of the enormous range in some of the values shown in the tables – aluminium (commonly used as a spacer in insulated glazing units) has a thermal conductivity of 198W/mK, while the silicone used in superspacer is just 0.158W/mK!

Even some green products may involve aspects which you might decide to avoid. A green designer has to consider an incredibly wide range of information and possibilities and then select the best solution. Do local materials really exist and would their use be appropriate for a low-energy, green building – and is quarrying or mining ecological, desirable and sustainable? If we all demand and specify materials with the highest green credentials, we can encourage and develop new green businesses, lifestyles and maybe - lower prices.

In order to lighten the burden we place on the environment, we can create buildings mainly from renewable, 'biological' materials, which rely on the income, rather than the capital resources of the planet. We now have a wide range of green materials and we can use glass, metals and plastics efficiently, where greener alternatives do not yet exist. Non-PVC pipes and cables are available. Kitchens can be made from real wood or pine-board and do not have to be full of energy consuming appliances. And if we claim to be green, do we really need to fill our floors and walls with a spaghetti of plastic pipes and electrical cables?

Timber frame, recycled paper insulation, straw bale and earth are all becoming popular materials for green building. Each brings its own strengths and weaknesses – no one method or material offers the only solution for all situations. We may need to combine the properties of materials in order to create successful buildings. A strawbale wall, with external timber cladding and internal earth plastering might be a logical strategy. Vapour-diffusive materials which transport moisture from the interior to the outside air are increasingly popular. Green (planted) roofs are often used to visually soften the roofline of buildings, delay solar admittance and attenuate rainwater flow.

Timber (from sustainable sources) is versatile as a beautiful, structural, easy to work material which may be locally available. New vapour-diffusive membranes enable us to build timber frame buildings with high levels of airtightness and greatly reduced heat loss. Very simple and affordable walls can be made using

140, 200 or 235mm timber studs, clad externally with rendered 60mm wood-fibre board to reduce thermal bridging, such as shown below.

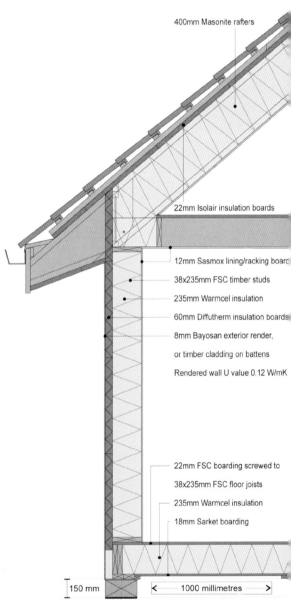

400mm Masonite rafters

22mm Isolair insulation boards

12mm Sasmox lining/racking board

38x235mm FSC timber studs

235mm Warmcel insulation

60mm Diffutherm insulation boards

8mm Bayosan exterior render,

or timber cladding on battens

Rendered wall U value 0.12 W/mK

22mm FSC boarding screwed to

38x235mm FSC floor joists

235mm Warmcel insulation

18mm Sarket boarding

150 mm

1000 millimetres

Eco-friendly roofing, thermal storage, foundations and ground floor insulation are aspects of green building which could benefit from new ideas and innovation in the use of materials. Design details of a lightweight, thermally efficient, timber framed building. © and courtesy of Ecologic Design

PRIMARY EMBODIED ENERGY

(approx)	kWh/m³
Lead	157,414
Copper	133,000
Steel (iron ore) blast furnace	63,000-80,000
Aluminium	55,868
Plastics	47,000
Steel (recycled) electric arc furnace	29,669
Glass	23,000
Fibre cement slates	12,783
Cement	2,860
Aluminium (recycled)	2,793-3,910
Clay tiles	1,520
Bricks (non flettons)	1,462
Plastic insulation	1,125
Gypsum plaster / plasterboard	900
Autoclaved bricks	800
Concrete 2 : 4	800
Imported softwood	754
Foamed glass insulation	751
Concrete Tiles	630
Concrete 1 : 3 : 6	600
Lightweight clinker blocks	600
Local slate	540
Local stone tiles	450
Sand cement render	400
Bricks (fletton)	300
Mineral fibre insulation	230
Home grown green oak	220
Crushed granite	150
Cellulose (recycled paper) insulation	133
Home grown softwood (air dried)	110
Sand and gravel	45
Sheeps wool insulation	30

Sources: Centre for Alternative Technology;
Environmental Science Handbook; Pittsburgh Corning;
Timber Trade Federation; CIRIA; GreenPro:

THERMAL CONDUCTIVITY OF MATERIALS

	W/mK
Copper	380.000
Aluminium	198.000
Steel	48.300
Granite	3.810
Limestone	1.530
Dense brickwork	1.470
Dense concrete	1.440
Sand / cement render	1.410
Very packed damp soil	1.400
Sandstone	1.295

Bricks (engineering)	1.150
Dry soil	1.140
Clay bricks (compressed, unfired)	0.950
Brickwork and tile hanging	0.840
Damp loose soil	0.700
Water	0.580
Adobe	0.520
Glass	0.500
Glaster (recycled ground glass encapsulated in lime plaster)	0.378
Earth blocks	0.340
Thermalite blocks	0.140-0.190
Plaster board	0.180
Recycled wood-fibre and Gypsum plasterboard	0.176
Hardwood	0.160
Superspacer (flexible silicone warm-edge glazing spacer)	0.158
Clay Board (alternative to plasterboard)	0.140
Oil tempered hardboard	0.120
Softwood / plywood	0.120 - 0.138
Chipboard	0.108
Stellac Wood / ThermoWood	0.100
Thermoplan multi-cellular clay blocks	0.100-0.120
Strawbales (dry)	0.080-0.100
Strawboard	0.098
Snow (average density)	0.090
Woodwool slab (light)	0.082
Stony soil (normal)	0.052
Sawdust	0.051
Bitvent 15 sheathing board	0.050
Foamed glass Insulation	0.036-0.046
Diffutherm T&G wood-fibre boards	0.044
Cork	0.043
Fibre-glass insulation	0.040
IsoNat hemp/recycled cotton insulation	0.039
Hemp and recycled cotton insulation	0.039
Thermafleece sheeps-wool insulation	0.039
Inno-Therm (recycled cotton) insulation	0.038
Warmcel 500 (recycled paper) wall insulation / hair	0.036
Warmcel (recycled paper) roof insulation	0.035
Mineral wool insulation	0.032
Rigid polystyrene insulation	0.029-0.036
Rigid polyurethane foam insulation	0.022-0.028
Rigid phenolic foam insulation	0.021-0.024
Still air	0.020

Thermal mass and storage

The ability of the interior of a building to admit, store and release heat energy at the appropriate time, is significant for the provision of user comfort, energy efficiency and passive solar heating. There are various schools of thought on how much thermal mass to include in a building. All buildings include a level of mass, which will take up heat, depending on its conductivity, which can be re-radiated after a time-lag if the ambient temperature falls. The decision on how much to include will depend on site and climate, the building design and the uses the building has to fulfil. (It should be noted that many people are living in thermally lightweight structures with appropriate glazing detailing, shading and insulation and report no significant experience of summer overheating).

Studies of heavy-weight buildings reveal the need for constant background heating to provide thermal comfort – hardly a sustainable concept. Since mass has to be heated, too much mass can be as much a problem as too little. The mass has to be cooled effectively at night, or it will be unable to take up heat the next day. The usefulness of solid materials as a thermal buffer reduces with thickness and is highly influenced by surface area. Hot thermal mass will not cool a building but can contribute to overheating. The technical problems of reliably achieving passive night-time cooling of mass in a global-warming scenario should not be underestimated.

As the tables in this section show, the materials commonly specified for thermal mass have poor thermal capacity and poor ecological credibility. A relatively small amount of water could be a simple solution to the provision of thermal storage in lightweight, super-insulated buildings. Water is more than twice as efficient as dense concrete, while being ecological, non-hazardous and available at zero cost. Glaster (recycled ground glass) encapsulated in lime plaster has thermal storage potential for ceilings, walls and floors. Ceilings are ideally placed to act as a heat-exchange medium, whereas floors and walls are often rendered ineffective by furniture and insulating coverings.

Phase-change materials (PCM) allow the selection of heat take-up and release temperatures and are a much more effective thermal buffer than even water or glass. A range of PCM products are becoming available in Europe for incorporation into ceilings and walls, to increase the thermal capacity of both lightweight and existing buildings. There is real potential for the development of PCM using plant-derived oils and waxes.

We live in interesting times which demand us not to take the environment for granted. Building material suppliers will have to rethink how they survive in a world of increasingly expensive and scarce energy and resources. ☙

THERMAL CAPACITY OF MATERIALS

	Wh/m³ K
Phase change material (PCM)[2]	5,000
Glass	1,250
Water	1,158
Cast iron	1,104
Lead	1,040
Steel	1,014
Slate	653
Stone	650
Dense concrete blocks	483
Sasmox gypsum-wood board	458
Alluvial clay - 40% sand	457
Plaster on render	440
Quarry tiles	418
Brickwork	374
Earth	356
Lightweight concrete blocks	336
Gypsum plaster	314
Dry oak, beech or ash	252
Woodwool slabs	250
Wood chipboard	224
Gypsum plasterboard	219
Softwood flooring	217
Aerated concrete blocks	140
tradical hemp / lime wall infill	157

The heat (watts per hour) needed to raise the temperature of one cubic metre of material by 1°C gives an indication of thermal capacity.

References

1. www.bre.co.uk/envprofiles

2. Gypsum plaster with encapsulated PCM (room temperature swing 22°C to 27°C).

© Green Building Press

Thermal mass

The surfaces around a room in a building will absorb and release heat to the room depending on the temperature conditions. Heavyweight building materials, such as concrete blocks, brickwork or stone, have the ability to absorb large amounts of heat. **Keith Hall** and **Jerry Clark** discuss the results of a survey carried out by energy consultant, John Willoughby.

Lightweight materials, such as timber, insulation or plasterboard, will not be able to absorb so much heat. The physical property that describes the ability of a material to absorb heat is the specific heat, that is the heat required to raise the temperature of 1kg of material by 1°C. In buildings a more relevant unit is the volumetric specific heat, or heat capacity, which describes the heat needed to raise a cubic meter of material by 1°C. The table

below shows the specific heat of a small range of building materials.

The way thermal mass works is another thing that is often misunderstood. To be effective the mass needs to be well connected or 'coupled' with the space. Spreading the mass around the surfaces is much more effective than having one very heavyweight wall, for instance, mixed with other lightweight walls or partitions. Thus the effectiveness depends on the mass and the area coupled to the space[1]. During a normal diurnal cycle, 90% of the recoverable heat flow is limited to a depth of about 50mm in dense concrete, and 50% to the first 25mm[2]. Thus for thermal storage over a 24 hour time-span, there is very little to be gained from very thick concrete masses. It can be seen from this that providing a double thickness of plasterboard

The specific heat of several common building materials, (source: John Willoughby).

Material	Density (kg/m³)	Conductivity (W/mK)	Specific heat (J/kgK)	Heat capacity (kJ/m³K)
Mineral fibre	25	0.04	750	20
Carpet	190	0.06	1360	260
Fibreboard	300	0.06	1000	300
Timber	630	0.13	1200	760
Lightweight aircrete concrete block	600	0.16	1000	600
Plasterboard	950	0.16	840	800
Brick	1700	0.62	800	1360
Medium density concrete block	1400	0.51	1000	1400
Stone	2180	1.5	720	1570
Dense concrete block	2300	1.63	1000	2300
Water	1000	1.9	4200	4200

It can be seen from the table that generally heat capacity increases with density. Also the thermal conductivity increases with density - i.e the denser materials conduct heat faster. This may sound obvious but often people confuse insulation and thermal mass. An old stone cottage will have a very high thermal mass but the wall U-value may be as high as 2W/m² K. This means that, without insulation, the cottage walls will act as excellent conductors to remove the internal heat from the dwelling during winter.

in a lightweight building would go a long way towards providing reasonable thermal mass. Effective thermal coupling depends heavily on access of the 'spare' heat to the storage mass. Fitted carpets, soft furnishings and even wall-hangings will all effectively reduce the efficiency of any available thermal mass.

Another concept is that of primary, secondary and tertiary thermal mass. Primary thermal mass is the small area of the interior which is warmed by direct sunlight. But for all other gains, from cooking, lights, appliances etc, the larger area of secondary mass (in the same room as the primary mass, but not directly sun warmed) and tertiary mass (in adjacent rooms with no direct sunlight) is more important.

Overheating and cooling down

Anyone who has gone into a stone cottage on a hot summer's afternoon will appreciate the effectiveness of thermal mass in reducing summertime temperatures. In modern houses, which are often closed up during the day, the danger of overheating is very significant. Lightweight houses can be much more prone to overheating than heavyweight ones, unless they are very well insulated. The following gives an example of the predicted effect of thermal mass on controlling temperatures on a hot August day. A 15m² unoccupied living room has been modelled using the admittance method[3]. It has 3m² of south facing glazing and 1.4m² facing north. If the house is built with standard timber frame walls, timber floors and stud partitions, peak temperatures are likely to reach over 30°C, whereas a masonry house will only reach just over 27°C. The average temperatures in the two houses are much the same - around 25°C, but the swing about the mean is 2.3°C in the heavyweight house and 5.6°C in the lightweight one.

If the south facing window is replaced by patio doors, the situation is even more extreme. Temperatures in the masonry house are predicted to reach 29°C whereas the timber frame house is likely to peak at over 34°C.

A recent worrying trend is the advertising of domestic air conditioning to combat high summertime temperatures. Not only is air conditioning expensive to run, it is also a significant source of carbon dioxide emissions. In addition the refrigerant gases often contribute to the depletion of the ozone layer. So, from this it is possible to deduce that thermal mass could have an important role to play in combating the extravagant and unnecessary use of domestic air conditioning by helping to slow and reduce diurnal temperature swings. However, attention to window design and size of roof overhang, along with increased levels of insulation, could go a long way towards reducing the temperature swings in lightweight buildings.

A 1997 simulation study[4] investigated the difference in energy use between heavy and lightweight designs. Five sites around the UK were chosen, ranging from Plymouth in the south, to Aberdeen in the north, and the difference in energy use between the two types of construction was never greater than 5%. The lightweight buildings fared better than the heavy when heating was intermittent, due to the lesser mass of material which needed warming before the occupants could feel the benefit. It was apparent that the heavyweight buildings performed better at evening out diurnal temperature swings in the summer. However, although the heavy buildings heated up more slowly during the day, their effect in a prolonged heatwave was to cool down more slowly at the end of the hot period.

During cold weather a modern, well insulated building, will not cool down so rapidly that heating is needed during the non-occupied part of the day, even if it does not contain significant thermal mass.

Passive solar versus conservation

Interest has grown, over the past 20 years, in the use of solar energy in buildings by passive means. This has placed the spotlight firmly on the role of thermal mass as a means of storing the surplus heat provided at times when there is plenty of solar radiation. In all but extreme

© Green Building Press

situations, the storage period involved was that of day to night, or possibly to the following early morning. It became possible to calculate the theoretical volume of thermal mass required in relation to the proposed area of south facing glazing.

The Pennylands housing development in Milton Keynes was one of the earliest passive solar schemes in the UK, consisting of around 180 houses with large south facing windows and an unusually large provision of thermal mass, including dense concrete inner partitions and concrete ground and first floors. These buildings were extensively monitored for energy consumption. It became apparent that the 100mm of rockwool insulation, in the outer cavity, had a far greater effect on fuel consumption than did the thermal mass. Unfortunately, due to the density of the development, the large windows led to a perceived lack of privacy for the occupants, resulting in profligate use of net curtains, thereby reducing the solar gain. Additionally, the British love affair with fitted carpets, considerably reduced the effectiveness of the thermal mass.

More recently a smaller number of Scandinavian style lightweight 'super-insulated' houses have been built, using prefabricated timber sections. These houses were also monitored. There was no particular attempt made to collect solar energy, but these houses had a smaller fuel consumption than did the passive solar designs of the day.

Many scientific papers on the 'light versus heavy' subject have since been published, unfortunately often funded by a vested interest, such as the concrete block industry, or those providing materials for lightweight buildings. However, the balance of evidence points out that the benefit of thermal mass in storing solar energy became a disbenefit in intermittently heated buildings. In buildings with a large area of south facing glazing, plus the provision of adequate thermal mass, around half of the heating needs could be provided from the sun. However, the need for auxiliary heating often remained greater than that of a well insulated lightweight design.

Winter energy consumption

As we have seen, the ability of thermal mass to absorb heat and smooth out swings in internal temperature, is also important in reducing heating use in winter, in a well insulated building. In poorly insulated houses, mass can be a disbenefit in winter, as in the example of the old stone cottage. Extra energy is needed to heat up the mass, which then rapidly cools down. In well insulated houses, thermal mass can help to reduce energy used for heating. As we have intimated, this is because the mass has the ability to absorb heat gains and store them for use later in the day or during the preheat period in the following morning. In some poorly designed lightweight constructions, the daytime heat gains can occasionally result in unacceptably high temperatures, possibly causing the occupants to open the windows, thus losing the solar gains before they can make a useful contribution to the heating. In well insulated houses this effect can be significant, because often over half the heating requirement of the house can be met by incidental gains: from people, cooking, solar radiation, lights and appliances.

Airtightness

The main point to make is that good insulation alone will not be enough to keep houses comfortable if they leak air like a sieve. Thus, the aim is to build an airtight shell, regardless of whether the construction is heavy or light. Most of the work on airtightness was done in Scandinavia and Canada where lightweight buildings predominate, airtightness being achieved with liberal use of sealants and membranes. Airtightness in heavy buildings relies more on wet plastering of walls and ceilings, along with good seals around windows and doors. The weak points here are the points where the intermediate floor joists penetrate the inner blockwork, and some would suggest the use of joist hangers to circumvent this. More recently, bespoke joist shoes (sometimes called boots) have been launched on the market in an attempt to address this serious heat loss route, but it is too early to decide if the products are achieving the desired goal.

Attention to detail on the sealing of the inner wall is of great importance in preventing interstitial condensation, which could pose a greater long term risk in lightweight constructions.

Sound insulation

Mass is very effective in reducing noise transfer, but so is insulation. Internal walls in lightweight buildings could include some insulation to reduce sound transfer from room to room, and thereby compete with heavyweight internal walls in this field.

Summary

The energy consumption of buildings is only weakly influenced by thermal mass; the better use of solar gains by heavy buildings tends to be compensated by extra heating energy when intermittently heated. Thermal mass plays an important part in limiting the diurnal swing in temperature - and hence peak temperatures during occupancy.

Provided solar and casual heat gains can be limited to moderate values, sufficient mass can be provided easily in all but ultra lightweight constructions. Moderate amounts of thermal mass, when combined with high standards of envelope insulation, lead to a long cooling time constant (time taken for the building temperature to drop to halfway between its original heated temperature and the external temperature).

Since all buildings are, to some degree, intermittently heated, the slight increase in solar utilisation of the heavier type is compensated by the saving in warm-up energy in the lighter type.

To be effective, thermal mass must be coupled to the space in which the gains are made, either by radiant or convective heat flow paths. Highly insulative internal finishes (e.g carpets) will almost completely negate the beneficial effects of thermal mass.

Very heavyweight buildings will perform better than lighter buildings during heat waves - the build up of heat will be slower, but will remain longer. To benefit from night ventilation buildings must have thermal mass coupled with the cooling air, and also coupled with the occupied space.

Conclusion

From the foregoing it can be seen that, in terms of comfort and energy use, there is not a huge difference between heavy and lightweight buildings. The occupants of heavy buildings may benefit from reduced temperature swings, but this is at the expense of slightly higher energy consumption. However, there are other issues which require consideration when making a reasoned choice. The most important of these is the lower embodied energy in lightweight structures. The foundations can be less substantial and many of the major components use short term renewables in their manufacture (i.e timber products). Against this must be set public perceptions – many house purchasers in this country are still in love with bricks and mortar for a good 'solid' investment, and it will probably take a while yet before 'timber frame' buildings are no longer clad with brick. ☏

References

1. 'Energy and Environment in Non-domestic Buildings - A technical design guide'.by N V Baker. ' Cambridge Architectural Research Ltd.

2. 'Environmental Performance and the Role of Structure and Materials' by N Baker. The Martin Centre for Architectural and Urban Studies, University of Cambridge.

3. Guide Book A 'Environmental Design. (CIBSE) Chapter 5 Thermal Response and Plant Sizing'.

4. 'Should it be Wood?' by P Smithdale (1997). Thesis submitted for MSc to University of East London.

Acknowledgements

Many thanks to John Willoughby BSc, MPhil, CEng, MCIBSE.

© Green Building Press

Using waste materials

Can we build our new buildings using reclaimed components from demolition? Are there opportunities for establishing closed loops for the flow of materials in construction? **Mark Gorgolewski** considers ways in which the construction industry can reduce the use of primary materials by using waste.

The concept of waste does not really exist in nature. All material is used in some way; the residual products from one species are utilised by another. Yet the way we design and construct our buildings creates a huge amount of waste and uses large amounts of non-renewable, primary materials, which are extracted with great environmental damage. In an ideal industrial ecosystem, resources are not depleted any more than those in a biological ecosystem; a piece of steel could potentially show up one year in a drink's can, the next year in an automobile and 10 years later in the structural frame of a building, "Manufacturing processes in an industrial ecosystem simply transform circulating stocks of materials from one shape to another; the circulating stock decreases when some material is unavoidably lost, and it increases to meet the needs of a growing population. Such recycling still requires the expenditure of energy and the unavoidable generation of wastes and harmful by-products, but at much lower levels than are typical today." (Frosch and Gallopoulos,1989)[1].

Currently, standard construction and demolition practices focus on the fastest, easiest and most economical way to get the job done. When this is combined with a lack of clear information and guidance for designers and owners about the implications of specifying reclaimed components and recycled materials, it creates barriers to a more ecologically sound use of resources. To move significantly towards an ecosystem based approach, there needs to be changes to the way things are done in the construction industry and, in particular, the availability of reclaimed components and recycled materials needs to increase. We should employ construc-

tion methods that will make disassembly of buildings easier, so that components used today can become valuable resources for the next generation of buildings.

There are four ways of reusing previously used materials or components in a project:
1. Reuse an existing structure on the site and possibly add to it or extend it. It may be possible to use this approach, often called 'adaptive reuse', in many urban developments. It is now relatively common, for example, with heritage structures, as they are seen to have cultural value, but is also appropriate for many existing buildings.
2. Move most or all of an existing building to a new location. Relocation sometimes occurs for pre-engineered buildings, such as industrial buildings and warehouses, and occasionally for other building types. Temporary buildings offer lessons for designing to allow future relocation.
3. Reuse individual components extracted from the demolition of one project in a new building. This form of reuse is commonly known as 'component reuse'. Thus, structural components, such as beams,

Typical demolition practices are destructive, and do not take care to extract valuable components for reuse.

columns or non-structural components, such as cladding panels, bricks or staircases, are taken from one project and used in another. This is not yet common, other than for heritage components. It is important to consider, at the design stage, how a building will be deconstructed to make it more feasible that components are reused.

4. Traditional recycling approach of using materials that have a high recycled content. For example, most metals have a significant recycled content, and other materials, such as mineral wool insulation materials, are increasing their recycled content.

Reuse is different from recycling, where a material is fed back into the manufacturing process. From an environmental, and economic, point of view, reuse of buildings or reclaimed components (1 to 3 above) are usually more beneficial strategies than recycling of materials. Reuse of components or whole buildings, generally requires little reprocessing, so greater environmental benefits often result, compared to recycling. Reuse is not usually possible for materials, such as in-situ poured concrete, which are destroyed during the demolition process (and can be crushed for use as aggregate – down-cycling), but is more realistic for many components, which can be deconstructed

These open web steel joists were taken from an old building for use in a new project.

undamaged. However, when reusing components, designers and contractors need to be more flexible in their approach. Designers who have attempted such an approach say that "using reclaimed materials adds a whole new level of complexity to the project"[2]. Reclaimed components may not be readily available off the shelf, and may be difficult to source. One of the principal problems with reuse is to co-ordinate demand with supply, and this can affect the whole design and construction process – "reclaimed materials do not show up at the right time, in the right amount or the right dimension"[3].

With a traditional approach to design, the construction components are specified and sized to suit the performance requirements of the architect's proposals, usually using standard sizes and other established performance criteria. But reclaimed components do not generally come 'off the shelf' and sometimes their specification needs to be established. Rather they are identified on demolition sites by salvage contractors. Thus, when proceeding to construction, the required size or type of component may not be readily available. This may necessitate redesign to suit available salvaged components or choosing whichever oversized components are readily available.

To maximise the potential for reuse, the starting point for a new design may, in the future, be an inventory of the available materials from salvage. For structural design, the size and length of the available members will then determine the spans and spacing possible in the new structure, so that structural efficiency can be maximised from the available components. This requires that the available components are identified early in the design process, and that these are purchased or reserved to prevent the salvage contractor from selling them elsewhere. One problem is that few, if any, salvage contractors will guarantee the availability of specific materials or products for the duration of the design and tender period, that may last years. This has severe cash flow implications and management consequences as the client may be required to dedicate resources to the

© Green Building Press

purchase of components early in the design phase, when a contractor has not yet been appointed. It may involve the design team in considerable additional research at the front end of the project to identify, locate, inspect and choose appropriate components: "Creating a workable structure for a new building using salvaged materials can be the single biggest challenge for architects. Many other materials and products are straightforward to use, but may be more difficult to source. .....Procuring all the materials in advance of tender requires money up front and a great deal of research, but enables tender documents to be complete, and contractors to view the materials before submitting a bid", (Taggart, 2001)[4].

If components cannot be pre-purchased it is essential to design in flexibility, particularly into the structural design, so that it is possible to use alternative options and adjust the design depending on the availability of components later in the process. This requires appropriate contractual procedures to be used, since the final materials may not be specified at the time of tendering. It is helpful for engineers and architects to develop working relationships with salvage and demolition contractors so they can easily find available salvaged materials, thus improving their choices when these components are required. Alternatively, it may be possible to purchase a suitable building already condemned for demolition, that contains appropriate components, and reuse as many of these as possible in the new project.

At present, the difficulties inherent in the incorporation of salvaged materials into new buildings often discourage clients and designers from embracing reuse, unless it is for principled, rather than financial reasons. Although the cost of materials can be lower through reuse, these may be offset by higher labour costs and increased design fees resulting from more research required by the design team. There is also likely to be greater uncertainty over costs, and schedule as delays can occur if key components cannot be readily sourced or there are delays in the demolition process. However, in some areas, specialist materi-

The steel at BedZED was reclaimed mainly from a railway building in Brighton. Some of the old features of the steel are still visible.

als' procurement consultants are emerging and their experience can reduce the risks of disruption or delay. For example, as a result of their involvement in the BedZED project, the environmental charity BioRegional Development Group decided to establish a new company, BioRegional Reclaimed[5], as a trading subsidiary specialising in the supply of reclaimed building materials for construction projects. Their aim is to take demolition, salvage or scrap materials and find uses for them. They offer advice to architects and their clients on the potential for reclaimed materials and disposal of materials on construction projects, and can provide a quantified assessment of the potential reduction in environmental impact from using reclaimed materials. They also locate and supply reclaimed materials to order. Furthermore, the demand for reclaimed components is likely to quickly change with altering priorities, and as salvage contractors become more aware of the value of the components they extract. ☯

References

1. 'Strategies for Manufacturing' by Frosch, Robert A. Gallopoulos, Nicholas (1989) , Scientific American. 189(3) pp152.

2. Mountain Equipment Co-op Ottawa Store, CBIP-C2000 Case Study by Chapman. & Simmonds, NRCan: Ottawa, (2000).

3. SCI, Environmental and economic assessment of a steel frame building using recycled and reused materials, Steel Construction Institute Publication P305, Ascot: UK, (2000).

4. 'Salvaged materials in new buildings' by Taggart, Canadian Architect, 46(1), pp. 32-33, (2001).

5. http://bioregional.salvoweb.com

Cement, concrete and alternatives

Cement is a wonderful material but its manufacture is responsible for massive CO_2 releases to the atmosphere. **Rob Scot McLeod** examines our addiction to cement and wonders if the alternatives already or soon to be available, might be worth considering.

Cement is a major industrial commodity that is manufactured commercially in over 120 countries[1]. Mixed with aggregates and water, cement forms the ubiquitous concrete which is used in the construction of buildings, roads, bridges and other structures. In countries even where wood is in good supply, concrete also features heavily in the construction of residential buildings.

In fact twice as much concrete is used in construction around the world as the total of all other building materials[2]. Despite its relatively low embodied energy, this scale of cement use is alarming given that cement production is responsible for 7-10% of total CO_2 emissions worldwide[3,4]. This places cement as the third biggest greenhouse gas culprit after the transportation and energy generation sectors[4]. With the cement industry growing at a rate of about 5% per year[5], increasingly severe CO_2 reduction measures will be required to keep cement emissions in line with levels set by the Kyoto Protocol[6].

There is no doubt that carbon taxes and other legislative measures to reduce carbon emission levels will provide the cement industry with an economic catalyst for change. But whilst such environmental weighting drives up the production costs for carbon emitters to the benefit of their non-emitting (or less emitting) competitors; there remains a practical need to find solutions to the problem.

With many industries it is obvious how we can make them greener or less polluting; buildings can be better designed or retro insulated and vehicle engines can be made to run more efficiently or on alternative fuels. Cement manufacture however is a well-established process and any improvements are likely to be incremental as old plant is upgraded.

So what CO_2 reduction options are available to the cement industry, and how can we establish whether these improvements are substantial enough to meet this sectors' share of the Kyoto CO_2 targets both now and in the

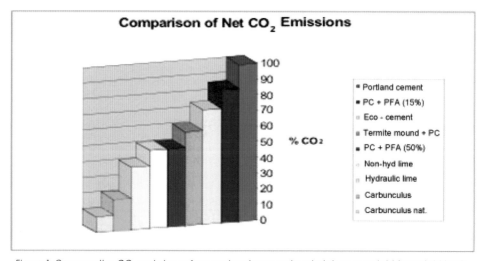

Figure 1. Comparative CO_2 emissions of cement replacement materials on a weight for weight basis, assuming portland cement = 100 (1 tonne CO_2 per 1 tonne cement).

© Green Building Press

future? Although there are several different types of cement, portland cement (PC) is the most widely used, and for simplicity I will refer to PC and cement interchangeably.

Cement production emissions

In 1994 Professor Joseph Davidovits of Caen University was the first to document the climate change implications associated with high levels of PC production. According to Davidovits a worldwide freeze of CO_2 emissions at 1990 levels, as agreed under the Kyoto Protocol, is not compatible with the high cement demands of developing countries[4]. China and Japan are increasing cement production by 5% per year and Korea and Thailand by approximately 16%. On average global cement production is rising by 5% per year. At this rate world cement production would reach 3,500 million tonnes by 2020, a figure which represents a 3-fold increase on 1990 levels[7]. Assuming this prediction is correct, then only by implementing replacements that emit one third or less of the CO_2 produced by current cement manufacturing can we keep to this target in fifteen years time. Redirecting the building industry away from its reliance on cement and steel will take time and in the interim there is an urgent need to promote lower CO_2 cement replacements.

CO_2 reduction options for cement

Essentially there are three ways to reduce the CO_2 emissions from cement manufacture. Perhaps the most obvious is to scale down production immediately, but this concept would not be popular with cement manufacturers or developing nations currently expanding their infrastructure. Therefore, we are left with two options: to reduce emissions within the existing industry; and to replace cement with viable alternatives, where possible.

Alternatives in the cement industry!

There are a number of cement and concrete making initiatives that are tackling CO_2 emissions both in the manufacturing of the product; the end use; and via the waste stream.
Industrial wastes: the proportion of 'pure' cement in a cement based mixture can be reduced by replacing some of it with other pozzolanic material (i.e. material which has the ability to act as a cement like binder). Industrial wastes, including fly ash slag, a by-product of the coal power industry, silica fume and rice husk ash, all have the combined benefit of being pozzuolana that would otherwise be destined for landfill.

Whilst every tonne of pozzuolana effectively saves a tonne of cement, there are often engineering constraints limiting the percentage of cement that can be replaced. In the past these limits have typically been in the range of 10 -15%[4] but more recently structures containing high volume fly ash at 50 - 60% replacement levels have been built[8].

Autoclaved aerated concrete (aircrete): quicklime is mixed with cement, sand (or pulverised fuel ash - PFA), water and aluminium powder to form a slurry which rises and sets to form lightweight structural blocks. These blocks are then heated in a pressurised autoclave to give them strength. AirCrete blocks have excellent thermal and acoustic properties, and are suitable for load bearing walls in low and medium rise buildings. Typically the cement component of an AirCrete block is approximately 20% by dry weight[9], which is comparable with a conventional aggregate block. Since AirCrete blocks are less than half the density of conventional medium density blocks, less than half the cement is required for an equivalent built volume. Autoclaves operate at relatively low temperatures and use far less energy than traditional brick kilns.

CaO⁻ and MgO⁻ waste stream carbon sequestration: This is a method of using waste products from the cement industry to reabsorb CO_2 directly from the ambient air. Waste stream sequestration is estimated to cost in the region of $8 US/tonne of CO_2 absorbed[10]. This figure represents a small fraction of the price that the Intergovernmental Panel on Climate Change places on the value of carbon credit, whose bottom estimate is $55 US/tonne of CO_2[11]. Given that mandatory carbon taxes may soon be on the agenda, waste stream sequestration could become a financially viable alternative for the cement industry.

Alternatives to cement

There are a number of products with similar properties to cement, the most obvious of which is probably lime, which need to be re-evaluated in light of their potentially lower CO_2 emissions.

Lime and limecrete: before delving into the intricacies of lime it is important to remember that lime is essentially formed in the same way as cement. By converting limestone to quick-lime, the raw product from which all calcium based lime is made, carbon dioxide is released. Burning fossil fuels to provide the heat for this reaction also releases CO_2, although temperatures required by lime kilns are lower than cement kilns thereby producing less CO_2. Cement is in fact composed predominantly of lime, the lime content of portland cement being around 63.5%[1]. There are two forms of lime commonly referred to. These are hydraulic and non hydraulic lime. Hydraulic lime mortars are formed by burning and slaking chalky limestone which contains a high silica content allowing stronger bond formations than non hydraulic

mortars. The more hydraulic a lime is the more cement like its properties are. However it is the traditional non-hydraulic lime putties, known for their permeable and flexible characteristics that have a greater ability to reabsorb CO_2 by carbonation during their prolonged setting process.

Hardening by carbonation occurs when calcium hydroxide in an aqueous state breaks down to bond with dissolved carbon dioxide, forming calcium carbonate with water as a by product. Some non hydraulic limes are capable of reabsorbing nearly all of the CO_2 released in their chemical formation, but this figure does not account for the CO_2 released by the kiln which can be on a par with PC[12]. In practice carbonation occurs gradually over a long period of time and is often only partially achieved. John Harrison (the founder of TecEco, see below) attributes this situation to the use of aggre-gates that are too fine to permit water and gas vapours to pass freely through the material[13]. Limecrete can be made by mixing lime with a suitable aggregate or for insulation purposes, e.g. Leca[16].

CeramiCrete: this American product combines magnesium oxide with a phosphate instead of

Figure 2. Comparison of relative energy consumption and Net CO_2 emissions for cement replace-ment materials, assuming portland cement = 100.

Cement type	Manufacturing temperature	% Energy consumption	% Net CO_2 emissions
Portland cement	1450-1500° C	100	100
PC + PFA(15)†	1450-1500° C	85 (-15%)	85
Eco-cement (TecEco)	unknown	70 (-30%)	73*
PC + Termite(40)**	1450-1500° C	60 (-40%)	60
EcoSmart concrete + PFA(50)	1450-1500° C	50 (-50%)	50
Non hydraulic (lime putty)	1350° C	100	50
Hydraulic lime (NHL2)	<1000° C	50 (-50%)	40
Carbunculus (TM)	750-800° C	40 (-60%)	20
Carbunculus (TM) nat.	750° C	30 (-70%)	10

NB Carbunculus is a brand of geopolymeric cement, * assumes maximum 12% carbon sequestration (Harrison, 2005) ** termite mounds at 40% PC replacement levels.
† PFA (15) and PFA (50) refer to pulverised fuel ash at 15% and 50% PC replacement levels respectively.

© Green Building Press

portland cement's calcium based chemistry. It still emits CO_2 in the same manner as PC but is significantly stronger so builders need less of it thereby reducing CO_2 emissions. Furthermore CeramiCrete is less dense than PC and this in turn reduces transport related CO_2 emissions. There are numerous other advantages to this product including its ability to bond to a variety of materials such as soil and straw[14]. However, it is likely to remain more expensive than PC to produce.

Eco-cement: produced by TecEco, a small Australian company, this product is undergoing considerable research and development. Their products combine reactive magnesia with fly ash and a small amount of portland cement in variable proportions depending on the end use. According to TecEco an average PC block containing 1.4kg cement can sequester 0.1kg CO_2 over time (this is a net CO_2 reduction of 7%). An equivalent eco-block is said to carbonate 50-75% more than this, giving net CO_2 reductions of 11- 12.5%[13]. Because Magnesium carbonates can be formed at lower temperatures than Calcium carbonate, TecEco have begun developing kiln technologies that will directly utilise waste heat (such as from power generation) and concentrated solar energy as the primary heat source[13]. If shown to be feasible net CO_2 reductions of up to 50% could be achieved over conventional cement kilns. Other beneficial properties include high early tensile strength compared to lime, good acid resistance and a high tolerance to salts. Due to the relative abundance of the raw materials, it may also prove cheaper to produce than PC.

Geopolymeric cements: this type of cement has its origins in the original Roman cements first used over 2000 years ago. Geopolymeric cements are formed in a different manner to PC and lime and do not involve the release of bound CO_2. The raw materials for geopolymeric cements are aluminium and silicon rich materials that are activated by alkali compounds. This silicate based chemistry can be achieved at relatively low temperatures, with the added benefit of requiring far less capital investment in manufacturing plant and equipment. The net

result is a product that sets in a matter of hours with CO_2 emissions that are 80% - 90% less than PC[4].

High quality earth bricks have been made by the addition of small quantities of geopolymeric cement to laterite soils, and then firing the bricks at low temperatures (85°C). The resulting bricks have excellent hygroscopic and breathable properties and contain less than 1/8th of a conventional bricks embodied energy[4]. Further research and development of geopolymeric cement products is currently underway prior to their commercial release.

Earth: locally sourced alternative materials have been in use all over the world since man first began building shelters. In the western world we, oddly, need to proove its capabilities once more to the regulating bodies. One fantastic example of proof is the work that Tom Morton and Arc Architects have been carrying out with earth bricks and mortars. Other earth building systems have been well documented in Building for a Future magazine. Cob, adobe and rammed earth will all have major parts to play in reducing cement/concrete use in the future. Another localised example might be that of termite mounds which are widespread throughout the African savannah and are often destroyed by farmers[15]. If an environmental impact assessment could establish that their use as a local cement substitute was relatively benign then significant financial and CO_2 savings could result. This low tech approach demonstrates that this global problem can be tackled locally and on many levels.

Conclusions

In summing up, we must remember that to prevent rapid climate change, it is necessary to reduce net CO_2 emissions drastically. Based on current consumption rates there will be a 3-fold increase in cement manufacturing CO_2 emissions between 1990 levels and 2020[7]. Using the Kyoto Protocol's 'first commitment period' CO_2 reduction target of 5.2% below 1990 levels as our initial base line target, we will need to cut our cement CO_2 outputs by two thirds plus

5.2%, i.e. 73% by 2020[7]. Subsequent Kyoto commitment periods set even greater reduction targets.

Geopolymeric cements and earth (for low rise buildings) are the only products/materials reviewed here that are clearly capable of achieving CO_2 reductions of this magnitude, whist still maintaining some of the beneficial characteristics of portland cement. This is because all of the other products use either a large percentage of PC, or rely on a similar calcination process to cement, which releases large quantities of CO_2 by virtue of the chemical reaction and furnace heat required.

Eco-cement and other magnesium based cement alternatives are possible exceptions to this finding because they have the potential to be fired at much lower temperatures than PC (possibly utilising waste heat) and are potentially stronger and less dense than calcium based cements. Future developments may well see large CO_2 reductions achieved by these products particularly as they begin to incorporate higher proportions of waste pozzuolana.

Rather than awaiting the final stages of R&D that will see this new generation of eco cements on the market, we should turn our attention towards specifying the most environmentally benign products from those currently available. Products like Canadian EcoSmart concrete have already demonstrated that by using high volume fly ash, CO_2 emissions can be halved overnight whilst creating cement that is both structurally superior to PC and cheaper to produce. Carbon taxes, mandates, assessment ratings and other incentives that drive all cement manufacturers and building specifiers to adopt such practices are urgently needed. ◉

Comment from the cement industry

In response to this article, Martin Casey, Director of External Affairs at the British Cement Association (BCA) pointed out that he disagrees with the figure of 7-10% as the global CO_2 contribution of the cement industry. The cement industry has always stated that the figure is 5%.

Casey also made the point that magnesium is not available in the UK, meaning that for the cement industry to use this technology it would need to be imported, increasing embodied energy. A fair comment.

Casey also said that the BCA represents the British cement industry, while the article is global and that he could not comment on what was beyond the boundaries of the BCA, other than to say that all the developing nations are using the most efficient methods possible to produce cement and have invested heavily in plant upgrades to this end.

His final point was that the BCA has an overt sustainability policy, and has recently published a performance report detailing how the industry is addressing corporate responsibility and sets out plans for delivering real environmental benefits. This can be found at www.cementindustry.co.uk

References

1. IUCC. (1993) Why Cement Making Produces CO_2. Information Unit on Climate Change: *www.cs.ntu.edu.au/homepages/jmitroy/sid101/uncc/fs030.html*

2. Sustainable Settlement in South Africa (2002) Climate Change: *www.sustainablesettlement.co.Za/issues/climate.html*

3. Godfrey, P (2000) TecEco Magnesium Cement Project: *www.tececo.com/technologies.tececo_cements.php*

4. Faludi, J. (2004) Concrete: A Burning Issue. World Changing, November: *www.worldchanging.com*

5. Davidovits, J. (2004) Up to 80% reduction of CO_2 Greenhouse Gas Emissions during Cement Manufacture. Geopolymer Institute: *www.geopolymer.org/library*

6. European Commission. (2004) Kyoto Protocol. European Union @ United Nations: *www.europa-eu-un.org*

7. Davidovits, J. (1994) Global Warming Impact on the Cement and Aggregates Industry. World Resource Review, 6 (2) 263-78: *www.geopolymer.org/library*

8. EcoSmart Canada (2004): *www.ecosmart.ca/facts_using_levels.cfm*

9. Spong, C. (2005) Durox Topblock Technical. Telephone interview, April 9.

10. Stolaroff, K et al. (2004) Using CaO˙ and MgO˙ Rich Industrial Waste Streams for Carbon Sequestration. Energy and Conservation Management 46 (5) 687-99: *www.sciencedirect.com/science*

11. IPCC. (2001) Climate Change 2001: Mitigation. Intergovernmental Panel on Climate Change Third Assessment Report: *www.grida.no/climate/ipcc_tar/wg3/index.htm*

12. St Astier (2001): *www.stastier.co.uk/index.htm?articles/mortars.htm~rbottom*

13. Harrison, J (2005). Carbonating and Hydraulic Mortars: *www.tececo.com*

14. CeramiCrete: *www.anl.gov/techtransfer/Available_Technologies/Material_Science/Ceramicrete/index.html*

15. Olusola, K et al (2005). Studies on Termite Hill and Lime as Partial Replacement for Cement in Plastering. Building and Environment, 33 (11): *www.sciencedirect.com/science*

16. *www.limecrete.org.uk*

© Green Building Press

Build a healthier, energy efficient home...
...Build Well, Build For Life, Build Sustainably

Ecological Building Systems provides intelligent building solutions & effective answers to sustainable building concerns, creating a living atmosphere for you which is environmentally sound & affordable. *Build For Life - Build Sustainably*

ECO ROOF — TOTAL SOLUTIONS

ECO WALL — TOTAL SOLUTIONS

Diffusion-Open Breathable Roof Structure (External to Internal)*

A Slates / Tiles
B Counter Batten
C Battens
D **solitex PLUS** - High Performance Diffusion-Open Breather Membrane
E Rafters filled with **100% Natural Hemp Insulation**
F **pro clima INTELLO** Diffusion-Open Intelligent Airtight Membrane - Vapour Check
G Service Cavity
H **Sasmox** - Gypsum Bonded Wood Particle Board

Diffusion-Open Breathable Wall Structure (External to Internal)*

A **pro clima solitex WA** - Breathable Wall Lining Membrane
B **PANELVENT** - Natural Woodfibre Sheathing
F **100% Natural Thermo-Hemp Insulation**
G **pro clima INTELLO** Diffusion-Open Intelligent Airtight Membrane - Vapour Check
H Service Cavity filled with **100% Natural Thermo-Hemp Insulation**
I **SASMOX** - Gypsum Bonded Wood Particle Board

WINNER BEST ECO PRODUCT

2006 GRAND DESIGNS MAGAZINE AWARDS

THERMO HEMP
100% Natural Thermal & Acoustic Hemp Insulation

PANELVENT
EXTERNAL SHEATHING

SOLITEX PLUS
Breather Membrane
Diffusion-Open

INTELLO®
High Reliability Vapour Check

holzFlex® 040
Natural Thermal & Acoustic
Wood Fibre Insulation

SASMOX
GYPSUM BONDED
WOOD PARTICLE BOARD

SOLITEX WA
Wall Lining Membrane

Samples & advice available exclusively from
Ecological Building Systems
Tel.: 00353 (0)46 94 32104
Fax.: 00 353 (0)46 94 32435
E Mail: info@maccannandbyrne.ie
www.ecologicalbuildingsystems.com

ECOLOGICAL BUILDING SYSTEMS
A DIVISION OF MACCANN & BYRNE
INTELLIGENT SOLUTIONS

*Products may be combined differently depending on structural requirements
Products may also be used independent of each other*

291

Healthy heating

Most of us in the eco-building community are familiar with the idea of efficient heating systems. With space heating being a major drain on fossil fuels, this makes sense, but we are perhaps overlooking the effects heating systems may have on our health. With this in mind, **Chris Morgan** argues that we run the risk of solving some problems only to create others.

In our drive to reduce energy use, and in particular, fossil fuel use, we risk creating new problems for ourselves. We shake our heads sagely at the poor decisions which led to sick building syndrome in buildings of the seventies and eighties, but we may find we create similar problems with the increasingly airtight and efficient eco-homes of the 'noughties'.

Let's take a step back and think of our biological heritage. The two heat sources with which we have evolved for millenia are the sun, and fire. Both deliver light, and heat in the form of infra-red radiation. In terms of our evolutionary make-up, it is probably fair to say we react well to a source of radiating heat, warm surfaces, cool air and probably a little air movement.

It is no surprise, therefore, to read that our biological needs for thermal comfort go far beyond the number '20°C' on a dial, and in fact are influenced by a complex matrix of:
- surrounding surface temperatures
- surrounding air temperatures
- air movement
- moisture in the air and objects nearby
- and the type of heat emitter.

In addition we know that certain parts of our body are more susceptible to heat loss (or gain) than the rest. We know that a cool head (speaking in strictly thermal terms!) aids concentration, while cold feet are particularly uncomfortable, and that in general, we require a cool head and warm feet (and to a lesser extent hands) to be comfortable and function well.

All of these aspects and more need to be considered when deciding on the heating regime of a building and its occupants, bearing in mind too that occupants' needs change with the days, the seasons, with age, and from person to person.

Characteristics of a healthy heating system

Warm surface temperatures
This is possibly the most important aspect of thermal comfort, yet it hardly registers in discussions about heating. We gain and lose a significant percentage of our heat through radiation heat exchange. What we need are surfaces which are a few degrees warmer than the ambient air temperature. Within certain tolerances (see diagram) the warmer the surfaces, the cooler the air can be whilst still maintaining comfort. The subsequent potential to save energy through lower air temperatures, whilst improving health, has yet to be fully appreciated in the eco-building community.

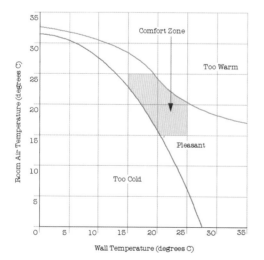

© Green Building Press

The way to achieve warm surfaces, generally, is to use radiant heating, either from a point source, like a stove or fireplace, or from a large surface area, as in underfloor heating. This tends to heat the surfaces and the objects in a room without heating the air in between – just like the sun. Some heating of air takes place of course, but it is minimal (see diagram).

Air temperature

Air temperature dominates our common understanding of temperature, yet it is only one constituent part, and unfortunately, the most problematic. In trying to keep warm, many people simply increase the air temperature, which in addition to being only partly success-ful, tends to exacerbate health problems.

Excessively warm air temperatures reduce concentration and performance, increase pulse rates, skin moisture and likelihood of fatigue. Warm air heating and air conditioning systems have also been associated with common colds, dried mucous membranes, headaches, irritabil-ity and weakened circulation. Cool air, on the other hand, tends to have the opposite effect, and aids deeper breathing which is particularly important when sleeping.

Warm air is lighter than cold air so rises and collects below ceilings. This can be very helpful in summer where high level windows and vents readily exhaust warm air and aid comfort, but in winter, it means that most of the warmth is where people aren't! This means more heat has to be generated to 'swell' the warmth down to where people are operating (or move the warm air down using fans), which leads to excessive heat input and, significantly, excessive warmth to the head, whilst feet remain too cold. This is exactly the wrong way around for human comfort and health.

Since we have to maintain fresh air levels at all times, ventilation is critical, but in exhausting air for freshness, we are also exhausting heat. Heat exchange ventilators are now common, but it remains the case that by heating the one thing that we need to get rid of, we are to an extent making a rod for our own backs. With warm air heating, lobbies become crucial to stop heat escaping each time we come in or go out, and if windows or trickle vents are left open, we are simply heating the sky. When the building fabric itself is warm and the air is cool, as it should be, such draughts are much less of a worry.

So all in all, warm air heating makes for a sorry tale, and since all heating systems will heat the air to some extent, it is unavoidable. Clearly though, we can seek to minimise this, whilst optimising the benefits of cooler air in the process.

Air movement

Moving air, however warm, will tend to cool the body by evaporation. Thus there is something strangely counter-productive of first heating, and then moving something which by moving it, serves to cool things!

What is needed for health is a small degree of air movement. Think of a warm day and a light breeze and the truth of this is apparent. Too little air movement and we cannot get rid of our moisture (sweat) or odours through evapo-ration, respiration is impaired, we get warm and tired; too much air movement of course and we will get cold. Bear in mind however that occu-pants sitting for long periods will appreciate less air movement while those working manually will need more. Air movement is also related to the airtightness of the building and to the ventilation strategy.

Excessive air movement tends to lift and circulate dust which creates further health problems. In forced air systems, the movement of air also creates friction in the ducts and positive ions in the process. In (overly) simple terms positive ions are relatively bad for respiratory health, whilst negative ions are relatively good. Think of yourself by the side of a mountain stream with fresh, gurgling running water for an image of an environment with higher negative ions and you can get a sense of this. Positive ionisation of the air also creates problems for the respiratory system.

Humidity levels

Whilst humidity levels do not directly affect the heating regime, the interactions between air, temperature and moisture levels are subtle and complex. Low humidity levels, for example, will increase respiratory problems associated with higher air temperatures, greater air movement, dust scorching and circulation, electrostatic charges and positive ionisation, while higher humidity levels will mitigate against them. On the other hand high humidity levels are associated with condensation and mould, which themselves lead to other health problems. In general, relative humidity levels should remain between 40 and 60%. This is harder to achieve with warm air heating, since the heating of the air itself dries out the air.

Heat emitter surface temperature

Fires and hot surfaces on stoves and radiators etc. have the effect of scorching dust, which is unhelpful for health, but more significantly they stir up air movement creating convection currents which then move all that scorched dust around.

Low surface temperature emitters which reduce this problem, have become more common, largely due to quite separate health and safety concerns surrounding children and other vulnerable people burning themselves. However, radiation is more effective with a higher temperature, so to achieve the same heat input, these heat emitters need to be larger to make up for the lower temperatures, which can sometimes be a problem.

Temperature gradients

I have already mentioned the problem of hot heads and cold feet created by warm air systems. But since most systems contain a large percentage of convection (air) heating, temperature gradients are common. Radiators, for example, hopelessly mis-named, produce more of their heat output through convection than radiation. Place your hand beside, and then above a radiator to see for yourself.

Fans can be used to disturb the heat pockets which develop at ceiling levels, but again these

Heating options at a glance?

Underfloor heating, and wall heating (almost unheard of in the UK until recently, but more common in Europe) are close to being ideal.

Kachelofens and other massive masonry stoves are also close to ideal.

Forced warm air heating is really to be avoided.

Systems, such as radiators and electric convectors, are effectively, warm air systems and are probably not ideal.

Open fires are wonderful, but so wasteful of fuel that they need to be seen as 'mood' heating, rather than a main source of heat these days. Individual room stoves are often OK because they emit heat largely through radiation.

Ceiling radiant heaters (like you see in churches and village halls), are often useful in large open spaces, but creating hot heads is never a good idea. Ceiling panel heating is to be avoided.

It is important to stress, that, quite apart from the times when the 'ideal' approach isn't possible, there will always be circumstances where the above advice does not apply!

have the effect of moving the air and thus cooling occupants at the same time. Reducing temperature gradients can only really be done at the design stage. One of the major advantages of underfloor heating is that heat is delivered in arguably the best place – the floor – and at low temperatures which reduce the air movement such that you strategically reduce stratification.

Temperature monotony

Most of us are familiar with the welcome cooling

© Green Building Press

effect of moving into a cold stone building on a hot day, or of entering a warm room after a snowball fight! Passing between areas of different temperature is invigorating. Conversely, experience suggests that having all rooms the same temperature has a deadening effect on the body as an organism. It is important therefore to zone areas of the building with this in mind; some rooms warmer and some cooler.

Controls

Heating systems which cannot easily be controlled can be both wasteful and uncomfortable in equal measure. Controllability (along with low installation costs) was often the rallying cry of the warm air heating brigade, and it is true that, in general, air heating is easier to control than radiant heating, especially the large surface, thermally massive systems (like underfloor heating) which in most other respects are preferable. In practice though, controllability is not just about the controls of the heating system itself, but about the way the system interacts with the thermal mass of the house (or lack of it) and the lifestyle of the occupants. Care needs to be taken at the design stage.

Conclusion

Hopefully it is clear that a healthy heating system is relatively easy to create if you use mostly radiant heating, whilst it is relatively difficult to create using convective, or air heating. You are looking then, for a system which creates warm surfaces, but relatively cool air, but a system where the heat emitter itself is not too hot. You are looking for a system which does not create excessive air movement, avoids excessive gradients but allows for different temperatures in different rooms. It needs to be quiet and easy to control, working well with the ventilation system and with the control of humidity.

The issue is likely to become more compelling as we tighten up our homes and start to see heat transfer from exhaust ventilation as the main heat losses in very low energy homes. Such heat exchange makes perfect sense in energy efficiency terms, but it is really just

convective heating and as such needs to be looked at cautiously for those concerned about health.

Heat can also be stored passively, along with moisture. My own view of the future of low energy housing is that it is the capacity of buildings to absorb and desorb heat and moisture ('thermal mass' and 'moisture mass') which is the key to super-efficient energy use, rather than warm air heat exchange technology. It is the buildings themselves, a holistic approach and the laws of nature, rather than applied technology that will help us out.

As we make our homes more airtight, the quality of the air and the warmth becomes more important still. Energy efficiency and healthy buildings can be mutually exclusive, but with good design they can also be mutually supportive. Let's get this right for our own, as well as our planet's health! ☯

Resources

Information on radiant heating:
www.constructionresources.com/products/services/radiantheating.asp
which describes the 'Variotherm' range of radiant heating products.

"Natural Heating", magazine BBE No.21, Winter 1995. Available from Building Biology and Ecology Institute of New Zealand at: www.ecoprojects.co.nz

Venolia, Carol, 'Healing Environments', Celestial Arts 1988 USA.

Underfloor heating

Underfloor heating is often specified for eco-homes. What are the advantages of this form of heating, and why is it a 'green' option? Are there any disadvantages? This article by **Olwyn Pritchard**, provides us with an introduction to the technology.

The concept of underfloor heating is not a new one. The Romans introduced it to Britain about 2000 years ago. Their systems were basic, but ingenious; flues running under a tiled floor, circulated hot air and gasses from a furnace to heat the tiles. Although this method may have produced hotspots, a problem which should not occur with a modern system, it would still have been more fuel efficient than simple fireplaces or braziers. The building would also have been comfortably warm throughout, avoiding the burning on one side and freezing on the other, effect of an open fire.

Modern systems (certainly the eco ones), use water passing through coiled pipes, running under or in the floor, rather than hot gasses, but the advantages remain the same. It is a fuel saving and energy efficient method of achieving a comfortable ambient room temperature, without having radiators taking up wall space, or indeed the need for a fireplace of any sort. This has many advantages from an aethestic point of view, allowing much greater flexibility in room layout.

Why is underfloor heating more efficient than radiators or stoves? To heat a space sufficiently to maintain a comfortable body temperature, without lowering the humidity so much as to cause discomfort, requires a large area of radiant heat emitter, (such as a floor) with the mean radiant (radiator) temperature a few degrees above air temperature.

Conventional radiators, however, being relatively small and operating at high water temperatures, create localised hot spots in a room, and only emit 15-20% of their heat by radiation, the rest is convection . The air heated by the radiator will rise to the ceiling, flow across the top of the room and down the other side, cooling as it does so. Cool air will then be drawn in at floor level and the convection current so formed will carry dust and have lowered humidity, causing problems for allergy sufferers, etc. The overall effect is to create a scenario where the occupants head is warmer than their feet, and the air is uncomfortably dry. One side of the room will probably be warmer than the other, and so on.

Underfloor heating, on the other hand, produces a large gently radiating floor area which is usually only a few degrees warmer than the air in the room. This difference is too low to create convection currents, and because radiant heat energy works like sunlight, the heat from the floor warms the occupants directly, rather than the air. Therefore, comfortable conditions can be acheived using much lower temperatures, without drying the air, and with no localised hot or cool spots in the room. A feeling of freshness will be maintained, simply because the mean radiant temperature is only a few degrees above air temperature and the relative humidity remains at a comfortable level.

From a 'green' point of view, underfloor heating is desirable, not only because it uses fuel more efficiently (lower temperature water circulation), but by avoiding wasting heat by drying out the air too much and moving it around unnecessarily, and because it can often offer health benefits to people with sensitive respiratory systems. It is green because the water circulating in the pipes does not need to be very hot, usually 45 - 50°C will be sufficient. The system can be operated using a variety of heat sources. Any kind of fuel can be used to warm the water, including condensing boilers, if a boiler is required. Condensing boilers operate at much higher efficiencies than conventional

© Green Building Press

boilers, and the lower the water return temperature, the higher the efficiency.

Again, because the systems work at low temperatures, they are even suitable for use with microgeneration and renewable energy sources. In fact they are ideal for connecting to alternative heat sources, such as solar panels, a heat recovery system, a ground source heat pump, or a wood or other biomass stove (e.g. straw, wood chips or pellets). One or more of these systems can also be used in combination.

Underfloor heating need not break the bank, either. Underfloor heating systems can be up to 25% cheaper to operate than a traditional radiator system when used with a high efficiency condensing boiler[1]. Such systems are generally no more expensive to install than a comparable radiator system.

A further advantage of this heating is the low maintenance required. Once the pipework, a (continuous winding loop - usually one large multi-loop per room), is installed, there is little to go wrong and the in-floor part of the system should last the life of the building.

Pipe can either be laid within a structural floor slab during the laying of the slab, within a floor screed on top of a structrural slab or directly beneath floor systems, such as boards or sheet material. Underfloor heating can also be installed between joists in upper floors and attached to the sides of floor joists. If you have a suspended timber ground floor then take care about a decision to put underfloor heating in as these floors tend to be very draughty and some clever design strategy will need to be adopted for the system to perform efficiently in these circumstances.

Lastly, virtually any kind of floor covering can be used with underfloor heating. Tiles, stone or slate are probably the best, as they transmit the heat effectively and are unaffected by changes in temperature or humidity. Wood floors are fine – so long as the wood is perfectly dry before it is laid, or warping can occur. Many people opt for laminated wood flooring as it is thought to

be more stable than real wood boards but there may be other environmental issues to consider, such as adhesives or origin on the species used within the laminations. Carpet, being somewhat insulating, is the least desirable, it will likely require the system to run at a slightly higher temperature, and could, with the added warmth, provide a potential breeding ground for dust mites, etc. The eventual covering should be decided upon at the design stage, as it will affect the required height of the slab and the finish.

Case studies
Underfloor heating systems
A slate floor

A self build system installed in the ground floor of a renovated farmhouse in West Wales has three circuits, and heat is supplied by a high efficiency wood fired boiler. The floor surface is of reclaimed roofing slates bedded on cement mortar and the effect is very pleasing. To the uninitiated observer it appears that original slate slabs have been retained. Unlike a normal slate floor, however, which is cold and not the sort of thing to walk on barefoot, this one radiates a gentle warmth and maintains the very well insulated house at a comfortable temperature.

The basic details of construction can be seen in the diagram – 150mm of polystyrene insulation was laid over a DPC, followed by 75mm concrete and reinforcing mesh laid on top. This served to hold the polybutylene barrier pipe, which was tied on to the mesh, in place as the final 50mm concrete was poured. Barrier pipe is so called as it has an oxygen impermeable layer built in to prevent the plastic degrading or filtering oxygen through to the water which would otherwise corrode metal parts of the system.

The heating system generally works well, except for two design faults which have had to be 'chalked up to experience'. The first is that no insulation was installed between the edge of the floor and the thick stone walls. The builder initially thought the heat radiating to the walls would help to keep them dry in the absence of any kind of damp proof course, but he acually found that it simply acts as a heat drain and cools the edges of the floor. On future projects, he has concluded that he would run the polystyrene up to just below the slates at the junction of floor and wall. The other mistake was in having overly long runs of pipework. The system consists of a 50m run, a 75m run and one 100m run. The main problem is that the 100m run requires far more pumping pressure than the two shorter ones and he is having to 'over-throttle' the shortest run to balance the flow pressure. In future pipe runs will be limited to 75m.

An oak floor

This system was installed by a builder for clients who wished to extend their living space to include a barn adjoining the house. The heat source is an oil fired boiler in the corner of the barn/room, which measures 5 x 8m, and there is a single circuit of approximately 100m. The rest of the house has a conventional central heating system. Again, the building is in Wales and the floor is finished in 150 x 25mm tongued and grooved boards of locally sourced oak. The client was very keen to use this particular supplier specifically because the wood was local and they thought that oak would be superior to the usual softwood floor boards.

The 'business part' of the floor is made of 100mm insulation above a DPM with 100mm concrete on top, above which are 50 x 50mm wooden battens at 400mm centres laid length-ways down the room with the pipe, again polybutylene barrier pipe, running between them. There are two lengths of pipe in each bay. The system was tested, found to work leak free, and screed was used to fill the spaces.

All seemed to be well until the boards arrived, supposedly well seasoned and very dry. They were loosely laid with the heating on very low to 'acclimatise' them before fixing to the battens. Within a week the planks both cupped and warped end to end – it wasn't dry enough. Everyone involved blamed each other

and eventually the wood supplier agreed to sort it out, which they did by turning the planks over and screwing them to the battens, rather than the secret nailing which was intended, as they began to warp in the other direction. The resulting floor is pleasantly warm and rustic looking, but there are gaps between the boards in places and it is marred by the many visible screw holes. The builder says the moral of this story is to be very careful with wood floors above underfloor heating and make sure the wood really is extremely dry. Otherwise, the job was a success. ✍

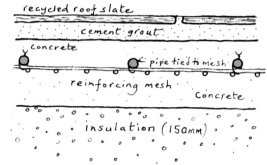

The Slate Floor

recycled roof slate
cement grout
concrete
pipe tied to mesh
reinforcing mesh
Concrete
insulation (150mm)

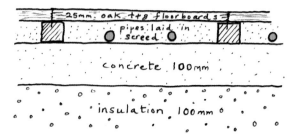

The Oak Floor

25mm oak t+g floorboards
pipes laid in screed
concrete 100mm
insulation 100mm

© Green Building Press

See also: 'Keeping warm without fossil fuels' in Chapter 4

Heating with logs

Recent price hikes in the cost of heating and cooking fuels are causing us all to reconsider our reliance on fossil fuels. From now on the UK will be dependant on gas supplies from Europe, particularly eastern Europe, and we are at the end of a very thirsty pipeline. Until the winter of 2005 we were all complacent about the fuel that we chose to heat our homes.
Keith Hall explains other options ...

If you planned to heat your home with a gas or oil condensing boiler, it may be prudent to think again! There are other eco-friendly and healthier options that may well also offer some security of supply in the event of fossil fuel scarcity in the future. When my family and I first moved to our farm in west Wales we made a conscious decision to avoid the use of fossil fuels in the heating of the farmhouse and nearby farmyard buildings. We therefore opted for a 50kW log burning boiler.

Why burn wood?

With only about 10% of the UK covered in woodland, and most of that is coniferous, you might imagine that there is not enough firewood to go around. This would be true if the whole country switched to wood burning overnight but this is not going to happen. What we are seeing is a gradual re-afforestation the UK as we learn to 'value' and re-assess our native woodlands rather than plunder those of far-off lands.

The resources that we need to nurture are those that are sustainable. It all has to be balanced of course. There has always been a need to grow food but now we are seeing that there is a need to grow fuel too. Most native woodlands in the UK have been neglected over the past 50 years and these neglected woodlands therefore offer us a massive, under-managed resource. In the past, landowners with woodland or potential woodland sites have been reluctant to plant or maintain woodland because there has not been a 'market' for the wood. We should and are beginning to see a change in attitude and the woodland cover of the UK has risen over the last two decades by about 2%, from roughly 9% to 11% now, and increasing.

Historically, native UK woodland would have been managed for construction timber, firewood, coppice crafts: charcoal, fencing, hurdles etc. Many of these uses have all but died out, other than as novelty craft revival interests. Most construction timber is imported but if more of us were to burn wood to heat our homes, offices and factories it would offer encouragement to owners of native woodlands to invest more time in growing high quality construction and joinery timbers, as firewood is usually harvested from thinnings during the growth of quality timber.

Contrary to popular belief, neglected temperate woodland is not as good for wildlife as managed woodland, so re-introducing sustainable management techniques, such as coppicing, will actually encourage more diverse and dynamic flora and fauna.

Burning wood helps the environment

It is now widely agreed that, when burnt efficiently and sustainably (from re-forested areas), wood gives off far lower pollution than fossil fuelled appliances. Efficiently burned wood only releases the same amount of carbon dioxide (CO_2) as the wood has locked up during its growth (even less if the timber originates from coppiced woodland, as the roots remain in the ground to grow again, therefore acting as a real carbon sink). Comparisons of CO_2 output from various fuels[1] indicate that wood is the best option, either logs, chips or pellets. See following table.

LEEDS COLLEGE OF BUILDING
LIBRARY

Fuel	kg CO₂/kWh
Wood pellets and logs	0.03
Gas	0.19
Oil	0.27
Coal	0.27
Electricity	0.42

CO_2 pollution from various fuels. For more detailed information please refer to the chart opposite.

Burning wood is healthy!

Almost every day we hear of new techno-gadgets promoted to make our lives easier and more satisfying. But the reality is that far from making us more satisfied with life they just separate us further from the natural environment, making us lazier. As a result our waists expand and obesity is fast becoming the UK's biggest killer.

Most of us are very separated from the need to provide ourselves with basic food, shelter and warmth. This alienation may cause a negative imbalance in our lives. Putting in at least a little physical effort towards making our homes warm and comfortable reconnects us, both mentally and physically, with the natural environment, and you do not have to live in the countryside to experience it. Even with the best, most energy efficient and mechanised equipment, wood burning offers a measure of laborious input. With the right attitude from the outset, wood cutting, collection, converting, stacking and burning is one of the most satisfying, enjoyable and health promoting tasks that you could undertake. It's real satisfaction too, every log stacked in the shed becomes an investment - not only financially, as we all tend to measure things these days, but as an investment in your own personal health and well-being.

The sustainable heating fuel

Prices for oil and gas are unrealistically low at present, although they have at last begun to rise. Demand will soon outstrip supply (recent suggestions are 2020). Improvements in energy efficiency are barely keeping pace with our insatiable demand. On the other hand, wood when used for heating, has everything going for it - the sustainable cycle for wood is well within human life-scales.

Whenever you mention wood burning to anyone they immediately think of a focal stove in the living room. Few people know of the technically advanced systems that are now available from long established European manufacturers. Whilst the UK turned its back on wood burning decades ago, other countries, particularly Scandinavia and Denmark, pursued the technology and invested heavily into refining the technology that we have available today.

Capital costs

The capital cost of a woodburning boiler system will vary depending on the sophistication of the equipment chosen (for sophistication, read mechanisation, not efficiency - efficiency is essential in all systems) and the fuel (logs, pellets or wood chips). As a very rough guide you could expect to pay the following + VAT costs for a fully installed system in an average sized detached home using a 15-30kW boiler:

Logs	£7-11,000
Wood-pellets and chip	£9-19,000

The Low Carbon Buildings Programme grant scheme is now available for domestic wood fired boilers up to a boiler size of 30kW[2]. For industrial sized applications there is the Enhanced Capital Allowance scheme which allows 100% capital allowances tax relief for the first year on investments in energy saving equipment listed on the Energy Technology List[3].

As far as efficiency is concerned, all of the systems compare well with the best condensing gas or oil boilers. As for running costs, the comparison between the various wood fuel option are: logs £65 -£85 per tonne; pellets £246[2] per tonne. Prices include VAT and delivery. Wood chips would fall somewhere in between.

Wood fuel efficiency is highly dependant on the moisture content of the wood fuel used.

JOHN
WILLOUGHBY'S   DOMESTIC FUEL PRICE GUIDE No 31   April 06

FUEL	PRICE		p/kWh	£/GJ	Quarterly Stand. Chg	Relative to Gas	Rank	kg CO₂/ kWh
GAS	3.44 2.55	p/kWh $ p/kWh $$	3.44 2.55	9.57 7.10	£ 9.72++	1.00	4	0.19
ELECTRICITY (on-peak)	14.36 10.62	p/kWh** p/kWh***	14.36 10.62	39.92 29.52	£ 6.81++	5.62 4.16	10	0.42
ELECTRICITY (Economy 7) night rate	20.04 11.04 4.21	p/kWh** p/kWh*** p/kWh	20.04 11.04 4.21	55.71 30.69 11.70	£ 16.38++	7.85 4.32 1.65	11 7	0.42 0.42
OIL (35 sec)	39.32	p/litre*	3.74	10.38		1.46	6	0.27
OIL (28 sec)	34.90	p/litre*	3.63	10.09		1.42	5	0.27
COAL	£177.00	/tonne +	2.12	5.90		0.83	3	0.29
ANTHRACITE	£190.00	/tonne +	2.09	5.81		0.82	2	0.32
LPG	32.80	p/litre*	4.59	12.77	£13.65	1.80	8	0.23
Wood Pellets	£258.09	/tonne@	4.89	13.58		1.91	9	0.03
Logs (B'leaf)	£65.00	/load@@	#REF!	#REF!		#REF!	1	0.03

$ based on B Gas DD price for first 12 kWh/day
$$ based on B Gas DD price for over 12 kWh/day

** based on nPower first 182 kWh/q
*** based on nPower for over 182 kWh/q (£20/yr discount available for DD)
* based on 1000 litre delivery
+ based on 1 tonne delivery
@ 15 kg bags. 1 tonne + delivery (£55+VAT)
@@ cost in Lydney. Stacking ratio 0.56, 9 GJ/m³
All prices include VAT at 5%
CO₂ figures from SAP 2005

Prices obtained from nPower, B Gas, Welsh Biofuels, RHP and 'best price' from local suppliers. Thanks to Alan Clarke for logs' cost

Price relative to gas now distorted by two tier tariffs and no standing charges. Second tier used for relative prices. ++If consumption over first tier you can use 2nd tier price plus equivalent stdg chg

Pellets have a guaranteed moisture content from the manufacturer that is below 12% . Logs, with a good storage regime, can easily be brought down to 15-20% (well within high efficiency levels) in two to three years, so a minimum of two year's storage should be allowed for. Wood-chips are the most difficult to dry and unless mechanical turning equipment for drying and large storage areas are available, then this might not be a good choice.

Of course if you are lucky enough to own your own woodland then your ideal system choice would be logs. If you have plenty of space but want more mechanisation and less manual labour, wood-chips.

The downdraught log boiler

I chose a Baxi Solo Innova[4] log burning boiler rather than a pellet or wood-chip (even though I have a chipper) for two reasons. Firstly, the price of log burning boilers are, at present, significantly cheaper than pellet boilers due

mainly to the more straightforward technology involved. Secondly, I have more than ample supplies of timber at the farm and enjoy managing my own woodlands. I might have considered a pellet boiler if machines were available to make pellets from your own timber (a long way off yet).

There is only one efficient method of burning wood. It has to be done fast and in a high temperature environment. A water jacket around the combustion zone is a definite drawback as it cools the temperature of the fire. So how have manufacturers overcome this problem? Well, in my boiler, the water jacket is behind the chamber rather than around it (see picture). It is in a pre-chimney where gasses leaving the combustion chamber are sucked by an inbuilt fan, at temperatures around 900°C, through a collection of water filled baffles (heat exchanger). This is where the heat is effectively transferred to the water without having any cooling effect on the combustion process at all. This arrangement allows the boiler to operate at an efficiency of 89-91%, which in reality is probably better than most condensing gas boilers perform. The real work of the boiler takes place in a ceramic flame tunnel (ceramic is one of the only materials able to withstand such high temperatures) directly below where the wood is loaded and this combustion takes place at full output with an appropriate mixture of primary and secondary air.

The Baxi Solo innova is a downdraught boiler which causes less pollution to the room when opened for loading.

Once lit the boiler needs no further adjustment and switches itself off at the end of a burn. My boiler is rated at 50kW which means that when running it will output 50kW of heat per hour. A full load of ash species timber will burn for up to 4 hours, therefore creating towards 200kW hours of heat as hot water which is stored in a well-insulated accumulator tank (large water vessel) sized appropriately for the boiler - in my instance 2,500 litres. The accumulator tank serves as a large battery which reduces firing times. In my case, depending on the weather, I usually fire up once every two days in the spring and autumn and each day during the winter.

The accumulator

Accumulator tanks are beginning to become more widely available but are still expensive. I converted an old oil tank with a view to replacing it sometime in the future when there is more choice and lower prices. Most of the suppliers of log boilers should be able to offer something. www.greenbuildingforum.co.uk has regular discussions on the availability and installation issues of log boilers, tanks and associated subject matter.

The Akvaterm accumulator tank. A few makes are now available in the UK. Until recently the only option was to have them made to order.

During recent research I found that Akvaterm accumulator tanks are now available in the UK and their website shows a complete list of their tanks (which are thankfully priced in UK sterling)[5]. For anyone not wanting to use an accumulator tank due to space limitations etc, most boiler suppliers produce log burning boilers that have advanced modulating controls which allow the boiler to be coupled with a much smaller accumulator tank. These are known as 'lambda controlled'. However, the boiler costs are far higher, the refuelling would be more frequent and the efficiency does drop, (though not by much if you believe the literature). Pellet and woodchip boilers use a hopper and or auger systems that are automated, therefore they have less need for accumulators. Personally I like the accumulator concept as it allows me to run the boiler at times when it is most suitable and most safe, i.e when I am around. They also allow the system to perform much like any other heating system - very nearly fully automated.

Conclusion

I see woodburning as the future. No doubt systems will continue to become even more sophisticated. There is little doubt in my mind that pellet fuelled appliances will ultimately find the lion's share of the market as they have the potential to appeal to those users that want minimal input into the running of the system. If you choose a log burning boiler you can rest assured that you will have chosen the most environmentally friendly system possible - whilst at the same time contributing towards the reforesting of the UK. ☙

References

1. The 'John Willoughby domestic Fuel Price Guide' April 06: www.johnwilloughby.co.uk

2. www.lowcarbonbuildings.org.uk/micro/biomass

3. www.eca.gov.uk/etl

4. Baxi: www.fbcgroup.co.uk

5. www.accumulatortanks.co.uk

© Green Building Press

Solar for space heating

The use of the sun to provide space heating, even during our darkest, UK winter days, is one of the smaller but growing markets of the UK solar industry. There's a simple reason why it has been a small sector. When we need our space heating most, the sun is at its least. It is an expensive matter to make headway against this over-riding fact, although many are willing to consider it. **Chris Laughton** discusses the options ...

In winter the sun is low in the sky, frequently hiding behind storm clouds if not invisible for days on end. Never-the-less, with some forward planning, it is possible for an active solar system to contribute nearly 20% to the annual space heating of a well-insulated new home. Perhaps with passive solar heating as well, this figure can be greater. But, in either case, be prepared for significant re-designing of your home. Serious solar for space heating is no simple task and rarely justified by cost-effectiveness based on current fossil fuel prices. But for the fully committed enthusiast, read on.

Those lucky enough to be building fresh, the first strategy is to orientate the roof and living spaces towards the south during the design process. Its the lower sun tracks of spring and autumn we are most interested in with solar space heating, so watch out for the long shadows of hills and don't forget the trees may not have dropped their leaves at that time. It's the 'shoulders' of the winter that is the target for solar space heating. Deep winter has too little sun to be bothered about and during the summer we don't need much space heating. But on those bright but sunny days in spring/autumn, useful gains can be made.

As with all forms of solar thermal energy, storage is the key to success. Active solar systems, intended to also provide domestic hot water, tend to start around 8m² of collector area in the UK, accompanied by no less than 750 litres of water storage. This forms

Many homes in mainland Europe have low energy design and take advantage of solar power for space heating.

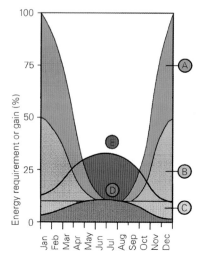

A   1984 typical German house
B   'Low energy' house
C   DHW
D   5 m² solar collector yield
E   15 m² solar collector yield

Left: diagramatic profile showing how the contribution of space heating can rise, as a percentage of the total heating needs, as buildings become more energy efficient.

The dream of space heating a house 100% from the sun is becoming the merest possibility, given the recent trend in warmer winters, combined with high insulation construction and heat recovery ventilation systems. So called 'passive' houses have previously relied on people's body metabolism, with electrical appliance's providing auxiliary top-up heat when the sun cannot provide all. Despite the best plans, many resort to occasional electric heaters to achieve full comfort throughout the year.

Pursing a high renewable fraction for space heating can lead to a dilemma on sizing appliances for the shortfall. For what may only be a few kW to find on the coldest nights, it barely makes sense for fitting a gas or oil boiler when it will be hardly used. Wood and electric are often chosen first, either for their smaller footprint, less capital cost, less maintenance or for their ambience.

It can't be emphasized enough that if the dwelling is not first extremely well insulated and airtight, then solar space heating is a very expensive pursuit. In all cases, domestic hot water heating should be the priority for the solar system, since it is first easier to transfer heat to the cold water entering the dwelling from the ground. Thereafter, heat is transferred to the cool return of the under-floor space heating before being heated further by other sources.

The physical area of solar collector necessary, for reasonable space heating contribution significantly exceeds the typical area where just solar domestic hot water is required by at least 3:1. This can lead to overheating problems in summer, unless care is given to the system

the backbone of the common solar 'combisystem' common in Sweden and Austria. Expect a store of this size to be found in the cellar or otherwise a lean-to outhouse. However, the vital feature of the space heating layout is to use under-floor heating, designed to flow at temperatures well below 50°C., ideally nearer 30°C. This critical step allows the lower grade solar heat in the store that can no longer heat domestic hot water (DHW), to be used instead to heat the floors, and even walls. Providing the dwelling is extremely well insulated and wind tight, the injection of modest amounts of stored solar heat from earlier in the day, will provide a welcome background heat to start the evening off in the living areas. With the use of timers and pumps, this heat is fully controllable.

Passive solar heating, without the use of pumps, is often discussed but rarely practised to a fine degree in the UK. There lies great potential to make greater use of thermal 'mass' (masonry, concrete or water) behind glazing to store heat for later release into the living space. Yet so often the result is overheating, glare and a lack of privacy or security. Worse still, the risks of a net annual loss of heat through increasing the glazing can actually increase fuel bills. Under-floor heating and passive heated areas, when adjacent, make poor companions, since stored passive heating is difficult to control and requires fast responding auxiliary heat emitters to make best use of the solar heat, without sacrificing comfort.

© Green Building Press

design, although most modern sealed system designs can cope with over-sizing without necessarily loosing fluid through boiling in the summer when the house is possible empty. Assume between 0.8 to 3.0m² of collector area per 10m² of heated floor area. Each square metre of collector should give 350kWh per annum with sufficient storage.

Collector orientation can help with large collector areas by pitching them up steeply to naturally shade out in the high peaks of summer and yet remain well targeted for the low winter sun. Commercially available software simulation programs, such as TSOL, greatly simply the design of solar space heating systems. The variety of equipment can easily be compared, along with sizes to achieve a balanced solution.

Water in insulated steel or concrete containers is normally the first choice for storage of solar heat, as it is cheap and readily available. Heat can also be stored in swimming pools, insulated 'ponds' or similar underground reservoirs. Rocks or other masonry can also hold heat, although here the inability to pump heat out quickly is a disadvantage. Heat storage over several days is quite possible, and indeed necessary for solar space heating to work well. However, 'inter-seasonal' storage is much more difficult to do well. The use of heat pumps does allow low temperature heat to be 'upgraded',

although it is arguable that the soil itself makes a good enough natural store for this purpose, without the need for water based stores. Assume a water storage size between 50 litres up to 1000 litres for a square metre collector for space heating.

Overall, a solar contribution of up to 3000kWh can realistically be made to the space heating of a UK house. This assumes a net space heating load of less than 13,000kWh, after considering useful free heat from passive solar, cooking and metabolic gains. Even the better insulated houses are likely to still require 4000kWh from non solar sources. ☻

Commercial solar heating

Solar heating can be successfully used in commercial properties. For assistance with process heat, hot water preparation and even space heating. The successful integration of solar heating systems into buildings where we work is significantly affected by how the building is being /to be used. For those buildings that contain a lot a glass, such as some office blocks, the sun's energy can even cause a net energy loss due to the electrical cooling loads necessary during summer from air condi-

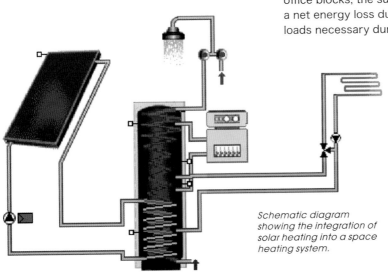

Schematic diagram showing the integration of solar heating into a space heating system.

tioning. Compared to domestic properties, commercial properties need greater care at the system design, generally to ensure that there is no conflict with other technologies and that the installed equipment is robust enough to survive working environments. The techniques for solar pre-heating of hot water and space heating are similar to residential properties. However, process heat requires special attention.

Some of the largest solar collector areas in the world are located on hospital roofs, indicating the huge hot water demand of medical laundries and canteens. Combined with hotels and care homes, such buildings provide a consistent hot water load ideal for solar pre-heating, and often containing existing floor space for the location of vital solar storage cylinders. Such buildings also require much greater attention to the risk of bacterial poisoning, that a poor quality design can magnify.

With the right equipment, such as plate exchangers, solar pre-heating need not increase bacterial risks beyond that of any typical hot water heater. Scalding risks can also be eliminated with accurate thermostatic pump control, now routine equipment in high quality systems. Compared to domestic properties, far greater liability falls on the solar system designer and owner in respect of the law. Written risk assessments are an essential start of compliance to such regulations as COSHH (Control of Substances Hazardous to Health regulations). Commercially available software simulation packages become invaluable in pre-empting temperatures around a system which can then be used in such assessments.

Schools have an unfortunate habit of breaking up when the sun is at its best! Unless there is an onsite school canteen to provide a steady after-lunch hot water demand of hand dish washing, a disappointing utilisation factor can result. Club houses for field sports also have a poor overall efficiency as the hot water demand for canteens and baths tends to occur in peaks at weekends and often during the winter. Furthermore, the hot water appliances are rarely centralised, making a single solar

system, serving the whole building, difficult to integrate. Nevertheless, using a well insulated store, solar can be allowed to build up during the week and significantly reduce energy demand at the weekend when the sports events tend to be held. Summer sports clubs, such as cricket or tennis, would work well, being in harmony with the solar high season.

Other ideal commercial locations

Process heat, such as that used in car washes or food preparation, provides excellent solar efficiencies since the daytime cold water passing into the hot water system use is high and readily accepts solar pre-heating. In these cases, the normally vital storage of solar heat becomes less important as the heat can be used almost as it is produced. As usual, a back-up heat source provides the shortfall, whenever the solar is not available.

Dairies require very hot water for sterilisation both early in the morning and in the late afternoon. To contribute to both times requires good storage volumes to hold over through the night. Agricultural buildings typically have lightweight roofs that provide a challenge for structural fixings but in rural areas, the cost of bottle gas or peak electricity, often makes the solar capital cost seem more attractive.

Camping and caravan sites, particularly those with swimming pools, provide an excellent accord with the seasonal increase of solar energy. However, finding space for extra solar storage vessels is difficult in already cramped plant rooms. Municipal pool plant room areas are often more generous but can contain heat recovery apparatus that makes solar integration difficult. Flat roofs, that often accompany swimming pool enclosures, provide difficult structural issues with wind and snow loading in some exposed regions during winter, although evacuated tube type collectors provide a simple way to lay the collector flat with minimal visual impact. Tube collectors can also be used to great architectural effect on balustrades, awnings and vertical facades on all buildings. Their ability to rotate the absorber within the

© Green Building Press

tube mounting permits this flexibility.

For any commercial concern, feasibility starts with assessing the heat demand that could usefully accept pre-heated solar input. Look for cold feeds and cool returns on available circuits and check that 'downstream' top-up heating appliances will accept pre-heating and thermo-statically respond to it. A significant number of appliances are not compatible with pre-heating, including most dishwashers, many new washing machines, combination boilers and even electric point-of-use heaters. Adequate thermostatic control and heat resistance of materials are necessary for safe and efficient performance. In new builds, careful specification of compatible appliances and short-run distribution of DHW can help make best use of solar.

Grant aid for businesses remains possible through the government's Enhanced Capital Allowance (ECA) **www.eca.gov.uk** where a list of the more stringently tested solar collec-

tors can be found. Significant capital funding can sometimes be found with local schemes in regenerative areas or with educational concerns. Progress towards procurement of solar energy through results purchasing (no sun = no pay !) is advancing for larger commercial systems, where results can be guaranteed over the long term and payment is made on a per kWh basis. Here, the contractor uses remote monitoring of the solar plant using the internet or other methods, with responsibility for performance falling to them and not the building owner.

Further reading

Low or zero carbon sources – a strategic guide - Department of Communities and Local Government

Solar Thermal Systems – Successful planning and implementation - James & James

IEA Task 24 Solar Procurement

IEA Task 26 combisystems Stiftung Warentest April 2003– Solaranlglen

Planning and Installing solar thermal systems - James & James

SOLAR ENERGY TECHNOLOGY, TRAINING & TECHNICAL SUPPORT

SOLAR WATER HEATING SYSTEMS
— SOLAR COLLECTORS
— PRE-ASSEMBLED COMPONENTS
— DESIGN & INSTALLATION TRAINING

PHOTOVOLTAIC SYSTEMS
— PV SYSTEM KITS
— INSTALLATION TRAINING COURSES

High quality and high efficiency solar energy systems at **competitive prices**

Tel: 01269 860229 / 860097
Web site: www.filsolsolar.com

Fax: 01269 860979   E-mail: info@filsol.co.uk
Filsol Solar Ltd, 15 Ponthenri Industrial Estate, Ponthenri, Llanelli, Carmarthenshire, SA15 5RA

FILSOL SOLAR

THE SOLAR ENERGY SPECIALISTS

Solar for water heating

Many thousands of solar water heating systems have been installed in the UK since the 1970's and while the majority of early systems continue to perform well, a new generation of commercially produced solar water heating systems has evolved. **Iain Calderwood** explains system types and controls.

Solar water heating systems are capable of providing up to 60% of annual domestic hot water requirements in the UK, dispelling the myth that there 'is too little sun in the UK for solar to work'.

Domestic hot water requirements in the typical UK home remain constant throughout the year and during the summer months, the operational efficiency of even the most modern gas, oil and solid fuel boilers, will fall off as they short cycle on part load. A well-designed solar water heating system should provide around 90% of the hot water requirement during this period, falling to around 20% during the winter.

Types of collectors

Solar thermal collectors typically comprise three types and all collectors should be certified to BS EN 12975.

Unglazed plastic collectors, used for swimming pool applications, where the temperature requirements are lower than for domestic hot water production.

Flat plate collectors, containing a specially treated absorber plate to maximise solar gain. The collector is glazed with either solar glass or plastic and is highly insulated to minimise heat loss. Collectors are available for both roof integration and above roof fixing.

Evacuated tube collectors in which the absorber plate is enclosed in an evacuated glass tube. These collectors can operate at higher temperatures due to the vacuum insulation and are usually more expensive.

With suitable specialised components, systems are straightforward to install, reliable and durable. The collectors will work during overcast days, even when there is no direct sunlight, but work best when in direct sunlight. Heat from the sun is transferred to water contained within the collector and circulated to a special solar cylinder, where it can be topped up to a useable temperature, as and when required by a conventional boiler or immersion heater.

Collector performance will be optimum when facing due south un-shaded and inclined between 25-60°C but, in practice, any situation between south-east and south-west will result in only a 10% fall off in efficiency and can be considered acceptable. Even east or west facing elevations will provide around 80% of optimum and should be considered since an oversized collector can be fitted. Some evacuated tube collectors can also be rotated within their manifold by up to 30°C in order to compensate for an unfavourable position. Consideration should also be given to mounting the collectors vertically on a wall or at ground level or flat roofs on purpose built 'A' frames, available directly from most collector suppliers.

Resultant savings in CO_2 emissions will vary according to the fuel being displaced and the hot water demand. A typical 4m² flat plate solar collector will save around 1000kg of CO_2 when displacing electricity or 450kg when displacing natural gas.

Hot water storage

Hot water stores are best designed to encourage heat from the solar collectors to work effectively in combination with input from a conventional heating system, such as a boiler or immersion heater. A well-designed store will ensure that water is pre-heated prior to reaching the boiler heat exchanger.

The most common way of achieving this is to

© Green Building Press

use a dual coil type of cylinder and this is the most common system throughout the UK and mainland Europe.

When selecting hot water cylinder size, consider that high performance showers, often operating at up to 3-bar pressure, require a large volume of stored water and this should be taken into account in the design stage.

Care must be taken, when designing this type of cylinder, to ensure that there is sufficient volume for the occupants requirements to be heated by the boiler, whenever there is insufficient solar gain to heat the contents – typically a minimum of 120 litres.

Additionally there should be sufficient volume below the boiler coil to enable the solar system to perform efficiently whenever the boiler is firing. Typical storage ratios are around 50-60 litres of stored water per square metre of flat plate collector installed or 80-100 litres per square metre in the case of very high performance evacuated tube collectors.

Ideally stores should be designed to ensure stratification, in order to maximise the efficiency of the solar system, typically a height /

diameter ratio of 2.5 or 3.1. The heat exchanger should be located as low as possible and have a large surface area (0.2m² minimum per square metre of collector) in order to maximise solar contribution at times of low solar radiation.

Solar collectors can be connected to a traditional open vented cylinders, mains pressure cylinders or thermal stores, although the performance of the latter is likely to be lower due to the lack of water movement and the need to maintain higher temperatures.

Solar primary circuit

The most common types of solar primary circuit are either the traditional fully filled and pressurised type, containing a special solar heat transfer fluid to provide frost protection or drainback, in which the solar collector is filled only when the solar primary pump is running and contains only water.

Controllers and other equipment

Unlike a conventional heating system, the temperature, in the solar primary circuit, will vary continuously. The sun cannot simply be switched off and high efficiency solar collectors can easily reach temperatures in excess

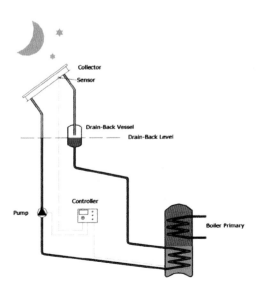

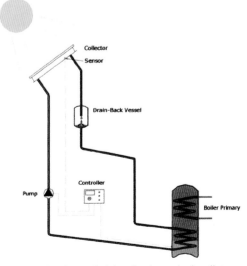

Diagram showing a drainback solar water heating system by night and by day.

of 200°C. Careful control of the solar system is therefore essential in order to prevent over-heating and to ensure that water previously heated by fossil fuels is not pumped back round the solar circuit to warm the sky.

A differential temperature controller ensures optimum performance from most types of solar water heating system. The controller measures temperature in the solar collector and compares this with the temperature in the lower part of the cylinder. When the controller senses that the collector is hotter than the store, the circulating pump is energised and heat trans-ferred. When the temperature difference falls, the controller switches the pump off.

In most controllers, the switch on and switch off differential is adjustable, enabling the installer to programme the unit to match the operating characteristics of the individual systems and types of solar collector.

Water must be distributed at a safe tempera-ture. If the temperature is too low, then there is a risk of legionella. Most controllers incorporate a thermostat, control-ling a second relay, in order to switch on a boiler, although many installers prefer to use a traditional cylinder thermostat. If the water temperature is too high, then there is a risk of scalding and potential lime scale deposition (in hard water areas). All controllers should have an adjustable 'top limit' thermostat.

Fault diagnosis

Many controllers have the capability to indicate faults. For example, sensor defects, reverse circulation, (the collector heats up at night) or too high temperature differential (indicating that the pump is not running when it should).

Heat meters

Units are available to provide a heat quantity

measurement enabling more precise monitoring of the performance of the solar system.

The location of the cylinder sensors is critical. In a cylinder with an internal coil type heat exchanger, the lower sensor should be no lower than the mid point between the flow and return connections. Ideally sensors should be fitted into pockets to give a good contact with the stored water. ✍

Grants

Grants are available for solar installations:
www.est.org.uk/housingbuildings/funding/

Solar Slates

Solar heating roofs for -

- Domestic hot water & heating
- Swimming pools
- Industrial process heat
- Commercial premises heating
- Agricultural processing

Unique roof integrated design, used in place of conventional roof tiles or slates.

Solex

01305 837223 - www.solexenergy.co.uk

© Green Building Press

ARE YOU STILL BURNING MONEY
TO HEAT YOUR WATER?
FREE HOT WATER FROM THE SUN
HIGH QUALITY SOLAR THERMAL SYSTEMS
FROM *celtic solar*
FOR HOT WATER AND SWIMMING POOLS
FULL DESIGN AND FITTING SERVICE
THROUGHOUT THE SOUTHWEST
SOUND ADVICE FROM EXPERIENCED INSTALLERS,
NO OBLIGATION FIXED PRICE QUOTATIONS.
01566 781509
www.celticsolar.co.uk

Software for solar thermal engineering
Design and analyse from your own computer

T*SOL® *Professional*

- *simulation*
- *sizing*
- *comparison*
- *performance*

www.solardesign.co.uk

SECON SOLAR LTD

Secon Solar is a family owned business supplying high quality solar products to the UK solar thermal industry.

Secon is the UK distributor for RESOL – electronic controllers, PAW – pump stations for solar and central heating systems, and SOLAR METALFLEX – flexible pre insulated stainless steel pipe.

Tel: 0191 5166554. Fax: 0191 5166558
info@seconsolar.com. www.seconsolar.com

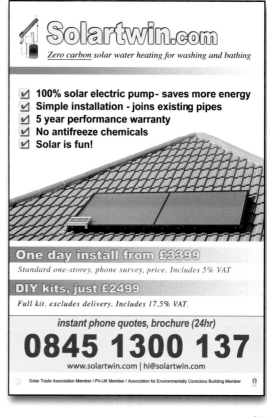

Solartwin.com
Zero carbon solar water heating for washing and bathing

- ☑ **100% solar electric pump- saves more energy**
- ☑ **Simple installation - joins existing pipes**
- ☑ **5 year performance warranty**
- ☑ **No antifreeze chemicals**
- ☑ **Solar is fun!**

One day install from £3399
Standard one-storey, phone survey, price. Includes 5% VAT

DIY kits, just £2499
Full kit. excludes delivery. Includes 17.5% VAT.

instant phone quotes, brochure (24hr)
0845 1300 137
www.solartwin.com | hi@solartwin.com

Solar Trade Association Member / PV-UK Member / Association for Environmentally Conscious Building Member

Minimise electricity use

Many people are mislead by the idea that if they buy their electricity from companies offering 'green' tariffs, they can continue using the same quantities, or even more electricity, under the illusion that they are no longer harming the planet. **Cath Hassell** and **David Olivier** dispel a few myths ...

Electric central heating systems have been enjoying a growth in popularity in recent years, especially in the new homes' market. This is due to a number of reasons:
- the privatisation of the power supply companies
- good marketing strategies by these new, highly competitive businesses
- simpler installation and cost savings for the housebuilder or installer (many electric resistance heating systems do not use plumbing).

However, for the consumer there is:
- less controllability
- less options for keeping warm in an electricity power failure
- the prospect of rising electricity prices
- the difficulty of changing to another fuel in the future.

The above points aside, the fact is that there is not currently enough green electricity to satisfy demand. So, even if you are paying a green tariff, the chances are the electricity you are consuming now is, in reality, either nuclear or fossil fuel generated.

Increasing energy use is the problem

Since 1990 energy use in the domestic sector has risen by a staggering 19% and now accounts for 30% of all energy consumption in the UK. Once we have insulated our buildings to the maximum levels possible we should then look to use the lowest carbon fuel source for our heating and other energy needs. See the tables in '*Heating your home with logs*' earlier in this chapter for a comparison of the CO_2 pollution of various fuels.

Obviously, we have to use electricity for lights and most appliances, so we should choose the most energy-efficient options. However, there are better environmental choices than electricity for heating, hot water and cooking in our homes. These include gas, oil, LPG, wood pellet or wood chip, ground source heat pumps and solar power for hot water. Most of these are discussed at length elsewhere in this book.

Electricity generation is the most significant source of emissions of greenhouse gases in the UK, as well as a source of air pollutants. Given the current generating mix for UK electricity, 0.42kg of CO_2 is produced for every kWh of electricity generated. Therefore, any increase in electrical demand will lead to an increase in CO_2 emissions, especially as more inefficient coal fired power stations are brought back on-line to meet increased demand.

Of the current electrical generating mix, only 3% comes from renewables. Yet 20% of the UK's total electricity generation is consumed on just lighting our buildings and streets. Not until 2020 (and that is if the government's target of 20% is met) will renewables cover merely the lighting demand.

No spare capacity

All the renewable electricity produced in the UK is eagerly purchased by electricity suppliers under a Renewables Obligations scheme. This will remain in place until 2010, thus ensuring a growing market and encouraging more invest-ment in new renewables' generating capacity. Due to the great demand for 'green' electricity there is none spare. Therefore, our collective aim should be to 'reduce' our consumption of

© Green Building Press

electricity, not to generate 'extra' demand. If we install electric central heating, then we will be increasing demand and this demand can, at present, only be met from fossil fuel generation with its associated greenhouse gas emissions. There is also great concern that our increasing use of electricity has lead to Tony Blair throwing his lot in with the idea of new nuclear power stations being built as the UK desperately tries to reduce the rising CO_2 emissions.

Some building specifiers use the argument that by specifying electric heating they are future proofing against the time that supplies of natural gas runs out. However, if the supply of natural gas does run out, it would be simple enough to change from a gas boiler to another fuel.

Facts and figures

It is interesting to note that in a dwelling built to the new 2006 Part L amendments of the Building Regulations, the hot water energy consumption could well be greater than the heating load. For example: a family of four, heating their hot water using a gas condensing boiler, would produce 1 tonne of CO_2, while heating the same hot water using electricity, would produce 2 tonnes. That extra tonne could not be offset by improving the insulation standards of the dwelling beyond the statutory requirements.

Another example: in a block of flats, over 1 tonne of extra CO_2 would be produced per 60m² floor area per year if electric space heating is specified instead of a condensing gas boiler. (These are emissions from a flat built to the 2002 Part L standard with an 'A' rated gas condensing boiler). We can more than double this penalty if a 90m² rural semi-detached house is fitted with electric heating instead of a condensing LPG boiler, because the heating demand of the house is much larger than the small flat.

Denmark has restrictions on the use of electric space heating in permanent dwellings. 60% of Denmark is now supplied by district

heating, fed by CHP plants and industrial waste heat. The heat mains extends to detached houses in suburbs and even some nearby villages; there are no complaints from home-owners about lack of control but there are comments about the convenience of receiving mains hot water and heating compared to main-taining an individual boiler.

Conclusion

Electricity use for purposes other than those where there are no alternatives, (lights and appliances), cannot be justified, even by those signed up to 'green tariffs'. The likelihood of there being an abundance of renewable gener-ated electricity is so far off that it is not worth considering as a serious heating load energy source.

In a district heating situation, the idea of future proofing is incompatible with electric resistance heating. A building heated by electri-cal resistance could not participate easily in a community heating scheme. For example, the entire centre of Southampton is now heated this way - this would not have been an easy option if the hotels, hospitals, council offices etc, had originally had electric heating. District heating schemes commonly use industrial waste heat, waste heat from a CHP plant or season-ally-stored solar heat (developed par excellence in Sweden and Germany). Genuine future proofing would be to specify versatile heating systems that can use any type of fuel, not to lock owners or tenants into a blind alley with buildings heated by electric resistance wires. Electric resistance space and water heating is not environmentally sustainable. ◐

Both of the authors buy their electricity from a 'renew-able' supplier and urge readers of this article to do the same; it is important to show support for renewable electricity. Neither author uses electricity for space or water heating and both have energy-efficient lights and appliances.

Solar for electricity

When people talk about putting 'solar panels' on their roofs, many assume these are for producing hot water. This is not always the case as solar panels for generating electricity are becoming increasingly popular. Here **Gavin Harper** explores solar panels which produce electricity – the solar photovoltaic cell.

Solar photovoltaic cells (PV's) offer a clean way to produce electricity to power your home. The benefits of your own solar array are not immediately apparent, but when you begin to think about the safeguard they offer against rising energy costs, the prospect of being sent a cheque by your energy supplier, and the knowledge that the energy you are generating is clean, green and carbon free, you begin to realise what an asset they are potentially to any home. In this article, we are going to be exploring what is entailed if you wish to generate electricity, using solar power, for your home.

Whilst a solar cell will produce the largest amount of power on a clear, bright sunny day, even on comparatively dull days, a solar array will still be providing cheap, green electricity. The amount of power a solar cell produces is proportionate to the amount of light that it receives. The more light, the more power. For this reason, you want to try, as far as possible, to minimise any obstructions and large objects which might overshadow your solar panels, siting them in an area where they have a clear view of the sun. Ideally, we want to face our cells due south to receive the most light throughout the year. However, any angle between 45 degrees of due south will produce satisfactory results. Similarly, cells which are placed on a pitch between 20 and 50 degrees will yield best results.

PV's do not necessarily need bright sunlight to work – of course the amount of power produced is governed by the availability of light, but even on overcast days some power will be produced.

Types of collectors

There are a couple of ways of integrating solar PV collectors. You can integrate them into the fabric of the building or they can simply be 'bolted on' to a suitable roof. Integrated tiles allow for the solar cell to perform the same function as an existing roof tile. In a new build, or where a roof needs to be replaced, this can be a practical proposition as it saves a little of the costs by eliminating the need to buy a separate set of tiles or roofing system as the solar array performs this function.

Solar slates are an innovative product, visually, they do not appear dissimilar from conventional roofing slates. Laing homes installed solar slates in a development of nine houses in north London. For each kW of power, solar slates require 10m² roof area.

You will need to size your systems based on the energy consumption of the building, and the amount of power produced per square metre of panel. The amount of power produced by an array is directly proportional to its surface area. Of course, this will all be governed by the amount of money available for the project, but even partially meeting your buildings energy requirements using clean renewable energy is to be seen as desirable.

Solar slates being installed in the same manner as normal roofing slates.

© Green Building Press

elegant efficient electricity

C21e solar roof tiles

Using the most efficient solar cells available, solarcentury's C21e is easily installed by any roofer, avoiding all the problems of traditional 'bolt-on' solar panels.

Integrated with your standard tiles, C21e sits flush with the roof without detracting from the design of your property.

(And 'yes' they do work in the UK...)

solarcentury

Call **020 7803 0100**
email **C21@solarcentury.com**
or visit **solarcentury.com**
to find out more about C21e solar roof tiles

Traditional roofing tile manufacturers, such as Redland, Marley and others, now offer a range of roof integrated PV tiles – these are designed to integrate with their own brand tiles. The solar tiles comes pre-wired with connectors that can be joined together and connected to the electrical system. Some have base tiles so the solar panels need not be exposed to damage during construction and can be clipped into the base tile after completion of the roof.

When installing any device onto a roof, whether its a new roof or retrofitting onto an existing one, it needs to be carefully considered whether the structure of the roof is adequate to support such a load. Always obtain the correct figures for the hardware that you are using, but as an example, the Marley solar tile weighs 40kg per square metre.

For commercial buildings, there are a wide range of solar claddings which can be used to generate electricity, whilst simultaneously protecting the building fabric from the elements.

Planning permission is generally one of the first concerns that people voice. Planning permission is not required in the majority of cases, although check with your local authority. Exceptions to this rule are buildings which are listed or of special historical interest, or buildings which are located in areas of outstanding natural beauty. For government grants, where planning permission is required, it must be sought before a grant is awarded.

Most of the houses in the UK are within easy reach of a grid connection. This is very convenient as it allows us to use the 'national grid' as a giant battery. Energy can be 'sold' to the grid at times when the building produces a surplus which is not being used by the occupants. When the solar arrays do not provide enough power for the buildings requirements, power can be 'bought back' from the grid.

If you are going to connect to the grid, you will need to seek the appropriate permissions from the local DNO (Distribution Network Operator). If you are having your PV's professionally installed, your installer should take care of this for you. You will be paid a different rate for 'exported' electricity depending on your supplier. As the amount paid varies so widely, it could be worth changing supplier to take advantage of better prices for your exported electricity. Again, your installer should be able to find you the best deal.

One decision that you need to think about is whether you wish to store any energy when there is a surplus. If you want to live in a manner that is wholly self sufficient, then you can consider an 'off-the-grid', battery system solution for storage.

This might involve storing the electrical energy in batteries. Lead acid batteries are currently the most pragmatic way of storing electricity. However, in the next couple of decades there might be interesting opportunities opened up by hydrogen fuel cells, which would allow storage of power as hydrogen gas. However, for widespread adoption this is not currently practical.

The other option is to store the 'energy' in a dump load, such as by heating water. This method is popular in third world countries, or areas where there is not a grid. However, in the UK it is not desirable to convert 'high quality' energy – electricity to a 'low quality' energy

Atlantis energy solar slates used on a house in Fordingbridge.

– heat. Where there is no other alternative this represents a better solution than wasting the power, but in the UK it makes more sense to feed that excess power into the grid and get paid for doing it.

Solar panels produce direct current electricity – this is the sort of electricity we would get from a battery. Electrons flow round the circuit in one direction. They also produce electricity at relatively modest voltages. By constrast, our mains electricity supply is alternating current. This means that electrons flow back and forth through the circuit – and they do so at much higher voltages.

This means that there must be an intermediate step between our solar PV's and mains electricity wiring. There is! It takes the form of a device called an inverter. An inverter takes the low voltage direct current, and using solid state electronics, turns the low voltage DC into high voltage AC, at a frequency that is appropriate for the mains supply, which in the UK is 50 hertz. The inverter is sized appropriately for the solar installation. It is important to note, that although the voltage increases, no electricity is 'made' – as a result of the voltage increasing, the current available decreases, so whilst the PV array might be producing high current DC, the output of the inverter is AC at a higher current.

If the installation is connected to the grid, a new metering system will need to be installed which can take account of electricity going back into the grid. Think, if you like, that when electricity is fed back into the grid, your meter needle 'spins backwards' - this is a good way of visualising the balance between electricity coming to and from your home. In reality, with peak and off peak tariffs, the metering arrangement is a little more complicated, but essentially, the detail is all the same - the electricity you feed into the grid is subtracted from that which you use from the grid.

One concern that many people have is that over the life cycle of a solar cell, it will produce less energy then was used producing the PV. This is not the case. Marley estimate that the

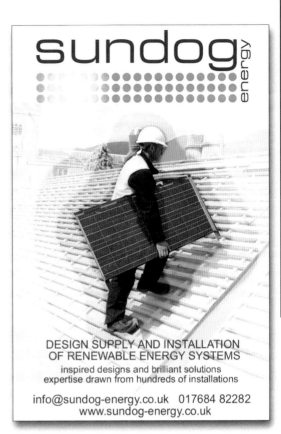

sundog energy

DESIGN SUPPLY AND INSTALLATION
OF RENEWABLE ENERGY SYSTEMS
inspired designs and brilliant solutions
expertise drawn from hundreds of installations

info@sundog-energy.co.uk   017684 82282
www.sundog-energy.co.uk

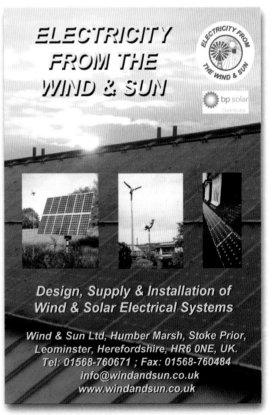

ELECTRICITY FROM THE WIND & SUN

ELECTRICITY FROM THE WIND & SUN

bp solar
Distributor

**Design, Supply & Installation of
Wind & Solar Electrical Systems**

Wind & Sun Ltd, Humber Marsh, Stoke Prior,
Leominster, Herefordshire, HR6 0NE, UK.
Tel: 01568-760671 ; Fax: 01568-760484
info@windandsun.co.uk
www.windandsun.co.uk

energy payback period is between four and nine years for systems which are grid connected and last for twenty five years. You will also want to consider access to the roof. Scaffolding and mobile towers are expensive – if these are required, they must be added to the cost of the installation when calculating payback periods.

Similarly, people often ask about the financial payback of photovoltaic systems. This will obviously be dependent on the cost of the installation and whether there were any factors which 'pushed up' the cost of the installation. However, for smaller systems, a payback period of 15 years is a reasonable assumption, falling to around 12 years for a larger system. Of course, these figures are not set in stone. As energy becomes more expensive, solar PV power will start to look more attractive! Of course, with any solar system, you should be looking for a warranty to provide some guarantee of system operation in the long run. Most solar module manufacturers guarantee that their cells will produce energy for around 25 years.

the technology, the psychological impact that it had on the family of 'generating their own electricity', and the effect that had on their energy usage habits. ☙

Grant information

Photovoltaics were previously funded by the major photovoltaic demonstration programme, however, more recently, this has been replaced with the Low Carbon Buildings Programme. There are two streams, Stream 1 is for smaller projects, Stream 2 is for larger micro generation projects. Most domestic solar installations will fall into the first stream, whilst larger commercial installations will fall into the second.

Grants are available for solar installations. They are managed by the Energy Saving Trust:
www.est.org.uk/housingbuildings/funding/solarpv

Case study

PVs on private house

Solarcentury put a solar installation, capable of generating 3.8kWp, which equates to 2,930 kWh annually, in the home of the Garside Family who live in Hertfordshire, England. The size of the collector was 25m², of the 'Sunstation' kind manufactured by Solarcentury. Though the house did not have the 'ideal' orientation to the sun, the system generated 351kWh over and above the Garside family's consumption. They were paid for that electricity by their supplier, who also provided electricity at night when their PV setup was not operating. The Garside's can feel righly proud – in their first year they avoided 1.2 tonnes of carbon from entering the atmosphere. Also, as a result of their new found 'ownership' of the electricity they were producing, the family found that the amount of electricity they were using fell from the previous year by 16%. It is important to note, aside from

Safe with **SUNPOWERED** Solar...

Solar Hot Water

Solar Electric (PV)

Underfloor Heating

Nationwide Coverage

Swimming Pool Heating

Domestic & Commercial

DTI Accredited Installers

www.**SUNPOWERED**.co.uk
Government Accredited
Full Design, Consultation and Installation

90 Albert Road Southsea PO5 2SN
02392 614 924   REA   08000 18 22 12

Fuel cells, heat pumps and CHP

The next few years could see significant changes in the way we heat and power our buildings. **Kevin Boniface** introduces us to three of the technologies that could become commonplace - fuel cells, heat pumps and Stirling engines.

Fuel cells

Fuel cell technology draws on the fundamental principle of combining hydrogen and oxygen to produce electricity, heat and (and usually as a waste product) water. In comparison to combustion, fuel cells use an electrochemical process to generate energy which leads to an inherently clean, quiet (and arguably the most important) very efficient fuel conversion process.

Fuel cells can be connected to the grid to provide supplementary power, or can operate independently to provide electricity where on-site generation is the only practical and economically feasible option. Although commonly referred to in texts as a 'renewable energy technology', fuel cells can only be truly classified as a renewable source of energy if the electricity used (in producing the hydrogen fuel) is, itself, generated by a renewable energy source, such as a photovoltaic array or a wind turbine.

Fuel cells are similar to batteries, but they do not run down or require recharging – provided that hydrogen fuel is available. Figure 1 shows the basic operating principle of a fuel cell. A fuel cell consists of two electrodes separated by an electrolyte. Generally hydrogen gas is fed to the anode and oxygen enters the fuel cell at the cathode. A catalyst is then used to split the hydrogen into protons and electrons, with the protons able to pass through the electrolyte. The electrons however, have to take the long way round, which creates an electrical current, before they return to the cathode. They then reunite with the hydrogen and oxygen to form a molecule of water.

Unlike most combustion based generation systems, there are no moving parts, although as with other types of battery, the electrical output is quite low per individual cell, typically about 0.7-0.8 volts. For this reason, fuel cells adopt a similar structure to batteries. in that they utilise multiple cells connected together in series to produce a useful working voltage.

Applications

Although the fuel cell was invented by Sir Charles Grove in 1839, serious development work only started in the 1950s. Fuel cells are essentially a family of technologies and there are several types in existence today for a range of applications. The five main types are summarised in Table 1.

Future developments

Fuel cells do offer huge potential for high efficiency power generation in homes. It was

Figure 1. Simplfiled fuel cell operating principle.

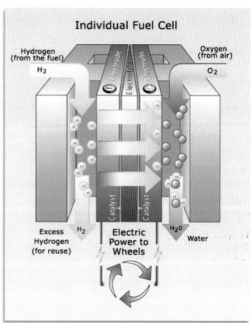

Solid polymer (SPFC)	There are two distinct types of SPFC, the proton exchange membrane (PEMFC) fuel cell and the direct methanol fuel cell (DMFC). The PEMFC is ideal for residential, portable and transport applications and is available in sizes from a few watts up to 250kW. It has already been demonstrated in households in North America, Japan and in Europe. The DMFC uses poisonous methanol as the fuel, but as a fuel it is easier to handle than hydrogen. Although still at the development stage, DMFCs could potentially be used for transport and portable applications; indeed in the US, Motorola is looking into using small cartridges of methanol (like an ink cartridge) to power small fuel cells in mobile phones.
Alkaline (AFC)	The AFC was the first fuel cell to be developed and was used by NASA during space programmes in the 1960s. They are relatively simple and cheap to manufacture, but require any CO_2 to be removed from the air supply to prevent contamination of the electrolyte.
Phosphoric acid (PAFC)	PAFCs have undergone a substantial amount of development and are commercially available in sizes from 50kW up to 11MW. As it is a higher temperature system, PAFCs tend to be used for larger applications and are often packaged with steam reformers to allow them to run on natural gas.
Molten carbonate (MCFC)	In this type of fuel cell, the cathode is normally supplied with carbon dioxide and the fuel is a fossil fuel, such as natural gas. These units operate at high temperatures (about 650°C) and can achieve high efficiencies. Because of the high temperatures, these have high potential for use in large scale power generation.
Solid oxide (SOFC)	As with PAFC and MCFC types, these operate at high temperatures with potential applications in areas such as power generation or industry. However, continued development has led to the adaptation to the small stationary sector, i.e. for units upto 10kW for residential use.

Table 1. Types of fuel cell and their applications.

estimated by 'Fuel Cell Today' in 2003 that about 1900 small stationary units had been developed and operated around the world. Many of these were in the USA, but the percentage of units installed in Japan and Europe has increased dramatically. Although certain types of fuel cell are commercially available, more research and development is needed, particularly on the technology itself and infrastructure issues, before more widespread uptake can occur in domestic applications.

A major application for fuel cells in the future could be in powering micro-CHP units. Stirling engine technology is more advanced and likely to lead the domestic market for micro-CHP initially, but the high fuel efficiencies possible with fuel cells make it an attractive technology for micro-CHP. For more information on fuel cells and their developments in the UK, see the Fuel Cell Network.

Case study

Fuel cells

Valliant in Germany has developed a prototype fuel cell unit for domestic use in conjunction with Plug Power. They are leading an EU backed

© Green Building Press

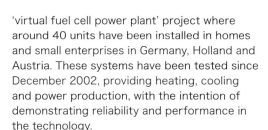

'virtual fuel cell power plant' project where around 40 units have been installed in homes and small enterprises in Germany, Holland and Austria. These systems have been tested since December 2002, providing heating, cooling and power production, with the intention of demonstrating reliability and performance in the technology.

Heat pumps

Heat pumps use the refrigeration cycle to transfer heat from a source (such as the ground, the ambient air or water) through a heat distribution circuit to an internal space. A working fluid (or refrigerant) is driven around a circuit comprising of an evaporator, compressor, condenser and an expansion valve. The heat source transfers heat to liquid refrigerant, which causes it to evaporate. The refrigerant is now at a low temperature and pressure; it then enters the compressor, where the temperature and pressure are increased, as a result of work done by the compressor.

The refrigerant gas enters the condenser, where the heat absorbed by the refrigerant in the evaporator, is released to be used in the dwelling, via a low temperature distribu-

tion system, such as underfloor heating or low temperature radiators. The refrigerant, which is still in the form of a gas but reduced in pressure and temperature, is throttled back further in the expansion valve before the cycle starts again.

Heat pumps will consume electricity, since it is required by the compressor. However, for every one unit of electricity used, 2-4 units of heat energy are produced as the total amount of heat energy delivered to the building is equal to the energy input through the compressor, plus the energy extracted from the heat source. Figure 2 shows the basic operating principle of a heat pump, using the ground as a heat source.

The technology in heat pumps is essentially the same, whether the heat source is from the ground, the air or water. However, as there is an inherent difference in temperature stability between these sources, the overall efficiency (commonly described as the 'coefficient of performance' - COP) will tend to vary.

With a ground source system, the earth absorbs a large proportion of the incident solar radiation, which in the UK helps to ensure that the ground stays at a relatively stable 11-12°C

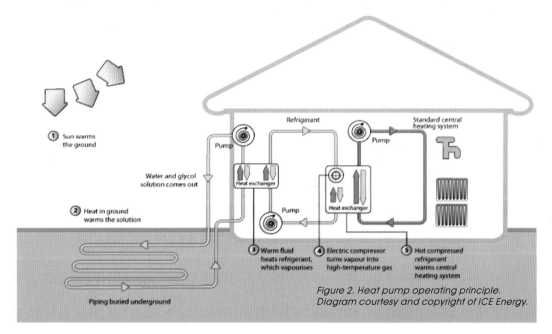

Figure 2. Heat pump operating principle.
Diagram courtesy and copyright of ICE Energy.

all year round. Air-source systems, however, cannot offer the same year round efficiencies, since the ambient air temperature is far more variable. This means that efficiency tends to drop off, just when there is a demand for heat. Spring-water sourced systems potentially offer the best COP; however a viable water source will only be available for a small proportion of potential applications.

Heat pump systems will be at their most cost-effective in applications where high levels of insulation have already been installed and mains gas is not available. Although it is possible for a heat pump to produce hot water at up to 55°C (depending on the heat source and heat pump type), the COP will increase as the required water temperature reduces. In other words, if a distribution system can be designed to effectively heat a dwelling using water heated to only 35-40°C, then the COP will be significantly better than a similar system that is required to heat water to 55°C.

For air source heat pumps, there are obvious space benefits, since the unit sits outside the building, and most other infrastructure works will be internal. A ground collector, however, will require a substantial amount of space, since they will either use a vertical borehole or horizontal trench, depending upon the land available, local ground conditions and excavation costs[1].

Future developments

Heat pumps are much more widespread in domestic application across Europe and in North America, but are gaining in popularity in the UK. Although often queried by some as a true renewable energy technology (since they require electricity to run), they can offer significant reductions in running costs and carbon emissions in comparison to heating systems using electricity, LPG or oil. Using on-site renewables, such as PV, wind or hydro to supply power for the compressor and circulat-

EARTHENERGY™

Renewable Geothermal Heating & Cooling

- **Cost-effective CO$_2$ reduction**
- **10% on site Renewable Energy for Planning (PPS22)**
- **Compliance with 2006 Building Regulations Part L**
- **Eliminate risks associated with boilers**
- **Available 24 hours a day, 7 days a week**
- **Doesn't require planning permission**

EarthEnergy Limited, Falmouth Business Park, Bickland Water Road, Falmouth, TR11 4SZ. Tel 01326 310650 Fax 01326 211071
enquiries@earthenergy.co.uk   www.earthenergy.co.uk

322

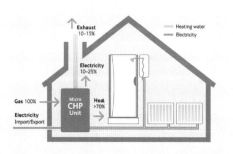

Figure 3: A typical micro-CHP unit (source:Whispergen)

ing pump, will help to boost the COP, and in the future it is possible that they will be competitive with gas-fired systems, in cost terms as well as carbon savings.

Stirling engine CHP

The Stirling heat engine was originally invented by Robert Stirling in 1816 and uses the behaviour of a 'working' gas in terms of pressure, temperature and volume and how these properties vary, with increases and decreases in temperature. Stirling engines have the potential to be much more efficient than conventional combustion engines, and could be run by anything that provides a source of heat, including solar energy and biomass.

The engine works by repeatedly heating and cooling a sealed amount of gas (typically air, hydrogen or helium). This is achieved by transferring the gas from a 'hot' heat exchanger, comprising a chamber and external heat source, to a 'cold' heat exchanger, which has heat sink attached for cooling. As the gas is heated its pressure also increases and this acts on a piston to produce movement. When the gas is then cooled, less work needs to be done by the piston to recompress the gas on the piston's return stroke, meaning there is a net power gain. In its simplest form, the gas simply flows cyclically between the hot and cold chambers.

Applications

Stirling engine technology has been used in a variety of different applications and of different scales. Currently they are only used in specialised applications such as in submarines, as power generators for yachts, and wherever conventional engines would be too noisy. A successful mass-market application for Stirling engines has not yet been found, however micro-CHP could provide the opportunity for Stirling engines to be a household name.

Future developments

One promising application is micro combined heat and power (micro-CHP). This involves an engine (such as the Stirling engine) driving an electrical generator that allows dwellings to generate a proportion of their own electrical supply, whilst also supplying heat and hot water. Dwellings with micro-CHP units would usually require supplementary electrical power from the grid at times of peak demand; any surplus power not used in the dwelling can be sold back to the grid when the demand is less than that generated. A typical micro-CHP unit is shown in Figure 3.

Case study
Sterling engine CHP

One example of a Stirling engine being used for micro-CHP is the 'Whispergen' unit, currently being tested by Powergen in the UK. Developed by Whispertech in New Zealand, the Whispergen has a 1kW electrical output and a thermal output of between 7.5-13kW. The obvious application for the Whispergen is in small, well insulated dwellings, with low heat loads or small groups of dwellings in urban locations, as larger CHP units may not be appropriate, and the system capacity (for heat and power) is closely matched to demand. ✆

References

For more detailed information on heat pumps, their suitability to different environments and costs, download a copy of 'Domestic Ground Source Heat Pumps: Design and installation of closed loop systems (CE82) from the Energy Saving Trust: www.est.org.uk.

Heat pumps in detail

Of all low carbon technologies, heat pumps are probably the most perplexing. At first they seem counter-intuitive, since the concept is far from obvious. Furthermore, there are many variants and many different applications. No wonder people are confused. **John Cantor** trys to sort the myths from reality.

There should be little mysticism about this technology as it has been around for well over a century, mostly used for cooling. Yes, your fridge is a heat pump, an established technology and far from magic.

The idea of getting 3 to 4 times the heat energy output, as compared to the electrical energy used to run it, truly does sound magic. This gets many people excited about the concept. Add to that a bit of sales-hype, and you may be left with a somewhat distorted view of the subject, since heat pumps are often compared alongside the worst forms of heating; - normal electric heating. It is surely only fair to also compare a heat pump to a gas condensing boiler, or wood burning for that matter.

In a nutshell, heat pumps can provide heat

equivalent to 2 to 4 times the power input. This is because heat is being extracted from an external source. But the electricity used to run them is potentially the most polluting of fuels, since it is mostly generated at between 30 and 40% efficiency, and therefore not ideal for heating. On balance, only a high efficiency heat pump will show significant advantages over burning the fuel efficiently in a conventional manner.

The renewable status of heat pumps is not all together clear. In reality they are not pure renewables, they are partly renewable, since for the vast majority of applications, the electrical power input is non-renewable. However, it would be true magic if the heat pump process didn't require some input. This would be perpetual motion. True renewables sit idle when there is no wind or sun etc. But heat pumps can operate on demand at any time.

The most important factor to consider must be the CO_2 emissions for all heating methods. A comparison of the environmental worth of various systems can then be made.

CO2 Emissions for various heating methods

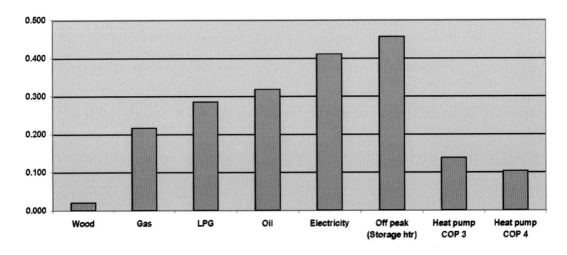

Variation in efficiency vs heated water temperature for a typical ground source heat pump (COP = coefficient of performance).

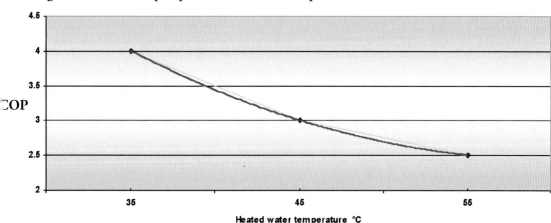

Wood can rank as the lowest carbon fuel commonly used (depending on how it is sourced and burnt). However, heat pumps normally rank second, but this all depends on the efficiency of the heat pump installation.

If your concerns are with the environment, your priority will be with energy efficiency. (If you were buying a car, you would want it to achieve 60, not 35mpg), to achieve the highest efficiency, you need to attend to every detail. All houses and households have different needs and requirements, so a standardised system may not be ideal for achieving the best from a system.

There is one vitally important fact that you need to understand, if you want to know how to get the best output from a heat pump. The energy efficiency of a heat pump system is greatly affected by the temperature difference between source (ground outside) and sink (underfloor heating). In simple terms, the hotter the water produced, the lower the system efficiency.

As can be seen, to attain a high efficiency, the temperature of the 'hot' side needs to be kept as low as possible. This is why underfloor heating is so desirable when connected to a heat pump; it only needs to be luke-warm to heat the house (depending on design). Since

it is the temperature 'lift' that we are trying to keep to a minimum, it therefore follows that the 'cold' side be high as possible.

A good analogy to illustrate these issues is to consider a car having to go uphill. The steeper the hill (bigger the temperature 'lift') the harder the engine has to work, and the lower the mpg. A well-designed system in a low energy house with a good ground collector, is effectively running up only a slight incline, so the energy efficiency is high.

How can high efficiency be achieved?
Heat pumps work better in low energy houses. It may not, at first, be obvious why it is better to install a heat pump in a well-insulated building. One might ask –'surely the savings are of more benefit when installing in an old energy guzzling property?' Well, it's back to that very important fact. In a low energy building the heated water temperature for the underfloor might be only 35°C resulting in COP's of 4, but in a badly insulated house, you will need water at least at 45°C. resulting in a COP of maybe 3. Yes, the incline is steep, and we therefore have a low mpg.

Use weather compensation - this is a must

if you want high efficiency. It reduces (adjusts) the heated water temperature as the outside temperature gets warmer. Without this facility, it's like driving a car up the same gradient hill, when at times it could be flatter, thus using less energy.

Use underfloor heating - underfloor heating generally works at a lower temperature than do radiators. But beware, it can be difficult to persuade underfloor heating companies to take seriously the crucial need to keep the heated water temperature as low as possible. The flow rate should also be significantly higher with a heat pump, so the pipe design will be different.

What about hot water?

Some heat pumps can reach 60°C, others only 45°C. But when heating water up to high temperatures, the efficiency drops (back to driving up our steep hill). However, you must consider the alternative. Even if the COP is as low as 2.5, you are still getting 2.5kW for only 1kW of electricity. This is 2.5 times better than an immersion heater. The domestic hot water (DHW) cylinder design is critical. Unless the area of the heat-exchanger coil within the cylinder is very big, the temperature difference will be undesirably large. The cylinder should be specifically designed for use with the heat pump, and not of the 'thermal store' type.

What about the heat pump unit itself? The size of the heat-exchangers inside units vary. Small temperature differences are desirable, but will come at a cost, since the heat-exchangers need to be efficient, and probably large. Be cautious of cheap heat pumps, they rarely have a high efficiency and may not be so long-lived. A well developed integrated control unit, that all of the best heat pumps have, is well worth having. Refrigerants vary too and unfortunately the best heat pumps do not use hydrocarbon refrigerants.

Exact efficiency figures (at realistic working temperatures) will be available from the manufacturers, i.e heat output(kW) and electricity in (kW) at source temperature (the cold bit) of °C, sink (the hot part) at 35°C, or sink at 50°C etc.

Beware of ratings that don't specify the conditions. (The graph on the previous page is for a typical good unit.)

Off peak electricity!

If your system is designed to use a large percentage of off-peak electricity, be mindful that you could actually use significantly more energy in terms of kWh of electricity consumed. But on the other hand, you could save significantly on running costs. Most houses using off-peak need to become 'toasty' warm at breakfast time, apart from the obvious energy loss, your COP is bound to be worse at such times, and since you cannot tell what outside temperatures the day will bring, the resulting system's controls are not ideal.

Glossary

The **COP** (coefficient of performance) is a commonly used efficiency term, (like mpg for a car). It is the ratio of heat output to energy input (usually electricity). Conventional electric heaters would have a COP of 1, a heat pump maybe 2.5 to 4.

The **SPF** (Seasonal performance factor) is simply the estimated total heat output delivered over the year as compared to the electricity bill. This is the figure you really need to know and is more informative than the COP which varies as seasons change. The SPF figure must reflect any use of an internal electric back-up 'immersion' type heater. The SPF is often lower than claimed COP's.

The CO_2 emission graph is based on expected efficiencies for typical good appliances. Figures taken from www.johnwilloughby.co.uk The figure for wood will vary greatly depending on many factors. Off peak electricity is given a poorer rating since it tends to overheat the building at night.

Useful websites

www.heatpumps.co.uk
www.heatpumpnet.org.uk
www.feta.co.uk
www.nef.org.uk/gshp/gshp.htm

© Green Building Press

Wind power

The UK is blessed with the best wind energy resource in Europe. Yet - despite all the efforts of a number of pioneering individuals and companies, our use of this renewable and pure energy source lags far behind other EU countries. **John Shore** suggests that we should give wind power, in all possible locations, a chance to prove itself.

In the past, large windmills (often made mainly of timber) were commonplace and provided an essential local energy source. Later, throughout the UK, the familiar wind-pumps provided water supplies and before the widespread introduction of grid electricity, small stand-alone wind turbines were used to provide lighting. Today, although wind technology has made some major advances, we currently only have perhaps a few thousand small turbines (to which this article mainly refers) and most of these are recreational (yachts and caravans) with perhaps a thousand or so domestic-sized machines installed for eco and off-grid houses. The use of medium-sized turbines for horticulture and industry has hardly begun.

Domestic-scale wind turbines can be beautiful, highly efficient, and can have a very long working life - in the USA, turbines dating from the 1900's are still bought, sold and are fully repairable. A carefully designed eco-house can power its basic needs from a 500 watt or 1kW turbine, depending on household numbers and lifestyle.

What is available

Small wind turbines can be classified in the following main categories:
- low or high voltage turbines, which directly provide heat, pump water or drive a suitable motor (no battery required)
- low-voltage (12, 24, 36 or 48V) turbines, which charge batteries and power low-voltage lights, appliances, pump water
- low-voltage turbines, which charge batteries

and power high-voltage lights, appliances, pump water etc via an inverter
- high-voltage (115 or 230 V) turbines, which feed into the mains electricity grid, usually via a special inverter, (no electricity is available during grid failure, unless a charger/battery/inverter is also added).

Despite the current optimism and media hype about roof-top, micro, grid-connect turbines, we should not assume that low-voltage turbines have had their day. Not only are batteries recyclable, but alternative power storage methods are being developed. We may yet live to see a whole new range of low-voltage domestic products, especially designed to work efficiently with low voltage renewable energy!

Location of the turbine

I have worked with wind energy for over 30 years as a researcher, designer, manufacturer and supplier and I passionately wish to see small wind turbines used on, as well as around, buildings. Since many of our customers install their turbines on yachts and often sleep in a cabin underneath, there is no reason why suitable turbines should not be mounted on buildings and we have already supplied building-mounted turbines in this country and abroad.

Turbines are usually mounted on steel tube masts, ideally hinged near the ground to enable the turbine to be safely lowered for inspection and maintenance. Batteries and inverters can be housed near the mast, so only low-cost, high-voltage wiring is run to the point of use. To obtain good performance the turbine should be sited 10m above any obstruction within 150m. Building-mounted turbines should be mounted on a steel or aluminium stub mast which attaches to the building structure through twin rubber noise and vibration isolation mountings.

The ability to operate safely in high winds is paramount. While larger turbines usually incorporate a furling mechanism, some small turbines have little or no protection. Some new companies are selling inadequately engineered designs and are also making performance claims which are impossible to achieve. Take independent advice from experienced consultants before specifying or buying!

The AIR wind module was one of the first small turbines intended to be mounted onto buildings. The design concept was for a

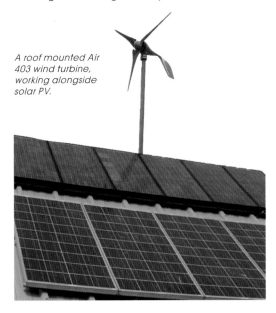

A roof mounted Air 403 wind turbine, working alongside solar PV.

powerful, low-cost, modular unit which could be installed in a row and make use of the enhanced wind flow that a large flat or gently curved roof can provide. The design was so popular that 70,000 were supplied world-wide in the first 10 years, and the latest version offers a programmed cubic power curve, automatic shut-down in gusty winds or beyond 500W output and built-in voltage regulation. However, high blade speed and noise are two aspects of the AIR which could and should be improved and a number of established UK manufacturers are now working to develop turbines much more suited for mounting on or near buildings. Turbines should not be mounted on chimneys (for obvious structural reasons) and building insurance will also be an issue. Because a smooth, steady air flow is rarely found close to buildings (or trees), a careful assessment should be made as to whether the turbine/s will produce enough power to be a sustainable concept.

There is no doubt that roof-mounted turbines have great potential, especially on larger buildings, but a completely new design approach and type of turbine may be required to deliver safety and cost-effectiveness.

Guide costs and outputs

Currently, a 1.1m turbine, providing 200W at 11m/s with a peak output of 500W at 13.5m/s, costs £700 excluding installation or any additional items.

A 2.7m, 1.0kW grid-connect turbine/inverter system will cost around £3,300.

A 3.5m, 2.5kW grid-connect system, will cost about £5,500 (all prices exclude VAT, installation or any savings from grants).

For comparison, a 1kWp (7.72m²) grid-connect PV roof-mounted PV array would cost around £5,000 and deliver around 750kWh/year.

Average urban wind speeds are quite low and while a 1kW wind turbine might deliver 750kWh/year on a domestic urban roof - assuming 3.85m/s average windspeed, the same turbine

© Green Building Press

will easily exceed 3000kWh/year in an open rural area. Resource assessment is an essential indicator of project viability, and matching demand to seasonal variation is important. PV can provide power in summer when winds may be light - wind can provide power in dull winter weather when heat and lighting loads are greater.

Grants

The present system of grants for wind energy equipment is not entirely a good idea, as it stifles the DIY approach which has been so popular with wind power enthusiasts, and many reputable dealers do not have the resources needed to support installation teams. £1,000 per kW of electrical output (£5,000 max) and limited to 30% of the installed cost, is only available if installation is carried out by a very limited number of accredited contractors, who will often need to charge for travel, B&B, and labour costs. Because the level of grant relates to the rated power specified by the manufacturer and not to a standardised wind speed or to actual energy production, some turbines get more grant than their output justifies.

Future systems

New designs for building-integrated wind turbines are being developed, some as ridge-mounted arrays and others hidden from view in ducts which enhance wind flow and power production. For safety and public confidence turbines will need to operate at much slower rotational speeds and with lower noise levels than most currently available turbines. Minimum weight, combined with high strength, low installed costs, zero maintenance and fail-safe operation in high winds, will be prerequisites for any successful roof-mounted product.

Fossil-fuel energy will have to be targeted for essential uses in the near future, so using the ambient energy around buildings for power generation is bound to increase. 🌏

New developments in domestic scale wind energy in the form of the Swift wind turbine (top) and the Windsave 'plug and save' turbine (below). Both are being developed for grid connect and not battery storage and both are causing controversy in the industry.

Further reading

'Green Building Bible, Volume 2', for an in-depth analysis of the potential output from 1 - 2m diameter wind turbines.

'Its not easy being green, part 3' earlier in this book for a potential customer's musings and research into the value/payback of a Windsave turbine.

BFF magazine Vol 15, No 3. for more opinions of potential outputs from roof mounted turbines:

www.buildingforafuture.co.uk//winter05/index.php

Useful websites

www.renewabledevices.com/swift/
www.windsave.com
www.shorepower.co.uk

Roofing

Getting the design of the roof and the rest of the building envelope right will give considerable benefits in terms of reduced energy use. But which roofing materials carry the least embodied energy? Is there a best choice? **Jerry Clark** and **Olwyn Pritchard** investigate.

You have probably learnt by now that approximately 50% of all energy use is caused directly from the operation and use of our buildings. Of the energy currently used by buildings, 90% is the energy consumed while the building is in use, with only 10% of this being embodied energy, i.e. that consumed in the construction of the building. With this in mind, vast improvements could be made in building structures and insulation levels, possibly reducing energy use during occupation by around 75%. This would then, of course, make the energy embodied in the fabric of the building of far greater significance.

Roofing materials comparison

Roof coverings can be manufactured from a wide range of materials. Some of these are described briefly below.

Clay tiles are one of the UK's most traditional materials. The clays (and natural minerals found within) are fired at high temperature in excess of 1100°C. This binds and cures the materials into the durable roof tile that adorns many UK homes. The higher the firing temperature, then the longer the life of the tile. On the down-side, of course, the high temperatures involved lead to a high embodied energy but this embodied energy component is offset by a longer lifespan of the product.

Concrete tiles are made in essentially the same way as any other concrete product, with the proportions of 1:4 portland cement and aggregate. Mixing and chemical curing takes place in highly technical and controlled conditions. From this the manufacturers are now able to offer

very long service guarantees – most offering a minimum of 50 years (remember though clay tiles have proven to last many hundreds of years).

Natural slate, as the name suggests, has no man made components other than the skill of the craftsman to 'hew' them from the larger slab. Quality of natural slate can vary, with Welsh slate renowned worldwide as one of the most durable roofing materials ever discovered. Some European slates, though cheaper (due mainly to lower labour costs), have been found to have far less durability due to mineral pockets (usually iron) within the slate seams. These irons eventually rust and expand causing the slate to crack and decay.

Steel is becoming a popular roof cladding material again. Traditionally it was used as corrugated sheets, either galvanized or self colour, but latterly colour-coated or with a plasticised coating. More recently we have seen the emergence of fake tiles and slates which are actually sheets of steel, coated with a mineralized surface to mimic the desired appearance. The two main advantages of this type of roofing has been weight, cost and speed of installation. The largest market for these products does seem to be roof refurbishment. Steel is produced from mined iron ore, coke and limestone melted together in a high temperature furnace. The coke turns to carbon monoxide, reducing the iron oxide to iron. Between 25 and 40% recycled material is used in the final steel making process.

Bitumen is the residual material produced after removal of all the volatile products from crude oil, such as petrol and diesel. Asphalt is manufactured from bitumen blended with limestone powder and fine limestone aggregate. Another source is lake asphalt, a naturally occurring material mainly imported from Trinidad. Asphalt tiles make up 75% of the US roofing market, but unfortunately these products have low durability. Timber shingles are riven or sawn from suitable timber, such as oak or western red cedar.

Embodied pollution

One important aspect of the sustainability of roofing materials, which is not highlighted in the above table is the pollution caused during manufacture and supply of the various materials. The 'embodied energy' column gives a good indication of the relative quantities of

pollutants produced in the manufacture and application of the now common PVC (Plastisol) coating. PVC manufacture involves considerable amounts of chlorine (a nerve gas) and results in the release of further dioxins when the steel is recycled.

Aluminium is a highly durable and very recyclable material but its main hamstring is the very high energy consumption of the manufacturing process (though high recycling percentages

In the table below, the figures in the first two columns refer to a square metre of roof cladding material, thus making it easy to compare various materials.

Environmental criteria for the selection of roofing materials	Embodied energy (MJ/m²)	Weight (kg/m²)	Lifespan (years)	Material resources (years)	Recyclability
Clay tiles	270 – 430	40 – 60	30 – 100	abundant	good
Concrete tiles	40 – 90	40 – 90	30 – 100	abundant	good
Natural slates	130 – 160	20 – 30	100+	150 (Welsh)	very good
Coated steel	180 – 290	7	30	230	fair
Aluminium (virgin)	550 – 920	<10	100+	260	good
Aluminium (recycled)	30 – 90	<10	100+		good
Asphalt shingles	285	low	20 – 30	75	poor
Timber shingles	very low	low	50	renewable	fair
Membranes	high	very low	15 – 25	75	poor

carbon dioxide produced during manufacture, but says nothing of all the other more toxic pollutants. It is therefore recommended that materials should be selected to perform the set task while minimising all impacts, including pollution. Direct comparisons of the various pollution risks are difficult to make, but the following gives a rough indication of the kinds of pollutants involved.

Clay tiles - although the embodied energy is high, there are few toxicity issues involved in their manufacture.

Concrete has a lower embodied energy, but more CO_2 is released (see 'Can we manage without cement' earlier in this chapter).

Steel production releases dioxins and other localised pollutants during smelting, and the

help to keep consumption comparable with steel. See 'Choosing the right material' earlier in this chapter).

Lead and copper both have a high degree of corrosion resistance, but their use for large areas of roofing can lead to a degree of contamination in the rainwater runoff. Copper is extracted from sulphide ores and the mining process is associated with pollution of waterways by heavy metals.

Bitumen and asphalt systems are renowned for their short product life. Due to their being very difficult to recycle, this leads to further use of precious oil reserves, unless an alternative replacement material is used. Both slate and shingles have no pollution implications, apart from that involved in extraction and transport.

>>>

Green or turf roofs

Green roofs are not a new idea, although they haven't been popular (until recently) in Britain since the days of earth walls and sod roofs. They are far more common on the continent, but over the last few years there has be a renaissance in the UK. Partly responsible for the new trend in green roofs are steelmaker, Corus, who introduced a simple but highly effective profiled steel tray system called Kalzip Nature Roof, suitable for creating simple but effective, thin soil sedum roofs. Buildings boasting this new breed of roof include the House of the Future at Cardiff's St. Fagans Museum, office blocks, supermarkets, railway terminals and some new homes across the UK.

Green roofs offer a number of advantages in terms of the environment generally, and some to the building and user specifically. For instance, in urban areas, green roofs can provide a useful habitat for birds and invertebrates. So much 'waste' land has been redeveloped that there are few habitats to support the insects on which birds depend[1]. Brownfield city developments often result in the destruction of specialised, drought resistant habitats. These can be recreated on roofs, and if recycled crushed aggregate, from the original site, is used this saves on disposal costs. Green roof/brown roof habitats are ideal for insects to breed and as more are installed we could see the return of certain bird species.

Tangible benefits of green roofs

Durability of green roofs need not be a concern as one green roof in Switzerland is known to date from 1914. In fact it could be argued that a green roof might actually improve the durability of the building as a whole by protecting the underlying membrane. Another major advantage is its absorbency, the ability to temporarily store water during a storm, with up to 85% of the rain being delay-released, thereby helping to alleviate pressure on storm drainage systems. Green roofs also absorb heat from the sun, which acts to reduce what is known as the 'heat island effect', a phenomenon now common in built-up areas where temperatures

can rise quickly on hot summer days. Noise too is much improved by the use of green roofs and greenery in general will act as an acoustic muffler, both inside the building and outside.

Demonstrable health benefits

Green roofs have proven health benefits for people living nearby. In Germany, the roof of a Bundepost Office in Stuttgart was 'greened' and absenteeism due to sickness among the workers fell dramatically compared to neighbouring blocks with conventional roofs.

Localised air quality is improved by green roofs. Ozone, a major contributor to air pollution in cities, is exacerbated by 'heat island' conditions, hence, more green roofs equal less ozone pollution. As a bonus the plants on the roof absorb carbon dioxide, and give out oxygen, further improving local air quality.

A Texan study of post-surgery recovery in hospitals demonstrated that recovery was quicker if patients could look out onto green space. Since then architects have been incorporating green roofs into hospital designs more frequently. A few community hospitals in the UK are now being designed with more green-space provision, and the good-practice work on hospital design being developed by the Commission for Architecture and the Built Environment (CABE) is likely to address this[2].

There is a growing body of evidence that visual and physical contact with natural greenery provides a range of benefits to people. These include both mental benefits (such as reduction of stress) and physical benefits (including the provision of cleaner air). Access to green space can bring about direct reductions in a person's heart rate and blood-pressure, and can aid general well-being. Also, widespread installation of green roofs in cities could, by lowering localised temperatures, reduce the number of heat related deaths during the increasing summer hot spells.

Types of green roof

Green roofs are often referred to as 'intensive' or 'extensive'. Either can be flat or with a shallow/medium pitch.

Intensive roofs usually have a significant depth of growing medium and support grass, small plants, herbs, etc. A roof garden, at the furthest extreme, could have shrubs and small trees. Simple turf roofs are usually referred to as 'intensive', and these are within the construction capabilities of most self-builders. Intensive roofs usually need some maintenance, such as watering in dry weather, mowing, and weeding. The weight of the soil can be a disadvantage and needs to be considered at the design stage, when water retention and snowloading need to be addressed. A turf roof with 150mm of soil can be 2 or 3 times heavier than a slate roof[3].

Extensive roofs usually have a much thinner soil layer, are lighter, and are usually planted with drought resistant succulents of the sedum species. These are usually grown on a fibrous mat with a thin layer of porous growing medium (called sedum mats). Sedums are used because they are wind, frost and drought resistant and because they absorb water. The sedum mat is rolled out on a specially designed roof, with several manufacturers now offering complete systems. Although these can be expensive, they are a simple solution and have proven to be very popular in recent years. Like intensive roofs, extensive roofs still provide habitat for insects and therefore a feeding ground for birds. Maintenance is minimal and they are not usually suitable for walking about on like intensive roof gardens, but they are a good choice for a large area of commercial or industrial roof.

Brown roofs

Brown roofs are another form of 'extensive' system which has been tried out in inner city areas, to mimic industrial wasteland habitat for biodiversity. As more brownfield land is grabbed for development, then groups like the Wildlife Trusts, are encouraging developers to consider putting a brown roof on their buildings. Brown roofs can, in some cases, use recycled aggregate from the site on which the building is built. Such roofs can then be

left to colonise naturally or be seeded with a wildflower mix that requires poor soil fertility. Materials may include sand, gravel, stones or timbers, all creating a range of habitats. Some seed and small creatures will be imported with the rubble, and recolonisation takes place much more rapidly than with a sterile growing medium. In most cases, no maintenance is needed or even desirable, as old stems provide necessary nesting places for certain wasps and small bees.

Conclusions

Considering all the roof materials that are available, the most sustainable options for traditional roof cladding are timber shingles, closely followed by natural slate, as long as these materials are obtained from a local source (or at least within the country). After this, selection can be made on the basis of embodied energy, pollution and length of life. Consideration can also be given to recyclability, and it is likely that slates, concrete and clay tiles will be available second hand somewhere quite local. Green roofs offer the alternative to traditional roofing, and are particularly useful where water retention, biodiversity and health benefits are goals.

❧

References
1. *www.blackredstarts.org.uk* or *www.wildlondon.org.uk*
2. *www.livingroofs.org*
3. John Talbot, Findhorn Foundation: *www.ecovillagefindhorn.org*

Useful links
www.optigreen.com/start.html
www.greenroofs.org

Further reading
'Planting Green Roofs and Living Walls', by Nigel Dunnet & Noel Kingsbury (2004), available from the Green Shop, 01452 770629 www.greenshop.co.uk

'Building Green (A guide to using plants on roofs, walls and pavements)' by Jacklyn Jonston & John Newton, London Ecology Unit.

Acknowledgements
Some of the information in this article is based on 'A Guide to Sustainable Roofing' published by Redland Roofing Systems.

Extensive green roofs

There are a growing number of voices extolling the virtues and benefits of 'green roofs.' There are currently some good manufactured roofing systems that can now be applied to domestic properties. Is this just a trend, or are there some real and tangible benefits to the installation of green roofs? Here **Peter Aceston-Rook** considers the construction and cost implications of extensive green roofs and what they can achieve?'

Green roofs are living roofs, planted living surfaces, rather than the traditional type of roof of tile, slate or bitumen based flat roof. There are two main types of green roof, extensive and intensive, and there is a wide difference between the two. Intensive green roofs are what one would, in the past, often refer to as a roof garden. Deep soils of 15cm and over,

trees, and other features, these roofs are often suitable for human use. Intensive roofs support a diverse range of vegetation, grasses, trees, shrubs, even ponds and hard landscaping.

Extensive green roofs differ in the fact that they are not designed for walking on, and the soil/substrate depth is anything from as little as 1cm up to 15cm. Often monoculture in their growing species, the most commonly used plants being sedums, these sedums are chosen for their durability and the fact they can survive on shallow substrate depths. Mainly from more arid climates, sedums are succulent plants that survive in dry conditions by storing rainwater in their tissues.

Nowadays these plants are commercially grown on matting of set sizes so that the plants

Extensive green roof detail at the BedZED development, near London.

© Green Building Press

Sedum matting on a roll

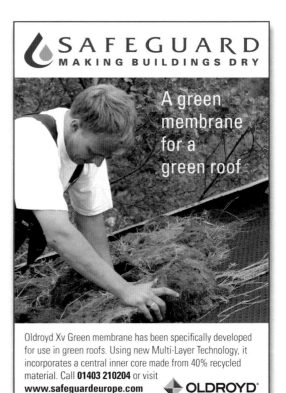

streams and rivers and therefore channels large quantities of water in sometimes short spaces of time, possibly leading to flooding scenarios or at the very least putting extra water into the river systems that would have otherwise been absorbed into the ground and into the ground-water system.

A green roof has the advantage of absorbing this water to a certain extent, and acting as a replacement to the lost permeable layer at ground level in the context of an area to harbour both bird-life and insects. Although it cannot act in the same way as the soil that has been built upon, it does have the effect of slowing down storm water run off, when compared to a standard pitched tile roof or a flat felt roof.

The main environmental advantages of extensive green roofs
● storm water management

can be harvested on rolls and taken to site to create instant green roofs of any size.

Germany is widely accepted as the centre of expertise in modern extensive and intensive green roof installation. This expertise has developed over the past thirty years and Germany boasts the unrivalled estimation that around 10% of all roofs have been 'greened'[1]. This equates to around 8,000 acres of green roofs, way beyond installations anywhere else in the world at present. The technology involved in green roofing systems is expanding rapidly as more and more research is carried out world-wide.

Green roofs are moving upward in the focus of designers and architects. They are becoming more popular as increased interest and legislation changes lean towards sustainable development, thereby promoting greater awareness of the effects of the built environment on nature and the environmental impact of buildings.

One of the key issues in the built environment is the fact that the footprint of a building, whether industrial/commercial or domestic, replaces the permeable surface of the earth with an impermeable surface. That surface area can no longer absorb rainfall or moisture, and therefore any water falling on that area must be channelled or directed elsewhere. Usually any rainfall is directed into storm drains,

SAFEGUARD
MAKING BUILDINGS DRY

A green membrane for a green roof

Oldroyd Xv Green membrane has been specifically developed for use in green roofs. Using new Multi-Layer Technology, it incorporates a central inner core made from 40% recycled material. Call **01403 210204** or visit **www.safeguardeurope.com** for further information. **OLDROYD** The ultimate membrane system

- reduction in heat island effect in urban areas/cities
- sound proofing
- insulative qualities
- absorption of carbon dioxide
- protection of roofing membrane from the elements
- microclimate
- biodiversity.

Advantages of green roofs

Storm water management

One of the main manufacturers of green roofing systems suggest that with a low substrate depth of 2 to 4cm, 40% of rainfall will be retained annually in their roofs, leaving the other 60% to run off naturally. Other manufacturers, like ZinCo, claim retention figures of up to 90% reduction in storm water run off, and they claim that 'the increasing use of extensive green roofs in cities significantly reduces the risk of flooding'

Even DEFRA, in their publication 'Greening the Gateway, claim up to 70% water retention on green roofs[2]. One of the leading research bodies conducting thorough experimentation in extensive green roofing is Penn State University in Portland, Oregon, USA. They put the figure more realistically at around 50% of a 2.5cm rainfall event being retained on the roof. They do state that annually, 50-70%

of rainfall could be retained. This is a figure backed up in an article in by Theodore Eismann in Landscape Architecture magazine, stating the same 50–75% storm water run off reduction on the recently greened 1,300,000 square feet Montgomery Ward Building in Baltimore USA[3].

Most studies and publications are in agreement that there are major advantages in attenuation of storm water in extensive green roofs. In the past rainwater has been channelled off roofs and roads into drains. In storm conditions run off combines with sewage, and has to be released into rivers in order to prevent sewage combining with storm water and being released into the streets.

After the August 2004 storm conditions in the southern UK, warnings had to be issued about bathing in the seas after large quantities of storm water and sewage discharged into the Thames. In one 24-hour period, 3 million cubic metres of sewage were discharged into the Thames in London. The discharge carried 10,000 tonnes of screenable solids, including faecal matter[4] which flowed out into the Thames estuary and its bathing beaches, destroying wildlife in the Thames and killing many thousands of fish.

The urban heat island effect

Urban heat island effect (UHI) is the effect that causes air temperatures around heavily built up areas to be 2-10°C warmer than the

Heat island profile

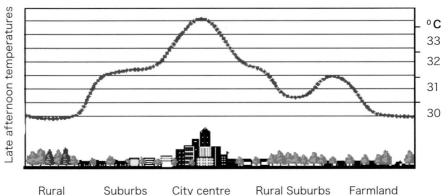

Late afternoon temperatures

°C
33
32
31
30

Rural   Suburbs   City centre   Rural Suburbs   Farmland

© Green Building Press

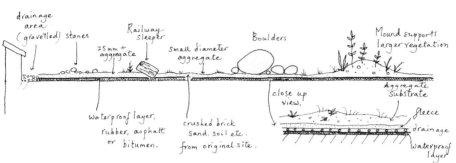

drainage area (gravelled) stones

25mm + aggregate

Railway sleeper

small diameter aggregate

Boulders

Mound supports larger vegetation

waterproof layer, rubber, asphalt or bitumen.

crushed brick sand, soil etc. from original site.

close up view.

Aggregate Substrate

fleece

drainage

waterproof layer

Sedum Mat - Lightweight

sedums

fleece/ 'geotextile'

drainage

waterproof membrane

Simple details of green and brown roofs

drawing by Olwyn Pritchard

150mm aprox soil + turf

floor boards

cork or polystyrene insulating layer.

EDPM or similar waterproof membrane

Rafters 200 × 50 @ 400 cntrs.

A Simple Turf Roof

flashband or similar

100 × 50 kerb

'geotextile' fleece or blanket water permeable

stones (pebbles) for drainage + perforated pipe.

Below: sedum roof being installed on the continent, using the Oldroyd system.

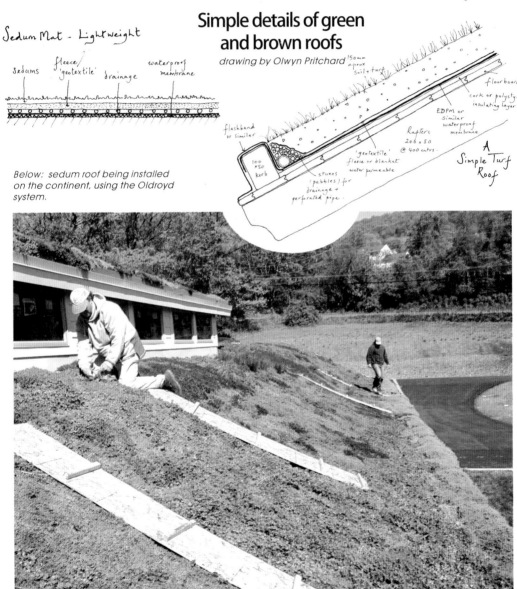

surrounding countryside or suburban sprawl. It is caused simply by large quantities of thermal mass in cities and towns where there is a lack of vegetation; vegetation allows the principle of evapotranspiration (ET) or the sum of evaporation and transpiration from trees and plants. Quite simply vegetation breathes in much the same way as a human breathes, that 'breath' is moisture rich. Research by the US geological survey found that up to 10% of the moisture in the atmosphere is transpired from plants[5].

A large oak tree can give off as much as 415 litres of water per day; an acre of cornfield can give off around 11,400-15,100 litres per day according to the USGS. This water is taken up by plant roots and given off by the trees leaves. Sedum, although a succulent, still gives off this moisture, and although at a much lower quantity as compared to an acre of cornfield, it is still going to be a far more useful surface for roofing than a conventional pitch and felt flat roof system, in relation to reduction of the UHI effect.

One of the contributory factors toward the UHI effect is the increased demand for air conditioning systems in cities and towns. This used to be confined to the warmer climates, but with a succession of hotter summers in the UK, it is more or less standard in the commercial districts, and certainly on the increase in the domestic market. Clearly then this increased demand for electricity means more power generation and more carbon emissions from our power stations. Possibly the worst thing about the UHI effect is that the increased heat encourages the increase in air-conditioning units, which in turn produce more heat. Air-conditioning units are notoriously inefficient as around 40% of a unit's energy is wasted in the form of heat transfer directly to the outside of the building in the form of heated air into the atmosphere.

The warmer a city's atmosphere, the higher the demand for air-conditioning, the more the air-conditioning systems heat the external air, the higher the temperatures will rise, an extremely damaging cycle.

Construction and weight

A typical modern, manufacturered green roof system has the following components installed and the weights are as follows

Product	Use	Weight saturated
Extensive substrate	Growing medium	1200kg/m³
Sedum Blanket	Vegetation	44kg/m²
Fleece layer	Filter layer	Nominal
Reservoir board	Water storage 10L/m²	10.65kg/m²

Most extensive roofs increase the weight by around 70 to 170kg per square metre (when dry), over the weight of a roof constructed from small plain clay tiles

Product	Weight per M²
Small clay plain tile	68-78 kg
Concrete pantile	46-52 kg
Welsh Slate	17-23kg

Even with the worst-case scenario of a saturated extensive roof, there are modern lightweight and low cost products strong enough to cope with such a weight, i.e Masonite 'I beam' as an example for flat roof constructions, as opposed to the standard pitched roof constructions seen in most houses today.

It has conventionally been the case that most extensive green roofs are of flat or lightly pitched construction. Sedum need not be restricted to flat roofs, as modern technologies have been utilised to secure sedum roll in place on pitched roofs of up to and sometimes over 20 degrees. One major consideration with green roof construction is the possibility of leakage. With modern methods of joining roofing membranes, they can now be tested for leaks pre-installation, both electronically and by simple flood testing (on a flat roof), before the rest of the roofing layers are built up.

Cost considerations

For a conventional detached house of 160m²,

© Green Building Press

**With Ecoseal
Single Ply Membranes,
you'll have nature covered**

Figures show that in recent years, specifiers still used PVC on approximately 70% of flat roofed projects in the UK. Ecoseal Environmental Roofing System is a non-PVC, toxin and halogen free TPO, and is the world's most widely used membrane of this type. Ecoseal comes with a guarantee of up to 20 years and meets all major UK and International code approvals. Technical and field support is provided by Trelleborg Field Engineers. This exceptional membrane protects roofs and the environment for longer.

Ecoseal – **high specification product,
low environmental impact.**

TRELLEBORG
BUILDING SYSTEMS

Suite 3D, Willow House, Strathclyde Business Park,
Bellshill, Lanarkshire ML4 3PB
T: +44 (0)1698 464620   F: +44 (0)1698 464621
E: tbselastomers@trelleborg.com   **www.tbselastomers.com**

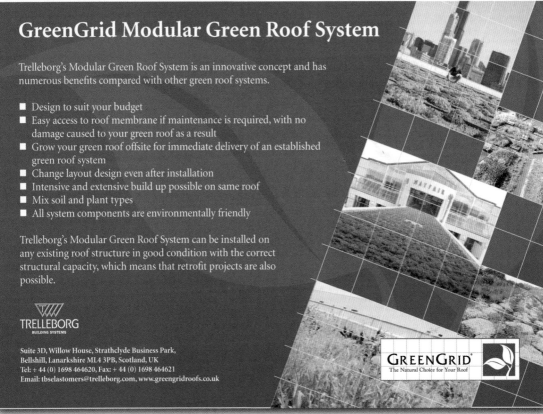

GreenGrid Modular Green Roof System

Trelleborg's Modular Green Roof System is an innovative concept and has numerous benefits compared with other green roof systems.

- Design to suit your budget
- Easy access to roof membrane if maintenance is required, with no damage caused to your green roof as a result
- Grow your green roof offsite for immediate delivery of an established green roof system
- Change layout design even after installation
- Intensive and extensive build up possible on same roof
- Mix soil and plant types
- All system components are environmentally friendly

Trelleborg's Modular Green Roof System can be installed on any existing roof structure in good condition with the correct structural capacity, which means that retrofit projects are also possible.

TRELLEBORG
BUILDING SYSTEMS

Suite 3D, Willow House, Strathclyde Business Park,
Bellshill, Lanarkshire ML4 3PB, Scotland, UK
Tel: + 44 (0) 1698 464620, Fax: + 44 (0) 1698 464621
Email: tbselastomers@trelleborg.com, www.greengridroofs.co.uk

GREENGRID
The Natural Choice for Your Roof

the roof structure would be broken down in its simplest form to attic trusses of costing £2,666 and a roof covering of tiles, 110m², costing £1,813, giving the cost of a basic roof of £4,479 or £59.50 per square metre of roofing space for a standard detached house[6]. Bauder quotes around £95 a square metre for an intensive green roof of sedum matting installed and water tested. As the industry is in its infancy here in the UK, the costs at present are quite high, but the more popular and common that green roof installations become, the more likely that costs will begin to fall.

If a green roof is being considered for a conventional flat roof replacement, then there are other considerations in cost savings, as the thicker the substrate level, the better the insulative and cooling qualities. In hot weather the surface of a roof becomes extremely hot, with bitumen flat roofs reaching temperatures in excess of 70°C. This can cause damage to roofing membranes as the constant expansion and contraction from hot day-time to cool night-time temperatures causes wear and stresses to the roof. UV damage also occurs and this will reduce the lifespan of a roof. Even with clay tiles or slates, degradation occurs through the effects of freeze, thaw etc.

Placing a layer of vegetation over these membranes in the form of an extensive green roof delays the effects of ageing and damage caused by the above. Due to the many and distinct advantages of green roofing it is an extremely viable option to reducing the stresses and strains placed on roof surfaces. Some manufacturers estimate that this would double the life of a roof structure's waterproofing system. In considering costs, although a small gain, the cooling effects and insulation properties of a green roof will contribute to lower energy bills, in respect of either winter heat or summer cooling.

Conclusions

With the requirement for over a million houses in the UK in the coming decades, green roofs are a real possibility for a change in the way we deal with the rainwater run off from the surface of our roofs, especially in large-scale developments. Moreover, it could alter the whole way we require and design high-pitched roofs for domestic homes. The many advantages of having a living natural roof surface must surely see this medium increasing in use over the coming years. Extensive sedum roofs could be important in large-scale development in preventing the spread of the urban heat island effect. Integrate sedum roofs with sustainable urban drainage systems, and we may go a long way to helping replenish underground water supplies, by diverting storm-water run off back into the earth, rather than through the easily overloaded sewerage systems.

References

1. *http://hortweb.cas.psu.edu/research/greenroof/ background.html*

2. *Office of the Deputy Prime Minister, Greening the Gateway Creating sustainable communities, Crown copyright 2004*

3. *Theodore Eisenman, Sedums over Baltimore, Landscape Architecture Aug 2004 (article)*

4. *www.guardian.co.uk*

5. *Evapotranspiration and Droughts, USGS, U.S. Global Change Research Program*

6. *'The Housebuilders Bible 5th edition' by Mark Brinkley, (2002).*

Further reading

'Planting Green Roofs and Living Walls', by Nigel Dunnet & Noel Kingsbury (2004), available from the Green Shop: 01452 770629 www.greenshop.co.uk

Building Green (A guide to using plants on roofs, walls and pavements) by Jacklyn Jonston & John Newton, London Ecology Unit.

Green Roofs Ecological Design and Construction by Leslie Hoffman et al., Earth Pledge, Schiffer (2005).

Useful websites

www.greenroofs.org

www.safeguardeurope.com (Oldroyd)

www.kalzip.com

www.enviromat.co.uk

www.greenroof.se

www.greengridroofs.co.uk

www.flaguk.co.uk

© Green Building Press

COPPER RAINWATER SYSTEMS

COPPA GUTTA

Newly installed   After a few weeks   With Verdigris finish

Easy to Install
Lasts 100yrs
Eco Friendly
Affordable
Low Maintenance

www.coppagutta.com   01489 797774

MILBANK ROOFS

Milbank Warm Roof Systems

- Complete Supply & Fix Package
- Finished Soffits including Decorative Ply & Plaster Board
- Mineral Wool & Polyurethane Sandwich Panels

Tel: 01284 852505

Milbank Roofs Ltd Hargrave Meadow Cottage, Church Lane, Hargrave, Suffolk IP29 5HH
web:www.milbankroofs.com email: info@milbankroofs.com

The shining light
in natural daylight solutions

The bright idea in energy-free lighting

Glidevale Sunscoop™ brings natural daylight where normal windows can't be used, guiding daylight from the roof to dark areas below.

- energy saving, cuts the need for artificial lighting
- ideal for bathrooms, stairways and corridors
- colour matched roof interface
- simple to install
- 95% or 98% reflectivity with 25 year warranty
- domestic, commercial or industrial applications
- pitched or flat roofs

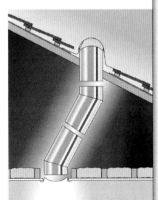

glideVALE    **SUNSCOOP™**
TUBULAR ROOFLIGHTS

Glidevale Limited
2 Brooklands Road, Sale, Cheshire M33 3SS
Tel: 0161 962 7113 Fax: 0161 905 2085
email: info@glidevale.com www.glidevale.com

BPD
A member of the Building Product Design Group

Insulation standards

Insulation is a fundamental component to any energy efficient and sustainable building. The type of insulation and its thickness needs to be considered. But what is the most environmentally sustainable option? Recent reports suggest that over the lifetime of a building the energy saving potential of insulation should be the dominant factor in its specification, and that the lifetime differences between various products are small. The most important factor is to ensure that the insulation is correctly installed. **John Garbutt** reports.

In the past few years choosing an eco-friendly insulation was quite simple. All you needed to do was select one that did not use CFC or HCFC blowing agents in its manufacture or avoid those that were an irritant in use. However, with the successful phase-out of ozone destroying gasses by EU law (based on the Montreal Protocol)[1] and the clearing of mineral wool of suspicion of being a possible carcinogen by the International Agency for Research on Cancer (IARC)[2] it is becoming a less clear-cut decision (if we ignore price).

So how can we choose the most environmentally sustainable products to insulate our buildings? Many might argue that 'natural is best' but others will counter with 'natural cannot promise durability'. It is true that some insulation applications are accessible enough for us to replace them occasionally throughout the lifetime of the building, if we so wish but, likewise, some application decisions are 'whole building life' choices. Let's take a look at some of the other environmental issues that may apply to building insulation.

Embodied energy / impact
Do they matter?

In recent years insulation materials, among many other materials, have been compared on the basis of embodied energy. However, I believe that it is the balance of the embodied

energy, the energy used to build the construction elements, and the 'in-use' energy consumption over the lifetime of a building that is more important. Indeed, due to the fact that insulation, by its very nature, is there to save energy, it has become widely accepted that the embodied energy of any insulation material is insignificant, compared with the energy saved by it over the lifetime of the building in which it is installed.

Having said that, we should not be complacent. The above statement will only hold true whilst we continue to design buildings with quite high levels of energy consumption. All this will change when our buildings have low or zero heating requirements or zero CO_2 emissions. The former can only be achieved by using insulation wisely at appropriate thicknesses and by detailing our buildings properly to ensure air tightness, the latter if we discover more efficient ways of generating renewable energy and if we do the low or zero heating part first in order to install renewables without over-egging our capital outlay. Only when our buildings get to low or zero heating levels will the embodied energy of the materials used become significant.

Embodied energy is also an inappropriate tool to use to compare the full 'embodied impact' of any product. It measures just one

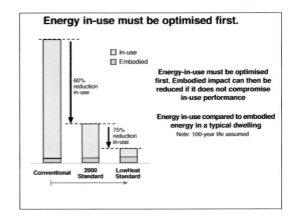

Energy in-use must be optimised first.

☐ In-use
☐ Embodied

Energy-in-use must be optimised first. Embodied impact can then be reduced if it does not compromise in-use performance

Energy in-use compared to embodied energy in a typical dwelling
Note: 100-year life assumed

60% reduction in-use

75% reduction in-use

Conventional | 2000 Standard | LowHeat Standard

© Green Building Press

Thermal design of buildings is central to cutting CO_2 emissions!

European energy use by sector
Source: European Commission

Domestic energy use by end-use
Source: European Commission

facet of the harm that the manufacture of a product can cause.

Arguably, the best available measure of embodied impact is the rating system used in the BRE's Green Guide to Building Specification[3]. This publication rates products from A to C on a basket of embodied impacts, including embodied energy. These ratings are based on generic life cycle assessment (LCA) data. You will find that almost all insulation materials, for which data is given, get the top rating of A. The exceptions are cellular glass, extruded polystyrene and high-density (>145 kg/m³) mineral wool; this is a clear reflection of the fact that the embodied impact of insulation materials is relatively insignificant. However, it does illustrate that it is important to consider the density of the insulation material, as more dense insulants may have a low embodied impact per kilogram, but not per m³ or m².

It should also be noted that when the impacts for insulation are combined with the impacts for all other materials that make up, say, a wall or a roof, the different ratings of insulation products become largely irrelevant as they are masked by the impacts of the other materials in the construction. A fact which illustrates my earlier point.

It is perfectly possible for a wall insulated with extruded polystyrene to get an overall A rating, even if the insulation itself does not, (some might argue that this is a failure of the rating system but we have to start somewhere). It is equally possible for a wall insulated with an A rated insulation material to get an overall B or C rating. It is the rating for the whole construction that counts as far as the Green Guide data is concerned.

The production and publication of embodied energy/embodied impact data by insulation manufacturers is therefore, if anything, an issue of corporate social responsibility (CSR) rather than environmental sustainability. Some manufacturers have now produced independently certified LCA data. Most of those have done this work with BRE Certification. However, the production of such data is effectively meaningless unless manufacturers are able to demonstrate a commitment to reducing the environmental impacts of their production processes. It is a shame that the DTI made a u-turn on introducing a requirement that all publicly quoted companies report on CSR performance as of January 1, 2006[4] as it would have been interesting to see what manufacturers had to say about their environmental improvement programs.

Accurate and unbiased embodied energy / embodied impact figures for insulation materials are difficult to find other than in BRE LCAs, and therefore should be treated with care. No embodied energy / impact data is presented here because I found it very difficult to ascertain if the data available is comparable and used consistent methodologies.

Delivering what is promised

It is widely accepted that reducing 'in use' energy consumption of buildings is the key to their global environmental sustainability. Therefore, the major parameter on which to compare insulation materials must be their ability to deliver their specified thermal performance over the lifetime of a building. This is one of the key themes of an independently produced report on the sustainability of insulation materials funded by BING (the European trade association for manufacturers of rigid urethane insulation products)[5], which brought to bear the concept of risk factors. These are all factors which could detrimentally affect the thermal performance of individual insulation materials, sometimes in very different ways, and hence the global environmental sustainability of buildings. These risk factors may include the impacts of:
● liquid water or water vapour
● air-movement
● compression or settling.

On the whole it is poor sitework that will allow these risk factors to come into play. Installation practices are notoriously uncontrollable and all materials will perform badly if installed without due care and attention. However, for some insulation materials the problem may stem from what is claimed for the product in the first place.

Adherence to common rules for thermal performance claims should be checked. The EU Construction Products Directive has created a set of harmonised product standards for insulation which demand that the thermal performance of all products is quoted in a comparable way that takes account of ageing

and statistical variation. It is called the Lambda 90:90 method. All major UK insulation manufacturers have adopted this approach to quoting thermal performance. It is worth noting that the introduction of the harmonised product standards added about 10% to the thermal conductivity of the insulation products that are covered (i.e. made them 10% worse). However, at the present time there are a number of smaller scale products for which there is no harmonised standard available and therefore no consistent method that takes account of statistical variation. No doubt these will be brought into the fold soon, but until then inconsistency will reign.

One particular case in point is that of multi-foil insulation[6]. Please see my 'Resource guide to the properties of most commonly available building insulation materials' in the Green Building Bible, Volume 2, for a full in-depth review of these products.

From global to local

Once the global issues have been considered it is then time to consider less pressing, but still important, issues such as recycled content, local sourcing, disposability etc. The key to the national level environmental sustainability of any product is a balance of all these issues. However taking just one issue and over-focussing on it could be counter-productive.

Recycled content of products is about to go through something of a revolution in the UK construction industry. The government has funded a body called The Waste & Resources Action Program (WRAP) to promote materials that have a recycled content. It gives very specific rules as to what counts as recycled content and what does not. These rules follow the definition cited in the ISO standard on Environmental Labels and Declarations[7].

Some insulation already contains recycled content. However, when examining the recycled content of insulation materials please bear in mind that recycled content is the proportion, by mass, of recycled material in the product.

© Green Building Press

PEN Y COED INSULATION

WARMCEL

**The insulation giving you
the sustainable solution to
energy efficient building**

Southport Eco Centre

Six Bells, Bishops Castle

Pen y Coed Insulation are the most experienced
company installing Warmcel throughout the UK. We have an
extensive portfolio of work from large industrial projects,
schools, housing developments to individual houses.

Development of Eco Houses in Castle Caereinion, Powys.
Built - Insulated - Sold by Pen y Coed Construction & Insulation Ltd

PEN Y COED INSULATION is a division of PEN Y COED CONSTRUCTION & INSULATION Ltd
a company that specialises in the design, detailing and construction of energy efficient buildings.

PEN Y LAN, MEIFOD, POWYS, SY22 6DA

TEL/FAX - 01938 500643

WEB:- penycoed-warmcel.com

Only pre-consumer and post-consumer materials should be considered as recycled content[8]. This means that surplus material cut from the edges of products during their manufacture and shredded and added back in at the start of the process don't count.

Fire

Another, often overlooked aspect of the performance of insulation materials is their performance with respect to fire. This is quite a complicated area but roughly speaking there are two facets to consider: reaction to fire and fire resistance. Reaction to fire is measured by the 'Class O' type rating system enshrined in building regulations or the risk categories shown in the Building Standards in Scotland. These ratings can be achieved by reference to the new Euroclass system for reaction to fire or by the tried and tested BS 476 Parts 6 and 7. There is a debate in the insulation industry at present as to which route is best.

What has caused this confusion is the fact that the new Euroclass rating system for reaction to fire is arguably irrelevant when applied to 'naked' insulation products, as the system was developed for wall and ceiling linings and insulation is rarely used as such. The reaction to fire test has slightly more value when used for products tested 'in-application', since insulation products are then tested mounted as they would be in practice, for example behind plasterboard.

Proponents of the Euroclass system suggest that 'naked' products lie around building sites all the time and that the products are exposed when, say, holes are cut in walls but I cannot understand how testing a product as a wall or ceiling lining can relate to packs of products lying on the ground.

Regardless, the test still gives no indication of a product's ability to resist fire. It is this crucial distinction that can make all the difference to the ability of a building to withstand a fire and maintain structural integrity long enough to enable occupants to leave safely, and allow emergency services more time to get the blaze under control and salvage the building. Mistakenly choosing a material based on its reaction to fire without taking into account its resistance to fire may therefore at best be costly, and could at worst prove fatal.

The crux of the issue is that some materials have excellent fire resistance qualities but relatively poor reaction to fire ratings, whereas others have the best reaction to fire ratings but relatively poor fire resistance properties.

So, if the Euroclass system is not a reliable guide to the fire performance properties of insulation products, what is? The answer may well lie in large scale insurer approved test regimes such as the Loss Prevention Certification Board (LPCB) 'in-application' test, LPS1181: 2003 or those carried out by Factory Mutual (FM).

References

1. All insulation materials (in the UK) are now free from CFCs and HCFCs and have been since Jan 1, 2004. As the issue of CFC and HCFC use is now historic, no mention is made here of these blowing agents.

2. IARC decision.

3. Green Guide to Specification, an Environmental Profiling System for Building Materials and Components. Third Edition by J Anderson, D Shiers and M Sinclair (2002).

4. The consultation process for this closed in August 2004.

5. Insulation for Sustainability-A Guide XCO2 conisbee for BING 2002: **www.xco2.com**

6. A detailed discussion on multifoil insulation is being carried out on the Green Building Forum: **www.greenbuildingforum.co.uk/forum/index2. php?DATEIN=tpc_wlpssdlpg_1142805843**

7. BS EN ISO 14021: 2001. Environmental labels and declarations – self declared environmental claims (Type II environmental labelling). BSI. London. 2001.

8. Pre-consumer waste is material diverted from the waste stream during a manufacturing process. Excluded is reutilization of materials such as rework, regrind or scrap generated in a process and capable of being reclaimed within the same process that generated it. Post-consumer waste is material generated by households or by commercial, industrial and institutional facilities in their role as end-users of the product, which can no longer be used for its intended purpose. This includes returns of material from the distribution chain.

Charts taken from Insulation for Sustainability-A Guide XCO2 conisbee.

346

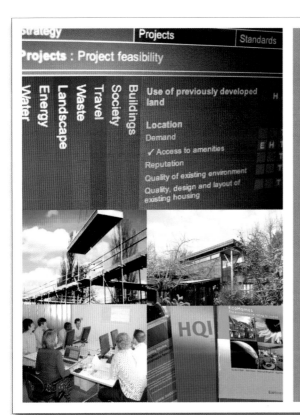

Sustainability Works 2005
Online software

Specifically designed to help housing professionals and their partners deliver sustainable development efficiently, from policy level to project delivery. Includes an extensive reference database and an EcoHomes prediction tool.

Sustainability Works is used by numerous architects and consultants, housing associations and their partners, developers, contractors, planners and local authorities.

To register visit www.sustainabilityworks.org.uk

Sustainability Works runs training courses nationwide on how to do sustainable development using Sustainability Works. See our latest programme on www.sustainabilityworks.org.uk/training.

Or book the team for customised training sessions, designed for your own organization.

To discuss your needs, call us on 020 7422 1777 or email us your details at contact@sustainabilityworks.org.uk

HOUSING CORPORATION   National Housing Federation   WWF   BRE   Sustainable Homes

www.sandbeps.com

WHERE LESS IS MORE...

"insulation that exceeds expectation"

...AND BONDING PROTECTS, THERE'S SIMPLICITY IN SOPHISTICATION, WARMTH IN PROTECTION.

Our castellated under-floor insulation panels are a thermoformed high-impact EPS with a polystyrene film [HIPS] bonded to its upper face. This protects the board from mechanical damage during its installation.

S and B EPS S1 panels are designed to simplify the procedure of preparing floors for laying under floor heating pipes. The pipes can be simply walked into place with no further fixings needed.

Cold bridging is eliminated by the board's interlocking profile. Its integral moulded skin acts as a vapour barrier eliminating the need to lay and tape polythene sheets. Environmentally friendly, the panels are CFC and HCFC free with a zero OPD.

S and B EPS S1 Castellated Under-floor Insulation Panel.

Further Details
Email: **company@sandbeps.com**
Phone: **0191 250 0818**
Fax: **0191 250 0548**
SandB EPS Limited_Dudley
Cramlington_Northumberland
NE23 7PY

See also: 'Energy and water saving advice' in Chapter 4.

Natural insulation

50% of the UK's energy is used within our buildings. The government is keen to see energy use in buildings reduced, to help meet both its climate change and fuel poverty targets, and is therefore undertaking a number of programmes to encourage increased insulation levels in buildings. In most cases, the type of insulation used is determined by its thermal properties, its costs and availability. However, the wider environmental impact of the insulation material is often not considered, therefore **Dave Barton** summarises the range of 'renewable' insulation materials available to us.

With many insulation companies and sectors promoting their own environmental credentials, there is still a lack of credible and independent research available to specifiers and householders. However, when choosing or specifying insulation, perhaps we should be giving consideration to the following aspects, alongside cost, thermal properties and efficacy as a building component:

- embodied energy (energy consumed within its processing and transport)
- raw material extraction
- high toxicity levels
- related health issues in manufacture, installation and for occupants
- use of ozone depleting chemicals and
- ability to be recycled.

In other words, the type of insulation used is an important consideration alongside that of the level of insulation fitted to a building. The right specification of insulation could be a significant part of reducing the overall environmental impact of a building. The current major players in the insulation market, mineral and glass wool, do not contain any chemicals and are quite inert, but they have high embodied energy and can create dust problems during handling.

There are a number of renewable insulation materials which are on the market at the moment, such as sheep's wool, cellulose and flax. These are currently only available at a few niche outlets. Compared to the major players in the insulation market, these materials tend to have lower embodied energy, do not involve mineral extraction and can be easily recycled at end of life.

Why isn't natural insulation in widespread use?

The UK construction industry tends to be rather conservative and slow to respond to 'new' materials. Not all materials are BBA or BSI approved; without such approval they are unlikely to be taken up by the market at large. Some products are relatively new to the market and consequently there is limited experience in specification and installation, limited availability and accessibility and generally a price premium (though this is claimed to be falling).

The natural benefits of the products tend to suit a breathing construction, and so their usage needs to be considered carefully and may be limited to specific applications, e.g. to lofts and internal wall insulation on existing buildings and to breathable walls and roofs in new buildings. Overall there are a number of alternatives for loft and timber framed applications but there are few suitable materials for cavity wall insulation although the Centre for Alternative technology (CAT) used cork for the AtEIC building, see photo.

The choice?

There are six main types of natural/renewable insulation, as summarised below.

Cellulose

Cellulose is currently the most common renewable insulation material available in the UK. It is made from post and pre-consumer waste paper and is available in boards of various thicknesses or loose fill in bags for loft applications.

© Green Building Press

Innovative use of cork in cavity walls for the AtEIC (autonomous environmental information centre) building at the Centre for Alternative Technology at Machynlleth. The cavity wall structure is compressed earth blocks with corkboard cavity fill insulation. A fact sheet on the whole building is available from CAT 01654 705980 and a building diary, featuring the project, can be found at www.cat.org.uk

A major benefit of sheep's wool (as with the plant products below) is its ability to absorb (and release) more than one third of its own weight in moisture without impairing the insulating properties of the fibres. This means it can control condensation in the insulated cavity and helps to cool the building in summer and warm it in winter. Wool insulation has low embodied energy and is completely biodegradable.

Flax

Flax is mainly used in the production of linseed oil but a few companies are exploiting its fibres for insulation. Flax insulation is made from the short fibres from the flax plant, currently from flax grown in Austria and Germany. Flax can be grown in the UK and is most suited to growing in Wales and the south west of England.

Flax insulation is available in rolls or batts in a range of thicknesses and lengths. It can be used in pitched roofs between and over ceiling

It can also be wet sprayed within timber frame construction. Cellulose is particularly suited for use in ventilated or breathing constructions. Of the renewable insulation materials available, it is also the cheapest and DIY is an option in some applications.

Sheep's wool

There are now a number of suppliers in the marketplace. Sheep's wool insulation is made from either new or recycled wool, some of which comes from sheep that have not been dipped in any pesticides. The insulation comes in rolls and batts of different sizes and thicknesses. Due to its hygroscopic properties, it is ideal for use in breathable roofs and timber framed walls as it allows water vapour to move through the structure. No special tools are required in its application. It can be cut with a sharp pair of scissors or a knife.

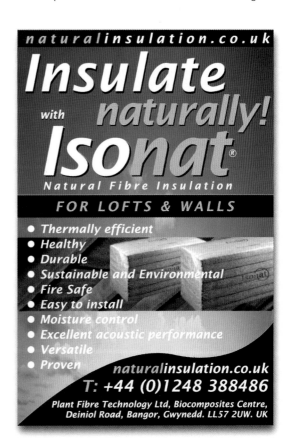

naturalinsulation.co.uk

Insulate with **naturally!**
Isonat®
Natural Fibre Insulation

FOR LOFTS & WALLS

- Thermally efficient
- Healthy
- Durable
- Sustainable and Environmental
- Fire Safe
- Easy to install
- Moisture control
- Excellent acoustic performance
- Versatile
- Proven

naturalinsulation.co.uk
T: +44 (0)1248 388486

Plant Fibre Technology Ltd, Biocomposites Centre, Deiniol Road, Bangor, Gwynedd. LL57 2UW. UK

joists, in suspended floors and in timber or steel frame walls.

Hemp

Hemp is thought to have great potential as an insulation product. Hemp fibre is increasingly being used in the automotive industry as a superior product to synthetic materials, typically for interior panels. It is also used for making prestige paper, horse bedding and garden matting.

Hemp is a fibre crop, well adapted for cultivation in the UK, and in fact can grow in many countries throughout the world and in a range of climates. Currently the largest European producer is France.

Cork

Cork has been available for some time as an insulation product and as wall and floor tiles. However, the insulation board is still not widely available at builders' merchant type outlets although it can be obtained from more specialised companies.

Cork comes from the cork oak grown mainly in Portugal as well as Northern Africa and Spain. The cork forests do not require pesticides, fertilizers or irrigation and the cork produced is both renewable and recyclable. Cork insulation comes in boards of varying thicknesses, which are generally used as insulation for warm roofs (i.e. on the rafters not the joists) and in timber frames. They can be used in dormer cheeks as well.

Cotton

Cotton is not suitable for growing in the UK and all cotton used in this country is imported. Cotton grows in warm, humid climates requiring a large amount of pesticide, fertilizer and water. Using 'new' cotton for a renewable insulation does not therefore make much environmental sense. However, using waste cotton and other fibres in an insulation product is a possibility. There are now three companies in the UK supplying insulation from waste cotton.

The future for natural insulation

Whilst there are a small number of niche suppliers currently marketing natural insulation, there is much interest in their market potential. Some suppliers are optimistic about the short-term potential, with the possibility that one of the big builders merchants will take on renewable insulation products. There are numerous market drivers to support this optimism, particularly climate change, healthy buildings and sustainable construction, as well as reduced building costs.

Cost remains the main barrier although those surveyed in the research felt that a 10% to 30% price premium would be attractive to the general market (premiums in the research ranged from 0% to 500%). The technical capability of many of the available products is impressive, even if there is limited experience of their application in the UK. Of course, they need to be specified correctly to optimise the overall thermal properties of the building and are more suited on the whole for breathing buildings (or breathable elements of the building). ☙

Further information

Further details can be found in 'Renewable Insulation Materials, A guide' published by Impetus Consulting. This contains:

- *information on thermal conductivity, density, U-values and energy consumption in manufacture*
- *feedback from users of the different materials*
- *a product use comparison table and*
- *examples of stockists.*

The report from which this information is extracted was created with some funding from the Pilkington Energy Efficiency Trust. This culminated in the production of a guide to using these materials. The key points from this research are summarised in this article:
www.impetusconsult.co.uk/what.htm

© Green Building Press

THERMAFLEECE™

Thermal and acoustic insulation

Healthy to use
Healthy to live with

For detailed information please contact:

Second Nature UK Ltd
BUILDING ON WHAT COMES NATURALLY

BBA BRITISH BOARD OF AGRÉMENT
CERTIFICATE No 02/3950

SOULANDS GATE, DACRE, PENRITH, CUMBRIA CA11 0JF
Tel: 017684 86285   Fax: 017684 86825   e-mail: info@secondnatureuk.com

www.secondnatureuk.com

SUSTAIN

DeltaGen -
Change energy

Total solutions for delivering
low carbon energy solutions.

- Feasibility study and options appraisal -
- Business case development -
- Detailed system design -
- Funding application -
- Tender preparation -
- Project management -

Sustain Ltd, 4 High Street, Wrington, Bristol BS40 5QA
Tel: 01934 863650 Fax: 01934 863649
www.sustain.co.uk

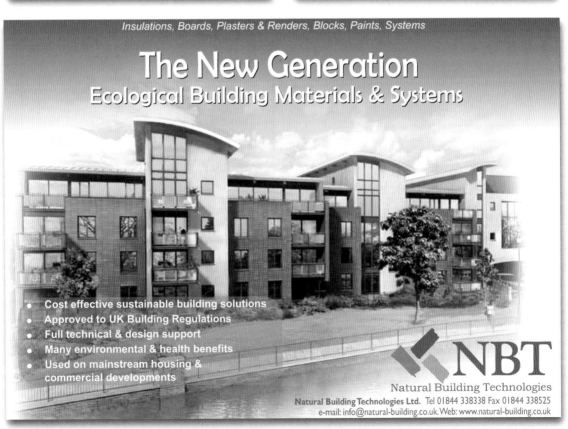

Insulations, Boards, Plasters & Renders, Blocks, Paints, Systems

The New Generation
Ecological Building Materials & Systems

- Cost effective sustainable building solutions
- Approved to UK Building Regulations
- Full technical & design support
- Many environmental & health benefits
- Used on mainstream housing &
  commercial developments

NBT
Natural Building Technologies

Natural Building Technologies Ltd. Tel 01844 338338 Fax 01844 338525
e-mail: info@natural-building.co.uk Web: www.natural-building.co.uk

Timber windows

Over the last few years timber window manufacturers have had to focus hard on their markets and products and ask themselves what the public really want from a window. They have been re-thinking, re-sourcing and considering environmental issues too. **Keith Hall** reports an an industry reborn ...

Concerned about sustainability, today's consumer might be forgiven for thinking twice before choosing timber windows. They certainly earned themselves a bad reputation in the sixties and seventies and this reputation for poor quality in workmanship and material opened the door for, first aluminium windows and then later, uPVC. Thankfully, the quality of timber windows has increased greatly but dispelling the perception that timber windows need intensive maintenance regimes that could carry hidden costs is not so easy to fix.

Lately, not just the materials and workmanship have changed. The industry has learned from its rivals and introduced modern production and finishing techniques, including offsite pre-finishing and quality assurance schemes.

From an environmental perspective, drivers such as the Environmental Protection (Prescribed Processes and Substances) Regulations of 1991, have led to a shift by the industry to using 'safer', preservative treatments and coatings, with some going even further and producing 'eco' windows specifically for this sector of the market. Manufacturers have also paid heed to performance expectations, adopting an 'holistic' approach to the specification of all materials used, and giving due attention to better component design.

Now, window manufacturers build into the design a very wide range of factors. For instance, which timber species should be used, chosen on the basis of its durability, dimensional stability and above all its sustainability and environmental impact with many now offering Forest Stewardship Council certifica-

tion as standard across their range.

The wood coatings sector has also responded to environmental demands by reducing solvent content and developing high-solids coatings and improved water-borne formulations, with lower dirt retention characteristics. However, the expectation of higher performance and sustainability carries with it its own demands. Pre-finishing of external joinery has many advantages which offer the end user a very high quality product. But in order for the end user to benefit from that quality, there needs to be a parallel responsi-

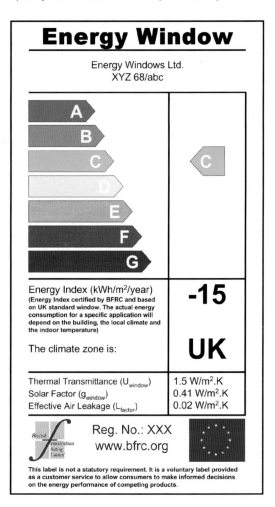

Energy Window

Energy Windows Ltd.
XYZ 68/abc

A
B
C
D
E
F
G

C

Energy Index (kWh/m²/year)
(Energy Index certified by BFRC and based on UK standard window. The actual energy consumption for a specific application will depend on the building, the local climate and the indoor temperature)

-15

The climate zone is:

UK

Thermal Transmittance (U_{window})	1.5 W/m².K
Solar Factor (g_{window})	0.41 W/m².K
Effective Air Leakage (L_{factor})	0.02 W/m².K

Reg. No.: XXX
www.bfrc.org

British Fenestration Rating Council

This label is not a statutory requirement. It is a voluntary label provided as a customer service to allow consumers to make informed decisions on the energy performance of competing products.

bility by the whole construction industry (the builder in particular) to handle and use this pre-finished joinery in a manner which reflects its value.

There are ways of ensuring that the products (windows and doors) are given adequate protection until the point of hand-over. This may require the adoption of such practices as installing windows into openings built around pre-fabricated formers.

The latest development in the industry has been the introduction of energy performance certification, similar to that given to domestic appliances. Look out for this next time you need to buy or specify windows or doors.

It is clear that the joinery and wood coating industries are responding positively to change through a process of integration and closer co-operation. It is only by further extending this approach, working with the installers, going beyond the manufacturing operation into the building process, and above all, meeting and addressing the requirements and concerns of the consumer, that timber windows will secure their rightful place back on our buildings. ☯

Double glazing

Double glazing is just about standard now on all new buildings but many existing properties still need to be upgraded. With our love of large glazed areas, it may well pay to consider enhanced double glazing. **Keith Hall** reports.

Whilst double-glazing can reduce heat loss through windows by up to 50%, our love of large glazed areas is undermining these reductions. However, technology is improving all the time, so we need to carefully consider the pros and cons of glazing options.

An air gap between the glass of 16mm and 20mm is considered to be the optimum, and the difference between the two is negligible. Below 16mm the direct heat transference between the panes reduces the effectiveness and over 20mm air convection between the panes that has a similar effect. The basic standard for sealed unit double glazing, as required by the Building Regulations, would be a 28mm thick unit combination as such: standard float glass / 20mm air gap / Pilkington 'K' glass. This would have a U-value typically of about 1.8W/m²K.

Low-e coatings

Low-e (low emissivity) coatings are a micro-

scopically thin metal oxide or semiconductor film applied on one or more surfaces of the glass, usually on a face between the panes of a double glazed or triple glazed unit. Double glazing, using low-e coated glass, gives energy conservation properties equivalent to standard triple glazing.

Average U-values	W/m^2K
Single glazing	5.4
Double glazing with 12mm air gap	2.6
Double glazing with hard low-e coating	1.8
Double glazing with hard low-e and argon gas	1.5
Double glazing with soft low-e and argon gas	1.2
Triple glazing	2.2
Triple glazing with argon fill	<1.0

Note: units should now be quoted to BS EN 673

The coating is usually applied on the outer face of the inside pane (or outer face of both inner panes in triple glazing), facing the air cavity. These coatings work by reflecting long wavelength heat generated within the room (radiators and heating appliances), back into the building, whilst at the same time allowing short wavelength, solar energy (from daylight and sunshine) into the room. The incoming short wavelength solar energy is re-radiated by internal building surfaces at longer wavelengths, which are then re-reflected by the coating back into the room.

Low-e coated glass looks identical to ordinary clear glass as the coating is almost invisible. Its effect on light transmission and reflection is hardly noticeable. It can be used everywhere, from the largest office block application to domestic conservatories, windows and doors and whilst designed for double glazing, it can also be used as the inner pane in secondary glazing, although hard coat low-e would be recommended for this application as it is tougher and more resistant to scratches (see boxout right for more details).

Advantages of low-e coating

The advantages include the following:
- improved insulation
- reduced heating bills
- reduced carbon dioxide emissions
- reduced condensation
- reduced cold spots and down draughts
- takes advantage of the sun's heat.

Gas fills and glazing bars

Argon and other gasses

Instead of air; argon, krypton or xenon gas can be injected between the panes. These gasses have better insulation properties than air and contribute to much better overall insulation (see table). For instance, with a argon fill the U-value would be reduced by over 30%. The gasses only displace a proportion of the air in the unit and it is generally accepted that the double glazed unit should achieve a 90% fill gas-to-air concentration. This concentration will gradually reduce with age, at a rate estimated from 0.5 to 1% per year. Units filled with argon do not degrade significantly until they reach 75% concentration, which adds up to about a 20 year performance durability, after which the unit will perform the same as an air filled unit

Comparing two types of 'low-e' glass

Hard coat 'low-e'

Also known as pyrolytic coating this coating is applied at high temperatures and is sprayed onto the glass surface during the float glass process.

Advantages include:
- *the coating is durable, which allows for ease of handling and tempering*
- *can be tempered after coating application*
- *can be used in single glazing applications*
- *utilizes passive solar heat gain.*

Disadvantages include:
- *higher U-values compared to soft coat 'low-e' products*
- *higher solar heat gain coefficient compared to soft coat 'low-e' products*
- *hard coat glass also has the possibility of a slight haze, which can be visible at certain angles.*

'K' glass is made by Pilkington.[6]

NOTE: Pilkington do supply a type of soft coat low E glass known as Optitherm but in the UK most of their Low-E supply is in the form of Pilkington 'K' Glass .

Soft coat 'low-e'

Also known as 'sputter coating', this is applied in multiple layers of optically transparent silver sandwiched between layers of metal oxide in a vacuum chamber. This process provides the highest level of performance and a nearly invisible coating.

Advantages include:
- *high visible light transmission with optical clarity - minimal color haze*
- *ultra-low emissivities giving optimum winter U-values*
- *up to 70% less UV transmission compared with standard clear glazing.*

Disadvantages include:
- *soft coat low-e must be used in a double glazed unit; the soft coating is sensitive to handling*
- *most soft coat Low-E products require tempering the glass prior to the coating application*
- *edge removal of the coating is required to ensure a proper seal in an insulated unit*
- *more expensive than hard coat 'low-e' glass.*

Made by Saint-Gobain [5] (Planitherm Futur N) Interpane[7] (Iplus) and Pilkington[6] (Optitherm).

© Green Building Press

(this may vary depending on the type of spacer bar used).

Not all double glazing manufacturers are able to offer double glazing with gas filling. Contact the GGF[1] for details of those that can. Other gasses, such as krypton and xenon, can be used but they are harder to source and more costly. Chris Herring of the Green Building Store[2] (GBS sells IPlus windows), said "Krypton and Xenon are only really appropriate where narrow cavity units are important. For example, we offer triple glazed units at 4-12-4-12-4 with 2 low-e panes and krypton which gives a centre pane (cp) U-value of 0.5, mainly because we can't easily adjust our system to fit the fatter 4-16-4-16-4 with argon which would give a cp U-value of 0.6. Windows in most passivhaus buildings (see Chapter 6) use argon filled 4-16-4-16-4".

Spacer bars

Advanced technology spacer bars are now becoming an essential part of any double glazed unit that intends to achieve seriously low U-values. There are currently three types available in the UK, with the foam rubber 'superspacer' from Edgetech IG[3] being the most common. Chris Herring of GBS said that "they all have pretty much equivalent characteristics but the 'Thermix' (stainless steel reinforced polymer bars) from Ensinger Gmbh[4] which we use, or the 'Swiss-spacer' from St Gobain[5], are rigid bars". He believes these are more suited to UK fabrication methods. However, I have personal experience of the Edgetech system and they have performed well.

Whichever of these advanced spacer bars you choose it will significantly reduce the heat loss around the edges of the units. Most people will have witnessed the condensation that forms around the edges of double glazed units, well the advanced spacers significantly reduce or eliminate this (condensation on glazing may vary with a number of environmental factors as well as technical factors to do with the composition of the unit). However, the most significant savings using these types of spacer bar will be achieved on windows where small (Georgian) type glazing units are used due to the edge to area ratio. However, their use on all sizes of double glazing units will enhance the energy saving potential of the window. Warm edge spacers can also reduce sound too – up to 2 decibels (according to Edgetech) compared to aluminium spacer bars. ✎

1. The Glass and Glazing Federation: *www.ggf.org.uk*
2. Green Building Store: *www.greenbuildingstore.co.uk*
3. Edgetech: *ukenquiries@edgetechig.com*
4. Ensinger: *www.thermix.de*
5. St Gobain: *www.saint-gobain.co.uk*
6. Pilkington: *www.pilkington.com*
7. Interpane: *www.interpane.de*

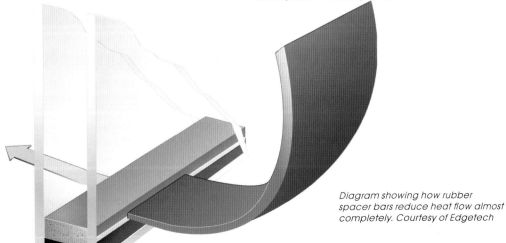

Diagram showing how rubber spacer bars reduce heat flow almost completely. Courtesy of Edgetech

See also: 'Don't get homesick' in Chapter 4

Paints and finishes

Choosing to decorate your home can be a challenging and rewarding process, but, domestic paint can contain a number of hazardous chemicals. There has never been a better time to use alternative products. **Gavin Blakemore** tells us more about what we can do to reduce our exposure to potentially harmful chemicals.

One of the prime sources of volatile organic compounds (VOCs) in your home is the paint that is on your walls and woodwork. When first applied, paint releases a lethal amount of fumes as it dries and will continue to do so for many months afterwards. Rigorous government testing classified that a tin of household gloss contains up to 50% VOC. However there are many steps you can take to proactively reduce the amount of VOCs that are present in your home.

Making the switch to natural paints and products is relatively easy although it could be made easier. At the moment it is down to the individual consumer to obtain enough information to make a proactive choice to use natural products. I believe there isn't enough education or resources at hand. Let me explain further. The average consumer who is considering redecorating their homes will usually visit their local DIY store to buy paint for the job. However, once they arrive at the paint shelves usually the only choice available is regular VOC loaded paint. Some may have concern over the way the fumes make them feel a bit sick or dizzy and opt for a 'low odour' paint, believing that by paying a little more for these, they are buying a healthier, more environmentally friendly option.

But don't be fooled! 'Low odour' paints can still contain a cocktail of nasty chemicals, such as formaldehyde and acrolien, meaning that they too have a VOC content. The majority of large DIY stores have yet to stock natural paint. However, I anticipate this will change fairly soon as the EU Solvents Directive aims to reduce the percentage of VOC's in paint by 2007 and plans to make it an absolute minimum by 2010.

Hopefully, before long, natural paints will be widely available. In the meantime they are available by mail order from stockists and distributors plus a few shops dotted around the UK that stock them. The internet is the best place to look, although I would advise that you shop around a bit, as prices do vary, just as do the range of colours and products available. Just because its natural doesn't mean you have to compromise on your choice of palette either. Like conventional paint, some companies offer a colour match service, with over a thousand shades to choose from. Natural paints are also scented with essential oils that make them a real pleasure to use and I offer the client the option of choosing their favourite scent. The fresh scent, and lack of noxious fumes, makes natural paint an ideal choice for schools or business premises, or anywhere that needs to remain an open and usable space whilst redecoration is undertaken.

Case study

Painting a nursery

Natural paint is ideal for internal and external walls. It covers the plastered surface with ease and what is more, the paint allows the surface to breathe, prolonging the longevity of the building. Mr and Mrs Jameson recently decorated a room using only natural paints and were more than pleased with the subtle colours and odourless paints. "We were at first, slightly cautious about using natural paints. We had heard that less colours were available and the finish could be inferior. We were, however, pleasantly surprised when we were offered a vast number of colours to chose from, as well as a superior finish to other conventional paints we had prevously used. It has been fun, too, to be involved in the mixing process and the lack of chemicals in the atmosphere is very satisfying".

Natural paints and wood finishes were used on a range of interior and exterior surfaces

© Green Building Press

Ecological
paints, oils
and finishes

livos
Naturally

helping to create
a healthier
environment
for you and
your family

Available from
Ecomerchant Ltd
Tel: 01795 530 130

livos@ecomerchant.co.uk   www.ecomerchant.co.uk

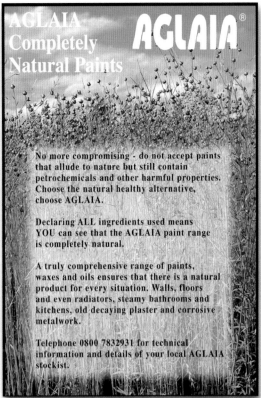

AGLAIA
Completely
Natural Paints

AGLAIA®

No more compromising - do not accept paints
that allude to nature but still contain
petrochemicals and other harmful properties.
Choose the natural healthy alternative,
choose AGLAIA.

Declaring ALL ingredients used means
YOU can see that the AGLAIA paint range
is completely natural.

A truly comprehensive range of paints,
waxes and oils ensures that there is a natural
product for every situation. Walls, floors
and even radiators, steamy bathrooms and
kitchens, old decaying plaster and corrosive
metalwork.

Telephone 0800 7832931 for technical
information and details of your local AGLAIA
stockist.

Green Paints

Water borne
paint
specialist for
20 years

Responsible modern technology combines traditional paint properties and renewable resources
in a water borne paint system free of petroleum
solvents.
True oil bound gloss enamels, anti-corrosive
metal primers, joinery primers, undercoats and
finishes, matt and satin wall coatings, low
energy wall coatings.

**Green Paints, Lock Farm, Alvingham, Louth,
Lincolnshire LN11 7EU
Tel: 01507 327362**

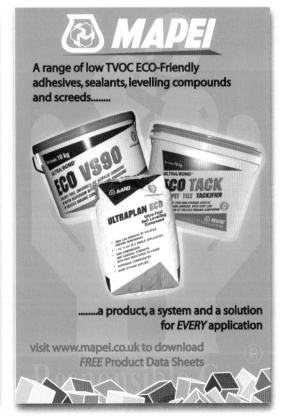

MAPEI

A range of low TVOC ECO-Friendly
adhesives, sealants, levelling compounds
and screeds........

........a product, a system and a solution
for *EVERY* application

visit www.mapei.co.uk to download
FREE Product Data Sheets

What are VOCs

VOC stands for volatile organic compound. Initially, this title sounds relatively harmless, especially the word 'organic' which seems to imply that it is from natural sources. Alas the truth is far from this. Organic compounds can be a potentially lethal mixture of benzene, toluene, methylene, chloride, formaldehyde and more. 'Volatile' means they evaporate easily at room temperature. According to the Environmental Protection Agency, exposure to VOCs cause symptoms such as nose and throat discomfort, headaches, breathing difficulties, nausea, asthma attacks, skin irritation and allergies. High levels of exposure may cause damage to the nervous system and there is emerging evidence that VOCs act as carcinogens.

Most household paint, emulsion, gloss and varnish all contain VOCs. Do any of the above symptoms sound familiar? Are you literally dying to paint your house? With just a little research one may find shocking evidence of how prevalent these toxins are in our day to day life, not only in paint, but also in synthetic furniture stuffing, carpets, even laminate flooring. The government are very aware of the health and environmental risks due to exposure to VOCs and are constantly working alongside EU Directives to reduce the use of VOCs in industry and manufacturing, which should lead to improvements in air quality and public health.

Limewashes (walls) and natural oils (floor and windows) in a renovated home in Wales. Natural finishes can provide opportunties for artistic shading, striking or subtle designs.

at the refurbishment of a prefab sectional building to form a new nursery unit at Cedar Integrated Primary School, Crossgar. Rachel Bevan Architects were keen to minimise the use of chemicals in the school environment and to avoid the off-gassing that can occur with conventional paints.

The nursery unit project was a small part of ongoing phases of work at the school, which provided the architects with an opportunity to experiment and try out new products and materials and influence the brief in future phases. As well as the natural paints and finishes, natural rubber flooring materials were specified, to avoid off-gassing and other environmental concerns associated with vinyl. The overall budget was only £30,000 and although the natural paints and finishes were slightly more expensive than conventional products, they only represented a small element of the total building contract.

A local painting contractor applied the paint and finishes and there were no complaints or problems with coverage, ease of application and mixing in the liquid mineral pigment colouriser,

© Green Building Press

although the paints and finishes sometimes took a bit longer than conventional products to dry. Rachel Bevan did have some concerns about the wall colouring when the yellow turned out to be somewhat paler than she had anticipated. Overall, though, the colours worked well together, particularly the blue shades on internal and external woodwork.

The nursery class teacher was reportedly enthusiastic about the colour scheme and the natural palette, as opposed to the bright primary colours often used in schools. Parents at the school were also pleased with the non-toxic and welcoming environment for their children. Rachel Bevan was satisfied with the quality of the natural paints and wood finishes and would definitely consider using such

products again if other clients were sympathetic. She suggested that the matt finish of paints would make them particularly suitable for use in historic buildings. She would encourage other architects wanting to use natural paints and finishes to plan ahead and give themselves time to try out samples and experiment with colours and to ensure clients and contractors are happy with the product before ordering.

Case study

Wood finishes

Simon Jameson is a Northumberland based wood craftsman and a fairly recent convert to using natural wood treatment products. "After using natural varnishes I have found the finished result leaves me with a strong sense of satisfaction. Obviously you get an enhancement of the wood's inner beauty. As with any standard varnish, the grain is brought to life and all the warm colours are enriched, giving a vibrancy of tones unique to each individual plank, beam or panel. However, I draw an equal sense of contentment knowing that we have just finished something beautiful that isn't going to poison the air, land or water around it.

He enjoys applying the natural products because most of them smell so wonderful. He gets none of the headaches and dizziness, experienced with previous treatments and he particularly like the fresh citrus scents. He also prefers to support the smaller businesses, rather than giving his custom to large companies who have limited or non existent environmental policies.

Simon's company, Karmacolour, treated a 10' circular, raised Yurt platform built from larch, which he collected locally from a large sustainable plantation. He got it planked at a local saw mill. Larch is a largely unappreciated wood by most carpenters and joiners, which is a real shame as there is an abundance, particularly around northern England and it mainly gets felled for chipping and pulping. The great thing about it for me is the transformation which

happens when the first layer of oil is applied, if you haven't seen it before then it is a total surprise. A seemly flat, uninteresting member of the pine family is suddenly brought alive into flowing patterns of deep, reds and glowing ambers. It is naturally rot resistant too.

The only disadvantage he has found in using natural oils and varnishes is the time they take to dry. This can be problematic in a house where there are small children (or pets) and dirty marks start to appear - if these marks are left unattended they are then sealed into the finished work, not ideal! However, from experience it comes down to how much the individual wants to do the right thing and use healthier alternatives which have less impact on the environment.

Conclusion

It would appear that natural paints are the future in home decoration and as we are all becoming more environmentally aware we seem to resort back to age old techniques. Natural paint is a fine example of this as its main ingredients are substances that have been used for thousands of years in decoration. The basic ingredients of natural paint consist of a binder that holds the ingredients together, a pigment

© Green Building Press

for colour and an extender that provides a good gloopy consistency.

Like conventional paint you can make both water and oil based paint. For oil based paint, the most commonly used ingredient is boiled linseed oil, although this can yellow slightly once dry. However, it is water resistant so it is excellent for kitchens and bathrooms. Water based paints contain casein which you can buy in most art shops or you can even make your own from curdled milk! You can use an array of substances for the pigment, anything which has a naturally strong pigment, for example, tea, beetroot, red wine, grass or clay. Or if you wish you can buy natural pigments again from your local art store.

You can of course buy natural paint from a number of companies dotted around the country. Many of these companies offer standard white paint, with the option to buy colour pigments that can be added at will. This is an exciting and creative way to making your own paints and wood oils. So give it a go, get creative and have fun. ☯

Further reading

'The Hand Sculpted House' by I Evans

Natural Paint Decorator by L Edwards, J Lawless & K Cathie (publishing date Feb 07)

Indoor Air Pollution by Jack G Kay, CRC Press

How Can We Save The Planet by Mayer Hillman, Penguin Books Ltd

The above books are available from the Green Shop, 01452 770629 **www.greenshop.co.uk**

Useful websites

www.karmacolour.co.uk

www.naturalshelters.co.uk

www.defra.gov.uk

www.opsi.gov.uk

www.paintquality.co.uk

www.ecosolutions.co.uk

www.greenshop.co.uk

Further research

GreenPro, is a database of eco-building products. For a one-off of fee (£10.00 +VAT) you get unlimited access at any time. It offers up to date listings of dozens of paint manufacturers, as well as over 1,000 other eco-building products that are currently available in the UK: **www.newbuilder.co.uk/greenpro**

Osmo's PolyxOil, the Original Hardwax-Oil and Still the Best

osmo
Polyx®-Oil
High Solid

For wood and cork floors and all internal joinery.
Interior use – satin.
Natural oil/wax based – micro-porous.
Water-repellent – treadfast.

highest coverage!

3032 Clear, satin

- Professional satin finish for wooden, cork and OSB floors.
- Offers highest coverage of any oil on the market (2.5 litre can covers approx 30m² with two coats).
- Extremely wear resistant, durable and easy to maintain.

PolyxOil from Osmo UK is the premium, wood finish guaranteed to keep wooden flooring and all internal joinery as beautiful as the day it was installed.

osmo
Osmo UK Ltd
Osmo House
Pembroke Road,
Stocklade Industrial Estate
Aylesbury HP20 1DB
Tel: 01296 481 220
Fax: 01296 424 090
www.osmouk.com
info@osmouk.com

NATURAL PAINTS

BIOFA

Ethical Consumer magazine best buy

- Made with renewable natural raw materials
- Toxic fumes free (no VOC's)
- 1000 colours
- Used in Brighton Library & Lewes School
- Nationwide stockists
- Free brochure

Enquiries: **01273 685 800**

CHILD FRIENDLY   NATURAL PRODUCT   PLANET FRIENDLY

www.biofa.co.uk

See also: various discussions on water management in Chapter 8

Water and appliances

The water flowing out of our taps has undergone a complex and energy consuming cycle that includes cleaning it ready for drinking and pumping it from the reservoir to our homes and places of work. Opportunities for saving water start with a change in our attitude to water utilisation. Here **Stephen Lawndes** reviews water saving techniques that can be incorporated into the design of our buildings.

We use water in our homes for drinking, washing, cooking, bathing and showering, flushing toilets and watering gardens. Other buildings, such as offices and community buildings, may consume water for large scale catering, swimming pools or even manufacturing processes. There are opportunities in all buildings to provide fittings, components and other measures that help reduce water consumption.

Taps

Taps left running can waste enormous amounts of water. New installations should incorporate either self-closing or spray-head taps. These can, of course, be retrofitted to existing installations. Spray taps are particularly suited to wash hand basins and can save up to 50% of water compared to conventional taps. However, the slow flow rate achieved when spray-heads are used for hot water taps can mean these savings can be compromised if the tap has to be left

Water saving inserts fit into many common taps and help save water without seeming to throttle the flow.

running for a long time to obtain sufficiently warm enough water. This is more likely to be a function of a badly designed hot water installation rather than the fault of the tap. 'Dead-legs', i.e. lengths of pipe work with un-circulated hot water, should be kept to an absolute minimum, so that hot water is readily available at all draw-offs.

Where a powerful flow at the tap is required, self-closing taps that close automatically after a preset period, usually set between 1 and

Water saving shower head with flow regulator..

30 seconds could be considered. These taps should significantly reduce the possibility of taps leaking or being left running. Some types incorporate an adjustable flow restrictor so that a lower flow rate can be set for even greater savings. Since water regulations now require all outlets to incorporate an isolating valve, fitting a flow regulating service valve, rather than a standard isolating valve would kill two birds with one stone.

The perception of good water flow can be achieved by fitting regulated aerators[1] on tap outlets and these work well if water flow is unchecked and there is sufficient water pressure.

There are a surprising range of sizes for wash basins and baths, mostly due to fashion. It would seem that it is a fashion statement

© Green Building Press

to have a large bath! The simple measure of ensuring wash basins and baths are no larger than necessary will mean the amount of water used and time taken to fill them will be minimised.

Reduced flush toilets

Flushing toilets are usually the principal consumer of water, after catering, within

The ifo Cera dual flush loo flushes 2 or 4 litres.

most buildings. Since conventional WCs utilise drinking quality water and generate sewerage for processing, it is in the interests of those who wish to reduce water consumption to seriously consider ways in which use can be moderated. Dual flush toilets[2] can save up to half the water used by old nine litre WC units, so the replacement of older existing units during refurbishment projects is usually worthwhile. It is possible to install WCs with ultra low flush capacity, utilising a four and two litre dual flush. If your loo flushes 9 litres (80% of houses

still use this size cistern) then there are retrofit systems available[3]. Once fitted, the average household of 2.4 people could save 27,000 litres per year, which equates to a saving of around £50 per annum and rising.

Composting toilets

Composting or waterless toilets compost the waste into a form that can be safely used as fertiliser. Human waste contains nitrogen as well as magnesium, sulphur, phosphorus, potassium and other trace elements that are, in the form of compost, beneficial for plants and help condition soil. Rather than flushing the waste away with water the user throws in a handful of 'soak' (sawdust or shredded cardboard). A chamber under the composting toilet receives the waste and the soak and facilitates the composting process.

Composting chambers range in size from a large box located within the toilet area, to a chamber under the floor. In most cases more space needs to be allocated for a composting toilet compared to a conventional WC and access must be provided for final removal of the compost and for interim turning and raking. Because human faeces contain pathogens, care

Separett Composting Toilet

needs to be exercised and contact with waste in its raw state avoided. Of course there needs to be a ready use for the compost. Without a garden you might need to rely on your friends to take your compost away.

Other types of waterless WCs include vacuum systems, usually employed on trains and in aeroplanes. These systems can be expensive, maintenance intensive and require the operation of electric vacuum pumps. Generally their use within buildings has been restricted to large installations that cannot utilise conventional gravity drainage.

Urinals

Water flush urinals are commonly installed in public toilets and in toilets within commercial premises. Where urinals are installed, automatic flush control should be installed as a minimum. With the older type of automatic flush, the urinal stalls are only flushed if the automatic flush valve senses a change in water pressure. Newer devices enable flushing if movement in front of the urinal is sensed, using an infra-red detector.

Although automatic flush control valves reduce water consumption, if you really want to save water in a urinal installation you might consider turning the water off to the stalls altogether. Waterless urinals, in essence, are just that – a urinal bowl without the flush. However, they need to incorporate a syphonic trap, or an outlet in the urinal waste with a perfume impregnated pad, designed to reduce the smell of urine.

Urine-separating flush toilets are a variation on the waterless urinal and ordinary loo. Aimed at the domestic application these toilets separate solid and liquid waste at source. They usually work on the principle of accepting liquid waste at the front of the toilet bowl and solid waste at the rear. Because the solids and liquids are separated in the toilet bowl, the former can be flushed in the conventional manner, while the latter requires no water to flush away.

Hot water systems

Although we have discussed taps and their use with hot water, there are some more particular issues relating to hot water outlets and distribution pipe work which will affect efforts to conserve water. For instance, the thermal insulation of all of the hot and cold water distribution pipes should not be overlooked. As hot and cold water pipes are usually run together, the mains cold water may be warmed up by the adjacent un-insulated hot water pipe and vice versa. Apart from the obvious heat lost from any un-insulated hot water pipe, users will also waste water by running the cold water for prolonged periods when they try to get a cool drink. There will also be condensation on the outside of the pipe if insulation is ignored. As previously mentioned if dead legs on the hot water system are too long, a great deal of water will be wasted before the hot water appears at the tap.

Showers and water pressure

Although taking a shower normally uses much less water than a soak in the bath, there is still scope to ensure that the water utilised by a shower is no more than it needs to be. The problem here, though, is that a low flow rate from a shower does not give a very invigorating experience. So whilst flow restrictors can be installed, their effect is likely to be at the expense of shower performance. The use of thermostatic shower mixer valves with a fixed maximum flow and mains pressure atomising shower heads can help maintain acceptable performance, even with low water flows. The available water pressure head plays an important part in water flow delivery. Direct mains fed outlets will almost always receive a higher flow pressure compared to tank fed outlets, unless you live in an area of low mains water pressure. The available pressure at outlets, such as showers and taps fed from loft tanks, rather than direct from the mains, is dependant upon how high the storage tank is above the outlet. The higher the tank, the greater the pressure head and therefore the strength of flow of water from the outlet.

© Green Building Press

Appliances

If you are fitting in new appliances such as washing machines and dishwashers you should be looking at 'A' or 'AA' rated units. In the case of washing machines and dish washers this label means that the appliance should be a low consumer of water, compared with a 'B' or 'C' rated machine. It is not always the case that an 'A' rated machine is more expensive to purchase over a lower rated appliance and of course it always pays to shop around.

It is possible to purchase hand operated 'pressure wash' devices, that are claimed to use only a very small amount of water and do not run on electricity[4]. Hot water is poured into and sealed in an airtight washer drum. The heat from the water causes the air in the drum to expand, which builds pressure, driving soap and water into the clothing. Hand operation is required to agitate the clothes within the drum and effect cleaning. However, whether in reality, these sorts of devices use significantly less water to achieve the same result as a conventional 'A' rated machine, is difficult to conclude without reliable data (but of course they will use less electricty). Other measures such as greywater harvesting, rainwater harvesting and off grid environmental drainage solutions are covered elsewhere in this book.

Conclusion

In this article I have introduced and discussed some of the technologies and systems that could be incorporated into a project with the aim of saving water. Some of these systems can be complex and is likely to require the involvement of experienced professionals in order to implement it successfully. At the other end of the scale there are comparatively simple solutions, such as the installation of water saving taps and retrofit components that are possible for a competent DIY'er to undertake and will go a good way to reducing consumption in a reliable and cost effective manner.

The way in which the building is used will ultimately have the biggest influence on the water consumption and occupiers need to be encouraged to adopt responsible usage patterns, so that water use can be optimised. With the cost of our water predicted to soar in the near future and the introduction of water meters on both existing and new buildings, there has never been a better time to take control of your water use. ☯

References

1. One example is Tapmagic: www.tapmagic.co.uk

2. A good example of a high quality, dual flush lavatory in the UK is the Ifô Cera range which is available from: www.greenbuildingstore.co.uk or www.rainharvesting.co.uk

3. One example of a retrofit WC flow limiter would be from a company called Interflush who make a Water Council approved product (also on Water Technolgy List for Enhanced Capital Allowance) that can be simply installed in most common WCs: www.interflush.co.uk

4. Hand operated washing machine. Available in UK from Mailspeed Marine: www.mailspeedmarine.com/ProductDetails/mcs/productID/101375

Further reading

'Sewage Solutions; answering the call of nature' by Nick Grant, Mark Moodie and Chris Weedon. This book deals with all aspects of non-mains sustainable sewage treatment.

'Lifting the Lid; an ecological approach to toilet systems' by P Harper and L Halestrap is probably the classic book on waterless toilets!

Both the above books are available from Green Shop: 01452 770629 www.greenshop.co.uk

The Wonder Wash. A hand operated pressure washing machine. Just turn the handle!

8 Outdoors

See also: 'Encouraging wildlife' later in this chapter

Sustainable garden design

The outdoor environment that surrounds our buildings is a vital part of our eco-system. It is our direct link to the natural environment, a place where you can relax and enjoy nature. Whatever the size of your outdoor space, there is much you can do to help save energy, conserve water and encourage wildlife and biodiversity. **Louise Zass-Bangham** introduces us to some sustainable garden and landscaping ideas.

There are many ways to reduce environmental impact by using sustainable materials and avoiding chemicals. This will ensure that your efforts to create a green building are not undone the minute you step outside the door.

Shelter from weather extremes

A combination of shelterbelts, shade trees / shrubs, foundation planting and climbers can modify the micro-climate around your home and even help reduce the heating needs of a house. A shelterbelt or windbreak is made up of rows of trees, planted to deflect wind. A mixture of evergreen and deciduous gives fast growth, winter protection and longevity. A row of shrubs on the windward side filters wind at ground level, where trunks are often bare. A shelterbelt needs to be much longer than it is high because otherwise wind deflects around it and actually increases wind speed in places. In a small urban garden, filtering the wind with a mixture

Is your house exposed to the weather or sheltered by planting?

© Green Building Press

of smaller deciduous trees and large shrubs will be a more realistic option than a complete shelterbelt. Careful positioning of the plants will balance the need for shelter, sunshine and root space. Remember that if you try to block wind completely with a solid fence or wall, it creates intense eddies on both sides of the fence.

Planting evergreen trees/shrubs around a house can also help reduce energy costs. Foundation planting filters wind nearer the building and creates a dead airspace between shrubs and the building. When the shrubs are mature there should be a 30cm gap between them and the structure. Refer to the chapter on trees regarding planting near buildings.

Here hard paving has been colonised by species such as black medick, hawkweed and clover, providing sources of nectar for bees and other insects.

Climbing plants, providing support where necessary and choosing species carefully so the building fabric is not damaged, can act as an additional layer of insulation, trapping a thin layer of air against the building. The soil layer in a green roof (decribed in more detail in Chapter 7), will also provide thermal insulation in winter.

Cooling the house in summer

To help reduce problems associated with over-heating in summer, deciduous trees can block 60-90% of the sun. Bare winter branches will still block around 30-50% of sunlight so there has to be careful planting to avoid shading solar collectors. A pergola, arbour or awning-frame alongside the house, clothed with a decidu-ous climber, gives shade to the building and windows during the summer, while allowing more sun through in winter months. Air is also cooled by transpiration from the plant's leaves - like sweating - so plenty of plants will create a cooler summer garden. Climbers and green roofs will take heat out of the air right by the building, whilst providing shade.

Hard landscaping materials

Hard landscaping means all the built garden structures, e.g paving, paths, fencing, shed, and pergola. In a new garden, install these first. It's really tempting to plant immediately but restrain yourself until the basic structure of your garden

Top 10 sustainable garden tips

Ten, at a glance tips for caring for your garden and the wildlife that lives in it and the wider environment. Further informa-tion relating to all of the tips can be found throughout this chapter.

1. Plan a new garden to scale before you buy anything

2. Use the garden to help conserve heat and reduce overheating in the house

3. Choose sustainable and preferably local or recycled/reclaimed materials

4. Look after your top-soil during building works

5. Avoid using any chemicals, use natural controls instead

6. Plant for your local climate conditions and soil type

7. Take every opportunity to save water and use it wisely

8. Mulch

9. Encourage bio-diversity with your planting choices

10. Start a compost heap.

is ready, as the plants may not survive being trampled during construction.

Sustainable surfaces

Firstly, consider minimising hard surfaces - for several reasons. If an area is paved then it isn't growing plants, so it isn't cleaning the air or supporting wildlife. Rainwater runs off down the drain rather than gradually returning to the water table through the soil. Sustainable drainage systems (SUDS), which are discussed in detail later in this chapter, are an essential part of our contribution to the environment and ensure our access to clean drinking water.

Some areas of hard surface are usually needed for easy access to the house and garden. There are a number of different options, which reduce environmental impact. These include reclaimed paving and brick stocks, which are widely available via paving and architectural salvage merchants. Don't use stone obtained from the natural rock formations known as limestone pavements. Such

areas are scarce and declining habitats that support a unique range of flora and fauna.

Cement is frequently used in laying paving and can be substituted with lime mortar. Paving can be laid so that it is permeable, by using sand in the joints and bedding it down in a very weak mortar. Make sure water that runs off will go into a flowerbed or soak away, rather than to the drains.

If you really want new stone, despite the environmental consequences of extraction, at least choose local stone that has not been transported around the world to reach you. Stone from overseas may seem cheap but ask yourself why - the environmental and human costs are often hidden. Investigations into quarrying practices in developing countries have uncovered child labour, bonded (slave) labour and a scant regard for workers' health and safety.

Dry stone walls are great for attracting invertebrates, such as lizards and newts.

© Green Building Press

A loose surface, such as gravel, has the advantage that it can become a diverse wildlife habitat if planted into. If you have off-street parking, you can plant low-growing plants between the tyre tracks and to the sides. The plants will be kept in check automatically by occasionally being driven over. However, bear in mind that gravel is extracted from land or sea. Millions of tonnes are effectively strip-mined from the seabed, destroying marine life in the process. The UK even exports 30% of its marine aggregate production to other European countries. More sustainable alternatives to gravel include recycled glass chips. These are available in a more natural look as well as a range of colours. Some companies now sell recycled gravel, if you look hard enough. Also consider organic materials, such as bark chips or shells - which are more sustainable and a waste by-product.

Outdoor structures

Reclaimed materials are gaining in popularity for garden structures and can be integrated if chosen carefully. If you need a solid wall, consider reclaimed bricks and lime mortar. It is possible to do away with mortar altogether and build a dry stone wall, an excellent habitat for insects and other wild creatures. However, there

is the issue of sourcing the stone for the wall as this has got to come from somewhere, unless it is reclaimed too. Alternative sustainable building techniques would be equally suitable for use in the garden – from rammed earth to cob. If you want an individual and obviously recycled look, old tyres or other discarded items can be used as experimental bed edgings. Mesh gabions filled with old terracotta or other materials are also popular choices at the moment.

Timber is a great material to use in the garden, providing it is certified sustainable and preferably locally sourced. Destruction of the world's rainforests is sadly a continuing problem, devastating local habitats and the global environment. Always check that timber is from a well-managed, sustainable source - look for the trademark of the Forest Stewardship Council (FSC) and choose wood that is FSC certified. This includes bark chips too.

Oak and sweet chestnut should not need treatment and will age to a beautiful silver. If you do want to preserve the original colour, however, you will need to put on some sort of coating. Linseed oil can make oak go black so do test samples to ensure you will be happy with the finished result. Be sure to only use natural finishes that are harmless to humans and wildlife.

Other hardwoods are available, but mainly imported. One popular choice is western red cedar but whilst it is possible to obtain some local supplies, most is imported. Timber structures that will be bearing a lot of weight and are in contact with the ground, such as fencing or a pergola, should have an appropriate footing that keeps them off damp soil.

Coppicing is still practiced in a few managed woods in the UK, usually for sweet chestnut, hazel and willow. This is highly sustainable because the trees are not felled but instead rods or poles are cut off at the base. The tree re-grows new stems, which can be coppiced a few years later. Coppiced hazel and willow rods are used to make wattle hurdles, a very tradi-

Homegrown cedar is available. It tends to be paler than the imported species but very nearly as durable. Most of the imported cedar is still harvested from old growth forests and is therefore not a sustainable option.

tional form of fencing. Sweet chestnut poles are used for a wide range of garden features, including fences, arches and arbours.

Be aware that timber and fencing materials for outdoor use may already have been treated with preservative (pressure treated) but not labelled, so you should always ask for details. If you do decide to buy treated timber, make sure the chemicals used are non-hazardous.

Reclaimed wood, including oak and other hardwoods, is available from architectural salvage specialists. Old railway sleepers are banned because of the creosote content. If you see wood for sale advertised as railway sleepers, ask for more information because it probably isn't recycled. You can always ask for sustainably sourced wood to be supplied to the same chunky dimensions.

Sustainable gardens are not new. Here is a living willow fedge, low hurdles, shady pergola and a permeable surface in a restored Medieval garden.

Care during building work

Topsoil is the upper layer of soil, where most soil-life and nutrients are found. It is usually 15-60cm deep and darker in colour than the stony sub-soil underneath. If the topsoil becomes heavily compacted - by machinery, building materials or heavy boots - plants struggle to grow. Contamination with building products and construction waste needs to be avoided too. Trees are particularly vulnerable around the root collar at the base of the trunk: an inch or two of extra soil built up around it can be all it takes to let in infection. It will take up to 7 years for damage caused during building work to finally kill a tree, so it is difficult to diagnose or remedy later. Damage to roots must therefore be avoided, to give trees and shrubs the best chance of survival.

During any construction works remember:
- make clear paths to prevent the whole site being trampled
- fence-off whole areas or individual trees

© Green Building Press

- lay boards or a very thick mulch to spread the weight of heavy machinery
- don't mix-up turf, topsoil and sub soil - make separate heaps and cover them
- keep soil heaps to a maximum of 1-2m high to avoid compaction
- never move or work soil when it is wet
- don't move extra soil onto the area under a tree canopy
- avoid digging a trench through tree roots - dig a tunnel or work by hand around tree roots.

Hedges and fedges

Even more sustainable than wood that has been harvested, is wood that is living. A good old-fashioned hedge absorbs carbon dioxide, helps recycle your compost, filters the wind and could outlast your house. A mixed hedge is excellent for providing food and shelter for wildlife. Some of the most effective intruder- and live-stock-proof boundaries include spiky firethorn or blackthorn, but consider how you will tackle them yourself if they need trimming.

A fedge, or living fence, is commonly made of willow rods or whips. These are traditionally woven or tied into open diamond patterns, in a technique that has been used for centuries. Many different willow species are available for different uses, several with brightly coloured stems. A fedge is easily trimmed each year, like a hedge. The main advantage is that a willow fedge takes up much less room than a hedge, being about as slim as an average fence. The principles of weaving living willow can be applied to garden structures too, such as arches, arbours, a summerhouse, seating or sculpture - there is plenty of scope to be imaginative. Turf banks also have good design potential, but are more time consuming to maintain.

Ecological planting

This is not about bio-diversity or saving plants; this is about growing plants that are in tune with your local environment or ecology. You wouldn't expect a penguin to survive in the desert or

a camel to enjoy the South Pole. Plants are equally adapted to their native climate. If you get the planting right, once garden plants are established, you shouldn't have to water them. This is particularly important now we are seeing many areas of the UK hit by drought and hosepipe bans.

Many of the plants available to buy today are descendents of plants brought back to this country by the Victorian plant hunters from expeditions overseas. Certain species have become popular over the years - particularly those that continue to be used in the showy annual bedding schemes that the Victorians so adored. The wild parents of many garden plants come from habitats as diverse as tropical rainforests and mountain ranges. We have been conditioned to believe that we need to water our gardens constantly, raise plants from seed in heated greenhouses and buy special growing mediums. However, if we focus on plants that suit our climate and our soil type, our garden will be naturally low-maintenance, with strong, healthy plants that can fend for themselves.

Such plants are usually our native species, or ones that originated in a climate similar to ours. If your soil is sandy and free-draining, plant things that like it dry. If the soil is naturally boggy, grow things that love the wet. Whatever your situation - chalky soil or heavy clay, salt spray or blazing sunshine - there are beautiful plants adapted to cope. Find out what your soil conditions are. Do a really simple pH test (available from your garden centre) and find out the sunny areas of your garden. You can then choose from a wide range of beautiful plants that will thrive in your garden. Remember though that hybrid species do not tend to be so rich in nectar so are not as desirable to insects.

Use water wisely

New plants will all benefit from some watering during their first year. This is because a pot has restricted their root systems. They need time to reach out to obtain the best water supplies. If you are going to water, do it thoroughly. Water sprayed lightly around the plant encourages the roots to come to the surface, exactly where you don't want them to be. Water should be directed at the base of the plant to reach the roots easily, not splashed around the foliage. Make sure the plant receives a thorough soaking once a week for the first few weeks, and that should be enough. Try to always water in the early morning or evening. Don't water in hot midday sun because most of what you apply will soon evaporate or little droplets of water will act like magnifying glasses, scorching the leaves.

Keeping water in the soil

Mulching is essential to retain moisture. A thick mulch layer, 5-7 cm deep, is one of the best methods of water conservation. The most sustainable materials to use are organic, such as cocoa shells, bark chips, well-rotted stable manure, compost or grass clippings. Mulch after heavy rain or thorough watering. The mulch also keeps weeds down, reducing competition for water. Avoid mulching right up to plant stems, so rot is not encouraged. When planting, mix a handful or two of compost or other well-rotted organic material into the planting hole. This will help the soil hold moisture around the roots, assisting with nutrient uptake and improving soil structure.

Avoid planting too close to the base of walls or fences, in the rain shadow. Plant climbers about 40cm away from the wall, tilting the stems back in. A shelterbelt helps prevents soil evaporation and protects plants from the drying effects of the wind.

Improving the soil

One of the most sustainable things you can do is to start a compost heap for your kitchen and garden waste. Add compost to the soil when planting, or use it as mulch. Urine is an excellent activator when added to compost heaps. For more information on this subject most good gardening books and websites will cover composting. Many local authorities can provide compost bins at much reduced prices so contact your local council to see if you are eligible for any such offers.

The use of peat in your garden is unneces-

sary. The Royal Horticultural Society (RHS) considers the use of peat to be unacceptable for soil incorporation and mulching. Peatlands are an important carbon sink - removal of this sink exacerbates climate change. The UK's peatlands are globally important and the effects of extraction are irreparable. Due to increasing government restrictions on peat extraction, the majority of peat used in the UK is imported, simply shifting the problem to countries with weaker legislation. Prior to the 1960s gardeners used soil conditioners from a whole range of sources. Sadly, despite long-running media coverage of peat bog destruction, peat products remain on sale. If you don't make your own compost, choose local, non-peat-based products, such as well-rotted stable manure – available at most garden centres. Check labels carefully before buying.

If you must water...

In an ideal world, you've planted a garden full of things that do not need watering, and it's all got a nice deep mulch. However, there may still be times you might need to water, such as helping to establish new planting or a thirsty food crop. Consider using wastewater from other household uses. For more information on this please refer to the rain harvesting section that follows this article.

You could also install water butts, an economical option for storing rainwater for garden use. Some local authorities can offer special deals on water butts so contact your local council for details. Water butts fill very quickly when attached to the down-pipe from the main roof, or even just from a shed or greenhouse roof. Always ensure water butts have tight fitting lids. Remember young children can easily drown in exposed water - so can birds and other creatures.

Biodiversity

There are many reasons for supporting diversity of plant and animal species. Man has yet to understand a fraction of the relationships that make our eco-system work. There are things that nature could provide for us that are

© Green Building Press

currently undiscovered so it's important to help a wide variety of species survive – remember that the raw material for aspirin was discovered in willow bark and new drugs continue to be found in plant material. Try to support your local wildlife, even if in a small way. There are hundreds of beautiful native plants that make great garden plants.

Some garden-escapees (alien species) have caused big problems in the countryside, such as Japanese knotweed and Indian balsam. Such plants provide little value to native wildlife and can quickly colonise vast areas, crowding out beneficial native species. However, other non-natives, such as buddleia much favoured by many of our butterfly species, are suitable to include in your planting. Many common plants arrived here relatively recently – for example sycamore and horse chestnut – so check what is actually native to your area. The Natural History Museum website will give you a long list appropriate to your postcode, covering everything from annuals and perennials to shrubs and trees.

If you are going to be developing land consider a wildlife survey before building work starts. Your local wildlife trust should be able to offer advice on this. This will reveal any rare species and enable you to take appropriate action if there are any species of interest. ☙

With grateful thanks to Sally Hall for providing some of the text and pictures for this article.

References

Sustainable Housing Design Guide for Scotland, covers a wide range of topics in some detail. See particularly 'The site and the dwelling': www.archive2.official-documents.co.uk/document/deps/cs/shdg/index.html

Planting for shelter and shade, University of Minnesota: www.sustland.umn.edu/design/index.html

Preventing construction damage to trees, University of Missouri: http://muextension.missouri.edu/xplor/agguides/hort/g06885.htm

Conserving water in the garden, Thames Water & Gardening Which?: waterwise.fortune-cookie.com/domestic/tips-for-the-garden.asp

Encouraging wildlife - English Nature: www.english-nature.org.uk/Nature_In_The_Garden

Natural History Museum: www.nhm.ac.uk/nature-online/life/plants-fungi/postcode-plants/index.html

Gardening issues

Royal Horticultural Society: www.rhs.org.uk

This is the general website for the UK wildlife trusts, but each area also has its own website, which can be located at this main site: www.wildlifetrusts.org

For an international directory of UK suppliers of architectural salvage, including used timber, bricks, stone and cast iron: www.salvo.co.uk

'Peat and the Gardener', Royal Horticultural Society Conservation & Environment Guidelines: www.rhs.org.uk/Learning/research/documents/c_and_e_peat.pdf

'Briefing: Lowland Raised Bog', Friends of the Earth: www.foe.co.uk/resource/briefings/lowland_raised_bog.html

'Peat Alert!', Do or Die Issue 10, Eco-action, 2003: www.eco-action.org/dod/no10/peat.htm

'Miracle-Gone: FAQ', Friends of the Earth: www.foe.co.uk/campaigns/corporates/case_studies/scotts/miracle_gone/faq.html

If you need information, news and networking on **global sustainable waste management** better than a hole in your head, contact the **Resource Recovery Forum**. 300 members in five continents already know how to avoid a headache.

Contact Kit Strange for more information.

Resource Recovery Forum, 1st Floor, The British School Otley Street, Skipton, North Yorkshire BD23 1EP. UK

Tel	+44 (0) 1756 709 808
Fax	+44 (0) 1756 709 801
Email	kit@resourcesnotwaste.org
www:	www.resourcesnotwaste.org

LEEDS COLLEGE OF BUILDING
LIBRARY

© Green Building Press

Rainwater harvesting

Forget the rising cost of mains water. Collecting rainwater from our own roofs may soon be the only way of ensuring an adequate water supply for our buildings during a drought.
Keith Hall explains how the systems work.

It is likely that rainfall patterns will continue to fluctuate and most predictions suggest we will need to get used to short sharp bursts of rain which will cause more flooding and soil erosion than we have been accustomed to in the past. Such rainfall patterns do little to top up the underground aquifers that most of us currently rely upon. Add to this the fact that household water consumption is increasing per capita and, as the climate warms, natural evapo-transpiration will increase, so we will have to find ways to reduce, retain and even reuse water.

Firstly we should look to reduce the amount of water we use. This we can do by installing water efficient appliances; air entraining taps, shower heads and low flush toilets should be installed. Alternatively install water reduction devices[1]. Next we should find alternatives to the high quality drinking water that we use for low grade uses, such as toilet flushing and watering the garden. There is no longer any justification in cleaning and purifying water to 'drinking' standards when most of it is used where lower quality would suffice.

Water should also be 'kept in play' for as long as possible; in other words, not flushed down the drain so quickly but retained for reuse (if it is not too dirty) wherever possible. Water from bathing and washing (commonly referred to as greywater) can be collected and essentially re-used for toilet flushing or car cleaning etc.

As water becomes more scarce we will all learn to improvise, but we should start to think ahead now. We are all used to the idea of water butts in the garden but at a more serious level, underground water storage tanks can be installed as part of a rainwater harvesting system which collects rainwater, usually from the roofs of the buildings. The advantages of rainwater collection and storage are twofold - not only will the system collect and store rainwater for reuse, but, if enough systems were to be installed, it will also assist in preventing flash flooding of rivers and streams.

If flooding is a problem in your region then a sustainable urban drainage systems (SUDs) might also be appropriate and on new developments may even be required as a condition of planning permission. These can also be used as giant reservoirs below car parks or grass verges on larger developments or housing estates. SUDs can include features such as swales (shallow, wide ditches channelling surface water overland from the drained area to a storage discharge) and basins (designed to hold back storm runoff reducing peak flows to rivers and reducing flood risk). Existing or new ponds can also be designed to accommodate peak variations in water levels to provide flood-storage capacity, but a risk analysis should be carried out by qualified ecologists before natural, established ponds are filled with water run-off from roofs and roads.

At the present level of water rates (metered), the pay back time on a full domestic rain harvesting system is typically 10-20 years. For commercial properties with high water consumption needs and large roofs, the pay back can be very much shorter, sometimes only months. The benefits however, are much greater

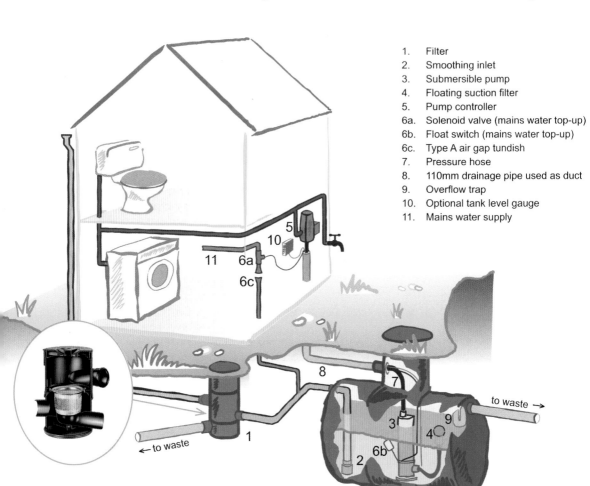

1. Filter
2. Smoothing inlet
3. Submersible pump
4. Floating suction filter
5. Pump controller
6a. Solenoid valve (mains water top-up)
6b. Float switch (mains water top-up)
6c. Type A air gap tundish
7. Pressure hose
8. 110mm drainage pipe used as duct
9. Overflow trap
10. Optional tank level gauge
11. Mains water supply

© Green Building Press

than just financial, the environmental aspects of capturing and retaining water are very great. It should also be remembered that because water is becoming a highly precious commodity, with demand beginning to outstrip supply, water authorities are now seeking permission from the government to apply considerable price increases. As this continues the pay back period will become shorter.

The principles of rainharvesting

Note: the numbers in brackets refer to diagram on left.

The principles of collecting and storing rainwater are fairly simple and easy to follow. The water must be stored in the dark below 18°C, then the system will supply clean, perfectly usable water for most purposes other than drinking.

The water is collected by normal roof gutters and is directed to the rainwater filter (1) where the water is separated from leaves and other debris at the bottom of the rainwater down-pipes. As much debris as possible must be removed from the water before storage, as any decaying material in the tank will consume oxygen (from microbial action) that is in the water. The result would be smelly, putrid water - the stored water must be oxygen rich.

The filtered water is then transferred to the storage tank via a water smoothing inlet (2) so as not to disturb the sediments on the bottom. The filter will have screened out all but the smallest of particles. The choice of mesh size of the pre-filter system has to be a compromise between maintenance intervals and water quality. The finer the filter screen, the more regularly it will have to be cleaned, if the collecting efficiency is to be maintained, because the filter is so designed that water which cannot pass through the filter is sent off down the normal stormwater sewer.

The floating particles will be organic material such as pollens, which must be flushed out as, if they were left in they would cause the water to become stagnant. This is done by designing the tank overflow so it has a skimming effect

on the surface of the water when it overflows. The system should be sized to overflow quite regularly but at least twice a year, and in doing so it keeps itself clean. The heavy particles that sink to the bottom of the tank (usually sand or grit in nature) accumulate at about 1-2mm/yr, a negligible amount - 50 years will result in 50-100mm. The overflow pipe to a soakaway will help recharge underground aquifers, or the system may be connected to the main's storm water system. If the latter, then an anti-vermin trap and an anti-backflow device need to be included if there is any risk of flooding and backing up.

The water thus stored can be delivered anywhere in the property on demand, using a submersible pump (3). The pump will be drawing water via a floating filter (4), ensuring the water is taken from just below the surface which will be the cleanest water in the tank. The pump is controlled by the flow control/pressure switch (5). The pump supplies the building directly on demand. This gives enough pressure and flow rate to feed commonly encountered appliances, including washing machines and garden hoses. Mains water is also connected to the underground storage tank via a solenoid, which includes a WRC statutory air gap to ensure that the rainwater in the tank cannot back up into the mains water system (6a and 6b). This connection will supply any small amounts of top-up from the mains to fulfil the requirement until the next rainfall replenishes the system.

The rainwater tank should never be allowed to become empty as this would have a detrimental effect on beneficial bacteria that have established in the tank, which will be keeping the water clean. Dry running protection for the pump should be built into the control system in case the water runs out and then an emergency switchover mechanism will revert to using mains water. Further incoming rainwater brings oxygen with it, keeping the system working. Simple monitoring equipment and system overrides can be conveniently located in a utility room or workshop (10).

>>>

The water collected has many uses, without any need for further treatment. It will be particle free, so uses that do not involve human consumption or skin contact, such as toilet flush, garden irrigation, and washing machine use, are ideal. If a wider range of uses are required, such as drinking or bathing, or the application is more sensitive, such as a hospital, then a risk assessment should be carried out to assess what further purification might be required. Further particle filtration, pH correction and UV sterilisation can be employed in such circumstances. This extra filtration/treatment costs more and uses more energy, so an evaluation of operational cost/benefit, also needs to be undertaken.

A well designed system will need no maintenance other than cleaning the rainwater collector filter four to six times a year; about 10 minutes work each time. Systems with extra particle and UV sterilisation will require maintenance as scheduled for these components, i.e changing of lamps etc. Commercial systems can be more sophisticated with double pump, duty-standby, or multi-pump systems, all sized for the specific application and often linked into a building management system.

The tank itself could be designed to perform more than one function, i.e it could act as a SUDS and rain harvesting system combined. A double sized tank could be employed, where the top half could have porous sides to allow slow water release, or alternatively, a floating overflow in a solid tank. This would slowly release excess storm water into the sewer or soak-away, the lower half would fulfil the rainwater harvesting function. Or, for other applications, perhaps where no mains water is available, the bottom half could be an emergency service reserve water supply, so the normal, 'usable' water from the tank would be from 50% to full but the remainder below could be called upon in times of severe drought.

Case studies
Rainharvesting

Domestic
Private home, Gloucestershire
One of the earliest domestic rainwater harvesting systems installed in the UK uses a modern German technology from Wisy. The system was installed in 1998 in a newly built house that, whilst fairly conventional in its construction, incorporated several ecological features. The rainwater system uses the downpipe type filter-collectors from Wisy, which collect and filter water from the roof directly into a 1500 litre holding tank in the basement. The tank contains a submersible pump, which delivers water directly to the WC's and the cold-fill on the washing machine. A low-level switch activates a top-up feed from the mains water supply should the tank run low on rainwater. The system saves approximately 38,000 litres per year.

Private home, Wales
Undoubtedly the easiest method of rainwater harvesting is the simple positioning of a butt below a rainwater downpipe. However, you can't do a great deal with the few gallons that the common or garden variety of butt will hold, so the owner installed two huge ones. They are about 2m tall, 1.1m in diameter and are black ex industrial fruit juice containers. They hold 400 gallons (1500 litres) of water each, ideal for use in the garden or for car washing. The house has two waterbutts collecting the water from the rear slope of the roof. These fill up with just 3 inches of rain from the roof, which, over a year, will equate to about 15 refills, given the rainfall in Wales. The water is primarily used for irrigation in a nearby polytunnel. The owner paid about £230 for three butts complete with taps during a 3 for the price of 2 offer from the Tank Exchange: www.thetankexchange.com/home.htm

Commercial
Market Bosworth Country Park WC block, Leicestershire
The block replaces a temporary toilet at the 87-acre park and its environmental features include:

- rainwater collection and use to flush the toilets which are low volume flush
- the gents' urinals are waterless
- meters record how much water is used
- the performance of the sewage treatment plant is monitored monthly.

The system uses the Wisy WFF vortex filter, which is wall-mounted within the building and picks up all the water from the shingle-clad roof. The filtered water is then directed to a small tank (1000 litres) at low level, and from here the water is then pumped using a 12v pump up to a break tank, at high level, to supply the WC's. The break tank also has an automatic back-up from the mains cold water supply. Despite this being a relatively small building, with a high water demand, the system saved over 4000 litres during the first six months of use. This is equal to about 900 flushes of the Ifo Cera ES4 WC units.

Industrial

Tolvaddon Energy Park, Cornwall
Built in 2001, the Tovaddon Energy Park in Camborne, Cornwall was designed to provide low cost, comfortable and work-inspiring business units that demonstrate a commitment to renewable resources and protection of the environment. The 17 industrial units include green building features, such as hot water and heating from geothermal source, heavily insulated floors walls and roofs, underfloor heating and rainwater harvesting. Eight of the units have rainwater harvesting systems for supplying water to WCs. Rainwater is collected and filtered using Wisy WFF vortex type filters.

These are indirect or gravity systems where the rainwater is pumped from an underground storage tank up to a break tank at high level within the building. The break tank then has a secondary feed from the mains water supply, which only cuts in if there is no supply from the rainwater pump.

This development has several units close together, so it was decided to use shared rainwater storage in order to save cost and ground works. The tank in this case is the only shared item, with each unit having its own pump and controls. Each system is therefore independent and can be isolated should one of the units

remain empty for any significant time. ✆

With grateful thanks to Roger Budgeon, Chairman of the UKRHA, and Derek Hunt of Rainharvesting Systems Ltd for providing the core data and the illustrations for this article.

Reference

1. One example would be a company called Interflush who make a Water Council approved product (also on Water Technolgy List for Enhanced Capital Allowance) that can be simply installed in most common WC's: www.interflush.co.uk

Further information

General design calculations for rainwater harvesting systems have been included in Volume 2 of the Green Building Bible: www.newbuilder.co.uk

UKHRHA: www.ukrha.org
The UK Rainwater Harvesting Association (UK-RHA) was formed in 2004 to serve as a focal point for organisations with business interests in the rainwater harvesting industry.

If you plan to install a commercial system and the components are on the Water Technology List, then the installation may qualify for enhanced capitol allowance. This means that you could claim tax relief on the whole rainwater harvesting system expenditure during the first year after installation: www.eca.gov.uk

Waste water management

Every litre of water piped into our homes has to leave again one way or another, mostly carrying away with it contaminants of waste and washing. Wiser management of our effluent, before it leaves our buildings could help reduce our environmental impact. But how easy would this really be? **Keith Hall** introduces the options...

In cities and large towns a network of sewer systems take away our effluent to municipal sewage farms but more remote properties have to fend for themselves. The common answer has been to use a septic tank with a soakaway field but it is widely acknowledged (especially by those living downstream of such installations) that they don't work! Percolation alone, on anything but the most suitable of soil and subsoil conditions, is doomed to failure and localised contamination.

System solutions

A newer solution is an on-site sewage treatment system. These work on the same principles as the municipal sewage farms but are now available sized for even single homes. The drawback with these systems is that they need power (electricity) to run air pumps to oxygenate the wastewater within a plastic or concrete tank. This simple process stops the waste from becoming anaerobic which would suffocate microbial action that helps break down the solid matter into harmless water and sediment.

While the treatment afforded to the wastewater by these package systems is quite acceptable, especially in situations where land is at a premium, if sustainability is your aim, both the long-term energy consumption (of the pumps) and the high embedded-energy of such systems are a downside, especially in times of power outages or pump failures.

These systems have actually been designed to exploit natural biological processes in a confined space, i.e natural organisms to do the work of breaking down the sewage into water and solids. Without the natural microbial activity the faeces would become a putrid, sticky and toxic mess.

More natural solutions

Useful systems then, especially in restricted space but with all this in-mind, if you wanted to avoid the use of electricity or power, achieve similar or even better results and have some space, then consider installing a constructed wetland or a reed bed system.

Constructed wetlands (or horizontal flow reed beds) are designed and built similar to natural wetlands; some are used to treat wastewater. Constructed wetlands for wastewater treatment consist of one or more shallow depressions, or cells, built into the ground with level bottoms so that the flow of water can be controlled within the cells, and from cell to cell. Roots and stems of the wetland plants form a dense mat where biological and physical processes occur to treat the wastewater. These work particularly well for low strength effluents, or effluents that have undergone some form of pre-treatment.

Vertical flow reed-bed systems can be more effective in reducing contaminant levels and eliminating smells than horizontal flow reed-beds. By their design they occupy a smaller space and can also cope with much stronger effluents. Single stage vertical flow reed-beds, when properly designed, can be used for the full treatment of domestic sewage - black and grey water - and, sludge, if required. There are also combination systems available - these incorporate one or two stages of vertical flow followed by one or more stages of horizontal flow.

Such systems use living plants and microbes to perform the same function that pumps and forced air do in a sewage treatment plant but, as stated earlier, without the need for any power supply. Nature provides this with sunshine which makes the plants grow. The

© Green Building Press

plants use nutrients from the sludge and water. They are also very beneficial for wildlife, attracting a host of wetland flora and fauna, such as dragonflies, butterflies and birds. In such systems, the reed beds would replace the soakaway field that would normally be used in conjunction with a septic tank system. Therefore, anyone with such a system already installed, could trace and intercept the outflow pipes and install a reedbed in-line to carry out further treatment to the outflow. This will greatly improve the underground water quality near the property. The septic tank will continue to perform the first settlement stage.

Separating waste - the options

The following solutions could be used with any system mentioned above, even standard septic tank systems or municipal mains sewage systems!

Black water

If you want to separate faeces from the sewer water, then a vortex separator unit, such as shown in the diagram below (Aquatron), could be used. This does not require any electricity

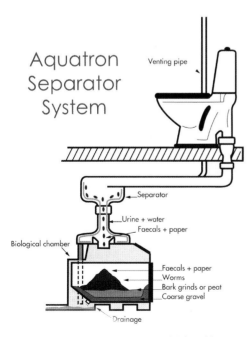

Aquatron Separator System

Venting pipe

Separator

Urine + water
Faecals + paper

Biological chamber

Faecals + paper
Worms
Bark grinds or peat
Coarse gravel

Drainage

www.solutionelements.co.uk/atron.htm

to operate. It will collect the faecal matter for composting in a chamber beneath the separator, while the flush water and urine continues to the septic tank or reed bed. The cleaner wastewater results in improved discharge quality or smaller treatment area. This type of system is very handy where you want to recoup the nutrients in the faecal matter but still wish to use a flush toilet in your home.

Another way to minimise the impact on the environment, and maximise the recovery of nutrients, is to use a urine separating toilet to take out nitrogen-rich urine before discharging the waste to the system. The urine can then be used as a liquid fertiliser. Used in combination, a urine separating toilet and a vortex separator unit can remove the vast majority of polluting matter from black water and save it in the form of re-useable nutrients. The final wastewater is thus much cleaner, entering the local environment of the treatment system for final cleaning.

Another approach might be to consider a dry (composting) toilet. This would also cut down your water consumption, as there is no flushing needed with such systems. There are many ways of achieving a composting toilet, with a number of off-the-shelf loos already available in the UK, or you could build your own. Organisations like the Centre for Alternative Energy (CAT)[1] or Intermediate Technology (IT)[2] and others produce easy to follow guides on constructing compost toilets.

Grey water

A reed-bed or constructed wetland can also be used on just grey water systems, i.e outflow from a kitchen sink or bathroom. You need to be fairly careful with your choice of cleaning products, and try to avoid harmful ingredients. You could even set up a simple irrigation system where the greywater flows down through pipes buried just below the surface in a vegetable plot in the garden. There are a number of resources on the internet that can provide more details of establishing simple greywater recycling systems. Ecosans Res, for instance, offer a free to download pdf document on the subject[3].

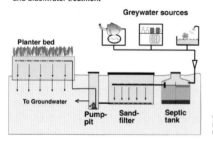

Separated greywater purification and blackwater treatment

Greywater sources

Ultra low-flush toilets

Planter bed

To Groundwater ←

Pump-pit   Sand-filter   Septic tank

Composting reactor in basement or ground

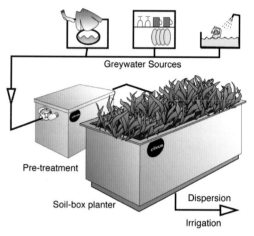

Greywater Sources

Pre-treatment

Soil-box planter

Dispersion

Irrigation

Above and right: diagram of a separated greywater and blackwater treatment system. This bespoke greywater treatment system from Clivus (www.multrum. com/uk/) may not be available in the UK but does show the principle workings and layout.

Images courtesy of Greywater Irrigation: www.greywater.com

With a little bit of filtration and storage in a cool tank, it could also be used for toilet flushing (though this might entail some serious re-plumbing), and car washing as well as uses in the garden. With a little imaginative plumbing you might be able to plumb the waste outlet from the wash hand basin to the toilet cistern to cut down on clean water use where it is not necessary, but be careful to ensure that the overflow is working properly or you could get a flood!. Even though the water from grey water systems is not used for drinking, bacteria should be removed and this is usually done with an ultra violet (UV) light filter. Although reported water savings within the range of 30% are potentially possible, installation and equipment costs, reliability and maintainability issues have all meant that the overall cost effectiveness of such systems has usually limited them to large scale projects, rather than domestic applications. ✆

With thanks to Féidhlim Harty for providing the original article upon which this article is based.

References

1. Centre for Alternative Technology: www.cat.org.uk

2. Intermediate Technology: www.itdgpublishing.org.uk

3. EcoSanRes (Ecological Sanitation)
Useful report on greywater management: www.ecosan-res.org/PDF%20files/ Fact_sheets/ESR8lowres.pdf

Further reading

'The Humanure Handbook - a guide to composting human manure' by J Jenkins available from Green Shop www.greenshop.co.uk

Water Works

Wales Water and Sewage Services

Dr Judith Thornton
www.water-works.org.uk

Advice and design for:
- Private water supplies
- Supplementing mains water supplies
- Sewage treatment systems including reed beds
- All aspects of sustainable sanitation

Looking for background information? Read
The Water Book. Chapters include:
- Reducing your water use
- Cleaning water
- Alternatives to the mains
- Rainwater harvesting
- Grey water recycling

available from www.cat.org.uk

Judith Thornton

The Water Book
Find it, move it, store it, clean it... use it

Constructed wetlands

Constructed wetlands are a cost-effective, low energy and robust way of treating industrial, agricultural and domestic wastewater - sewage and greywater. They have been used successfully to purify domestic sewage in the UK since 1903. They are suitable for treatment of sewage from single households or from small communities and are currently being used to treat sewage from populations of up to 10,000. **Jay Abrahams** explains the advantages that such systems have over normal sewage treatment methods and introduces a further advancement known as 'WET Systems'.

There are at least 500 constructed wetlands currently in the UK, treating a variety of wastewaters and there is substantial experience and expertise available here for the design, construction and operation of such systems to allow confidence in their widespread application.

How they work

Constructed wetland systems mimic the processes found in nature, which purify water in the global hydrological cycle. These systems use no electricity or fossil fuels in their operation, and rather than emit the greenhouse gas, CO_2, such systems absorb this gas and store it as plant biomass and soil. As well as purifying wastewater, these plant based systems purify the air and produce oxygen through the photosynthetic process. These systems are also visually very attractive and offer a haven for wildlife.

The basis of the purification process is, as with conventional mechanical treatment processes, microbiological; it relies on the biochemical transformations provided by the plethora of micro-organisms found in the gravel, sand or soil, which are used as the purification and growth media within the constructed wetland system.

The bacteria and fungi which transform

the waste are in a symbiotic, mutually beneficial, relationship with the roots of the wetland plants. In exchange the plant roots provide oxygen, sugars and attachment points for the microbes, whilst the microbes mineralise the organic matter found in the wastewater making this available to the growing plants.

A system to suit every need

There are several types of constructed wetland in use, ranging from simple unplanted pond systems, planted lagoons and reedbed treatment systems (both horizontal and vertical flow), as well as high rate planted sand filters, soil based multi-species wetlands called 'wetland ecosystem treatment' or WET systems. There are also the greenhouse enclosed, hydroponic tank-based 'living machines' which I have not discussed. Here I concentrate on reedbed and WET systems, in particularly the latter.

Reedbed treatment systems

Both horizontal and vertical flow, are the types most familiar to people in the UK whilst on the continent 'facultative pond' and 'lagoon systems' are often used for the purification of the sewage from small towns, villages and hamlets. In both horizontal and vertical flow reedbed treatment systems gravel is used as the purification medium and these systems are generally planted with only the common or Norfolk reed (Phragmites communis).

A reedbed treatment system comprises one or more lined lagoons filled with gravel. They usually have a relatively high aspect ratio (they are longer than they are wide) and the depth of the reedbeds is rarely more than 1m, as the roots of the reeds rarely grow deeper than 0.6m. There are often plastic pipes located within the system to avoid 'dead spaces' - to ensure that the wastewater flows throughout the whole volume of the lagoon and also to bring air to the lower reaches of the gravel bed.

Horizontal flow reedbed systems have the wastewater entering at the surface of the gravel on one side of the lagoon and flowing through it to the other side, the outlet being at approximately the same height as the inlet - the wastewater flows horizontally through the lagoon. This type of reedbed has only a limited surface area for aeration to occur - between the water surface and the atmosphere - and so the horizontal flow type functions mainly anoxically and anaerobically. Thus this type of reedbed is used mainly for polishing low strength wastewaters.

Vertical flow reedbed systems address the limited area for gaseous exchange in horizontal flow systems, because In these systems the inlet is at the surface of the gravel layer, whilst the outlet is located at the bottom of the gravel layer at the other end of the lagoon. Thus the wastewater has to flow 'vertically' downwards through the gravel, which is sometimes totally submerged with the liquid, but is periodically flushed through with air as the water passes through, and the water level varies from full to empty. This type of reedbed is able to function aerobically for more of the time and is therefore able to handle higher strength wastes such as sewage more effectively. This being the case it is usual to have a vertical and a horizontal type working together 'in-line', the vertical bed being dosed so that it fills and empties alternately and feeds a horizontal type for 'polishing'. It is also quite usual to have two parallel vertical flow systems working sequentially, with each taking its turn to be 'flushed' through with the waste-water, whilst the other is periodically 'rested'.

Although less energy intensive than conventional mechanical/electrical sewage systems, reedbed treatment systems have a high embedded energy content due to the sand/gravel which is used as the purification and growth medium, the requirement for plastic distribution and aeration pipes and the concrete/brickwork that is used to create the beds.

The embedded energy of reedbed treatment systems has led some practitioners and designers to develop soil based wetlands. These systems do not use imported gravel or cement; only topsoil found on site is used as the purification medium and the clay subsoil is compacted to form an impermeable base to the system.

Some designers also prefer to plant the constructed wetlands with more than just one species of reed, using reeds, rushes and sedges to create a range of root depths and a more varied habitat. Some advocate the use of wetland trees, such as willow, within the systems they create.

WET systems

A wetland eco-treatment system, or WET system, is the next stage in the evolution of constructed wetlands for wastewater purification. such a system is based on good ecological practice and permaculture design priciples. It mimics nature to a greater degree than simple reedbed treatment systems. It uses soil as the purification medium and employs a wide range of wetland plant and tree species, not just the common reed (Phragmites communis) which is the species used in conventional reedbed treatment. It treats the wastewater input, not as a problem to be got rid of, but as a resource to be transformed into a beautiful wetland environment, which purifies the water and grows useful wetland species which can be harvested for craftwork use or as a biomass fuel.

A series of swales are created to form a water reticulation system for the wastewater. This enables the wastewater to soak into and through the planted soil banks. It can therefore be created on slopes ranging from 1:500 to 1:25. This is in distinct contrast to conventional reedbed treatment systems which need to have relatively large areas of flat ground to be present, or to be created on site, for installation. This, in turn, means that the system responds to the landscape and looks far more natural than the rectilinear reedbeds, which always appear to have been imposed upon the landscape. This becomes more important and apparent the larger the constructed wetland needs to be.

© Green Building Press

WET systems are not simple reedbed treatment systems or conventional facultative pond or lagoon systems, although they do contain reeds, as well as a range of aquatic and marginal plants and a variety of willow types and wetland tree species. As the wastewater flows through the densely planted wetland trees and marginal plants, it is both purified by microbiological action and transpired by growing plants.

The systems generate a biomass resource; willow wands can be harvested from the coppiced willow each year. These are used for a range of traditional and contemporary crafts. The biomass yield from a well managed system can include one-year old coppiced willow wands for basketry, two-year old wands for hurdle making or living willow domes and tunnels, as well as binders - used for hedge-laying, and three-year old wands which are used for the construction of living willow structures and garden furniture. Rapidly growing, large, biomass willow types can also be planted and, when harvested and seasoned, these can be used to fuel simple woodstoves, ceramic stoves or combined heat and power (CHP) boilers and so contribute to the energy needs of the site.

A WET system, being soil not gravel based, can withstand intermittant loading without failing, whereas should the input to a conventional gravel based reedbed treatment system be cut off for any length of time and the bed dry out, the purification processes often fail or are severely curtailed as the gravel dries out and the reeds die off.

Case studies

WET systems

WET systems have now been created for a wide range of domestic sewage applications; these include systems for full time populations of one person up to 380 people; as well as an environmental education centre, which now has around 250,000 visitors per year, and a field studies centre with a maximum seasonal population of around 180. Systems have also been designed and constructed to purify a variety of effluents; a piggery and a dairy farm; an organic creamery producing cheese; a farm producing sheep's milk, ice cream; a large family owned cider mill in Herefordshire; and an expanding family owned 'micro-brewery' in Devon. These 'agro-industrial' systems purify wastewater of up to 80 times the strength of domestic sewage.

Hunters Inn Pub, Gloucestershire
This was the first system (established in 1994), to be created when the pub's new soakaway system (gravel/perforated pipe) failed within a month after it had been installed, due to the local heavy clay. It is a total absorption system with no outfall. The sewage passes from the pub to a holding tank fitted with a macerator pump, which pumps the finely chopped sewage up to the top of the hill. From here it bubbles out of the soakaway, down the hill, across a cricket pitch and into the next door farmer's grazing land, where it crosses a public footpath, as well as crossing the pub car park to end up in a road drain. The system was created and planted in under a month and as the original owner of the pub wanted it to become a wildlife haven, it has had no maintenance at all for over 10 years. It has become overgrown and is now virtually impossible to walk into it, but it is still effectively purifying the sewage.

Ivycroft Plant Nursery, Herefordshire
This system, established in 1996, purifies the settled sewage from a plant nursery which is open to the public on a limited scale. It thus has a base load of two people who live there, plus the two or three people who work there seasonally, and customers, as well as groups of up to 15 people who visit for tea and a tour of the garden. This system is an integral part of a beautiful garden. In winter, after exceptionally heavy rainfall, there is, very occasionally, an overflow of purified water from the final polishing pond into the local brook.

Little Marcle Court, Herefordshire
The system, established in 1995, here purifies the settled sewage from an oast house and barn conversion of a 17th century farmhouse,

which are used as holiday lets with a maximum population of 20 - 25. The owners originally wanted the system to be as small as possible and as far away from the house as possible - they now wish they had located it closer to the house and asked for it to be made much bigger, so as to become a garden feature. The sale of coppiced willow wands from the system to a local basket/hurdle maker has more than paid for the cost of the system creation.

Westons Cider Mill, Herefordshire

This 5 acre site, established in 1994, was initially designed as a total absorption system with no outfall required. The original volume of wastewater from the cider mill was around 17,500m³/year with 80% entering the system during the 3 month cider making season. The wastewater has an average biological oxygen demand (BOD) of around 5,000 (sewage is around 350) although there can be 'slugs' of up to 20,000. The wastewater has a pH of about 3.5, but fortuitously, whilst carrying out trial pits to see what the local geology could offer us for our design, we discovered a large area of 1.5 metre deep limestone gravel just below ground level over around one third of the site. This was integrated into the design to give us the pH modification we required with no chemical dosing system needing to be installed, as the acidic wastewater, when channelled through he

limestone gravel, has its pH increased from 3.5 to 7 - 8, or around neutrality.

Due to the increase in cider production, since the creation of the system and the building of additional processing facilities on the site, such as a new kegging plant, the wastewater input has grown to around 120,000m³/year. So the system has had two new swales added and the ponds enlarged and deepened. It is no longer a total absorbtion system per se, but the purified water in the polishing ponds is now pumped up to a trickle irrigation system, which feeds around 120 acres of orchard, thus increasing the apple yield by about 2.5 tonnes per hectare.

The site has been planted with 50,000 trees, mainly coppice willow (50 varieties), as well as 35 species of wetland marginals. The site (see photo below) is a wildlife haven and currently 60 species of bird have been recorded there. ☙

This 5 acre wetland treatment system at Westons Cider Mill was established in 1994. It was initially designed as a total absorption system, with no outfall required. The original volume of wastewater from the cider mill was around 17,500m³/year with 80% entering the system during the 3 month cider making season.

© Green Building Press

Sustainable urban drainage

Rainwater that falls on urban areas needs to be controlled and drained to avoid inconvenience, damage, flooding and health risks. Imaginative use of this water could provide habitat and amenity and prevent some of the problems that are created by conventional drainage systems. **Judith Thornton** explains ...

Understanding the water cycle

To understand the best approach to dealing with the rainwater that falls on a site, compare what would happen before and after development (Figure 1).

Before development of the site, when rain hits the ground, some of the water evaporates (or is transpired by plants 'breathing'), and some of the rain infiltrates into the ground. This infiltration is important to maintain groundwater supplies. A proportion of water will also run off the ground surface and become streams or rivers. If we cover the ground surface with something that's largely impervious, like a house with a tarmac drive, the rate of infiltration is drastically reduced, and the run off is increased (Figure 2).

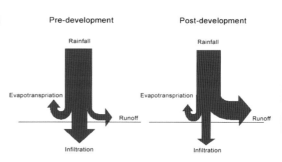

Figure 1. The fate of rainfall pre and post development.

Graphs of surface water run off over time are shown in Figure 3. Pre-development, run off is prolonged but is never very great. After development, however, the peak flow is much higher and occurs sooner than in the pre-development state. The end result of covering the UK in impervious surfaces is therefore an increase in the amount of surface water run off, and

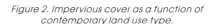

Figure 2. Impervious cover as a function of contemporary land use type.

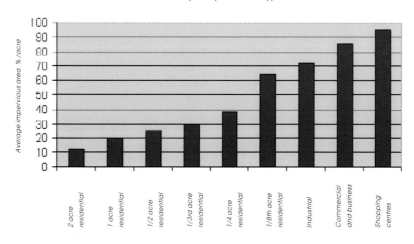

Flow patterns in developed and undeveloped areas

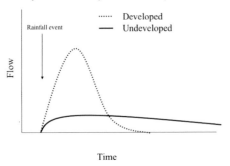

Figure 3. Surface water run off after rainfall events for a typical developed catchment.

the tendency of this flow to peak much more suddenly. This leads to flash flooding, and with a conventional approach to drainage requires pipes to be sized to cope with these big peaks in flow. But flow is only half the problem. Impervious surfaces also result in impaired water quality, since pollutants and sediments on the ground surface in urban areas, such as heavy metals, fuel and tyre rubber, will get washed straight into water courses, rather than infiltrating into the ground where they are naturally treated.

In much of the UK, this bad situation is made worse by connecting these stormwater drains into the foul sewer system, resulting in huge variations in the amount of sewage flowing to sewage treatment works, sewage being discharged untreated into rivers via combined sewer overflows and impaired sewage treatment owing to the effects of the pollutants on the microbiology of the sewage works.

Solutions for large scale developments

Enough of the problems, what about the solutions? In many instances, planning permission for new development will stipulate a maximum rate of surface water run off from the site that goes to storm drains after rainfall of given intensities, which in turn is based on a probability of that rainfall event occurring. In order to meet these requirements, the conventional solution is to install attenuation tanks with 'throttles' controlling the outflow, or tank

sewers. Both solutions are basically large underground voids, which store peak flows and discharge them more slowly into the mains drainage system. These have a lot to recommend them. They are a 'hard' engineering solution, with recognised design standards, and critically for small sites and commercial developments, the ground above the tanks is still useable. The provision of this type of temporary storage often makes little difference to the flood impact on the local river (since the events that cause river flooding are often low rainfall intensities over long durations), but does serve to prevent flooding of the drainage network itself.

Increasing emphasis on environmental water quality, flood prevention and amenity provision, as opposed to simply the hydraulic capacity of piped drainage systems is leading to increased uptake of sustainable urban drainage systems (SUDS). SUDS techniques are designed to mimic natural systems and allow treatment of pollutants to occur at the same time as preventing flooding. There are a number of types of SUDS that can be installed in large scale developments, but central to the approach is the idea that stormwater should be dealt with on site wherever possible. The first priority is preventing run off and pollution, wherever possible. This means minimising the use of impervious surfaces and preventing build up of pollutants on surfaces by regular housekeeping and spill prevention. The next step is to optimise infiltration where ground conditions are suitable. Permeable pavements may be an option; these are porous paved areas with a sub base that acts as a storage reservoir for gradual infiltration. Any flow remaining after the above measures is then dealt with by a large scale solution, such as a detention basin or retention pond. These are large ponds that fill during storm flows and hence buffer flow rates. They can also be designed to promote settlement of the particles in stormwater, for example by using forebay areas or wetlands at their entrance. Since the heavy metals in stormwater are usually bound to solid particles like grit, this sedimentation provides significant water treatment.

© Green Building Press

Small is beautiful

When looked at on the scale of large housing developments, many storm drainage installations (including some SUDS), look distinctly over engineered; unsurprising given the massive buffering capacity that may be required of them. But where does this leave the person looking for a pragmatic but ecological drainage system for their single eco build house? The first point is to ensure that you are maximising your use of surfaces that allow infiltration, so consider your ground coverings carefully. Grass is the obvious choice, but if you need a more hardwearing surface for part of your property, a range of materials are available, such as block paving with gaps in between, porous blocks and reinforced grass. Unfortunately, most of these products are based on concretes or virgin aggregates. Even in areas where you are using an impermeable surface, paved areas such as paths and driveways should be profiled to shed water onto adjacent permeable areas such as lawns and flower beds.

You may be considering a green roof, and these are promoted from a wide range of angles such as biodiversity, aesthetics, reduction of airborne pollution as well as reduction of stormwater run off. However the limited storage capacity of a green roof means they are unlikely to help flood control during prolonged rainfall, so you will want to make sure that you have other justifications for wanting one. It's also worth pointing out that green roofs are generally incompatible with rainwater harvesting systems where the water is to be used in the house (the water will contain a lot of solids and may well be discoloured).

We should all store as much rainwater as we can for garden use, rather than the token water butts normally installed. However this is more for reasons of water efficiency than SUDS. Standard water butts are of little value as part of a SUDS solution since they are generally small (less than 0.5m³) and you won't be using the water in the garden during rainy periods, which is precisely when the flow buffering would be useful. In the future, widespread use of rainwater butts with throttled overflows might provide worthwhile stormwater attenuation, but at present, use of water butts in a development does not allow for any reduction in other drainage measures required.

Test your soil porosity (details in Part H of the Building Regulations), and see how much water you will be able to infiltrate into the ground. If your calculations suggest that infiltration can only ever be a partial solution, you can look at SUDS as part of your overall landscaping scheme for your property. You might be able to incorporate a wetland and a pond into your garden, with only the overflow from your pond being discharged into a local watercourse, or failing that, local storm drains. Anything that slows the flow of water off your property, and provides some filtration and treatment will be of benefit.

Sewers for adoption?

Not a tug-on-the-heart-strings advertisement for abused drainage systems, but a critical issue in implementing innovative SUDS solutions. In the UK, developers pass on the long term responsibility for various aspects of their site to other organisations. These are known as 'adoption agreements'. In the case of piped drainage systems, this agreement is generally with the local water company, who take future responsibility for the drainage system from the point it leaves your property, provided that the developer builds it to recognised standards. These standards are set out in the delightfully named book 'Sewers for Adoption'. This system works pretty well for conventional piped drainage systems, but less well for SUDS, which water companies are reluctant to take on. So who else may adopt the system? In larger scale developments, planning permission is often dependent on provision of public outdoor space, and this space is 'adopted' by the local authority (LA). In some instances, LA's have adopted SUDS as part of this open space since the ponds, wetlands and swales created are of habitat and amenity value. The alternative is for the SUDS to be adopted by a housing association, formed by the local residents who then organise any maintenance necessary; an option worth considering on eco-housing developments.

The lack of definitive design guidance for SUDS and the unknown long term costs of maintenance mean that, to date, adoption and long term responsibility for SUDS are the main limiting factor in their more widespread use on a large scale. As a result of these problems the National SUDS Working Group has come up with an Interim Code of Practice and a set of model agreements, which will go some way to making larger scale SUDS a realistic proposition for developers.

Conclusion

Inevitably, some green builders will be disappointed by the lack of detailed guidance available on SUDS installation at the household level. However, when looked at from the point of view of your entire ecological footprint, your water use, sewage disposal and drainage systems are a very small part of your overall environmental impact (less than 5% in most cases). Consequently, if you have a limited amount of eco-enthusiasm, or a limited budget to dedicate to environmental aspects of your house design, you should not be concentrating on green drainage solutions. In most instances you would be better off focussing your eco-enthusiasm on energy or heating issues. With that proviso aside, you may be able to incorporate the basic principles of SUDS design into small scale building projects with little cost; store as much rainwater as you can use for garden watering, minimise your use of impermeable surfaces and infiltrate stormwater to ground via a soakaway wherever possible. If your property is large enough, consider using ponds to buffer any residual flow. ☁

Further reading

SUDS. Interim Code of Practice, model maintenance agreements, publications and further information **www.ciria.org.uk**

Sustainable drainage systems – hydraulic, structural and water quality advice. CIRIA publication C609.

Infiltration Drainage – Manual of Good Practice. CIRIA publication R156.

Drainage of Development Sites – A Guide. CIRIA publication X108.

Post-project monitoring of BMPs/SUDS to determine performance and whole life costs; phase 2. WERF, AWWA, UKWIR. – a detailed report into the long term effectiveness of SUDS and their costs.

A database of SUDS installations in the UK, with comments on performance, maintenance and monitoring. **www.suds-sites.net**

Case studies

Sustainable urban drainage (SUDS) for schools

The following two case studies were both developed by Robert Bray Associates, Sustainable Drainage Consultants, based in Stroud, and Property Services at Worcestershire County Council, who were the architects for the new schools in both cases. Both school sites required rainwater runoff attenuation and management; and the decision was taken to adopt an approach that combined these needs with an approach to SUDS, which enhanced the sites providing habitats, opportunities for study and visual interest. **Robert Lewin-Jones**, principal architect for the schemes reports.

Matchborough First School - Redditch

The site for this new school was a relatively low-lying flat greenfield site close to the Ipsley Brook. However, initial investigations through the Environment Agency confirmed that the floodplain does not extend a significant distance from the brook and that a flood risk assessment was unnecessary. There is a distinct low area associated with the brook and this was identified as the land that floods during heavy rainfall.

The site was drained in the past by a hedge and ditch to the west and another to the east. Nonetheless, the site was generally very flat which caused water to lie on all surfaces for a time following rain.

The SUDS scheme for the site addresses the immediate issues of site drainage as well as modifying ground form to encourage surface draining of hard and soft play surfaces.

Assuming a 1 in 100 year return period and a requirement to achieve a 'greenfield runoff

© Green Building Press

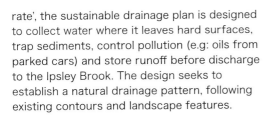

rate', the sustainable drainage plan is designed to collect water where it leaves hard surfaces, trap sediments, control pollution (e.g: oils from parked cars) and store runoff before discharge to the Ipsley Brook. The design seeks to establish a natural drainage pattern, following existing contours and landscape features.

The existing hedgerow ditch was re-profiled as a narrow swale to intercept overland flows from adjacent higher land and create a level access path along the eastern boundary. The swale protects the east elevation of the school from sheet runoff during heavy rainfall, when channel drains at entrances may surcharge, and to prevent constant saturation of the playing field.

An existing land drain was routed under the new playground into a swale collecting surface runoff from the hard play surface. Downpipes and channel drains on the eastern part of the school building also feed into the manhole. Runoff from the remainder of the roof collects in a pipe which discharges directly to the swale. The playground is profiled to collect runoff and deliver it as sheet flow into the collector swale. Water collected in the swale flows quickly to a detention area wetland along the western boundary to avoid standing water next to the playground.

As the school car park may generate modest hydrocarbon (petrol) pollution, runoff is there-fore collected and stored in a small detention basin where silt is trapped and pollution broken down naturally in wetland vegetation. Water flows slowly through a controlled outlet, under the access road, into the next collector basin and then to the boundary storage swale. Water from the school's main drive is treated in a similar way, flowing into a collector basin, and any light pollution which passes through the first basin is trapped in the storage swale.

Rainwater from the western side of the building is collected for use in toilet flushing. Surplus roof water overflows into the swale, and run-off from adjacent hard surfaces flows across the grass lawn to be stored in the swale.

The swale meets storage requirements for the main drive, roof and adjacent paving and discharges through a controlled outlet under the lower access footpath to the detention area wetland.

When rainfall is heavy or prolonged, then water is stored in a shallow detention area wetland along the western boundary to help prevent flooding downstream. The basin normally drains down in 48 hours and leaves a marsh habitat which is used for education purposes. Changes in level create temporary pools and an interesting mosaic of wetland vegetation.

Water is released from each storage basin in a controlled way to prevent flooding down-stream, reduce damage to the stream bed and generally mimic the natural pattern of drainage for the site. The drainage for the site is largely accommodated by shallow ground modelling, usually no deeper than 450mm, with water levels 300mm or less. Water levels will normally be no more than 150mm deep.

Maintenance of the SUDS drainage is under-taken as part of normal grass mowing together with checking inlets and outlets. These can easily be cleared by site staff, although overland flood routes will be present in case of any blockage. Capital and maintenance costs on the site are less than conventional drainage without a requirement to pay charges to the Water Company for storm sewer management.

Redhill Primary School - Worcester

This school is situated on a site of approaching 2 hectares, with the new school and surround-ing hard areas comprising over 5000m². The previous school, which was demolished to make way for the replacement, drained directly to the combined sewer with no on-site attenuation.

Discussions with the Severn Trent Water Company confirmed the requirement to discharge stormwater separately to the storm sewer at a controlled rate of 10 litres per second for the whole site. It was acknowledged that due to historical development there was no access to a watercourse nor an overland flood route from the site. Therefore flows in excess of the 30 year flood will discharge to the sewer directly as they have done in the past. The SUDS design endeavours to maximise storage of runoff wherever possible.

The site falls from higher ground to the east, where the sports pitch is, down to the new school, where runoff is directed around both sides of the building. The southern route flows from the play area, along a sett channel, into a short collector swale before entering a pipe taking water below the access road into the woodland basin. The sett channel also collects water from an outdoor terrace related to the new classrooms. The water is cleaned and stored in the basin before it flows slowly to the sewer or overflows, in extreme events, directly to the site outfall.

The northern route flows from the lower play area to the car park, where water with possible pollution from cars is cleaned, before collection, into below-ground storage using geo-cellular boxes where water is stored before it again flows to the outfall. An overflow grating allows extreme events to flow directly to the outfall. The SUDS scheme can therefore provide the storage to meet the 1 in 30 year attenuation required by Severn Trent, a minimum of one treatment stage for all runoff required by SUDS guidance and various amenity opportunities for the school.

The woodland basin forms the main landscape feature on the site. Close to the caretaker's house, and unsuitable for building on or for sports, with help from Bishop's Wood Environmental Centre, this area was identified early on in the design process for its potential as a urban wildlife and outdoor teaching area. A series of shallow turf-lined swales now curve around the existing mature lime trees that once formed part of an avenue. This area has been dubbed 'the swale maze' as it criss-crossed by sleeper bridges and will form the major habitat area on the site, planted with wetland species and including a permanent pond, giving many study opportunities. The woodland area will be bounded by an earth berm (allowing the water collection facility to temporarily rise to a higher level in extreme rain), as well as newly planted hedges and fences. The school has been carefully involved in developing the ideas for this spot and anticipate using it for activities related to Forest Schools, pond dipping, investigating mini-beasts and the identification of wild flower species. Bat and bird boxes will also be erected. Smooth newts, which had to be translocated from the old school pond, to a new pond adjacent to the school field, have already returned to the woodland basin area.

The use of a sustainable drainage system is seen as an environmentally-friendly complement to the new primary school itself, which is designed with ground source heat pump heating, timber framing, rainwater harvesting, and an emphasis on the use of recycled products in construction. ✎

Bio Bubble
COMBINED WASTEWATER & SLUDGE TREATMENT

ENVIRONMENTALLY FRIENDLY

Simple, hassle free, fully biological solution to off-mains drainage. Odourless, with minimum running costs utilizing our patented sleep mode. Highest quality discharge to Pond or Bog Garden if necessary.
Discharge can be re-used, typically ideal for irrigation with no tanker requirements.

Emsworth Yacht Harbour, Thorney Road, Emsworth, Hampshire PO10 8BW

Telephone: 01243 370100 Fax: 01243 370090
www.bio-bubble.com E: sales@bio-bubble.com

© Green Building Press

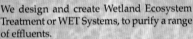

Above: swales at one of the schools, which are able to cope well with flash floods and add natural interest to the learning environments.

Biologic Design

Wetland Ecosystem Treatment
Integrated wastewater purification,
resource production and habitat creation

We design and create Wetland Ecosystem Treatment or WET Systems, to purify a range of effluents.
Existing systems include
- domestic sewage - from 1 person up to 380 people, larger scale also possible
- piggery and dairy farm
- organic creamery producing cheese
- dairy producing sheep's milk ice cream
- cider mill
- micro-brewery

Biologic Design specialises in the creation of WET Systems for
- ecologically minded people and organisations
- sustainable housing developments
- low input/organic farmers and food producers
- environmental, educational and Permaculture projects

WET Systems
- are sustainable soil-based wastewater purification systems, with minimal non-renewable energy use (no gravel is used)
- create beautiful, multi-species wildlife habitat which gives greatly enhanced biodiversity
- convert the wastewater into a biomass resource - the coppiced willow can be used for traditional and contemporary crafts, or as kindling and fuel for stoves

Biologic Design
Archenhills, Stanford Bishop,
Bringsty, Herefordshire WR6 5TZ
Telephone: 01 886 884 721
Web : biologicdesign.co.uk

See also: 'Sustainable garden design' earlier in this chapter

Encouraging wildlife

Residential areas, including gardens of all sizes, can be excellent and popular habitats for native flora and fauna, even acting as wildlife corridors to other areas. As the UK's natural wild habitats become degraded from the pressures of all kinds of development and intensive agricultural practices, our gardens become increasingly important for the survival of many of our species. **Sally Hall** encourages us to make our outdoor spaces wildlife friendly.

Witness the silence and lack of life when walking over land that is intensively farmed and compare this to a vibrant, living garden managed for nature, which is full of bird song and activity from a diverse range of creatures.

In our increasingly 'busy' society people are becoming more and more detached from the natural environment. Children spend much of their time indoors. Obesity and health problems are rife across all age ranges. However, encouraging an interest in our natural environment can be totally absorbing, stimulating all our senses and encouraging an interest in a healthy, active, outdoor life. The popularity of TV programmes, such as the BBC's Springwatch and Autumn watch series, prove that many of us already have an interest in wildlife. We now need to do more to safeguard our precious flora and fauna. Many species are declining and even species that used to be so common, such as the house sparrow and song thrush, are now absent from many areas. Our native species are at risk from pollution, chemicals in the environment, habitat destruction and introduced predators, such as cats.

Attracting wildlife

A garden that consists mainly of tarmac, concrete, showy borders and close-cropped lawns will support little wildlife. So how do you attract more insect and animal life? All species need the same things we do – water, food and shelter. The size of a garden and its location

will dictate the diversity and number of species you will be able to attract. If you are creating a new garden you can build the concept of biodiversity into the design right from the start. For example, if you are considering a hedge, plant some prickly species to keep predators away from nests and include species that produce berries that birds can eat. Choose native plants and shrubs that encourage beneficial insects, such as bees, butterflies, moths etc, and a good selection of species, so you will have flowers for most of the year. Consider too planting fruit trees, which will provide a crop for you and wildlife. There are many different species and sizes available to suit most gardens.

Leave as much as possible of your garden to go wild. A wild garden needs less management

A lawn left to grow longer will enable species, such as clover, to flower and attract bees, hoverflies and butterflies. The dry stone walling will attract invertebrates. The valerian in the foreground and marjoram in the background will also attract beneficial insects. The mullein is the food source for the striking mullein moth caterpillars..

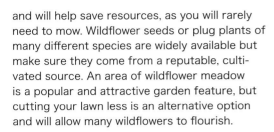

and will help save resources, as you will rarely need to mow. Wildflower seeds or plug plants of many different species are widely available but make sure they come from a reputable, cultivated source. An area of wildflower meadow is a popular and attractive garden feature, but cutting your lawn less is an alternative option and will allow many wildflowers to flourish.

Even in areas left wild you may want to control dominant species if they start to stifle other plants but remember clumps of nettles are the larval foodplant for butterfly species, such as the small tortoiseshell, red admiral, peacock and comma. A wild flower only becomes a weed when it is in a place where it is not wanted.

If you do have to clear areas, for example for growing food crops, refrain from using weed killers which can be hazardous to wildlife. Instead use discarded black plastic or cardboard, anchored down with heavy objects. This method clears most growth in a few months, although for areas of persistent perennial plants, it can take a year.

Any wetland area, from a tiny pond to a large lake, attracts a great diversity of life. Always make sure the sides are gently sloping to allow access for frogs, hedgehogs, birds etc. Even small areas of water will quickly attract species of dragonfly, damselflies, hawkers and their lava, all completely harmless and wonderful to watch, particularly if you are fortunate enough to witness the metamorphosis of lava to adult.

Most of us keep our gardens too tidy; removing plants that have died back, sweeping up leaves and clearing away grass clippings, bits of bark, logs etc. However, an overly tidy garden has very few hiding places for beneficial insects and mammals so leave piles of leaves, prunings and logs around as habitat piles. They will be quickly colonised by a diverse range of creatures and fungi. A pile of logs or large stones left in a corner makes an ideal habitat for many species. Lizards, who like the warm sun on their bodies at certain times of the year, will be attracted to slates, logs or even old tyres left

in sunny areas. Species like hedgehogs need somewhere to hibernate. Such mammals may use bonfire piles, so these must be checked thoroughly or preferably restacked, just before lighting. Similarly, hedgehogs and slow worms may inhabitant your compost heap so always take care when using spades and forks.

The ideal place to conserve and encourage species is in our garden. However, we may not be so happy to encourage wildlife into our buildings, so you should ensure that all buildings you wish to keep free of uninvited inhabitants are insect proofed, using good detailing and mesh over vents. Don't forget that for some species, for example swallows, owls and bats, buildings are important roosting and breeding areas. You can therefore leave appropriate openings in sheds and outbuildings, but ensure these are small enough to exclude cats. Small rodents will move into buildings and greenhouses during the cold months if they can. They will usually depart in the spring. If they cause a problem you can live trap them and release them elsewhere – do bear in mind that rodents are an important food source for species such as owls and other birds of prey.

Trees

If you have the space, consider planting trees and shrubs. We all know that trees grow, increasing in height and spread over a number of years and many will last for hundreds of years, so bear these points in mind before selecting where to plant. Many people take trees for granted, yet they are vital habitats with many benefits:

- trees absorb carbon dioxide
- timber is used for many purposes, including building, furniture, firewood and charcoal
- trees are an excellent food source (leaves, sap, bark, fruit and nuts)
- trees improve the landscape, they screen and improve the appearance of buildings
- trees provide shelter and wildlife habitats
- trees help stabilise easily eroded soils and spoil tips
- trees form hedgerows.

Trees near buildings

Not all trees growing close to buildings will affect the structure. Many other factors can be responsible for structural damage and so if you suspect any problems with existing trees, or you wish to plant close to a building, detailed site assessments by qualified professionals should be undertaken. Structural damage is generally limited to shrinkable clay soils. Trees, particularly species such as ash, take moisture out of these soils, thereby exaggerating soil shrinkage. This results in shifting foundations, which cause structural cracking. Conversely removing large trees from clay soils can cause the ground to swell, again leading to structural displacement.

Remember that roots, particularly species such as willow, may block drains, causing cracking and leaking problems. Branches can cause damage to roofs and guttering, suckers can disturb paving and stems can rub against walls. Many factors can affect root spread and roots often extend for a radius wider than the tree height. If unsure always seek professional advice before planting. A tree is the property and responsibility of the landowner, who may be liable for any damage caused. Always check with the local planning authority whether a tree preservation order is in place before working on a tree.

Birds

It is interesting to note that the government uses wild bird statistics as one of its 'quality of life indicators'. Birds are very important. They devour huge numbers of pest species, are visually appealing, wonderful to listen to and many different species can be attracted to gardens of all sizes and locations. They need all the help they can get as many species, even those common up until recent years, are now in decline.

Birds appreciate a wide variety of food, so providing feeding areas will definitely encourage them. Birds can come to rely on a source of food being present in a particular place, particularly in winter so ensure you can keep

feeders topped up. A birdbath is essential, particularly in hot dry weather but again, you must keep it filled and it should be positioned away from cats.

To discourage rats ensure you do not overfeed. All food on the ground should be consumed before nightfall or fit trays to feeders to limit the amount of food falling on the floor. If on the rare occasions we see rats, we never resort to poisoning, but discourage them by locating and blocking up their runs. We also keep all food out of their reach and the rats disappear quickly, probably falling prey

What about cats?

Cats are the number one predator of our wildlife, killing and injuring millions of species each year. There are 7.5 million cats now kept as pets in the UK with a further 1 million feral cats and the population is growing. In a recent RSPCA campaign urging people to neuter their cats, it was alleged that, even with a 10% mortality rate, a single cat, having two litters of kittens, each containing two females, could be responsible for 50 million cats in decade or so! Neutering is therefore vital, as well as dealing with feral populations.

For their size, domestic cats are very effective predators. They do not respect boundaries and have extensive territories, being difficult to keep out of any area. The domestic cat can hunt and eat about one thousand species. Many pet cats successfully hunt and kill rabbits, rodents, birds, lizards, frogs, fish, and large insects by instinct, but many do not eat their prey. It is estimated that domestic cats in Britain kill around 250 million items of prey each year. If you have a cat, a correctly fitted collar and bell can help reduce predation. So can piles of bramble or other prickly plants around a bird feeding area or a scattering of chilli powder at building entrances. If you don't have a cat, think twice before you get one!

© Green Building Press

Birds will benefit from feeding help all the year round. Feeding can be from bird tables or feeders, home-made or purchased. A diverse range of species use this station.

Sadly barn owls have declined significantly, due to the conversion of many old farm barns over the past few decades; decreasing habitat and road road kills. If you have this species in your area you can take steps to encourage them by providing the appropriare habitat and buildings. Contact the Hawk and Owl Trust for more information.

to the larger mammal species frequenting our garden.

Nest boxes will encourage birds to breed in your garden and can be installed where natural potential breeding sites, such as holes in trees, dense hedges etc are scarce. Nest boxes are available for a diverse range of bird species and can also be made easily from timber off cuts. Boxes must be designed correctly and hole size is important for many species. Advice on making boxes for different species and siting instructions are available from organisations such as the RSPB, BTO or your local wildlife trust, (see end of article for contact details). Ensure you site nest boxes well away from cats. Open fronted ones need to be camouflaged and well hidden by vegetation. We have had great success with the Woodcrete boxes, which are made from sawdust and concrete and come with a 25-year guarantee. However, the spotted woodpecker can predate even these boxes, both eggs and young. The problem with nest boxes is that they tend to be visible and it does not take long for a predator species to recog- nise them as a potential food source during the nesting season.

Thousands of birds are killed or injured each year from flying into glass, particularly young birds in their first year or ones fleeing predators. Birds are attracted to the bright reflections of sky and vegetation seen in the glass. Site feeding areas and nest boxes well away from glazed areas. If you have a problem you can brush a soda crystal solution on to the glass surface (internally will last longer) to make it opaque during the times of highest risk (summer and autumn).

Do bear in mind that if you have a healthy population of birds, they will attract natural predators, such as the sparrow hawk. While some may be distressed to see birds killed by hawks, remember that it is a native species, high in the food chain, that must eat to survive. The species is only just starting to recover from its previous decline due to widespread pesticide use. We have a resident pair but they take fewer birds than the feral and neighbouring cats.

Bats

There are seventeen species of bat in the UK but many are now rare. Development of all kinds destroys roosting sites and feeding grounds. Gardens are therefore becoming vital for these useful species. They cause no harm to people or buildings. You are most likely to see the pipistrelle (our smallest species) in your garden at dawn or dusk and it will eat, on average, 3,000 midges per night during the summer! Bats will use bat boxes and may even breed in them. Many shelter and breed in buildings, behind hanging tiles and boarding and in roof spaces.

Bats and buildings

In the UK, law protects bats and their roosts. A roost is defined as 'any place that a wild bat uses for shelter or protection', and the roost is protected, whether bats are present in it or not. If the roost is in a dwelling house and the works require planning permission then you should inform the local planning authority about the bats during the period of public consultation. The local Statutory Nature Conservation Organisation (SNCO) office will advise on the best way to carry out the work, causing minimal disturbance to the bats. If planning permission is not required (e.g. a re-roofing), then you need to contact the Bat Conservation Trust for advice. Always avoid using chemical treatments in a roof that is used by bats.

If the roost is in a structure that is not a dwelling, such as a church or a barn or a tree, then the developers will need to obtain a Habitats Regulations license in order to carry out any work. Someone with experience of bats must apply for the licence. In this situation you should write to the planning office to alert them to the presence of a bat roost, and to advise them that a Habitats Regulations licence is needed before any work goes ahead. They should then ensure the developer proceeds with the proposal only if a licence is obtained.

Bees

Bees are essential pollinators of a wide variety of plant and tree species. The decline in bumblebee populations has been receiving increasing news coverage over the last few years. Three of the UK's twenty bee species are already extinct. Agriculture depends on bees for pollination of crops. Certain species of

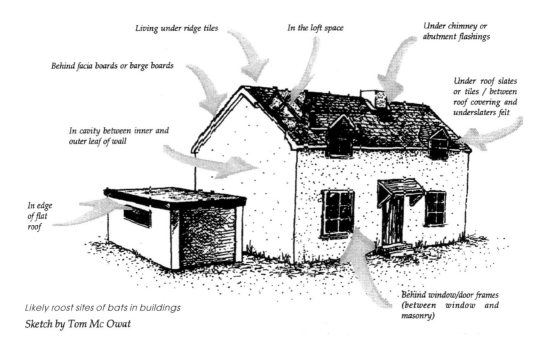

Living under ridge tiles

In the loft space

Under chimney or abutment flashings

Behind facia boards or barge boards

Under roof slates or tiles / between roof covering and underslaters felt

In cavity between inner and outer leaf of wall

In edge of flat roof

Behind window/door frames (between window and masonry)

Likely roost sites of bats in buildings

Sketch by Tom Mc Owat

© Green Building Press

As well as supplying us with honey, the honey bees pollinate a wide range of plants and trees, including fruit species. This hive is tucked away in the corner of a fruit orchard.

Natural pest control

The practical benefit of a bio-diverse garden is that it will attract more garden predators, such as birds, hover flies and ladybirds. The better the eco-system you create, the fewer pests you will have to worry about. Ponds are excellent for encouraging beneficial predators such as frogs, toads, newts etc, but remember the sloping sides so creatures can get out easily. If your garden has a healthy population of insects it will attract predators, such as birds, bats and hedgehogs. A hedgehog can eat its own bodyweight in insects in one night, naturally helping keep insects down to manageable levels. Hedgehogs will also help by eating slugs and snails. If you want to attract hedgehogs, create access under a gate or via a hole in a fence and do not use slug pellets.

Moles eat many pest species but many people are not happy with the molehills they produce. If you have a wilder garden you should hardly notice the earth mounds or you can easily clear these away - the soil makes an excellent, free potting compost.

Sadly many people still use slug pellets. These certainly kill slugs but the poisoned carcasses are eaten by creatures higher up the food chain, such as birds and hedgehogs, with disastrous results. You should not need to control slugs where garden plants and wildflowers are established. You may need to control them if you have young seedlings. Nematodes are the latest environmental control. This is a natural slug parasite which is watered into the soil. They are slug-specific, so can't harm other animals in the food web. Avoid using them close to ponds, however, as they will also affect water snails. The most environmentally benign method though is handpicking slugs from areas of young plants at dusk or dawn.

In general, choose plant varieties that have natural resistance to pests and diseases. A healthy soil will help build strong plants to help resist attack and companion planting can help. This is where research and experience has shown that certain species grow well together. You should not need to use any chemicals in

bees and the plants they pollinate, are declining together in numbers. This is because insects can develop specialised tongues for reaching the nectar in particular plants and therefore effectively specialise in pollinating only these plants. The Bumblebee Conservation Trust aims to help prevent bee numbers from falling further.

Unfortunately even the honeybee is declining and now almost all UK apiaries are infected with varroa, a parasitic mite which weakens the bees. Many hives are collapsing, unless managed carefully. However, if you have a large garden with plenty of space around, you could consider getting some bee hives and start beekeeping. If you decide to keep bees, locate hives behind fences or hedges to ensure the bees are encouraged to fly high and away from people. You should also consult your local bee keeping organsation for more advice.

your garden if you get the natural balance right. You may find that on occasions you get an explosion of pest species but it shouldn't take long for predators to bring them under control.

Surveying the natural environment

With the current concerns about climate change, on-going surveys of our natural species are becoming increasingly important for monitoring purposes. For example, the index of wild bird populations is one of the government's key indicators for sustainable development in the UK. Bird populations are considered as a good indicator of the broad state of wildlife and countryside because they occupy a wide range of habitats, they tend to be near or at the top of the food chain, and considerable long-term data on bird populations is available. Birds are placed on the red (globally threatened), amber (moderate declines) or green lists (stable). A total of 247 species have been assessed. Forty are red-listed and 121 are amber listed.

You can help with many surveys by reporting what you see in your garden and the surrounding area. See the contacts below for some of the on-going ones, (free unless stated otherwise). 🐞

With grateful thanks to Louise Zass-Bangham for providing some of the information for this article and Keith Hall jnr for the photos.

Survey opportunities

British Trust for Ornithology (BTO), different surveys, including Garden BirdWatch (£12 per annum): 01842 750050 www.bto.org

Royal Society for the Protection of Birds (RSPB), Big Garden Birdwatch: 01767 680551 www.rspb.org.uk

UK Phenology Network, Spring Watch and Autumn Watch: 0800 77 1234 www.naturescalendar.org.uk

PlantLife's annual Common Plants Survey: 01722 342730 www.plantlife.org.uk

Further information

For advice on trees and buildings, and contacts for professionals who can help in the case of problems with trees and buildings: www.rhs.org.uk/advice/ profiles0101/trees_buildings.asp

Information on planting, care, species: www.treecouncil.org.uk/info/packng2.html

Courses for builders re building near trees: www.nhbcbuilder.co.uk/Consultancyservices/Training/ BuildingnearTrees

Further reading

'Bringing a Garden to Life' by J Steel is an inspirational book with glorious photos and tips based on making the wildlife garden at the Wiggly Wigglers' farm.

'Wildlife Gardening for Everyone' by M Tait

'How to Make a Wildlife Garden' by C Baines

'Bob Flowerdew's Complete Book of Companion Gardening'

The above books are availabe from the Green Shop: 01452 770629 www.greenshop.co.uk

Useful contacts

Bird feed, boxes, wildflower seeds etc with an emphasis on local and sustainable materials:Wiggly Wigglers: 01981 500391 www.wigglywigglers.co.uk

The place to visit for information, news and discussion on Britain's wild predators: www.toothandclaw.org.uk

Useful organisations

Bat Conservation Trust: 0845 1300 228 www.bats.org.uk

The Bumblebee Conservation Trust: www.bumblebeeconservationtrust.co.uk

Garden Organic (HDRA), national charity for organic growing: 024 7630 3517 www.gardenorganic.org.uk

Hawk & Owl Trust: 0870 990 3889 www.hawkandowl.org

Royal Society for the Protection of Birds (RSPB): 01767 680551 www.rspb.org.uk

Royal Society for the Prevention of Cruelty to Animals (RSPCA): 0870 33 35 999 www.rspca.org.uk

Statutory Nature Conservation Organisation (SNCO) has links via www.bats.org.uk/helpline/helpline_help- withbat_SNCO.asp

The Mammal Society: 020 7350 2200 www.abdn.ac.uk/mammal/

The Wildlife Trusts: 0870 036 7711 www.wildlifetrusts.org

The British Dragonfly Society: www.dragonflysoc.org.uk

Butterfly Conservation: 0870 7744309 www.butterfly- conservation.org/index.php

British Hedgehog Preservation Society:www.british- hedgehogs.org.uk

Join Garden Organic – the UK's leading organic charity

FREE 3 months trial when you join by Direct Debit

We are the UK's leading organic charity. Garden Organic offers you a wealth of knowledge based on nearly 50 years promoting organic gardening, farming and food. Join and you'll grow in knowledge through our magazines and members' web pages, save money through members' discounts, enjoy free or cut-price admission to more than 20 UK visitor gardens, and you'll help our work in schools, in developing countries, and special research projects.

Choose your annual membership with a tick: Standard £26 ☐; Family £30 ☐ (couple and any children under 16)

Concessionary memberships (for pensioners, students, unwaged, disabled) Single £16 ☐ ;Couple £20 ☐

Name 1 .... Name 2 (for Family) ....

Address ....

Garden Organic is the operating name of the Henry Doubleday Research Association. Reg. Charity No 298104

Gift Aid Declaration: If you are a UK taxpayer, we could claim an extra 28% of the value of your subscription from the taxman, at no extra cost to you. "I would like Garden Organic to reclaim tax I have already paid on this and any future membership subscriptions or donations until I notify you otherwise. I have paid an amount of UK income tax or capital gains tax equal to any tax reclaimed." Please tick ☐

I enclose a cheque payable to HDRA, for £ ....

or: Credit Card VISA / MASTERCARD / SWITCH: ⬚⬚⬚⬚ ⬚⬚⬚⬚ ⬚⬚⬚⬚ ⬚⬚⬚⬚

Expiry Date: ....Issue No: ....Security No: ⬚⬚⬚ (last 3 digits on back of card)

DIRECT Debit

Originators identification Nº: 8 7 1 2 9 7

Membership No. (For official use only)

or: Pay by Direct Debit
I wish to join now free as a trial member. My membership will be collected in 3 months by Direct Debit.

Instructions to your Bank or Building Society: Please pay Direct Debits from the account detailed on this instruction subject to the safeguards assured by the Direct Debit Guarantee. Name and full postal address of your Bank or Building Society Branch -

To the Manager:
Bank: ....
Address: ....
....
.....................Postcode: ....

Branch Sort Code: ⬚⬚ ⬚⬚ ⬚⬚
Account Number: ⬚⬚⬚⬚⬚⬚⬚⬚
Name(s) of account holder(s):
Date: ⬚⬚ ⬚⬚ ⬚⬚
Signature:

Please send this completed form to:
Garden Organic Ryton,
Coventry CV8 3LG
Tel: (024) 7630 3517 Fax: (024) 7663 9229
Email: enquiry@gardenorganic.org.uk

How green is your garden?

Louise Zass-Bangham

Beautiful Practical Sustainable Gardens

Your garden is part of your home's ecosystem, so make it work for you. Create shelter for the house and reduce heat loss in winter. Use the garden to cool the house in summer. Conserve water with plants that suit your climate. Choose gorgeous, sustainable materials.

You don't need to sacrifice style to grow wildflowers or organic food – we offer creative solutions. From essential storage to fun and relaxation, our garden design service is personalised to your needs. Whether creating a new garden, rejuvenating a jungle or preparing to sell, we provide down-to-earth advice. The sooner you plan your dream garden, the easier it is to achieve.

To get the most from your space, contact Louise - **020 8867 2667** or **louise@zass-bangham.com**
Take the "How green is your garden?" quiz at www.zass-bangham.com

Member AECB & Sponge

Louise Zass-Bangham 17 Crane Road Twickenham TW2 6RX
www.zass-bangham.com
louise@zass-bangham.com   020 8867 2667

Natural swimming pools

Natural swimming pools are wonderful for people and nature too, providing beauty the whole year round. **Michael Littlewood** puts forward the case for natural swimming pools.

Many people can still remember the joy of bathing and swimming in natural waters in the countryside, whether it was a lake, river or a pond, in sunshine or moonlight, whatever the weather, with or without clothes, in groups or as a solitary soul, planned or spontaneous. Alas this has all changed and most children today are unlikely to experience such natural bathing due to numerous reasons, such as health and safety, trespass and land ownership, litigation and polluted waters.

However, not all is lost as there are now natural systems for private and public swimming that can be built for the enjoyment of everyone. Natural swimming pools are based on ponds and pools that were once found so abundantly in the landscape.

The comparison to a landscape pool is deliberate because that is what a natural swimming pool is – a large pond with special provision for people to enjoy the water as well as the various creatures that are attracted to it. Nature offers the best examples.

Most pools, ponds and lakes are cleaned and purified by the combination of plants and micro-organisms, including beneficial bacteria. These micro-organisms break down organic wastes into substances which plants can use directly as nutrients.

The pleasure of using natural water once again for bathing and swimming is now available to many people, whether it is in the privacy of their own home or publicly at a hotel, a park,

Children playing in their own natural swimmimg pool

© Green Building Press

or any recreational centre in the mountains or at the seaside! They are sheer bliss in which to swim and a joy to see.

The original concept was developed in Austria by a number of people, who were very conscious of the health benefits of bathing in natural waters found at spas and hydro places. It was not until 1985 that the idea was commercially developed by an Austrian based company, called Biotop, by the founder Peter Petrich who conceived the idea of a self cleaning biosystem for swimming ponds.

These have been favoured by many European homeowners and have also become very popular in hotels and resorts. Biotop was followed by Bionova of Germany, who planned and executed the first public pool in 1998, with considerable success. Biotop and Bionova were followed by Bioteich of Switzerland and during this period there were several other companies who undertook the building of natural swimming pools.

More than 1000 pools have now been built in Austria, Germany and Switzerland by many contractors. Each one has something unique to offer with their individual systems but all are variations on the same theme.

As part of my philosophy of ecological design I had, for some time, been looking for an alternative to chemical swimming pools. A visit to a Biotop in Vienna early in 2000, where I studied their system, resulted in bringing the concept back to this country. The first natural swimming pool was built in September 2001 for a client in Gloucestershire.

How they work

Natural swimming pools, are a chemical free combination of swimming area and aquatic plant garden. The swimming area merges with the planted area, creating an environment that is intertwined and mutually dependent on one another. These ecologically balanced, self cleaning swimming pools combine the natural cleaning properties of plants with filtration and

Pond or swimming pool?

David Nettleton of Clearwater Revival differentiates between the terms 'natural pond' and 'natural swimming pool'. The former is just an ordinary pond that you can swim in if you wish (see below), the latter being a pool created specifically for swimming in. Natural ponds are a balanced ecosystem, which achieve water clarity from natural cycles. A natural swimming pool, on the other hand, uses a more sophisticated filtration system that carefully controls water quality.

skimming systems, so that there is no need for harmful chemicals or intensive sand filtration .

The result is a biologically clean, chemical free swimming environment. The water is clear but not sterilised, as in the traditional swimming pool, and it is able to sustain the normal range of pond life, microscopic organisms, invertebrates and even frogs and toads. The aquatic flora and fauna are indicators of the state of the environment and at present their loss in the landscape is very worrying.

While designs of the natural swimming pools may vary, all consist of a swimming area and a regeneration (plants) zone. The swimming area can range between 1.2m and 2.2m deep and this area is kept plant free. It is usually lined with a rubber liner or foil to prevent water leakage and it is separated from the regeneration zone by a barrier wall. This prevents the invasion of plants and soil leakage from the regeneration zone into the swimming area. It also makes it much easier to service and drain each separately. The wall top will actually be approximately 100mm below the surface of the pool in order to allow free transfer of water between each area.

Within the regeneration zone the water is cleansed biologically by the roots of the aquatic plants and micro-organisms. The plants act as living filters and provide a very important function in the whole system by absorbing decomposing materials and bacteria, as well as pollutants, from the water and converting it into biomass (plant tissue), thereby cleaning water. Water plants rely on these nutrients for their growth.

Zooplankton is important for the natural swimming pool as they feed on single-celled algae and filter them out of the water. Through this natural self-cleaning process the use of harsh chemicals is unnecessary to keep the pool free from algae and safe. There is very little need for maintenance.

Plants

A range of aquatic plants are used covering submerged (oxygenators), floating, shallow marginals, deep marginals, bog/marsh and waterside species. Wherever possible indigenous plants are used but a definitive plant list is not always possible as each region should have plants from its own locality, if they exist, as this will provide for more interest. All aquatic plants grow far more quickly than soil based species and there is always the necessity of thinning and pruning.

Construction

A swimming pool requires a deep area of at least 1.5m to 2.2m, with near vertical walls, which needs to be constructed for the swimming area and waterproofed by means of a rubber liner with an underliner. The swimming area should be a minimum of 25m² (50m² is the minimum for the total area). The internal walls should be constructed from sustainable materials wherever possible such as recycled plastic, stone, timber or geotextile bags. As they will be acting as a retaining structure for the material and plants in the regeneration zone, they should be carefully engineered. The walls usually have a capping. They should finish 100mm below the water surface to maintain the visual effect of one pool. Ideally the liner should be placed behind the wall (but in some cases it goes over

© Green Building Press

The regeneration zone utilises a course inert substrate, such as shingle/gravel and not topsoil or any other growing medium as this would bring high levels of nutrients to the water and would counteract the cleaning effects of the plants, while contributing to the silting process. By planting the aquatic plants in shingle they must draw their nutrients from the water itself and so clean the pool. Also by cutting and removing the plant mass each autumn, the impurities held in the plants are physically removed from the water, allowing the cycle to begin again in the following spring. A surface leaf skimmer is also used to help remove floating debris from the water.

The construction sequence of a natural swimmimg pool is similar to that of an elaborate garden pond. The important notes to remember are that the swim area walls are kept 100mm below the surface water height to allow water to mix between the swim zone and the plant zones.

the wall) to ensure that it is both hidden and protected.

The water is drawn down through the substrate in the regeneration zone and through perforated pipework to the pump. The water is also taken via the surface skimmer to the pump where it is again filtered before returning to the bottom of the swimming area. The regeneration zone must be of the same size as the swimming area and have an average depth of 300mm of aggregate, usually graded from 50 to 450mm approximately.

In some pools the plants would surround the swimming area, giving a soft planted margin to the pool. In small pools it is better to plant on one side only so as to avoid a tight enclosed effect. Where space is at a premium, an alternative is to create a second pool, perhaps uphill, to allow the water to flow between the bodies of water, probably using a pump and waterfall.

Silt, a combination of decaying vegetation, dust and other detritus, will always form in any body of water, and depending upon the size and location of the pool, it can easily be removed by either a vacuum or bottom purge system. A drainage ditch is constructed completely around the pool to ensure that no water runoff enters the pool thereby causing any differences in the pH and the water quality.

It has been assumed by many people that the cost of building a natural swimming pool should be considerably cheaper than the conventional ones. Sadly, this is not the case, due to the many complexities with the biological, as well as the construction, processes. Currently the average cost is £350/400 per square metre with a minimum size of 50m². Existing swimming pools can easily be converted to the natural process providing that there is space for the regeneration zone, either as a separate pool or as a subdivision.

Water quality

The quality of the water is of special significance. The layout of the pool with its natural regeneration zone promotes the self-cleaning

	ADVANTAGES —	DISADVANTAGES
Sheet linings	✓ cheapest of liners ✓ light weight per unit area easily transportable ✓ conforms to minor ground undulations ✓ minimal skill and supervision required ✓ can be made up by manufacturer	✗ puncture very easily except butyl (which can be cut with a knife) ✗ sheets need to handled with care ✗ larger ponds require joining of sheets on site ✗ cheaper liners tend to deteriorate in sunlight. These are folly to use. ✗ slippery surface for children unless covered
Concrete	✓ cheaper than Bentonite ✓ less laborious to use than clay ✓ can be made to fit any shape ✓ extremely durable even when water levels drop.	✗ more skill necessary then other liners ✗ requires 'seasoning period' after construction. This is not mandatory ✗ difficult to repair ✗ concrete subject to attack by acids ✗ cracks under loads.
Puddled Clay	✓ cheap, provided suitable source available nearby ✓ no special equipment or tools required ✓ clay could be puddled by machinery where suitable access exists ✓ immune to leaks and decay if applied thickly ✓ pond can be cleaned by hand without fear of damage ✓ leaks can easily be traced and repaired.	✗ regular swimming will disturb the liner and cause turbidity ✗ plant colonisation across pond floor ✗ filter and bottom drain becomes clogged ✗ not 100% watertight and therefore will increase water consumption ✗ clay may have to be bought ✗ hand labour is usually used which is expensive ✗ clay liner could crack if not covered by water ✗ bottom collects silt and becomes muddy which is not good for bathers' feet.
Bentonite clay	✓ non-toxic and easy to handle ✓ large areas can be treated mechanically ✓ leaks in existing ponds can be easily repaired.	✗ expensive product ✗ thorough ground preparation is crucial ✗ not suitable for shallow ponds ✗ more easily damaged than clay linings ✗ cannot be applied to steep sloping bank ✗ bottom collects silt and becomes muddy which is not good for bathers' feet.

Pros and cons for the selection of various pond lining materials. Extracted, with permission, from the book 'Natural Swimming Pools' by Michael Littlewood. see review far right.

forces of the water and the mechanisms provide a long term stable and hygienic quality. The use of chemicals would only lead to the destruction of the biological balance in the water. The shallow warmer water of the regeneration zone circulates with the cooler deeper water of the swimming area and increases its temperature much more quickly. Solar methods can be used providing care is exercised and it is not used until the plants have grown to combat the algae. Fish are not allowed in the pool as they cause damage to the water quality and also encourage birds, such as herons, who could also damage the liner. Ducks, geese and any other waterfowl, are also discouraged and any pets such as dogs.

Wildlife

The natural swimming pool provides an attractive biosphere for various kinds of animals and is quickly inhabited after its creation. They stay mostly in the regeneration zone that serves them well with food and shelter. There are many predatory insects that feed on mosquito larvae. Amphibians use the regeneration zone

© Green Building Press

as a breeding ground too. They appear in early spring to lay their eggs. The amphibians usually migrate from the pool before the swimming season commences.

Health aspects

Numerous users state that the joy of using water free from chemicals is profound. Chlorine used in conventional pools is a skin irritant and can be associated with rashes like eczema and a number of serious diseases. Chlorine has been documented to aggravate asthma, especially in those children who make frequent use of chlorinated swimming pools. Chlorinated water contains chemical compounds called trihalomethanes which are suspected carcinogens resulting from the combination of chlorine with organic compounds in water. They do not degrade very well and are stored in the fatty tissues of the body.

Conclusion

There is no doubt that our landscape is in severe distress and the loss of wetlands, especially ponds and pools has now reached a critical stage. Natural swimming pools can, therefore, make a very important contribution to the restoration of aquatic flora and fauna. We must make every effort to design in harmony with nature. For, as many owners of natural swimming pools comment, it is that harmony, a seamless blending of environments that is the major advantage. Many have also said that it has enriched their lives. While you are separated from the plants you still feel surrounded by them when you swim, which creates a very special kind of mood. The colour of the flowers from spring throughout the summer and into the autumn, along with the chorus of the birds and the frogs, make people feel far closer to nature. It provides them with a very special place to be at any time of the day or night, throughout the whole year. It is their very own natural oasis. ☯

Useful contacts

Ecodesignscape, eco landscaping and natural swimming pools: ***www.ecodesignscape.co.uk***

Clearwater Revival: ***www.clear-water-revival.com***

Further reading

'Natural Swimming Pools' by Michael Littlewood ISBN 0-7643-2183-8

9 Listings

Regions of the UK and Ireland

A guide map for the inspirational places and the listings

Scotland

Northern Ireland

North East

Yorkshire and Humber

Southern Ireland

North West

East Midlands

West Midlands

East

Wales

London

South West

South East

Inspirational places

Putting all the theory into practice, there are now hundreds of energy efficient and low impact projects completed in the UK. The majority use reclaimed and sustainable materials with high levels of insulation. Some have already been mentioned in the stories but here **Sally Hall** has compiled a selection from across the UK, with very brief notes on some of the main features only, as more details are on the websites provided. Many welcome visitors but ensure you telephone or check the website before calling in. We have not had the space to list every scheme but some of the websites listed also include details of other interesting eco projects not included in this list.

London

The Calthorpe Community Centre, Kings Cross, is an early example built in1992, using natural materials with a green roof: 020 7403 2889 *www.architype.co.uk*

The Tree House, Clapham, completed 2006, on a tiny infill plot with a mature sycamore tree which influenced the design. Full story in the book, Diary of an EcoBuilder by Will Anderson: *www.treehouseclapham.org.uk/*

The Millennium Centre, The Chase Nature Reserve, Barking and Dagenham, completed 1997, uses a number of large 'helical screws', which anchor the building to the site, acting as foundations, so if the building were removed it would not leave a mark on the landscape: 020 8595 4155 *www.barking-dagenham. gov.uk/8-leisure-envir/park-country/millennium/ millen-c-menu.html*

The CUE (Centre for Understanding the Environment) building, (completed 1995) using sustainable materials with a grass roof. It now houses the Horniman Library: 020 8699 1872 *www.architype.co.uk/cue.html*

Construction Resources, eco builders' merchant in eco renovated building with exhibitions, courses: 020 7450 2211 *www.constructionresources.com*

Angell Town Estate, Brixton is a regeneration and refurbishment project. From 1998 refurbished and partly rebuilt in a series of separate packages designed by different architects. The London Borough of Lambeth Policies for Sustainable Housing has provided a policy basis for green construction and its translation into practice in this project: 020 7704 1391 *www.ecoconstruction.org/c_study_angell2.html*

Greenwich Millennium Village, recent eco residential development from one-bedroom apartments to penthouses: 020 8293 6900 *www.greenwich-village.co.uk*

Mile End Park, East End, an ecology park with lakes, themed areas and grass-covered buildings. Used for art, sport, play and the study of ecology. A 'green bridge' of shrubs and trees spans a busy highway, linking the two main areas of the park: *www.cleanersafergreener.gov.uk/en/1/london.rmxs*

Gherkin office building, (Swiss Re skyscraper) opened 2004, an innovative design (hence its name), which uses half the energy typically required by an office block: *www.fosterandpartners.com*

Bow, East London. Small block of four flats on a tiny urban infill site, It has a communal clean burn wood pellet boiler, a micro wind turbine, and wind driven heat recovery: 0208 8404 1380 *www.zedfactory.com/bowzed/bowzed.html*

The Creative Media Training Centre, Southwark Bridge Road, (opened 2006) is a refurbishment and extension of a disused Victorian library. Features include wind turbine, wood pellet heating system; passive ventilation, full building energy monitoring: 020 7403 2889 *www.architype.co.uk/southwark.html*

South East

Braziers Park, Oxfordshire features an eco-renovation, and low impact, community housing: 01491 680221 *www.braziers.org.uk*

Oxford Eco House, domestic dwelling and one of the most high profile low energy houses in the country, as featured in EcoHouse 2: 01865 484 075 *www. newbuilder.co.uk/books/reviews/Ecohouse_2.asp*

Sutton Courtenay, Oxfordshire (completed 2002) has sewage treatment system filtering liquids through an underground leachfield. Composted solids are used as fertiliser for tree planting. Mini reedbeds treat grey water. Set in a 13 acre nature reserve: 01235 862024 *www.bbowt.org.uk/content.asp?did=23503*

Redfield Community, Buckinghamshire, sustainable community living, eco renovation of large house with workshops and training areas, regular courses: 01296 713661 *www.redfieldcommunity.org.uk*

Holywell Mead Environment Centre, High Wycombe, Buckinghamshire, opened 2002, utilises a redundant building refurbished using sustainable and natural materials. Heated using a biomass boiler: 01494 511585 *www.ecobuzz.org.uk*

The Living Rainforest, near Newbury, Berkshire is an educational centre, jungle (in greenhouses) with the Human Impact timber educational centre, opened 2006: 01635 202444 *www.livingrainforest.org*

Taplow Court Estate, Berkshire, UK headquarters of SGI-UK, eco-build completed 2001. 020 7403 2889 *www.architype.co.uk*

Kent Wildlife Trust's Romney Marsh visitor centre, opened in 2004, has rendered straw bale walls, a green roof, rainwater conservation system and sustainable woodchip heating: 01797 369487 www.kentwildlifetrust.org.uk

Visitor Centre at Shorne Wood Park, Gravesend, Kent built from locally sourced sweet chestnut. Demonstrating sustainable building techniques and technologies with a wind turbine and solar panels, rainwater harvesting, a woodchip boiler: 01474 823800 www.kentdowns.org.uk/map_details.asp?siteID=53

Pines Calyx, Kent, an eco conference centre using rammed earth (chalk) walls, completed 2006: 01304 851737 www.pinescalyx.co.uk

Bedzed, Surrey is the UK's largest eco village of around 100 homes with community facilities and workplaces, exhibition centre and shop. Residents have been living in the homes since 2002: 020 8404 4880 www.bioregional.com

Pestalozzi Childrens Village Trust, Hastings, E Sussex is an education centre with some eco buildings, including straw bale, ancient woodland: 01424 870 444 www.pestalozzi.org.uk

Flimwell Woodland Enterprise Centre, E Sussex is a Gridshell building using chestnut with an automated wood-fired heating system, designed to be low-energy consuming, and recyclable at the end of its life: 01580 879552 www.woodnet.org.uk

Stanmoor Park Earthship Building, Brighton, built from recycled materials, including tyres plus renewables: 07974 122770 www.lowcarbon.co.uk/tours.htm

Diggers Self Build and Hedgehog Self Build, Brighton are timber frame (Segal) builds using natural materials: 01892 511652 www.forevergreen.org.uk

Ben Law's house, Prickly Wood, Wessex was completed 2002, using sweet chestnut cruck timber frame with strawbale walls and sweet chestnut wood shingles: www.permaculture.co.uk/info/Grand_Designs.html

Weald and Downland Open Air Museum of historical buildings, Chichester, Wessex, plus the Downland Gridshell timber (oak) building built in 2002: 0845 1210170 www.wealddown.co.uk

South West

St Werburgh's self build, Bristol was built in 2004, by the Ashley Vale Action group, a group of self builders on a 2 acre former scaffolding site, using sustainable materials and renewable energy: 0117 944 5797 www.ashleyvale.org.uk

Bordeaux Quay, Waterfront, Bristol City Centre, local timber, recycling, heat pump, solar hot water, rainharvesting: 01179 547333 www.white-design.co.uk

Heeley City Farm, Bristol is a community based and led training, employment and youth project employing over 30 people, on a range of environmentally based enterprises. Includes high thermal mass, passive solar design, powered by renewable energy from photovoltaics and a wind turbine. Living green sedum roof: 01904 468752 www.ecoarc.co.uk

Cherry Orchard, Bristol is a market garden and educational building, Camphill Community, low impact materials: 01952 433 252 www.simmondsmills.com

Create Centre, Bristol is an environment centre which features a purpose-built eco home and also hosts a range of events and exhibitions: 0117 925 0505 www.bristol-city.gov.uk/create

The Congresbury Home, Bristol is a new fast track erection house, shell completed in 24 hours, using sustainable materials: 0117 9557224 www.urban-e.com

The Eden Project, St Austell, Cornwall features the renowned 'Biomes', which represent three of the world's climate zones in domes, a visitors' centre and education facility with earth and timber buildings: 01726 811911 www.edenproject.com

Above: CORE building at Eden Project.

Timber Cabin, Redruth, Cornwall, timber cabin building with grass roof, classroom facility for horticultural students: 01209 891500 www.pioneercabins.co.uk

Cob buildings, Cob in Cornwall, involved in a number of mainly cob buildings in the Cornwall area but also other low impact projects that include straw, lime, turf roofs etc: 01326 231 773 www.cobincornwall.com

Mount Pleasant Eco Park, Truro, Cornwall is a 42 acre site with eco workshops for artists and crafts people. Also permaculture, training courses and eco holidays: 01209 891500 www.mpecopark.co.uk

Lanlivery CP School, Cornwall in 2003, added a 88m^2 super-insulated, low-energy construction built from local/recycled materials with a green roof planted with sedum: 01208 72100 www.arco2.co.uk

Oak Meadow, South Molton, Devon is 35 affordable eco houses for rent, built in 2005. Also features wildlife corridors and habitats. Every home has a garden, fruit trees and Devon hedge banks: www.dcha.co.uk

Neal's Yard Remedies, (retailer of natural toiletries and medicinal products), Gillingham, Dorset, new industrial building for manufacturing, office and associated facilities, surrounded by productive landscape:01225 852545 www.feildenclegg.com

© Green Building Press

Above: Neals Yard Remedies HQ.

The Genesis Centre, sited at Somerset College in Taunton, is a living exhibition of sustainable building materials and techniques promoting energy efficiency and sustainable courses: 01823 366 743 www.genesisproject.com

Tinkers Bubble, Somerset is a community of low impact dwellings and sustainable living: 01460 249204 www.tlio.org.uk/chapter7/photos.html

Lower Coxbridge House, Baltonsborough, Somerset, private dwelling, with renewables, water recycling: 01458 445100 www.markormearchitects.co.uk

Polbury Mill, Bruton, Somerset, community centre and nursery, cedar clad timber frame and recycled materials, an examplar building for the local authority: 01458 445100 www.markormearchitects.co.uk

Great Bow Yard, Langport, Somerset, 12 new timber frame houses, using natural and locally sourced materials and a variety of energy saving features built 2006: 01458 259400 www.swecohomes.co.uk

Keinton Manderville, Somerset, an eco self build timber frame house using sustainable materials, for visiting enquires contact STSD: 01458 259400 www.sustainablehousing.org.uk

Heelis Centre, Wiltshire, HQ of National Trust built in 2006, natural ventilation, passive solar, renewables, thermal mass, sustainable materials, visitors welcome, free tours: 01793 817400 www.nationaltrust.org.uk

Wiltshire Wildlife Trust Visitor Centre, Lower Moor Farm Reserve, Nr Oaksey, prefabricated off site, flowering meadow on roof, cladding leaving spaces for bats, wildlife habitat, renewables, natural finishes: 01380 725670 www.wiltshirewildlife.org

Kindersley Centre, Lambourne, Wiltshire is an eco conference centre built in 2005 on an organic farm: 01488 674737 www.sheepdrove.com

Stroud Co-housing, Gloucestershire was first new build co-housing scheme in the UK, built in 2004. Based on the Danish model, co-housing is a form of collaborative housing that aims to create a real sense of community. 35 private houses and flats with a shared common house at the heart. Timber frame construction from renewable sources, photovoltaic roof tiles: www.springhillcohousing.com

Green Shop, Gloucestershire is a builders' merchant, eco buildings, shop, renewables, rainwater harvesting, demonstration centre, new eco building in progress: 01452 770629 www.greenshop.co.uk

Oxstalls Campus, Gloucestershire, university buildings, renovation, sustainability as a key component with low energy consumption and environmental control as major objectives: 01225 852545 www.feildenclegg.com

HQ of Wildfowl and Wetland Trust, Slimbridge, Gloucestershire, with visitors'centre built in 2000 includes reed beds for recycling grey water: 01453 891900 www.ecda.co.uk/pdfs/slimbridge.PDF

Living Green Centre, Bourton-on-the Water, Gloucestershire, green choices in real home setting. Shop, garden, eco-trail, grass roof, renewables and rain-harvesting: 01451 820942 www.living-green.co.uk

Green and Away, Gloucestershire, tented conference centre with innovative and eco-friendly, low-impact structures, including straw bale building: 0870 460 1198 www.greenandaway.org.uk

West Midlands

Humber Marsh, Herefordshire is a renewables demonstration centre and timber building on nature reserve: 01568 760671 www.windandsun.co.uk

The Straw House, Putley, Herefordshire is made from straw bales: 01531 670 934 www.thestrawhouse.co.uk

The Wintles, Living Village Trust, Shropshire, new development of eco houses at Bishops Castle: 01588 630 475 www.livingvillage.com

The Woodland College, Shropshire, study and conference building (built 1999) for Green Wood Centre , innovative pole framed structure building, low impact: 01952 433 252 www.simmondsmills.com

Fordhall Farm, Shropshire, community land initiative bought in 2006, organic community farm with eco buildings planned: 01630 638696 www.fordhallfarm.com

Bishopswood Environmental Centre, Stourport, Worcestershire, timber educational building, wildlife landscaping, ancient woodland, green roof: 01299 250513 www.bishopswoodcentre.org.uk

Willans Green, Rugby, Warwickshire (completed 2005) new development of affordable homes built to BREEAM Eco Homes excellent: 01827 260600 www.debutbyredrow.co.uk

HQ of Organic Gardening (HDRA), Coventry, with a range of eco buildings together with demonstration areas relating to many aspects of organic gardening: 024 7630 3517 www.gardenorganic.org.uk

Centre of the Earth, Birmingham headquarters of Urban Wildlife Trust, built 1992, innovative timber structure, low impact wildlife gardens: 0121 515 1702 www.wildlifetrust. org.uk/urbanwt/education/coe/coeprospectuses/ primaryprospectus.htm

North West

The Underground House, Appleby, Cumbria, earth sheltered house started in 2002: www.greenbuildingstore.co.uk/case-ecoplus7.php

Solaris, Lancashire, demonstration centre for energy efficient systems, renewables and wildlife habitat, eco renovation, rainwater harvesting, CHP: 01253 478020 www.solariscentre.org

The Maharishi School Woodley Park Sports and Arts Centre, Lancashire, is the first public building in the UK that has been designed and constructed according to principles of an ancient and comprehensive system of architecture from India. Natural and non-toxic building materials including timber and clay, rammed earth for the external walls: 01695 729603 www.rammed-earth.info

Preston headquarters of the Wildlife Trust for Lancashire, Manchester and Merseyside uses recycled and local materials, woodchip-fuelled heating and renewables: 01772 750 001 www.lancswt.org.uk

Dunham Massey and the Stamford Brook Sustainable Housing Development, Cheshire, new eco housing estate on former National Trust land: 08459 335577 www.stamfordbrook.co.uk

Trafford Hall, Cheshire, (opened 2005) eco friendly training unit, timber frame, renewables, biofuels, biodiversity: 01244 300246 www.traffordhall.com/newdevelopments.html

North East

Alnwick Gardens, Northumberland includes one of the biggest tree houses in the world, using redwood and cedar: 01665 511350 www.alnwickgarden.com and www.treehouse-company.com

Nature's World, Middlesborough, high tech eco structure with geothermal bore holes, earth sheltered design, renewables, waste minimisation: 01642 594895 www.naturesworld.org.uk

Yorkshire and Humber

Heeley City Farm is a farm and environmental centre in Sheffield. The training and resource centre building is an innovative design linked with brown field urban regeneration utilising a local employment construction scheme. The building is high thermal mass, powered by renewable energy. It has a living green sedum roof: 0114 258 0482 www.heeleyfarm.org.uk

Anns Grove Primary School, Sheffield has a new building using glue laminated timber frame with load bearing masonry and natural materials: 01179 547333 www.white-design.co.uk

Earth Centre, Doncaster, eco demonstration centre with buildings, exhibitions, gardens, wetland: 01709 513933 www.architecture.com/go/architecture/debate/sustainability_2801.html

Above: the solar canopy at the Earth Centre.

Lockton Youth Hostel, West Yorkshire, eco renovation, one of first UK winners of European Eco Label: 01904 46875 www.ecoarc.co.uk

Ecology Building Society, new eco headquarters building at Silsden, West Yorkshire, plus straw bale meeting room building: 01535 650770 www.ecology.co.uk

York Zero CO$_2$ Environmental Centre, is a centre to promote sustainability. The building is high thermal mass with passive solar design powered by renewable energy from photovoltaics and a wind turbine: 01904 411821 www.ecoarc.co.uk/case_york.html

Meanwood Valley Urban Farm, Leeds Epi Centre, timber visitors' centre with turf roof, solar heating, composting toilets, reed beds, farmland: 0113 262 9759 www.wwf-leeds.org.uk

Gibson Mill, Hebden Bridge, eco-renovation of an old mill (National Trust), relying solely on renewable power and natural resources: 01422 844518 www.ecoarc.co.uk/casestudies.html

Above: Gibson Mill.

City of York Council's EcoDepot, exemplar of sustainable design, passive design, local materials, new system super insulated straw bale cladding: 01904 613161 www.york.gov.uk/cgi-bin/wn_document.pl?type=7072

East Midlands

West Beacon Farm and Whittle Hill Farm buildings, Leicestershire, renewable energy demonstration centre, biodiversity, biomass: 01509 610 033 www.beaconenergy.co.uk

Brocks Hill Country Park, Leicestershire, environment/ ecology centre, demonstrations and exhibitions: 0116 257 2888 www.oadby-wigston.gov.uk/Home/ Brocks%20Hill/Home%20Page.aspx

Leicster EcoHouse, converted 1920's house demonstrating eco features and ideas, internationally renowned environmental show home: 0116 222 0258 www.environ.org.uk

Hill Holt Wood, Lincolnshire, thirty-five acre woodland with straw bale buildings and other low impact initiatives: 01636 892836 www.hillholtwood.com

Sutton Work Life Project, Lincolnshire, earth sheltered house and office: 01406 364646 www.searcharchitects.co.uk

Northampton Academy independent secondary school building with south facing solar atrium, PVs, rainwater harvesting: 01225 852545 www.feildenclegg.com

Attenborough Nature Centre of the Nottingham Wildlife Trust, new building for visitors, mainly timber framed. Heat exchange system which transforms low level heat recovered from the lagoon, within which the building sits, into usable heat for the under floor heating system. Reed bed system. Rewewables: 0115 772 1777 www. attenboroughnaturecentre.co.uk

Nottingham Eco House, an eco renovation: 0115 9143893 www.msarch.co.uk/ecohome

The David Wilson Millennium Eco Energy House, test and demonstration house for energy systems: 0115 951 3157 www.nottingham.ac.uk/sbe/

Hockerton Housing Project (HHP), Nottinghamshire, earth sheltered, self sufficient and ecologically sustainable housing project. Regular tours and events: 01636 816902 www.hockertonhousingproject.org.uk

Millennium Green, Collingham, Nottinghamshire, 24 conventionally styled homes for the mass market: 01636 894900 www.emra.gov.uk/s_d_success/millennium_green.asp

Sherwood Energy Village, Nottingham, office units, industrial, new housing on former colliery site: 01623 860222 www.sherwoodenergyvillage.co.uk

East

Chilterns Gateway Visitor Centre, Dunstable Downs, Bedfordshire, (built 2006) community and education facilities; woodchip heating system, rainwater harvest-ing, timber frame with lime render finish to the external solid walls: 020 7403 2889 www.architype.co.uk

Guilden Gate, Cambridgeshire, organic smallholding, new timber-framed cottage, rainwater harvesting, straw and bark filters vertical and horizontal flow reed beds, solar pond, willow trench soakaway, dry twin vault compost toilet, renewable power: 01763 243960 www.guildengate.co.uk

Purfleet Environment and Education Centre, Rainham Marshes, Essex. New building, built to BREEAM 'excellent' rating on the RSPB nature reserve: 01708 892900 www.birdsofbritain.co.uk/features/rainham-marshes. asp and www.rspb.org.uk

Integer House, House of the Future, Hertfordshire, built by BRE, hight tec, recycled materials, sedum roof, reedbed: www.integerproject.co.uk

EcoTech Centre, Swatham, Norfolk, eco centre in large timber framed building with wind turbine which visitors can climb up: 01760 726 100 www.ecotech.org.uk

Welney Visitor Centre, Norfolk Fens, timber skin of larch, sustainably sourced, nature reserve: 01353 860711, 01620 825722 www.wwt.org.uk/visit/welney

Honingham Earth Sheltered scheme, Norfolk, the UK's first earth sheltered social housing scheme of four bungalows: 01406 364646 www.searcharchitects.co.uk

Suffolk Hemp Houses, Suffolk Housing Society. 2 houses built using hemp as an experiment to compare their performance to 2 adjoining brick and block built houses: 01284 767224 www.suffolkhousing.org/pages/hempage.html

Adnams brewery, Southwold, Suffolk, new warehouse, lime, energy efficient, renewables with largest sedum roof in UK, rainwater harvesting: 01502 727200 www.adnams.co.uk

Scotland

Craigencalt Ecology Centre, Fife, eco-building demonstration centre, community workshops, first UK example (completed 2004) of an earthship made from earth filled tyres and aluminium cans: 01592 891567 www.sci-scotland.org.uk

Findhorn eco-village project, Inverness, many buildings using diverse range of sustainable, natural materials and methods: 01309 690154 www.ecovillagefindhorn.com

Highland Eco Centre, Spinningdale, Inverness, an exemplar of autonomous technology and sustainable building as a demonstration of ecological best practice in the Highlands: 01862 881259 www.highlandeco.org.uk

Lothian Gridshell, Pishwanton, low impact, gridshell building: www.buildingforafuture.co.uk/winter02/index.php

McLaren Leisure Centre, Callander (built 1998), the largest dynamically insulated building in the world and the first to use the technique in a pool: 0131 557 9191 www.gaiagroup.org/architects/index.html

Glencoe Visitors' Centre, *built from locally sourced timber, woodchip heating and low impact:* *www.naturalspace.com/naturalworld_broadband/ glencoetext.htm*

Zero heated home, *Aberdeen, house built and monitored in collaboration with Robert Gordon University and Aberdeen CC: 01224 263714*

Low impact building, *Aberdeen, visitors welcome, larch building, post and beam, raw sheep's wool (waste from local mills), deconstruction, passive solar, renewables: 01330 830057*

Fairfield Housing Cooperative, *Fairfield, Perth (1997) healthy, energy efficient housing, sun scoop form, breathing walls and natural finishes: 0131 557 9191* *www.gaiagroup.org/architects/index.html*

Wales

St Fagans, *Cardiff, a museum of buildings, including the House of the Future with its sedum roof and high tech interior: 029 2057 3500* *www.museumwales.ac.uk/en/197/*

Assembly Building, *Cardiff, Sustainability is at the heart of this new building for the Welsh Assembly Government.*

West Wales Eco Centre, *Pembrokeshire, eco renovation, renewable power, pellet heating: 01239 820235* *www.ecocentre.org.uk*

Scolton Manor, visitors' centre, *Pembrokeshire, timber building, renewables, ancient woodland: 01437 731 457* *www.aboutbritain.com/ScoltonVisitorCentre.htme*

Brithdir Mawr, *Newport, Pembrokeshire, a community of people living and working together in a sustainable way, eco refurbishments, new builds (round houses) low impact, organic farming, wildlife landscaping, visitors welcome, eco tourism. Includes the world famous round house by Tony Wrench: 01239 820164* *www.brithdirmawr.co.uk*

Nant-y-Cwm Kindergarten, *Pembrokeshire, green roof, natural materials: 01437 563640* *www.nant-y-cwm.co.uk/kindergarten.htm*

The National Botanical Gardens for Wales, *Carmarthenshire, various buildings, including the largest single span greenhouse in the world and restored double walled (brick) garden: 01558 668768* *www.gardenofwales.org.uk*

New Art Centre, *Cardigan for Small World Theatre, eco building: 01239 615952* *www.smallworld.org.uk*

Rachels house, *Cardigan, first 2 storey straw bale house in UK:* *www.gwaliaessences.co.uk/sustainablelivin.html*

Centre for Alternative Technology *(CAT), Powys, visitor's centre with inspirational and diverse range of eco buildings, alternative technologies, demonstration centre, courses: 01654 705950* *www.cat.org.uk*

Ty-Mawr, *the Welsh Centre for Traditional and Ecological Building; products, courses, eco renovation: 01874 658249* *www.lime.org.uk*

David's House, *Monmouth, low embodied energy, super insulated, timber frame construction: 01904 46875* *www.ecoarc.co.uk/case_davejohnson.html*

Northern Ireland

Conversion of Old Mill *into two adjoining dwellings Crossgar, County Down, eco renovation, low impact: 028 4483 0988* *www.bevanarchitects.com*

Cedar Primary School, *Crossgar, County Down, load bearing strawbale building:* *www.buildingforafuture.co.uk/winter97/strawbale.php*

Southern Ireland

Ireland's first hemp building: *Co Monahham* *www.oldbuilders.com*

The Hollies, *Enniskeane, Co. Cork, creating a model of permaculture and rural sustainability in practice, cob, strawbale: 00 353 23 47981* *http://homepage.tinet. ie/%7Ethehollies/pages/contact.html*

The Spiral House, *Co Mayo, built in 2001, Europe's first 2 storey, load bearing straw building:* *www.strawbalefutures.org.uk/projects.htm*

For a range of eco buildings in Ireland, using hemp, lime and timber frame, visit: *www.oldbuilders.com*

Other sources of information

'Sustainable Housing Schemes in the UK'. available from Green Shop 01452 770629 *www.greenshop.co.uk*

Sustainable Homes Eco Database, listing 173 projects around the UK: *www.sustainablehomes.co.uk*

Chapter 7 – list of low impact dev in UK: 01460 249204 *www.tlio.org.uk*

Straw bale projects in UK and Irealnd: *www.strawbale-building.co.uk*

Professionals and suppliers

IMPORTANT INFORMATION

FOR MORE PRODUCT MANUFACTURERS, SUPPLIERS ETC, PLEASE SEE THE ADVERTISEMENT LIST AT THE BACK OF THIS BOOK.

ALL BUSINESSES LISTED IN THIS BOOK WERE REQUIRED TO PROVIDE EVIDENCE OF GREEN BUILDING EXPERIENCE OR MEMBERSHIP OF A RELEVANT ORGANISATION.

DISCLAIMER

THE PUBLISHER CAN ACCEPT NO RESPONSIBILITY WHATSOEVER FOR THE ACTIONS OF ANY INDIVIDUAL OR COMPANY, FOR WHATEVER REASONS, SELECTED FROM THE LISTINGS WHICH ARE PROVIDED IN GOOD FAITH. READERS ARE ADVISED TO OBTAIN PROPER REFERENCES FROM PREVIOUS CUSTOMERS AND DETAILS OF PAST PROJECTS PRIOR TO MAKING ANY DECISION TO EMPLOY.

Professionals by region

London

ARCHITECTS

ATAP
Fran Bradshaw
110 Elmore Street, London N1 3AH
T: 020 7704 1391
E: mary@annethornearchitects.co.uk
www.annethornearchitects.co.uk
ATAP is an well-established practice designing for both sustainable communities and a sustainable environment, working closely with those using the building to enhance the quality of peoples lives, developing healthy and environmentally sound solutions to design and specification.

CONSTRUCTIVE INDIVIDUALS (LONDON) LTD.
Peter Smithdale
Trinity Buoy Wharf, 64 Orchard Place, London E14 0JW
T: 020 7515 9299
E: info@constructiveindividuals.com
www.constructiveindividuals.com
An architects practice with particular experience of residential and community buildings. We have undertaken new-build, renovation and extension, including historic buildings, in rural and urban locations. We have extensive knowledge of low-energy design and incorporation of renewables.

MASS ARCHITECTURE
Charlotte Harrison
Unit 10, London Fields Studios, 11-17 Exmouth Place,
Hackney E8 3RW
T: 0207 275 9753
E: info@massarchitecture.com
www.massarchitecture.com
Mass architecture designs buildings using ecologically responsible approaches, techniques and materials. We create high quality, contemporary architecture by providing you with a service tailored to your project. Our workload includes housing (new-build and extensions), shops, offices and community buildings.

REID ARCHITECTURE
Stuart Barlow
11 Hills Place, London W1F 7SE
T: 020 7297 5600
E: stuart.barlow@ra-lond.com
www.reidarchtecture.com
REID architecture has offices in London, Birmingham, Glasgow and Madrid. Using its own Environmental Management system for Designing Buildings REID architecture provides sustainable solutions across a whole range of commercial building types. Environmental conscious solutions, innovatively designed, delivered with passion.

RICHARDS PARTINGTON ARCHITECTS
Richard Partington
Fergusson House, 124-128 City Road, London EC1V 2NJ
T: 020 7490 5490
E: post@rparchitects.co.uk
www.rparchitects.co.uk
Our broad portfolio covers urban expansion, regeneration, master-planning, housing, offices, small business, retail and industrial units and individual houses. With our understanding of low-energy, environmental and sustainable design, we advise on strategic issues and deliver buildable solutions. EcoHomes assessment service.

SHEPPARD ROBSON
Robert Keenan
77 Parkway, Camden Town NW1 7PU
T: 020 7504 1700
E: bob.keenan@sheppardrobson.com
www.sheppardrobson.com
Sheppard Robson provides archi-

© Green Building Press

tectural, town planning and interior design services. The practice has an in-house group-SR:Evolution-that promotes and assists its designers to provide credible, integrated and sustainable solutions to its clients. The practice has offices in London and Manchester.

CONSULTING ENGINEERS

FERGUSON BROWN SUSTAINABILITY AND BUILDING SERVICE
Matt Grace
Suite 804, 8th Floor, Capital Tower,
91 Waterloo Road,
London SE1 8RT
T: 020 7803 4230
E: matt.grace@ferguson-brown.com
www.ferguson-brown.com
FB Sustainability and Building Services provide clients with easy to understand solutions specific to their sustainable challenges. We offer a range of services, including: strategic planning, sustainable policies, low carbon strategies, renewable energy studies and environmental assessments (BREEAM and CEEQUAL).

HOUSEBUILDER

DEVELOPMENT INSIGHT LTD.
Aldhun Levitt
68 Tollington Park,
London N4 3RA
T: 020 7281 8497
E: info@developmentinsight.co.uk
www.developmentinsight.co.uk
We are a small progressive house-building company building houses in the north Norfolk area. Our future houses are to be super efficient in terms of insulation, energy and water usage and we would like to find potential purchasers who could be involved in the design process.

PAINTING AND DECORATING

ZACHARY HOLTMAN
35 Eagle Mansions, Salcombe Road, London N16 8AU
T: 020 7923 3408
E: zach.holtman@gmail.com
Experienced and trustworthy eco-painting/decorating. Working to extremely high standards, with a wide knowledge of environmental, sustainable materials. Genuine concern for the environment. Friendly and reliable. Call for a free quote. Working to create a healthy home.

STRAWBALE AND TIMBER FRAME

TOM MACKEOWN
Uncle Tom's Cabins,
Dyes Loke,
Aylsham,
Norfolk NR11 6EG
T: 07050 695 268
E: tom.mackeown@dsl.pipex.com
Tom specializes in straw bale and timber-frame construction. His current projects include a house in North Norfolk, an extension and eco-alterations to a house in Cambridgeshire and a group of 'affordable houses' (local houses for local people) in West Norfolk.

STRUCTURAL ENGINEER

TECHNIKER LTD.
Matthew Wells
13-19 Vine Hill,
London EC1R 5DW
T: 020 7360 4300
E: matthew.wells@techniker.ltd.uk
www.techniker.ltd.uk
Techniker sets out to make structural engineering a formative part of building design. Projects include all kinds of buildings, bridges, furniture and sculpture. We treat innovation with care and seek to make sustainable use of resources. Offices in London and Manchester.

SUSTAINABLE DEVELOPMENT CONSULTANT

ECOCONSULTING (UK) LTD.
Nanik M. Daswani
28 Marshalsea Road,
London SE1 1HF
T: 020 7939 0989
E: info@ecoconsulting.net
www.ecoconsulting.net
EcoConsulting consults on improving cost-effectively the energy-efficiency and eco-friendliness of developments. Our services include: BREEAM and EcoHomes NHER/SAP/SBEM energy ratings, Compliance with Part L and Section 106 requirements, 10% Renewable Energy analysis, Dynamic thermal modeling, Daylighting simulations.

South East

Berkshire

ARCHITECTS

CA SUSTAINABLE ARCHITECTURE
Isabel Carmona
83 Old Newtown Road, Newbury
RG14 7DE
T: 0163 548 363
E: isabel.carmona@ca-sa.co.uk
www.ca-sa.co.uk
We aim to provide lasting comfortable buildings. Architect led, CA-SA provides services to private clients and fellow professionals, and participates in research. Our Ecohomes assessor can help you make sustainable choices. Experience: residential, office, museum, libraries, retail.

BUILDING CONTRACTOR

MCCURDY AND CO. LTD.
Peter McCurdy
Manor Farm, Stanford Dingley,
Reading RG7 6LS
T: 0118 974 4866
E: info@mccurdyco.com
www.mccurdyco.com
Craftsmen and consultants in the repair and conservation of historic timber frame buildings and the design and construction of green oak buildings. Striving to be the best for 25 years, winners of two categories of the 2005 Wood Awards.

CHARTERED ENVIRONMENTAL SURVEYOR

DW ASSOCIATES
Dennis Wilkinson
Oak View Cottage, Church Lane,
Finchampstead RG40 4LP
T: 0771 040 3405
E: biodennisw@netscape.net
www.buildingphotographs.com
Freelance lecturer on 'green design' and the environment. Education advisors and provider of in-company training on various subjects, including building surveying, management and defects.

Buckinghamshire

DESIGN AND BUILD

DGS CONSTRUCTION LTD.
Doug Stewart
The Glebe, Nash Road, Whaddon,

Milton Keynes MK17 0NQ
T: 01908 503147
E: info@dgsconstruction.co.uk
www.dgsconstruction.co.uk
DGS Construction Ltd build sustainable and energy efficient homes for discerning clients. Managing Director, Doug Stewart, provides a consultancy service for all aspects of house building, drawing on his 40 years of experience in the building industry.

EDUCATIONAL

LOW-IMPACT LIVING INITIATIVE (LILI)
Dave Darby
Redfield, Winslow MK18 3LZ
T: 0129 671 4184
E: lili@lowimpact.org
www.lowimpact.org
Practical things that you can do to reduce your impact on the environment. Residential weekend courses, factsheets, books, products - biodiesel, straw-bale building, solar hot water, earth building, timber building, natural paints and lime, sustainable water and sewage, and more

OPEN UNIVERSITY
David Elliott
OU, Walton Hall, Milton Keynes MK7 6AA
T: 01908 653197
E: D.A.Elliott@open.ac.uk
http://eeru.open.ac.uk
Prof. David Elliott is Director of the Open University Energy and Environment Research Unit, and has been producing courses on sustainable energy and researching renewable energy development and deployment policy issues. He is editor of EERU's journal NATTA.

East Sussex

ARCHITECTS

KORU DESIGN - SUSTAINABLE ARCHITECTURE
Mark Pellant
4a Burton Villas, Hove BN3 6FN
T: 0127 320 4065
E: info@korudesign.co.uk
www.korudesign.co.uk
Architects specialising in high quality, contemporary design guided by sustainable principles. We undertake residential and small commercial projects including new build, extensions and refurbishments.

ARCHITECTURAL SERVICES

GREENERLIVING HOMES
Paul Mustard
Sussex Innovation Centre, Falmer BN1 9SB
T: 01273 488588
E: info@greenerlivinghomes.co.uk
www.greenerlivinghomes.co.uk
Self-build company offering a comprehensive service specialising in the design, specification, and sourcing for high quality, designer homes with low environmental impacts. Available for eco-minded newbuild projects throughout the South of England.

BUILDING CONTRACTOR

DOUCH PARTNERS LTD.
Toby Douch
Court Mead, Priory Road, Forest Row RH18 5HS
T: 01342 825766
E: info@douchpartners.co.uk
www.douchpartners.co.uk
A long established progressive building contractor that specialises in sustainable building techniques. Has extensive experience in timber and breathable structures, and uses many cutting edge products and practices. Douch Partners Ltd has a passion for improving the standards of the built environment.

EARTHWISE CONSTRUCTION LTD.
Mischa Hewitt
50a Park Crescent Terrace, Brighton BN2 3HE
T: 0845 6800015
E: info@earthwiseconstruction.org
www.earthwiseconstruction.org
Green building specialists. Design, consultancy and construction. New build projects and renovation. Extensive experience of low impact materials, including rammed car tyres, reclaimed timber, salvaged masonry, sedum roofs, eco-cement and lime. Builders of Earthship Brighton. Based in Sussex.

ECOLOGISE LTD.
Dan England
49 Newmarket Road, Brighton BN2 3QG
T: 01273 885458
E: info@ecologise.co.uk
General eco-building firm. Plumbing, carpentry, masonry, plastering, decorating. Specialists in energy and water efficiency, condensing boilers, solar thermal systems, insulation, reclaimed timber, eco-paint, lime plaster. Our main focus is eco-refurbishment of old buildings. Happy to take on any work, big or small. Free quotes and advice

CARPENTER/JOINER

SPECIALIST JOINERY (SOUTH) LTD.
David Pattenden
Sycamore House, Ringmer BN8 5SY
T: 01273 814555
E: info@westgatejoinery.co.uk
www.westgatejoinery.co.uk
Specialist Joinery (South) Ltd is the umbrella company encompassing our trading divisions Westgate Joinery, Hailsham Joinery and The Green-Wood Co. Over the years we have built up an enviable reputation for quality, providing complete joinery packages to private and commercial customers.

GLASS PANELS

THE GREENHOUSE EFFECT LTD.
Andrew Savile
Coach House, High Street, Alfriston BN26 5TD
T: 01323 871399
E: greenhouseeffectltd@hotmail.co.uk
www.greenhouseeffect.co.uk
Designers and distributors of Structuran 100% recycled float glass (without resins) as a sustainable and bio-gas fired glass sheet formed into 2.8m x 1.2m sizes for facades, stairs, memorials, kitchen surfaces, backlit screens, vanity tops etc.

SOLAR THERMAL INSTALLER

SOUTHERN SOLAR LTD.
Howard Johns
Unit 6, Allington Farm, Allington Lane, Offham nr Lewes BN7 3QL
T: 0845 456 9474
E: info@southernsolar.co.uk
www.southernsolar.co.uk
Southern Solar has offices near Brighton and Bristol, and installs a range of Renewable Technologies, including Solar Hot Water and Electric systems, Wind Turbines, Pellet Boilers and Heat Pumps, for domestic and commercial settings. Accredited for national and local grants.

Hampshire

BREEAM ASSESSOR

CLOUDS ENVIRONMENTAL CONSULTANCY LTD.
Carl Peat
327 Copnor Road,
Portsmouth PO3 5EG
T: 023 9263 9858
E: carl.peat@cloudsenvironmental.co.uk
www.cloudsenvironmental.co.uk
Our expertise in the field of energy and environmental management enables us to assist you in reducing your overheads and improving your environmental performance. We offer a wide range of services that can be tailored to suit your business requirements.

BUILDING SUPPLIES

GREENER LIVING
Simon Burnett
327 Copnor Road, Portsmouth,
Hampshire PO3 5EG
T: 023 9266 4700
E: sales@greenerliving.co.uk
www.greenerliving.co.uk
Supplier of environmentally friendly building and decorating products: Insulations, Lime Plasters and Mortars, Clay plasters and Clay boards, Clay and Oil based Paints, Wood Treatments, Oils and Waxes. Wooden and Natural Floor coverings. Solar Heating Systems and Micro power generation.

ENERGY CONSULTANT

CLOUDS ENVIRONMENTAL CONSULTANCY LTD.
Carl Peat
327 Copnor Road,
Portsmouth PO3 5EG
T: 023 9263 9858
E: carl.peat@cloudsenvironmental.co.uk
www.cloudsenvironmental.co.uk
Our expertise in the field of energy and environmental management enables us to assist you in reducing your overheads and improving your environmental performance. We offer a wide range of services that can be tailored to suit your business requirements.

ENVIRONMENTAL BUSINESS CONSULTANT

CLOUDS ENVIRONMENTAL CONSULTANCY LTD.
Carl Peat
327 Copnor Road,
Portsmouth PO3 5EG
T: 023 9263 9858
E: carl.peat@cloudsenvironmental.co.uk
www.cloudsenvironmental.co.uk
Our expertise in the field of energy and environmental management enables us to assist you in reducing your overheads and improving your environmental performance. We offer a wide range of services that can be tailored to suit your business requirements.

STRUCTURAL ENGINEER

TIMBER CRAFT
Palmer Smith
12-Beaulieue Close,
New Milton BH25 5UX
T: 0781 739 8086
E: palmer0120@hotmail.co.uk
Timber frame designer.

Kent

ARCHITECTURAL SERVICES

HELIONIX DESIGNS
Alistair Gould
Pines Garden Offices, St. Margarets Road, St. Margarets Bay, Dover CT15 6EF
T: 01304 851737
E: alistair@helionixdesigns.co.uk
www.helionixdesigns.co.uk
Ecological design consultants / Architects delivering optimum healthy and sustainable spaces for living, learning and working. Working with communities and individual clients, our collaborative approach includes partnerships with both other building professionals and academic institutions in the field of sustainable construction.

BUILDERS MERCHANT

ECOMERCHANT LTD.
Paul Whitlock
Head Hill Road, Goodnestone, nr Faversham, Kent ME13 9BU
T: 01795 530130
E: info@ecomerchant.co.uk
www.ecomerchant.co.uk
Ecomerchant is an environmentally friendly builders merchant based in Kent. We supply high performance doors and windows, paints, sunpipes and traditional building restoration materials. We are a national distributor of wool, hemp/cotton, recycled textile and cellulose insulations.

BUILDING SURVEYOR

CALFORDSEADEN
Anthony Kerr
St. Johns House, 1A Knoll Rise,
Orpington BR6 0JX
T: 01689 888 229
E: akerr@calfordseaden.co.uk
www.calfordseaden.co.uk
Calfordseaden is an integrated multi-disciplinary organisation comprising surveyors, architects, mechanical and electrical engineers, structural engineers and project managers. We have several Ecohomes, BREEAM and SAP assessors and can provide environmental assessments and advice on sustainability and renewable energy issues.

CONKER CONSERVATION LTD.
Paul Mallion
26 Highfield Close,
Canterbury CT2 9DX
T: 01227 764 260
E: paul@conkerconservation.co.uk
www.conkerconservation.co.uk
Kent's most dedicated specialists in sustainable building design. New build, conversion, extension, refurbishment and historic buildings. Rammed earth and chalk, straw bale, timber frame, passive solar, anything unusual or usual. Feasibility studies, planning applications, detailed design, contract administration. Green Apple Award winners.

RENEWABLE POWER

RENEWABLE SOURCES LTD.
Liam Harris
21 Bartholemew Street, Hythe, Kent CT21 5BY
T: 07706 313134
E: info@renewablesourcesltd.co.uk
www.renewablesourcesltd.co.uk
Wind turbine supply and installation. A complete service for domestic and light commercial customers from choice of product to installation. We offer a detailed site survey and independent advice to give you accurate costs, not just an estimate.

Middlesex

ARCHITECTS

BILL DUNSTER ARCHITECTS / ZEDFACTORY LTD.
Bill Dunster
The BedZED Centre, 24 Helios Road, Wallington, Surrey SM6 7BZ
T: 020 8404 1380

E: bill@zedfactory.com
www.zedfactory.com
Zedfactory offer architectural services and development appraisal services for step change zero fossil energy communities - ranging from a detached house to an urban block - including ranges of standard house types with integrated supply chains and volume discounts - in addition to site specific designs.

DEVELOPER

HOMEPOTENTIAL
Martin Leach
77 Colne Road,
Twickenham TW2 6QL
T: 0208 892 2298
E: martin@homepotential.co.uk
www.77colneroad.co.uk
A development designed to catalyse micro businesses, by providing small, affordable, office/ workshop space using sustainable, energy efficient building techniques. We are creating bright, comfortable and stylish workspace at the same time respecting the existing character of the neighbourhood.

ENVIRONMENTAL BUSINESS CONSULTANT

SUSTAINABLE HOMES
Sarah Butler
Harlequin House, 7 High Street,
Teddington TW11 8EE
T: 020 8973 0429
E: info@sustainablehomes.co.uk
www.sustainablehomes.co.uk
Sustainable Homes. Building on our respected reputation within the social housing sector, we can now offer a range of training and consultancy services, focusing on the sustainable built environment and sustainable communities.

LANDSCAPE ARCHITECT

LOUISE ZASS-BANGHAM
17 Crane Road,
Twickenham TW2 6RX
T: 07780 600980
E: louise@zass-bangham.com
www.zass-bangham.com
Sustainable garden design. Your garden is part of your homes ecosystem - create shelter and shade, conserve water, increase biodiversity. Our creative designs are sustainable, practical and stylish. Customised service - new garden, renovation or simple make-over. Consultancy and friendly advice.

Oxfordshire

ARCHITECTS

HESS-KINCAID-LEACH
Paul Leach
39 Radcliffe road,
Oxford OX4 4BX
T: 01865 249691
E: leachvenningpaul@yahoo.co.uk
www.hess-kincaid.co.uk
After 20 years in building, Paul studied Ecological Architecture at Manchester and Oxford, qualifying in 2002. He has designed and run community, residential and commercial projects. Now a partner in Hess-Kincaid-Leach, Paul offers Sustainable Design from the Basis of practical experience.

JOHN BLEACH ARCHITECT
John Bleach
47 Rosamund Road,
Oxford OX2 8NU
T: 01865 512114
E: john@bleacharchitect.co.uk
Architect with 30 years experience in new and existing buildings, including housing, university buildings and hospitals. MSc in energy efficient building. Can provide advice for controlling energy consumption and sustainable design solutions for small building projects.

OWEN CONSULTANCY LLP
Rhys Owen
Ivydene, Burford OX18 4AB
T: 01993 842036
E: rowen@owenconsultancy.com
www.owenconsultancy.com
Innovative Sustainable Buildings through partnership with Private Clients, Social Landlords and Contractors. We carefully consider the environmental impact each project has and balancing environmental performance with the need for a high quality of life and a safe and healthy environment.

BUILDING CONTRACTOR

GAVIN COOK
54a Cowley Road,
Oxford OX4 1HZ
T: 01865 243230
E: gavin.green-build@tiscali.co.uk
Sustainable Construction. Eco-build specialist.

EDUCATION

OXFORD ECO HOUSE
Sue Roaf
26 Blandford Avenue, Oxford
OX2 8DY
T: 01865 515001
E: s.roaf@btinternet.com
Architect, author, lecturer and city councillor. Consultant and designer specialising in ecohousing, and the integration of renewable energy and issues of sustainability into buildings and communities.

SOLAR THERMAL INSTALLER

THAMES VALLEY SOLAR
Marc Delman
Manor Farm, Oxford OX2 0NG
T: 07740 929305
E: info@thamesvalleysolar.co.uk
www.thamesvalleysolar.co.uk
Design, supply and installation of Solar Hot Water Heating Systems and Energy Efficient Heating Systems.

Surrey

ARCHITECTS

PRP ARCHITECTS
David Housego
Ferry Works, Summer Road, Thames Ditton KT7 0QJ
T: 020 8339 3600
E: david.housego@prparchitects.co.uk
www.prparchitects.co.uk
PRP Architects has been established for over 40 years specialising in residential design. We are committed to the sustainable design and specification of our buildings and seek to promote the use of environmentally-friendly materials and adoption of energy-efficient design.

BUILDING CONTRACTOR

NATURALLY AMAZING LTD.
Trudy Thompson
Lilac Cottage, Dye House Road,
Thursley, Godalming GU8 6QA
T: 01252 702717
E: tt@naturallyamazing.co.uk
www.naturallyamazing.co.uk
We are passionate about building eco-friendly, sustainable, low/zero energy homes that are healthy to live in. Specialists in green roofs and landscapes to encourage biodiversity. We also supply/install eco-friendly building materials, water harvesting, waste recycling and renewable energy systems.

HEATING ENGINEER

ROUGEMONT BUILDING SERVICES
John Fletcher
59 Rougemont Avenue, Morden SM4 5PY
T: 0208 404 7262
E: rougemontbuildingservices@blu eyonder.co.uk
www.rougemontbuildingservices. pwp.blueyonder.co.uk/
Domestic and commercial heating services; Installation and repair; Gas safety; Energy auditing and reporting Management services; Planned and preventative; corrective maintenance; Design and Installation.

HISTORIC BUILDINGS

OXLEY CONSERVATION LTD.
Richard Oxley
8a Friday Street, Henley on Thames RG9 1AH
T: 01491 414191
E: info@oxleyconservation.co.uk
www.oxleyconservation.co.uk
Oxley Conservation offers a broad spectrum of services to owners and custodians of old buildings. These services go beyond traditional building surveys to encompass project management, contract supervision, grant applications, consultancy and training.

West Sussex

ARCHITECT AND BUILDER

LIVING SPACE DESIGN
Bob Mousley
Cedarfield , Five Acres, Funtington, Chichester PO18 9LX
T: 01243 572604
E: bobmousley@aol.com
www.livingspacedesign.com
Living Space Design offers ideas, imagination and creativity for all aspects of organic environmentally conscious design. Contemporary or traditional. We create living breathing spaces that enhance the quality of life for those within and compliment the environment without. Design and Build service available.

ARCHITECTURAL SERVICES

R. E. OSBORNE BUILDING CONSULTANT
Ted Osborne
11 Danefield Road, Selsey, Chichester PO20 9DA
T: 01243 605122

E: reo@selseypc.net
New houses, extensions, conversions, alterations, remodelling (rethinking/reorienting spaces in older properties) - even the simplest project can use eco-design principles and site-specific opportunities to benefit clients and minimise impact on the environment.

BIOFUELS

BLOOMING FUTURES LTD.
Mat Bulba
Old Cement Works, Shoreham Road, Steyning BN44 3TX
T: 08453 372965
E: mat@bloomingfutures.com
www.bloomingfutures.com
We convert diesel engines to run on Pure Plant Oil (PPO) and can provide a fuel delivery service to access the greenest of transport options. We use the best equipment available in the UK.

BUILDING CONTRACTOR

LIVING SPACE DESIGN
Bob Mousley
Cedarfield , Five Acres, Funtington, Chichester PO18 9LX
T: 01243 572604
E: bobmousley@aol.com
www.livingspacedesign.com
Living Space Builders is an environmentally conscious company that loves working on projects that are different, difficult, interesting and unusual, own joinery. We are committed to leaving the world a better place than from which we inherit it. Contemporary, Traditional or Listed we love it. Full design service.

ENERGY CONSULTANT

IMPETUS CONSULTING LTD.
Dave Barton
Suite 4, 39 Aldwick Road, Bognor Regis PO21 2LN
T: 01243 869834
E: dave@impetusconsult.co.uk
www.impetusconsult.co.uk
Impetus Consulting Ltd., with offices in West Sussex and London, aims to assist people and organisations reduce their environmental impact. Specialising in sustainable energy and construction issues, we offer training, and independent and objective advice on specific buildings or projects.

LANDSCAPE ARCHITECT

JOHN AND KEREN ROBBINS LANDSCAPE DESIGN
Keren Robbins
Ivy Cottage, Duncton, Petworth GU28 0JZ
T: 01798 344076
E: jandkrobbins@supanet.com
Husband and wife team. Horticultural consultancy, advice on starting up/running horticultural holdings, landscape/garden design/in-house training for local authorities, arboricultural advice and tree reports, pest/disease advice. Our designs marry garden to site. Use local materials and craftsmen.

PROJECT MANAGEMENT

GREENLIGHT CONSTRUCTION LTD.
Richard Sabin
3 Chapel Street, Chichester PO19 1BU
T: 07947 486211
E: rs@greenlightconstruction.co.uk
www.greenlightconstruction.co.uk
Greenlight offers both construction and consultancy services with the overriding aim of increasing the use, awareness and acceptance of holistic and sustainable building methods, materials and processes that are good for you and the environment around you.

WASTE WATER TREATMENT

RICHARD IAIN WILKINSON
Iain Wilkinson
17 Hamsey Road, Sharpthorne, East Grinstead RH19 4PA
T: 01342 810885
E: iainwilkinson@tiscali.co.uk
www.reedbeds-treatment.co.uk
Reed beds and manufactured treatment units for domestic, industrial and agricultural waste waters. We offer a design, design with supervision, or design with installation service for projects throughout the UK.

South West

Bristol

ARCHITECTS

JOHN PEGRUM ARCHITECTS
John Pegrum
65 Gloucester Road North, Filton Park BS7 0SN

T: 0117 969 4820
Researching various green
solutions. Currently engaged in
domestic work involving timber
framing, renewables and other eco
methods. Domestic work of high
quality a speciality.

SOUTHPOINT
Jerry Evans
45 The Dell, Westbury-on-Trym BS9
3UF
T: 0845 644 6639
E: mail@southpoint.co.uk
www.southpoint.co.uk
Sound, practical advice is backed
up by a track record in designing
environmentally conscious new
buildings, alterations and extensions. Our flexible service can vary
from a few hours of consultation, to
taking your first idea through to a
completed project.

ASCENT ARCHITECTURE
Steve Mardall
81-83 Stokes Croft,
Bristol BS1 3RD
T: 0117 942 9515
E: info@ascentarchitecture.com
www.ascentarchitecture.com
Architects offering innovative and
practical designs which address
the issues of environmental impact
and sustainability. Commercial
and domestic work large and
small scale. New build, extensions,
conversion and refurbishment.
Listed Buildings. Feasibility studies.
AECB member.

DAVID HAYHOW ASSOCIATES
David Hayhow
Cedar High, Madams Paddock,
Chew Magna, Bristol BS40 8PN
T: 01275 333109
E: architecture@davidhayhow.
co.uk
www.davidhayhow.co.uk
A member of the AECB and on
The Green Register, we work with
individual clients and public bodies
in Health, Housing, Education and
Commercial fields. We aim for
quality design, sustainability and
inclusion.

QUATTRO DESIGN ARCHITECTS
Hugh Nettelfield
1 Great George Street,
Bristol BS1 5RR
T: 0117 929 9672
E: hugh@quattro-bristol.co.uk
www.quattrodesign.co.uk
Quattro is a talented ARCHITECTS
committed to designing buildings which enhance the local
environment both physically and
socially. We have built a reputa-

tion for creating innovative designs
through close collaboration with
users and clients within tight financial guidelines.

STRIDE TREGLOWN
Amy Thatcher
Promenade House, The
Promenade, Clifton Down,
Bristol BS8 3NE
T: 0117 974 3271
E: amythatcher@stridetreglown.com
www.stridetreglown.co.uk
Stride Treglown is a multi-disciplinary practice offering architecture,
landscape architecture, interior
design, planning, building surveying, BREEAM assessments and
project management. Recently
completed Great Bow Yard: the
first speculative green housing
development in South West,
commissioned as a prototype for
local sustainable housing.

ARCHITECTS AND BUILDER

GREENHEART DESIGN
AND BUILD
Bill Flinn and Malcolm McMahon
79 Effingham Road,
St. Andrews BS6 5AY
T: 0117 942 9717
E: info@greenheart.com
www.greenheartuk.com
Greenheart is a partnership which
practices and promotes environmentally responsible building.
The services we offer include
design, project management
and construction. We undertake
projects of both a domestic and
social nature and particularily
welcome ventures which are innovative and challenging.

DESIGN AND BUILD

CLEARWATER REVIVAL
David Nettleton
The Hub Bristol, 35 Kings Street BS1
4DZ
T: 07832 382 653
E: info@clear-water-revival.com
www.clear-water-revival.com
Specialist company for the design
and installation of natural swimming
pools. Concentrating expertise in
the development of efficient and
reliable natural filtration systems and
developing a network of partners
around the UK. Supply renewable energy systems designed for
swimming pools.

SLR
Oliver Mouland
28 Redland Grove, Redland, Bristol
BS6 6PT
T: 0777 339 9320
E: olivermouland@hotmail.com
Oliver Mouland CAD Draughting
and Visualisation Architectural and
structural CAD draughting services.
Specialising in concept visualisation and planning application
drawings for self build projects.
Build types include timber frame,
rammed earth, cob building, straw
bale and earth ship construction
methods.

THE GREENHOUSE PROJECT
Simon Lewis
35 King Street, Bristol BS1 4DZ
T: 0117 3700990
E: enquiries@thegreenhouseproject.net
www.thegreenhouseproject.net
Environmental building consultancy, design and construction.
A unique perspective built upon
years of experience in all aspects
of the building trades and willing-
ness to research and develop new
techniques, materials and ideas.
Simple advice, detailed designs,
project management, specialist
trades.

EDUCATIONAL

THE GREEN REGISTER
Sarah Derryman
The CREATE Centre, Smeaton
Road, Bristol BS1 6XN
T: 0117 377 3490
E: mail@greenregister.org.uk
www.greenregister.org.uk
The Green Register is an independent, self supporting organisation
that brings together all disciplines in the construction industry
committed to sustainable building
practices (including architects,
engineers, builders, surveyors and
tradespeople) by providing wide
ranging seminars, workshops and
networking opportunities

RENEWABLE ENERGY
CONSULTANTS

SUSTAIN LTD
Stephanie Franklin
4 High Street,
Wrington, Bristol,
BS40 5QA
T: 01934 863 650
E: stephanie.franklin@sustain.co.uk
www.sustain.co.uk
Energy and environmental consul-
tancy.

© Green Building Press

TIMBER FRAMER

TIMBER ROUTES
Diana Powell
42 Armoury Square, Easton, Bristol
BS5 0PT
T: 0117 952 2585
E: paul@timber-routes.co.uk
www.timber-routes.co.uk
We produce quality mortice and
tenon timber frames. Engineered
using sustainably sourced douglas
fir and oak. Traditional and modern
houses, extensions, roofs and
barns, including cost effective
solutions for self builders. Free
initial consultation and estimating
service.

Cornwall

ARCHITECTS

INNES ARCHITECTS
Mark Innes
Sunny Bank, Bossiney Lane, Tintagel
PL34 0AU
T: 01840 770099
E: markinnes@macace.net
Specialising in green domestic,
cultural and community archi-
tecture. Well researched green
designs and energy solutions
tailored to client and site.
Feasibility studies undertaken.
Specialist Planning Advice and
Expert Witness work.

DAREN THOMAS
1st Floor, 12A Cliff Road, Newquay
TR7 2NE
T: 01637 859494
E: atecdesign1@btconnect.com
A small practice, with a keen
interest in sustainable design both
for the developer and end user.
We are fluid in our approach to
design and environmental issues,
and prepared to explore innovative
methods of construction.

PARKES LEES ARCHITECTS LTD.
Robert Platts
4 Broad Street,
Launceston PL15 8AD
T: 01566 772035
E: parkes.lees@fsmail.net
www.parkeslees.co.uk
Chartered architects specialising in building conservation and
new buildings in sensitive environments. Our design approach
aims to use natural materials and
provide energy efficient solutions.
Our projects include residential,
commercial, retail and public
buildings in the South West of
England.

ARCHITECT AND BUILDER

ECOHOUSE LTD.
Robin van der Bij
Inglenook, West Polberro, St. Agnes
TR5 0SS
T: 0187 255 4014
E: info@theecohouse.co.uk
www.theecohouse.co.uk
Design and build company using
environmentally friendly and
healthy materials where possible
and cost effective. Build costs
are similar to conventional builds.
Good building practice, high
levels of insulation, effective solar
design and heating systems ensure
minimal future service bills.

ARCHITECTURAL SERVICES

CHARLES GREEN DESIGN
Charles Green
The Studio, Gethsemane, Church
Lane, Redruth TR15 2SH
T: 01209 216964
E: charles@greendsgn.freeserve.
co.uk
Environmentally sensitive design-
led architectural service able to
successfully interpret progressive
and traditional briefs. Preparation
of planning, building control and
listed buildings applications,
seeking tenders and contract
management. Straw bale, green
oak/larch, timber frame and
passive solar designs. Established
12 years.

DESIGN AND BUILD

ELLERSLEE LTD.
Pauline Stutt
15a Rear Lane, Clinton Road,
Redruth TR15 2LL
T: 01209 215419
E: accounts@ellerslee.com
www.ellerslee.com
We are suppliers and registered
contractors of Kingspan TEK
building system, offering an
affordable, mainstream solution
to sustainable building in Cornwall
and the expense and time delays
recurrent in construction. We also
offer modular (POD) building
options using SIPS technology.

EARTH BUILDERS

COB IN CORNWALL
Adam Weismann & Katy Bryce
Higher Boden,
Manaccan TR12 6EN
T: 01326 231773 /0778 978 0391
E: info@cobincornwall.com
www.cobincornwall.com
www.howtobuildwithcob.co.uk

We are ecological builders
specialising in cob building and
associated materials such as lime
renders, washes and earth plasters.
We build new cob structures, and
also sensitively restore ancient and
listed buildings with appropriate
materials. We are the authors of
Building with Cob: A Step by Step
Guide published by Green Books,
ISBN 1903998727

ENVIRONMENTAL BUSINESS CONSULTANT

ENVISION
Tracey Johnson
John Keay House, Tregonissey
Road, St. Austell PL25 4DJ
T: 0845 456 9350
E: cornwall@envisionsw.org.uk
www.envisionsw.org.uk
Envision is a not-for-profit part
funded South West environmental
business support programme. Our
service offers five days of bespoke
advice to reduce water, energy,
waste and transport resources as
well as training and implementation of BS8555 and ISO14001.

ENVIRONMENTAL CONSULTANCY

CORNWALL ENVIRONMENTAL CONSULTANTS LTD.
Phil Hills
Five Acres, Allet, Truro TR4 9DJ
T: 01872 245510
E: enquiries@cec.gb.com
www.cec.gb.com
CEC provide professional ecological and landscape architectural
services to the public and private
sectors. Services include desk
studies, habitat and protected
species surveys, master planning,
detailed design, site watching
briefs, management planning,
environmental impact assessments, planting design and
community consultation.

SOLAR POWER (PV) INSTALLER

PLUG INTO THE SUN
Andrew Tanner
Trebehor Farm Cottage, St. Levan,
Penzance TR19 6LX
T: 01736 871291
E: info@plugintothesun.co.uk
www.plugintothesun.co.uk
Solar PV and solar thermal instal-
lations. Full consultation, design,
installation and commissioning of
solar systems. Fully accredited with
Low Carbon Building Programme

grants system. Based in West Cornwall, working throughout the South West region.

TRUST

CORNWALL SUSTAINABLE BUILDING TRUST
Paul Bright
Watering Lane Nursery, St. Austell,
Cornwall PL26 6BE
T: 01726 68654
E: admin@csbt.org.uk
www.csbt.org.uk
CSBT exists to raise awareness and so minimise the impacts of construction on the Cornish and Global environments. It runs training courses in traditional and sustainable building skills, offers information, advice, and promotes and shares best practice in sustainable construction.

Devon

ARCHITECTS

CLIVE JONES ARCHITECT
Clive Jones
141 Irsha Street, Appledore,
Bideford EX39 1RY
T: 01237 421262
E: clivejones@waitrose.com
Environment friendly and energy conscious design.

MCCAREN DESIGN ARCHITECT
Robert McClaren
Floor 2, 26 Lockyer Street, Plymouth PL1 2QW
T: 01752 209 417
E: mail@mccarendesign.co.uk
www.mccarendesign.co.uk
McCaren Design provides tailored guidance on projects ranging from commercial developments to private residential extensions and community resource buildings. The company strives to achieve sustainability in all its buildings and working practices, specifying green and local products wherever possible.

ARCHITECTURAL SERVICES

PCA
Phil Collins
Langapark, Dunsford,
Exeter EX6 7HE
T: 01647 253084
E: philco@globalnet.co.uk
www.s-p-a-c-e.org.uk
An environmental design practice specialising in small and medium scale building design, building conservation, ecological and land-scape design projects. Expertise in environmentally sensitive building and landscape design, ecology, alternative technologies and the conservation of historic buildings.

TOM FOSTER ARCHITECTURE
Tom Foster
Holeland Farm, Dunsford,
Exeter EX6 7DJ
T: 01647 24436
E: info@space-and-light.co.uk
www.space-and-light.co.uk
My mission is to create space and light for modern living and working, whether in new build or within enjoyed, respected and trans-formed old buildings, in the lowest energy, least toxic, most natural way possible, anywhere in the West Country.

ARCHITECTURAL AND ENERGY CONSULTANT

DESIGNING NATURALLY
Michael Rose
Red Earth Studio, 1 Weston Lane,
Totnes TQ9 5UN
T: 01803 867510
E: michael@newbuilder.co.uk
Architectural and sustainable environmental design consultancy. Building sites and design drawings analysed for environmental impact, renewable energy potential, micro-climate and indoor comfort management, thermal storage and energy efficiency (prioritising passive solar, low energy, ecological and economic principles).

DESIGN AND BUILD

CARFRAE SUSTAINABLE DESIGN
Jim Carfrae
1 Ashleigh, Kingsbridge Hill, Totnes TQ9 5SZ
T: 01803 862369
E: jim@carfrae.com
Everything from consultation on aspects of sustainable construc-tion, into the design and build of a complete dwelling. Sophisticated straw-bale building. Passive solar design. Integrated solar thermal solutions. Timber frame and straw-bale integration. Selecting and sourcing appropriate sustainable materials.

EARTH BUILDERS

ABEY SMALLCOMBE
Jill Smallcombe
West Ford Farm, Cheriton Bishop,
Exeter EX6 6HP
T: 01647 24145
E: jackie@abeysmallcombe.com
www.abeysmallcombe.com
We design and create traditional and contemporary cob buildings and sculptures, including the cob shelter at the Eden project and art for the Met Office. We run practical courses on cob construction in both repairs and new build.

OFF-MAINS DRAINAGE

CRESS WATER LTD.
Rick Hudson
18 Forcefield Road,
Cullompton EX15 1QB
T: 01884 839000
E: info@cresswater.co.uk
www.cresswater.co.uk
We specialise in the design and installation of reed-beds, ponds and wetlands for sewage and wastewater treatment, recycling treated effluent, water conserva-tion, rainwater harvesting and water management, and the creation of attractive aquatic garden features. We provide a nation-wide service.

PAINTING AND DECORATING

THE GREEN BRUSH
Steve Coles
Tanglewood, Little Silver,
Exeter EX2 8XZ
T: 01392 832207
E: Info@thegreenbrush.co.uk
www.thegreenbrush.co.uk
We are a professional and depend-able painting and decorating business dedicated of using the highest quality, natural and envi-ronmentally-friendly paints and materials. Preparation is always the key. Just quality, clean, ethical work. Fully insured - City and Guilds Craftsman.

THE NATURAL DECORATING CO.
Pam Macdonald
5 Orchard Terrace,
Buckfastleigh TQ11 0AH
T: 01364 642893
E: naturaldecorating@phonecoop.coop
Paint and finishes consultant. Natural paints and finishes. Consultancy and specification for paints, fabrics, flooring and furni-ture for sustainable interiors. Design and decoration service available.

© Green Building Press

Dorset

ARCHITECTS

ECOPRIZE! LTD.
Philip Jordan
116 Monmouth Road,
Dorchester DT1 2DQ
T: 077 6666 4855
E: ecoprize@ecoprize.co.uk
www.ecoprize.co.uk
Buildings are our principal
environments - their building,
maintenance, sites are fundamental to sustaining us - Ecoprize!
can help by for instance: -Initial
inception meetings and service
plans -Condition inspections
-Space utilisation surveys -Related
drawings, models, studies, and
advice Reports.

BUILDING CONTRACTOR

D.C.R.S CONSTRUCTION LTD.
Rob Buckley
Dorset Centre for Rural Skills, West
Farm Barn, West Farm, Farrington,
Blandford DT11 8RA
T: 01747 811099
E: info@dorsetruralskills.co.uk
www.dorsetruralskills.co.uk
A dedicated team with 25 years
experience in the building industry,
from sensitive restoration and
refurbishment using traditional
building techniques and materials
to pioneering sustainable building,
producing straw bale, timber
frame, cob and earth structures.
Training courses also provided.

BUILDING SURVEYOR

SAVILLS (L AND P) LTD.
Jon Shears
Wessex House,
Wimborne BH21 1PB
T: 01202 856837
E: jshears@savills.com
www.savills.com
Savills, a multidisciplinary property
consultancy practice has over
65 offices throughout the UK. In
addition to EcoHomes assess-
ments, professional advice is
offered to Developers, RSLs and
Housing Associations through
Savills Building Consultancy Dept.
Development and Planning advice
is also available.

CONSULTING ENGINEERS

JULIAN BROOKS ASSOCIATES
Julian Brooks
2 South Street,
Bridport DT6 3NQ
T: 01460 77155
E: jb@julianbrooks.com
www.julianbrooks.com
Planning Advice, EcoHomes
assessments (BRE Registered), Eco
Materials advice, Energy advice
from a single home to complete
new towns.

DEVELOPER

**THE RURAL RENEWAL
COMPANY**
Alan Heeks
Cole Street Farm, Cole Street Lane,
Gillingham SP8 5JQ
T: 07976 602787
E: data@workingvision.com
www.ruralrenewal.co.uk
RRC is creating a sustainable
education centre and eco-village,
to include a visitor centre, eco-
hotel, co-housing for 200+ people.
Partner organisations, investors and
potential residents are welcome to
contact us. We offer consultancy to
similar projects.

Gloucestershire

ARCHITECTS

ANDREW BEARD ARCHITECTS
Andrew Beard
The Bakery, Cowle Road,
Stroud GL5 2JR
T: 01453 757485
E: a.beard@virgin.net
Working with ecological principles
of design and construction, we
place special emphasis on an
organic relationship between
the form of a building, its environment and the human activities it
encloses, thus enriching the lives of
those who use it.

HEATH AVERY ARCHITECTS
David Heath
3 Bath Mews, Bath Parade,
Cheltenham GL53 7HL
T: 01242 529169
E: architects@heath-avery.co.uk
www.heath-avery.co.uk
Established in 1980, Heath Avery
is creative Architects committed
to environmentally and socially
responsible design. We have
particular expertise in housing,
education and care as well as
being accustomed to working
with complex Conservation and
Planning issues.

**DAN STAINER-HUTCHINS
ARCHITECTS LTD.**
Dan Stainer-Hutchins
5 Bridge Street,
Nailsworth GL6 0AA
T: 01453 839121
E: dan@dstainer-hutchins.co.uk
www.dstainer-hutchinsarchitects.
co.uk
We are a firm of architects specialising in ecological design. With
extensive experience in both the
private and commercial sector, our
services include: surveys, statutory approvals, listed buildings,
fundraising, feasibility studies, town
planning and project management.

QUATTRO DESIGN ARCHITECTS
Pauline Dewhirst
Bearland Lodge, Longsmith Street,
Gloucester GL1 2HT
T: 01452 424234
E: pauline.d@quattro-glos.co.uk
www.quattrodesign.co.uk
Quattro is a talented ARCHITECTS
committed to designing buildings which enhance the local
environment both physically and
socially. We have built a reputation for creating innovative designs
through close collaboration with
users and clients within tight financial guidelines.

BREEAM ASSESSOR

PAVEL HOUZVICKA
92 St. Whites Road,
Cinderford GL14 3HB
T: 01594 826464
E: pavel@deanfern.org
A fully qualified BREEAM EcoHomes
Assessor.

BUILDERS MERCHANT

GREEN SHOP (THE)
Jane Powell
Cheltenham Road, Bisley GL6 7BX
T: 01452 770629
E: enquiries@greenshop.co.uk
www.greenshop.co.uk
We offer sales and advice on
products for a more sustainable
future. Including a host of different
environmentally friendly paints
and wood finishes, sheeps wool
and cellulose based insulation,
sunpipes and solar and wind
systems.

EDUCATIONAL

THE LIVING GREEN CENTRE
Diana Ray
High Street,
Bourton on the Water GL54 2AP
T: 01451 820942
E: people@living-green.co.uk
www.living-green.co.uk
Visitor attraction: green choices in real home setting. Top showcase for proven green products. Retro-fit Cotswold cottage. New build is sexy- but existing housing stock is where most people affect the environment. Fabulous shop, garden, eco-trail, grass-roof, solar, household stuff, rain-harvesting.

MARKETING AND MEDIA

GRAHAM BOND VISUAL COMMUNICATIONS
Graham Bond
85 Barrowfield Road,
Stroud GL5 4DG
T: 01453 758279
E: studio@gbvisual.com
www.gbvisual.com
Promote your business with a presentation folder, brochure, Website or a fresh corporate ID. Design for print: brochures, product data, catalogues; Web site design and maintenance; Creative graphics: corporate ID, logos, illustrations, digital imaging.

PLUMBER

EFFICIENT SOLUTIONS
Charlie Mackinnon-Little
14 Winterway, Blockley,
Moreton-in-Marsh GL56 9EF
T: 07979 460925
E: cml-plumbing@fsmail.net
Energy saving heating and water conservation plumbing: achieved through the design and installation of efficient heating systems, insulation specification, solar thermal, rain harvesting, water efficient fittings and appliances. Consultancy services also offered for all the above.

Somerset

ARCHITECTS

MARY C BON RIBA
Mary Bon
Elm View, Cottage White Hill,
Shoscombe, Bath BA2 8LU
T: 01761 436712
E: m.bon@ukonline.co.uk
I am a sole practitioner operating as a RIBA chartered practice,
involved principally in the private domestic sector, (including conservation and listed building work) but also in the education sector. I am also a registered architect in France.

WILF BURTON
DIPARCH RIBA, DIPTP, MRTPI
The Oak House, Lower Godney,
Wells BA5 1RZ
T: 0771 3408291
E: wilf.burton@virgin.net
Eco architect and town planner specialising in oak-framed, environmentally friendly houses, working closely with framers, craft builders, energy consultants and clients.

ECOLOGIC DESIGN
John Shore
16 Popes Lane, Wellington,
Somerset
TA21 9DQ
T: 01823 666177
www.shorepower.co.uk
Architectural design consultants for low-cost, self-sufficient, timber frame, self build and renovation. Passive solar space and water heating, water conservation, aerobic compost toilet design, wind and solar energy, education and training. Over 30 year's experience with ecological building and wind energy.

DEVELOPER

SOUTH WEST ECO-HOMES LTD.
Nigel Griffiths
Old Town Hall, Bow St.,
Langport TA10 9PR
T: 01458 259400
E: nigel@sustainablehousing.org.uk
www.swecohomes.co.uk
South West Eco-Homes - ethical developer of sustainably built housing, focusing on small and medium-sized brownfield sites in the south west. We also undertake master planning, consultancy and eco-homes assessment for housing associations, other developers and self-builders.

LANDSCAPE DESIGNER

MICHAEL LITTLEWOOD
Michael Littlewood
PO Box 25, South Petherton
TA13 5WZ
T: 01460 240168
E: michael@ecodesignscape.co.uk
www.ecodesignscape.co.uk
Bio-engineering, water harvesting, natural waste treatment, bio-
energy systems, organic edible production, nature conservation, natural swimming pools. International experience and expertise, Michael can demonstrate how 'Designing in Harmony with Nature' can be used to the advantage of people and the environment, as well as producing considerable financial savings and benefits.

SOLAR THERMAL INSTALLER

ECOFIRST
Jody Moorat
The Tithe Office, Abbey Manor Business Centre, Yeovil BA20 2FJ
T: 0845 257 5064
E: info@ecofirst.net
www.ecofirst.net
Ecofirst is an accredited installer of solar thermal systems. Our systems are designed by BPEC trained personnel using software simulation systems. We have highly trained teams throughout the UK to install our superior quality systems (flat plate or evacuated tube).

SUSTAINABLE DEVELOPMENT CONSULTANT

SOMERSET TRUST FOR SUSTAINABLE DEVELOPMENT
Charles Couzens
Old Town Hall, Bow Street, Langport
TA10 9PR
T: 01458 259400
E: admin@sustainablehousing.org.uk
www.sustainablehousing.org.uk
Promoting sustainable building and lifestyles through advice, consultancy, seminars, conferences and exhibitions. STSDs mission is to make sustainable building normal rather than exceptional by 2010. The Trusts sister company South West Eco-Homes builds real life examples of eco-developments.

TIMBER FRAMER, TRADITIONAL

GREEN OAK STRUCTURES
James Godden
20 Bushy Coombe gardens,
Glastonbury BA6 8JT
T: 01458 833420
E: timberframes@greenoakstructures.co.uk
www.greenoakstructures.co.uk
Design and build traditional timberframes in douglas fir and oak. Timber is sourced from managed reserves in U.K and France.

© Green Building Press

WATER AND WASTE APPLIANCES

WATERCOURSE SYSTEMS LTD.

Chris Weedon
Wills Barn, Taunton TA4 2PX
T: 01984 629 070
E: weedon@compuserve.com
Consultancy, design and build of appropriate wastewater treatment systems, reed beds, ponds, willow beds, composting toilets. Chris Weedon, company director, has implemented nearly 50 treatment systems, since 1991 established CAT's consultancy in alternative sewage treatment co-author Sewage Solutions.

Wiltshire

ARCHITECTS

EDWARD TUCKER

Edward Tucker
93 Kingshill Road,
Swindon
SN1 4LG
T: 01793 610593
E: ed@edwardtucker.co.uk
www.edwardtucker.co.uk
Edward Tucker is an RIBA chartered architect and member of the Association of Environmentally Conscious Builders specialising in sustainable residential architecture from eco-refurbishment of existing buildings to low energy new homes and self-builds.

MARK ELLERBY ARCHITECT

Mark Ellerby
The Studio, Rookery Cottage,
Uphill, Urchfont,
Devizes SN10 4SB
T: +44 (0) 1380 840800
E: mark.ellerby@virgin.net
Mark Ellerby Architect is an award winning practice specialising in the creation of imaginative, responsible designs that are ecologically sustainable and cost effective. The practice has a wide experience of many project types, especially Education, Community/Voluntary, and Housing.

BREEAM ASSESSOR

DEGREES OF GREEN

Stephen Parker
Glencairn, 17, South Street,
Corsham SN13 9HB
T: 07785 980 500
E: degreesofgreen@dsl.pipex.com
www.degreesofgreen.co.uk
Providing technical advice and

project management services to Housing Clients who want to benefit from expertise in the innovative and challenging field of sustainable development, including design reviews, renewable energy advice and assistance with grant funding applications. Registered EcoHomes Assessor.

TIMBER FRAMER, TRADITIONAL

WESSEX OAK FRAME CONSTRUCTION LTD.

James Reid
9 Longleaze Cottages, Lower
Wadswick, Box,
Corsham SN13 8JF
T: 01225 812484
E: info@wessexoakframe.co.uk
www.wessexoakframe.co.uk
Incorporating Radicle Oak Frame Design. 25 years experience in the Design and Fabrication of Original Oak-framed Structures to Traditional or Contemporary specifications. Conservation of time-served frames and Glazing of new-build are specialities.

West Midlands

Shropshire

ARCHITECTS

BAART HARRIES NEWALL

Robert Morris
1 Wilderhope House, Pountney
Gardens, Belle Vue, Shrewsbury
SY3 7LU
T: 01743361261
E: studio@bhn.co.uk
www.bhn.co.uk
We offer full architectural services and are committed to contemporary design of high quality whilst seeking to use best practice in low energy design to produce cost effective sustainable solutions. Experienced in repair and conversion of older/listed buildings.

ARCHITECTS

ENVIRONMENTAL AND ARCHITECTURAL DESIGN

David Gomersall
Studio 4, Lower down, Lydbury
North SY7 8BB
T: 01588 680693
E: david@eadstudio4.co.uk
Environmental and Architectural Design is a small ARCHITECTS specialising in contemporary

ecological design and construction. We produce practical, innovative and energy efficient designs for new buildings and extensions using environmentally sensitive techniques and materials.

SIMMONDS MILLS ARCHITECTS

Andy Simmonds
Workshop Office, Greenwood Trust,
Station Road, Coalbrookdale,
Telford TF8 7DR
T: 01952 433252
E: simmondsmills@f2s.com
www.simmondsmills.com
Established 1991, historic conservation, eco-renovation, new housing, public and educational buildings. We have a clear understanding of ecological building physics, and all our projects incorporate principles of energy efficiency and use sustainable materials. We support and promote the AECB's energy standards

Warwickshire

ENERGY CONSULTANT

ENCRAFT

Graham Eastwick
Perseus House, 3 Chapel Court,
Holly Walk,
Leamington Spa CV32 4YS
T: 01926 312159
E: graham.eastwick@encraft.co.uk
www.encraft.co.uk
Encraft provide independent technical analysis, design and evaluation services for low carbon energy systems. They deliver an individual service at design stage, with site visits and assessments for refurbishment projects. Encraft cover all low carbon energy technologies and are impartial.

Worcestershire

ARCHITECTS

HOWL ASSOCIATES LTD.

Phil Howl
Shrubbery House, 21
Birmingham Road,
Kidderminster DY10 2BX
T: 01562 820022
E: phil@howl.co.uk
www.howl.co.uk
We are architects committed to contemporary design and work with our clients to seek cost effective and sustainable solutions. We have experience of natural ventilation principles, light tubes, passive solar control, active environmental controls and ecological specification of materials.

North West

Cheshire

ARCHITECTS

COMMUNITY REGENERATION LTD.
Malcolm Seddon
The Studio, 12 Chiltern Drive,
Woodsmoor, Stockport SK2 7BE
T: 0161 484 0585
Small, friendly, RIBA registered
practice in the residential,
domestic and voluntary sector,
with experience in green design,
conservation, refurbishment
and newbuild across Greater
Manchester and adjoining
counties.

DESIGN AND TECHNICAL SERVICES
Simon Morris
20 Lilac Grove, Stockton Heath,
Warrington WA4 2DG
T: 07812 809333
E: design-tech@ntlworld.com
A small friendly practice offering
the full range of architectural
services. With experience in
residential, commercial and
education projects.

PLASTERER

LIME EARTH CONSERVATION LTD.
Stuart Furby
10 Haughton Street, Warrington
WA2 7DD
T: 0192 548 0600
E: furby@limeearthpaints.com
www.limeearthpaints.com
Traditional lime plastering contrac-
tors and repairs to old buildings.
Manufacturers of lime mortar, lime
patching plasters and lime/earth
paints.

Cumbria

TIMBER FRAMER

EDEN FRAME
Trevor Lowis
Midtown Barn, Appleby
CA16 6BD
T: 01768 353866
E: trevor@edenframe.com
www.edenframe.com
Tradis Panel Design, Manufacture,
Supply and Erection of Warmcel
pre-insulated floor, wall and roof
panels. Be-spoke Design: Houses,
Libraries, Schools, Village Halls,

Leisure Centres, Eco-Centres. 3-
Bedroomed Housed weather-tight
in 3-4 days with off site manufactured panels. Zero-heating
achieved!

Manchester

CONSULTING ENGINEERS

CLANCY CONSULTING LTD.
Alan Bramwell
Dunham Court, 2 Dunham Road,
Altrincham, Cheshire, Manchester
WA14 4NX
T: 0161 613 6000
E: marketing@clancy.co.uk
www.clancy.co.uk
Clancy Consulting is a multi disci-
plinary consultancy specialising in
innovative engineering solutions
for the Construction Industry. We
provide advice in the areas of civil,
structural and building services
engineering, building surveying,
sustainability and energy management, and health and safety.

North East

Tyne and Wear

ARCHITECTS

GLASS ARC LTD.
Henry Amos
Studio 6, Station Terrace,
Tynemouth, North Shields
NE30 4RE
T: 0191 257 4454
E: solutions@glassarc.com
www.glassarc.com
Innovative sustainable design solutions for domestic and commercial
clients with an enthusiasm for
natural light. We offer a full range
of services including new build
and refurbishment developments
informed by varied experience
and interests in listed buildings and
conservation areas.

NEWTON ARCHITECTS
Malcolm Newton
Burnaby Lodge, Ryton NE40 3BP
T: 0191 413 3996
E: mn@newtonarhcitects.co.uk
www.newtonarchitects.com
All projects address the sustainability agenda holistically, starting
with designing buildings with
climate then to issues such as
embodied energy in use balance
to renewable energy generation/
recycling/minimising waste. Typical

projects: training/community
centres, theatre, offices, housing
and conversions.

ARCHITECTURAL SERVICES

NBS
Michael Smith
The Old Post Office, St. Nicholas
Street, Newcastle upon Tyne
NE1 1RH
T: 0191 2445619
E: michael.smith@thenbs.com
www.thenbs.com
NBS publishes national master
specification systems (NBS
Building, NBS Engineering Services,
NBS Landscape), the Building
Regulations, and related info.
systems for construction specifiers.
NBS offers pre-written work sections,
clauses and guidance for use on
sustainable projects. Regularly
expanded and updated.

MARKETING AND MEDIA

NBS
Michael Smith
The Old Post Office, St. Nicholas
Street, Newcastle upon Tyne
NE1 1RH
T: 0191 244 5619
E: michael.smith@thenbs.com
www.nbsgreenconstruction.com
Is a top level information tool,
which features an extensive
bibliography relating to sustainability issues in construction.
NBS Green Construction is also
available as a twice monthly
newsletter. To subscribe, send an
email to Michael Smith at michael.
smith@thenbs.com.

Yorkshire & Humber

North Yorkshire

ARCHITECTS

ECO ARC
Andrew Yeats
Old Village School, Harton ,
York YO60 7NP
T: 01904 468 752
E: ecoarc@ecoarc.co.uk
www.ecoarc.co.uk
Andrew enjoys working with clients
to design beautiful and healthy
buildings built to the highest
ecological and spatial standards
incorporating best practice in
low energy, solar design, utilizing

© Green Building Press

renewable wind and solar technologies, etc all within a holistic
frame work.

South Yorkshire

BUILDERS MERCHANT

SUSTAINABLE BUILDING SUPPLIES
Matt Robinson
c/o 90 Stafford Road, Sheffield,
South Yorkshire S2 2SF
T: 0114 299 8559
E: matt@sustainablebuildingsupp
lies.co.uk
www.sustainablebuildingsupplies.
co.uk
Contract and retail supply of
sustainable building systems and
materials, natural insulations and
contract-eco or natural paints. We
are Northern wholesalers of the
superb BIOFA paint range. From
a tin of paint, to a new school, we
can supply.

West Yorkshire

ARCHITECTS

LEEDS ENVIRONMENTAL DESIGN ASSOCIATES LTD.
Jonathan Lindh
Micklethwaite House, 70 Cross
Green Lane, Leeds LS9 0DG
T: 0113 2009380
E: office@leda.org.uk
www.leda.org.uk
LEDA integrates architecture and
environmental building services
engineering to create sustainable
buildings. We can provide a full
range of services from full building
design and site supervision to initial
design advice.

OSA ARCHITECTS
Pamela Parkinson
31 Well Lane, Leeds LS7 4PQ
T: 0113 225 8240
E: design@osa-architects.co.uk
www.osa-architects.co.uk
We are committed to creating high
quality sustainable architecture.
Since establishing our practice in
1991, we have encouraged our
clients, from community groups to
the health service, to build green.
We are currently designing eco-
houses in West Yorkshire.

SENSE OF SPACE ARCHITECTS AND BUILDING SURVEYORS
Richard Addenbrook
35 The Grove, Ilkley LS29 9NJ
T: 01943 816489
E: enquiries@senseofspace.net
www.senseofspace.net
Sense of Space is committed to
sustainable forms of construction
and the use of environmentally
friendly products. Our innovative
approach means we design for the
future, embrace new technology
and most importantly work with the
varying needs of our clients.

BUILDERS MERCHANT

GREEN BUILDING STORE
Chayley Collis
11 Huddersfield Road, Meltham,
West Yorkshire HD9 4NJ
T: 01484 854898
E: chayley@greenbuildingstore.co.uk
www.greenbuildingstore.co.uk
Green Building Store specialises in
supplying products which promote
energy-efficient, sustainable
and healthy buildings. Our range
includes FSC-certified windows,
doors and solar spaces, natural
paints, boron timber preservatives,
natural insulation, ultra-efficient
toilets and steel guttering.

BUILDING CONTRACTOR

GREEN BUILDING COMPANY
Bill Butcher
11 Huddersfield Road,
Meltham HD9 4NJ
T: 01484 854186
E: build@greenbuildingco.co.uk
www.greenbuildingco.co.uk
The Company offers a high quality,
environment-sensitive regional
construction service. Recent
contracts include Manchester
Environment Resource Centre
(Bridge 5 Mill), Quaker Meeting
House (Huddersfield), Longwood
(Huddersfield) low energy house
and many local commercial and
domestic contracts.

ECOLOGICAL COMMUNITY

ECOLOGY BUILDING SOCIETY
Jenny Barton
7 Belton Road, Silsden, Keighley
BD20 0EE
T: 01535 650770
E: info@ecology.co.uk
www.ecology.co.uk
Ecology specialises in green
savings and mortgages for the
construction of ecological new
builds and the renovation or
conversion of dilapidated proper-

ties. Mortgages are advanced
against the land or the unimproved
property value, and funds can be
released in stages.

ENVIRONMENTAL BUSINESS CONSULTANT

CONSULTING WITH A PURPOSE
Gideon Richards
45 New Laithe Hill, Newsome,
Huddersfield HD4 6RF
T: 01924 261341
E: gideon@cwap.co.uk
CWAP provide consultancy in the
Energy, Energy from Waste and
Environmental sectors, predomi-
nantly at a strategic, regulatory,
business development and feasibil-
ity level. Gideon Richards also
chairs the UK mirror committee
for European Standards for Solid
Biofuels and Solid Recovered Fuels.

INTERIOR DESIGNER

MILESTONE DESIGN LTD.
Julian Richards
22 / 24 Leeds Road,
Ilkley. LS29 8DS
T: 0845 4567 153
E: julian@milestone.uk.net
www.milestone.uk.net
A kitchens designer/maker
business. We have created
the first, affordable, totally
recycled content kitchen project.
Contemporary in style, it fits
comfortably into the middle market
sector and features low energy
lighting. Check our website for
more in-depth information.

PAINTING AND DECORATING

ECODEC
George Bogojevic
27A Northgate,
Cleckheaton BD19 3HH
T: 07974 683111
E: eco-decs@tiscali.co.uk
www.ecodec.co.uk
EcoDec are happy to adapt to the
individual needs of our customers and execute a broad array of
residential work and commercial
refurbishments, including shops,
bars and offices along with new
build projects. Specification service
available for paints and wallcover-
ings.

East Midlands

Leicestershire

BUILDING CONTRACTOR

EARTH STRUCTURES (EUROPE) LTD.
William Swaney
The Manor, Hall Lane, Ashley,
Market Harborough LE16 8HE
T: 01858 565436
E: info@earthstructures.co.uk
www.earthstructures.co.uk
Rammed Earth building contractors, designers, consultants and researchers. We have a full set of rammed earth building formwork and equipment and can offer a full service from advice to completion of an environmentally friendly rammed earth building.

EDUCATIONAL

THE ECOHOUSE / GROUNDWORK LEICESTER
Caroline Harmon
Gwll, Parkfield, Western Park,
Leicester LE3 6HX
T: 0116 254 5489
E: ecohouse@gwll.org.uk
www.gwll.org.uk/ecohouse
The EcoHouse is Britain's original and leading environmental showhome open to the public. It demonstrates hundreds of possibilities for an eco-friendly building. See website for opening times and entrance fee. Guided tours for groups can be arranged.

ENERGY CONSULTANT

THIRD STONE LTD.
Richard Holmes
34 Glen Park Avenue, Leicester LE3 8GG
T: 0116 2875588
E: enquiries@third-stone.co.uk
www.third-stone.co.uk
Part L Compliance: Over 10 years experience in energy rating of buildings and provides cost effective advisory service in helping building designers comply with Part L of the Building Regulations Assessments are carried out using software approved by the BRE.

Lincolnshire

BUILDING CONTRACTOR

HILL HOLT WOOD
Bryce Gilroy-Scott
1 Badgers Lane Hill Holt Wood,
Norton Disney LN6 9JP
T: 01636 892 836
E: bryce@hillholtwood.com
www.hillholtwood.com
Eco-construction social enterprise, specialising in build of composting loos. Full contract services - design, planning guidance, materials sourcing. We work in wood, earth, strawbale and recycled materials. Also earth ovens. National portfolio of previous builds.

CARPENTER/JOINER

TITHE FARM OAK WORKS
Biff Vernon
Tithe Farm, Church End, North Somercotes, Louth LN11 7PZ
T: 01507 358413
E: biff@biffvernon.freeserve.co.uk
www.biffvernon.freeserve.co.uk
Maker of bespoke oak windows and doors, using sustainable methods and materials. Mouthblown plain and stained glass work. Consultant in traditional and sustainable building methods.

Northamptonshire

EDUCATIONAL

PERMORGANICS
Dawn Houghton
Northampton NN4
T: 07885 981789
E: permorganics@yahoo.co.uk
Workers co-operative providing adult and school education courses, team building and workshops/consultations in permaculture, green building and more. We also supply home grown and locally sourced fresh organic produce, useful and medicinal plants to local people, community and corporate groups.

DESIGNER

SQUEAKY DESIGN
Mark James
The Wheelhouse, Northampton NN12 7XU
T: 0790 454 0583
E: squeakydesign@aol.com
www.squeakydesign.info
DIY guidance to full project management. 21 years living without ANY mains services spent acquiring experience in multi-disciplinary ecological design, research and build, low-tech alternative solutions, including 12 volt electrics, historical reconstructions, real ergonomic interior/exterior design on land and afloat.

Nottinghamshire

ARCHITECTS

MARK STEWART ARCHITECTS
Gil Schalom
34a Musters Road,
Nottingham NG2 7PL
T: 0115 9455787
E: gil@msarch.co.uk
www.msarch.co.uk

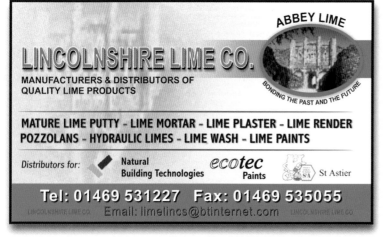

LINCOLNSHIRE LIME CO.
ABBEY LIME
BONDING THE PAST AND THE FUTURE
MANUFACTURERS & DISTRIBUTORS OF QUALITY LIME PRODUCTS

MATURE LIME PUTTY - LIME MORTAR - LIME PLASTER - LIME RENDER
POZZOLANS - HYDRAULIC LIMES - LIME WASH - LIME PAINTS

Distributors for: Natural Building Technologies   ecotec Paints   St Astier

Tel: 01469 531227   Fax: 01469 535055
Email: limelincs@btinternet.com

Designers of groundbreaking Nottingham ecohome. Experienced practice specialising in green new build, advanced sustainable retrofit and historic conservation. Focus on practical, true low energy solutions and use of appropriate materials. Excellent record in obtaining consents in sensitive locations.

East

Bedfordshire

WOOD ENERGY

ECONERGY LTD.
Dawn Riggett
Unit 12, St. Georges Tower,
Hatley St George,
Sandy SG19 3SH
T: 08700 545554
E: sales@econergy.ltd.uk
www.econergy.ltd.uk
Econergy is the UK's premier wood energy company. We deliver a full range of products to our customers from log, chip or pellet boilers for individual premises to larger turnkey installation, heat networks and CHP.

Essex

ARCHITECTS

INKPEN DOWNIE ARCHITECTURE AND DESIGN
Su Butcher
35 North Hill, Colchester
CO1 1QR
T: 01206 577 244
E: arch@inkpendownie.co.uk
www.inkpendownie.co.uk
A progressive practice of architects, interior designers and historic building consultants. Inkpen Downie's sustainable building work includes award winning community buildings, a naturally ventilated golf club house and a passive solar, CO_2 neutral house in the countryside.

BUILDING CONTRACTOR

JONATHAN COOKE
Stocking Green Farm, Saffron Walden CB10 2SS
E: jcooke@dragonbc.f9.co.uk
www.rotaloo.co.uk
Complete renovation and extension of period properties. Over 24 years of experience working with

listed buildings. Structural work in steel and green oak solar, underfloor and central heating design and installation.

ENERGY CONSULTANT

SPLENDID ENGINEERING
Daniel Kenning
Woolmers Mead,
Chelmsford CM3 1HH
T: 01245 237 524
E: dkenning@splendid.gb.com
www.splendidengineering.co.uk
Energy Consultancy, and the BEST Energy advice and support service for sustainable domestic energy, including Demand Optimisation, Efficiency, Renewables onsite Opportunities Reviews, Technical Feasibility Studies and support through Installation of the best energy system with the least hassle and least cost.

Hertfordshire

ARCHITECTS

ANDREW GOODMAN ARCHITECTURE
Andrew Goodman
90 Ware Road, Hertford
SG13 7HN
T: 01992 501073
E: andrew@goodarchitecture.co.uk
The practice has a philosophy of developing adaptable, environmentally friendly and energy conscious design for living and working.

ECOLOGGIA ARCHITECTS
Maurice Clarke
3a Canberra House, London Road,
St. Albans AL1 1LE
T: 01727 833331
E: mc@ecologgia.net
Ecologgia aims to: -Work with nature. -Avoid materials which: are remotely procured, have high embodied energy or damage the environment -Use materials which: save natural resources, are renewable -Design for carbon neutrality. -Minimise harm.

ENVIRONMENTAL BUSINESS CONSULTANT

BRE (CENTRE FOR RESOURCE EFFICIENCY)
Katherine Adams
Buknalls Lane, Garston, Watford
WD25 9XX
T: 01923 664471
E: smartwaste@bre.co.uk
www.smartwaste.co.uk

www.bre.co.uk
The Centre for Resource Efficiency is world leading in providing advice and research in all aspects related to waste management throughout the whole life cycle of a building. We provide a number of waste monitoring tools known as SMARTWaste to help industry improve their performance.

HEATING SUPPLIES

FBC
Heather Jackson
Sells Close, High Street, Barley,
Royston SG8 8HY
T: 01763 271271
E: info@fbcgroup.co.uk
www.fbcgroup.co.uk
Suppliers of Baxi log boilers and wood pellet wood chip and grain boilers, Futura wood pellet boilers, Dinak Flues, Akvaterm Storage Tanks, Acaso Controls and Valves for Heating Systems. Also importers of the Bilke firewood processor.

Norfolk

ARCHITECTS

JOHN PARDON MCIAT, CHARTERED ARCHITECTURAL TECHNOLOGIST
John Pardon
29 Newton Park, Newton St. Faiths,
Norwich NR10 3LP
T: 07776 357237
E: johnpardon@tiscali.co.uk
Sole practitioner with special interest in promoting sound sustainable development, alternative energies and energy efficient use of buildings. Projects include small scale housing developments, self-build and one off houses, commercial and industrial.

BUILDING CONTRACTOR

GREENBUILD
Mike Walker
The Garden House,
High Common, Swardeston,
Norwich NR14 8DL
T: 0794 902 0080
E: mikewalker@greenbuild.fsnet.co.uk
www.norfolkgreenbuild.fsnet.co.uk
GreenBuild is a friendly local business specialising in all aspects of sustainable building and contracting, using modern and traditional methods and materials. We will undertake barn conversions, extensions, renovations, new builds, lofts and almost any type of green building work.

KATE EDWARDS
Crescent Cottage, Surrey Street,
Cromer NR27 9EZ
T: 01263 519024
E: sheepie32@hotmail.com
www.edwardsecobuilding.com
Eco building specialising in the
beauty of cob/clay lump. Beautiful
sculptural buildings, garden
houses, art studios etc. renovations of clay lump building, lime
plastering and rendering working
with earth is the most environmet-
ally friendly and durable, method
possible.

ENVIRONMENTAL BUSINESS CONSULTANT

FRANCES FRANCIS
Frances Francis
Flint House, High Street,
East Runton NR27 9AB
T: 01263 514345
E: francesfrancis@tiscali.co.uk
Environmental Co-ordinator
specialising in promotion of sustainable construction, eco-homes and
green lifestyles. Extensive experience of organising exhibitions,
conferences, speakers, awards
schemes and judges, educational and practical projects plus
research and advice. Can also be
commissioned for other environmental projects.

SOLAR THERMAL INSTALLER

NORFOLK SOLAR
Lee Rose
26 Gunton Lane, Costessey,
Norwich NR5 0AE
T: 01603 734851
E: lee@norfolksolar.co.uk
www.norfolksolar.co.uk
Specialists in the design, installation and servicing of domestic solar
hot water systems. Also provide
training services to self builders and
professional installers.

Suffolk

ARCHITECTS

STUDIOMGM LLP
Ralph Carpenter
88-89 St. Johns St., Bury St. Edmunds
IP33 1SQ
T: 08700 508246
E: modece@studiomgm.co.uk
www.studiomgm.co.uk
Studiomgm is a practice with an
extensive and award winning
portfolio of work in East Anglia,
and Europe. The practice majors

in housing design, community
and educational projects with
particular strengths in areas such as
ecological design, climate change
design, beauty and a sense of
place and home.

Scotland

ARCHITECTURAL SERVICES

ZN DESIGN AND VISUALISATION
T: 0031 518 41 32 45
E: info@zndesign.co.uk
www.zndesign.co.uk
ZN Design creates digital artist
impressions of your design ideas.
We specialise in photomatching
the design in its context, create
photorealistic art work, use
computer animation for landscape
overviews and help present your
design on paper / powerpoint /
internet.

Aberdeenshire

BUILDING CONTRACTOR

SYLVAN STUART LTD.
Bryan Stuart
Pitmachie Works, Old Rayne, Insch
AB52 6RX
T: 01464 851208
E: sales@sylvanstuart.com
www.sylvanstuart.com
Long-established timber engineers
and processors with a record of
innovation, operating throughout
the UK. Anything in wood! is our
motto. Unique interlocking, double-
skin log construction system. Large
structures a speciality. Aqueous
boron pressure pre-treatment.
Extensive website.

Angus

CARPENTER/JOINER

BESPOKE TIMBERWORK
Dave Saville
Dalkilry, Kilry PH11 8HX
T: 01575 560 755
E: mail@bespoketimber.co.uk
Timberwork and joinery, both
contemporary and traditional.
Timber frame design and consulta-
tion. Timberwork surveys and repair.
Provide weathertight structures
including glazing, cladding, roofing
and insulation. Source local and
recycled timber.

Argyll and Bute

ARCHITECTS

CP ARCHITECTS
Iain Angus Campbell
110 George Street,
Oban PA34 5NT
T: 01631 563177
E: mail@cparchitects.net
www.cparchitects.net
We are an Oban based Practice
with projects throughout the
Highlands and Islands working with
Community Groups, Public Bodies,
and private individuals. We aim
to integrate appropriate renewable energies within the design
to ensure our buildings minimise
energy usage and impact on the
environment.

Dundee

RESEARCHER

EDG (ECOLOGICAL DESIGN GROUP)
Fionn Stevenson
School of Architecture, University of
Dundee, 13, Perth Road
DD1 4HT
T: 01382-385262
E: f.z.stevenson@dundee.ac.uk
www.dundee.ac.uk
EDG provides comprehensive
post occupancy evaluations in
the health and housing sector,
research and guidance on sustainable housing design, bioregional
and local sourcing of materials and
products particularly in relation
to Scotland, innovative material
applications and design for disassembly.

Edinburgh

ARCHITECT

GAIA ARCHITECTS
Howard Liddell
The Monastery, 2 Hart Street,
Edinburgh EH1 3RG
T: 0131 557 9191
E: architects@gaiagroup.org
www.gaiagroup.org.uk
Gaia Architects are the oldest
ecological design practice in
the UK, and have received many
awards. Experienced in housing,
community development,
commerical, sports and leisure
buildings, project management,
feasibility, training and specialist
advice.

© Green Building Press

LOCATE ARCHITECTS
Chris Morgan
30 High Street, Portobello Road
Edinburgh
EH15 1DD
T: 0131 620 0530
E: mail@chrismorgan.fsnet.co.uk
www.locatearchitects.co.uk
An innovative young practice
specialising in contemporary
ecological design, tailored
to circumstance and budget.
Services range from architectural
commissions to technical research,
masterplanning, consultancy
in construction and sustainable
development and lecturing.

Glasgow

ARCHITECTS

DALLMAN JOHNSTONE ARCHITECTS
Lillian Johnstone
The Studio 24 New Kirk Road,
Bearsden G61 3SL
T: 0141 942 3025
E: dallman-johnstone@dial.pipex.com
www.dallmanjohnstone.com
Chosen by the DTI as exemplar
for sustainability and energy
efficiency. Maximum effect
with minimum environmental
impact. Creative design backed
by sound project management
skills. Attention to orientation, site,
resources, renewable energies and
non-toxic local/recycled materials. Sectors:- leisure, commercial,
residential, health.

Highland

BUILDING CONTRACTOR

A J BUILDING SERVICES
Anthony Birdsall
Stonefield Farm, Upperbower
Tower, Bower,
Caithness KW1 4TT
T: 07790 111125
E: ajbuilding@ktdinernet.com
A complete Building Service,
est. 1997, all trades covered from
sympathetic renovations and
repairs to old buildings using traditional materials to custom made
small scale re-newable power for
off grid solutions. Also manufacture and installation of solar water
systems.

MARK THACKER (STONEMASON)
Mark Thacker
The Norwegians, Carloway,
Isle of Lewis HS2 9AG
T: 01851 643261
E: mark.thacker@virgin.net
Our stonemasonry business has
been trading for 10 years. A small
firm passionate about old buildings
we work to the highest standard.
Stone dressing and carving
rubblework Lime harling and
pointing lettercutting and drystone.
Anywhere in Britain.

Lanarkshire

CAMPAIGN ORGANISATION

ECO-RENOVATION NETWORK
Kat Jones
16 Victoria Park Drive North,
Glasgow G14 9NH
T: 01415 796967
E: info@eco-renovation.org
www.eco-renovation.org
We are a new organisation facilitating local networks (starting with
Glasgow) and promoting coor-
dination and communication for
people interested in eco-renovation. Our website has directories of
businesses and links. Talks, workpar-
ties and cooperative buying, we
welcome individual and business
members.

Lothian

ARCHITECTS

ICOSIS ARCHITECTS
Euan Millar
28 Albert Street,
Edinburgh EH7 5LG
T: 01315 552442
E: mail@icosis.co.uk
www.icosis.co.uk
ICOSIS aim to produce both
contemporary new buildings and
carry out sensitive conservation
projects, with an emphasis on the
use of natural and environmentally
sustainable materials.

ARCHITECT AND BUILDER

DICK PEDDIE AND MCKAY
Mike Henderson
The Stable Block, Society Place,
West Calder EH55 8EA
T: 01506 873851
E: mike@peddiearchitects.co.uk
Dick Peddie and McKay is a long
established Scottish practice which
takes a pragmatic approach to

the incorporation of ecological
principles in its current projects.
We always try and strike a balance
between cost efficiency and client
satisfaction.

Midlothian

ARCHITECT AND BUILDER

QUERCUS RURAL BUILDING DESIGN
Peter Caunt
Sunnyside Studio,
Heriot EH38 5YE
T: 01875 835220
E: quercus@ednet.co.uk
www.quercusrbd.co.uk
Quercus Rural Building Design
are Architects and Builders
based in the Scottish Borders. The
practice has a good knowledge
of Agricultural, Equestrian and
Holiday Lodge design. We are
members of SEDA and apply green
principles to all our projects

Perth and Kinross

LANDSCAPE ARCHITECT

SCOTTISH ORIGINS LLP
Erika Luukas BSc, MIEEM
3 Brewery Lane, Kinross KY13 8EL
T: 01577 861437
E: erikaluukas@scotorigins.co.uk
www.scotorigins.co.uk
Scottish Origins - Landscape
Ecology by Design. Providing
consultancy and landscape design
services to create ecologically
functional wildlife habitats in built
environments using native origin
plants and wildflowers grown at
our specialist nursery - ensuring
external landscaping truly comple-
ments green building projects.

Ross-shire

ARCHITECTS

DOUGLAS MURRAY, ARCHITECT
Douglas Murray
5 Kinellan, Strathpeffer IV14 9ET
T: 01997 421981
E: murrarch@aol.com
I have been practising as an
architect in the Highlands since
1979 and ploughing an ecological
furrow in my design work for last six
years, with several clients who want
the full ecological design.

FRANK BURSTOW ARCHITECT
Frank Burstow
Portnacloich, by Erbusaig,
Kyle of Lochalsh IV40 8DA
T: 01599 534040
E: architect@portnacloich.co.uk
Architect based in the Highlands
since 1978. Wide range of projects
including public and private
housing, leisure and recreational
buildings. Practise ethos is to
design buildings that fit into the
landscape using low energy and
sustainable solutions within budget
and timescale.

Wales

Cardiff

ARCHITECTURAL SERVICES

PARKINSON HOLT LTD.
Rodney Holt
Unit 143, The Business Centre, 61
Wellfield Road,
Cardiff CF24 3DG
T: 07921 767092
E: parkinsonholt@btinternet.com
www.eco-residence.com
As part of new building regulations part L1A, you will require a
new build dwelling to have a SAP
energy rating produced by an
authorised SAP Assessor at full
plans approval stage and as fitted
stage following an airtightness
pressure test. We provide both SAP
and Airtightness services and will
shortly be carrying out SBEM Energy
Ratings.

EDUCATIONAL

ROUNDED DEVELOPMENTS
Peter Draper
Sustainable Building Centre, Unit 93
Portmanmoor Road Ind. Est., Splott
CF24 5HB
T: 029 2040 3399
E: info@rounded-developments.
org.uk
www.rounded-developments.org.
uk
RDEs Sustainable Building Centre
encourages people interested in
their environment to explore all
aspects of sustainable building.
Themed displays and courses are
run throughout the year. Check the
website for updates. The centre
also sells a range of sustainable
goods.

Carmarthenshire

ARCHITECT

KBJ ARCHITECTS.
Katherine Jones
Carcartref, Rhanirmwyn,
Llandovery SA20 0PB
T: 01550 760271
www.kbjarchitects.co.uk
Creative solutions, environmentally
efficient healthy buildings.

Powys

ARCHITECTURAL SERVICES

AEDES
Deb Stephens
Boughrood House, 97 The Struet,
Brecon LD3 7LS
T: 01874 622800
E: aedes@mac.com
Emphasising energy efficiency,
renewable energy systems, water
conservation and environmentally-
friendly materials. Appropriate
solutions tailored to each client
and project. Experienced in new
build, conversions, extensions,
refurbishments and community
projects. Comprehensive service
including submission of all necessary applications. Wales/Borders.

HEATING ENGINEER

**THE VERY EFFICIENT HEATING
COMPANY**
Chris Laughton
Old Station, Doll Street,
Machynlleth SY20 8BL
T: 01654 700324
E: enquiries@veryefficientheating.
co.uk
www.veryefficientheating.co.uk
Heating engineers specialising in
solar and wood heating. Also quali-
fied for gas and other solid fuel.

TIMBER FRAMER,
TRADITIONAL

FRAMEWORKS
Paul Thomas
Trewalter Farm Trefeinon,
Brecon LD3 0PS
T: 01874 658586
E: paul.thomas99@btinternet.com
www.oakframeworks.com
Traditional timber framed build-
ings in oak and other timbers.
Specialising in the medieval
style with halls for sale and hire
for events and festivals where
an outstanding venue may be
required. All timber is sustainably

sourced from well managed forests
and woodland.

WATER & WASTE
CONSULTANT

WATER WORKS
Dr Judith Thornton
www.water-works.org.uk
Advice and design for private
water supplies, supplementing
mains water supplies, sewage
treatment systems (including
reedbeds) and all aspects of
sustainable sanitation.

Northern Ireland

Antrim

ARCHITECTS

JOHN K CHILVERS ARCHITECT
John Chilvers
10 Clare Road,
Ballycastle, Co Atrim BT54 6DB
T: 028 2076 8767
From industrial archaeology and
transport preservation through
community projects and heritage
interpretation to restoration/reuse
of vernacular buildings and AONB
design; now exploring crossover
between conservation and natural
building, with modest technologies, passive design, self help and
low capital.

Southern Ireland

ARCHITECTS

**SOLEARTH ECOLOGICAL
ARCHITECTURE**
Mike Haslam
Daintree Building, 62 Pleasants
Place, Dublin
T: 00 35 3140 05790
E: mike@solearth.com
www.solearth.com
Solearth aims to provide beauti-
ful, high performance, low impact
solutions to architectural, planning
and process problems.

© Green Building Press

Suppliers by trade

For more product manufacturers and suppliers please refer to Appendix D at the back of this book.

BUILDERS MERCHANTS

ECOMERCHANT LTD.
Paul Whitlock
Head Hill Road, Goodnestone, Nr
Faversham, Kent ME13 9BU
T: 01795 530130
E: info@ecomerchant.co.uk
www.ecomerchant.co.uk
An environmentally friendly
builders merchant based in Kent.
We supply high performance doors
and windows, natural insulations,
paints, sunpipes and traditional
building restoration materials all
with countrywide distribution.

GREEN BUILDING STORE
Chayley Collis
11 Huddersfield Road, Meltham,
West Yorkshire HD9 4NJ
T: 01484 854898
E: chayley@greenbuildingstore.co.uk
www.greenbuildingstore.co.uk
Specialises in supplying products
which promote energy-efficient,
sustainable and healthy buildings.
Our range includes FSC-certified
windows, doors and solar spaces,
natural paints, boron timber
preservatives, natural insulation,
ultra-efficient toilets and steel
guttering.

GREENER LIVING
Simon Burnett
327 Copnor Road, Portsmouth,
Hampshire PO3 5EG
T: 023 9266 4700
E: sales@greenerliving.co.uk
www.greenerliving.co.uk
Supplier of environmentally friendly
building and decorating products:
Insulations, Lime Plasters and
Mortars, Clay plasters and Clay
boards, Clay and Oil based Paints,
Wood Treatments, Oils and Waxes.
Wooden and Natural Floor cover-
ings. Solar Heating Systems and
Micro power generation.

GREEN SHOP (THE)
Jane Powell
Cheltenham Road, Bisley GL6 7BX
T: 01452 770629
E: enquiries@greenshop.co.uk
www.greenshop.co.uk
Products for a more sustainable
future. Including a host of different
environmentally friendly paints
and wood finishes, sheeps wool
and cellulose based insulation,
sunpipes and solar and wind
systems.

JACKSON BUILDING CENTRES LTD.
Colin Bartleet
Pelham House, Lincoln, LN5 8HG
T: 01522 511115
E: colinbartleet@jacksonbc.co.uk
www.jacksonbc.co.uk
Committed to green issues and
can supply a range of environmentally friendly products from
insulation to solar heating. Our staff
are knowledgeable in renewable
energy and are able to provide
professional advice whether you
are building an eco-home or
simply planning home improvements.

LIME FIRMS LTD.
Tim Strang
Corgam Farm, Bwlchllan,
Lampeter, Ceredigion SA48 8QR
T: 01974 821624
E: info@limefirmsltd.co.uk
www.limefirmsltd.co.uk
Suppliers of a wide range of
building and decorating materials
for historic and new-build projects.
A comprehensive advice and
support service is seen as inextrica-
bly linked to the supply of materials
- many of which are innovative. St.
Astier distributor for Wales.

LONG AND SOMERVILLE
Robin Somerville
Kingswell House, 453 Southbury
Road, Enfield, Middlesex EN3 4HR
T: 020 8804 1161
E: rjs@longandsomerville.co.uk
www.longandsomerville.co.uk
Supplier of a range of sustainable
heavyside and general building
materials as well as landscaping products. Comprehensive
customer service including online
account management loyalty
programme and delivery. A garden
design and installation service will
soon be available.

ONE PLANET PRODUCTS
Sarah Jeffcote
BedZED Centre, Wallington, Surrey
SM6 7BZ
T: 020 8404 4880
E: info@oneplanetproducts.com
www.oneplanetproducts.com
One Planet Products is a bulk-
buying initiative working with
partners in the construction and
refurbishment industries. Our aim
is to make sustainable building
products, materials and services
more cost-effective, and to
encourage their availability and
quality in the housing sector.

SEVEN GENERATIONS LTD.
Anton Saxton
10-12 Picton Street, Bristol, 5QA
T: 0845 330 3934
E: hello@sevengenerations.co.uk
www.sevengenerations.co.uk
Full range of natural paints (distributors for Biofa and Osmo) and
eco-building materials (including
Thermafleece). Using our paint
mixing machine, we offer thousands of delicious colours. Contact
us about our natural products for
home and health. We are quite
friendly.

SUSTAINABLE BUILDING SUPPLIES
Matt Robinson
c/o 90 Stafford Road, Sheffield,
South Yorkshire S2 2SF
T: 0114 299 8559
E: matt@sustainablebuildingsupp
lies.co.uk
www.sustainablebuildingsupplies.
co.uk
Contract and retail supply of
sustainable building systems and
materials, natural insulations and
contract-eco or natural paints. We
are Northern wholesalers of the
superb BIOFA paint range. From
a tin of paint, to a new school, we
can supply.

TRAVIS PERKINS PLC
Travis Perkins
Lodge Way House, Lodge Way,
Harlestone Road, Northampton,
Northamptonshire NN5 7UG
T: 0800 389 6611
E: marketing@travisperkins.co.uk
www.travisperkins.co.uk
Committed to buying timber and
forest products originating from
legally-harvested timber from well
managed forests and maintaining both FSC and PEFC chain of
custody certification across our
national network of more than 600
branches.

BUILDING BOARDS

SKANDA (UK) LTD
Tony Carroll
64/65 Clywedog Road North,
Wrexham Industrial Estate,
Wrexham LL13 9XN
T: 01978 664255

E: info@skanda-uk.com
www.skanda-uk.com
Skanda are the exclusive sole distributors for Heraklith materials for the UK and Ireland. Heraklith manufacture woodwool boards for external and internal cladding of timber frame structures which allows direct application of renders and plasters. Laminated insulation boards and Acoustic Ceiling panels. Heraklith also manufacture flax insulation.

EGGER (UK) LTD.
Sophie Read
Anick Grange Road, Hexham, Northumberland NE46 4JS
T: 01434 613314
E: sophie.read@egger.com
www.egger.com
Egger, Europes leading manufacturer of wood based products produces the Weyroc range of flooring boards for the building/refurbishment market, all are CE marked, FSC approved and manufactured to ISO 9001.

DAMP PROOFING

HOLLAND DAMP PROOFING UK LTD.
Evert de Graaf
Holland House, 89 Pickmere Lane, Knutsford WA16 0JU
T: 0156 573 4734
E: info@dampproofing.com
www.dampproofing.com
Holland Damp Proofing UK Ltd is a specialist company using a proven Dutch damp proofing method which works without the use of chemicals and is environmentally friendly. The system can be used to treat problems such as rising damp, condensation and mould in most types walls e.g. solid, cavity stone.

DECORATING SUPPLIES

AURO UK
Bryan Roe
Holbrook Garage, Bisley GL6 7BX
T: 01452 772020
E: sales@auroorganic.co.uk
www.auroorganic.co.uk
Auro paints, made exclusively from wood resins, plant chemicals and earth pigments, promoting a healthy atmosphere in the home. With 100% compostibilty of our process waste, we demonstrate a total commitment to the environment.

ECOMERCHANT LTD.
Paul Whitlock
Head Hill Road, Goodnestone, Nr Faversham ME13 9BU
T: 01795 530130
E: info@ecomerchant.co.uk
www.ecomerchant.co.uk
Ecomerchant is an environmentally friendly builders merchant based in Kent. We supply high performance windows and doors, natural insulations, paints, sunpipes and traditional restoration materials, all with countrywide distribution.

GREENER LIVING
Simon Burnett
327 Copnor Road, Portsmouth, Hampshire PO3 5EG
T: 02392 664700
E: sales@greenerliving.co.uk
www.greenerliving.co.uk
Supplier of environmentally friendly building and decorating products: Insulations, Lime Plasters and Mortars, Clay plasters and Clay boards, Clay and Oil based Paints, Wood Treatments, Oils and Waxes. Wooden and Natural Floor coverings. Solar Heating Systems and Micro power generation.

HOLKHAM LINSEED PAINTS
Amanda Taylor
The Clock Tower, Longlands, Holkham Park, Wells-next-the-Sea, Norfolk NR23 1RU
T: 01328 711348
E: linseedpaint@holkham.co.uk
www.holkhamlinseedpaints.co.uk
Holkham Linseed Paints are environmentally friendly and cost effective, providing protection for 10 to 15 years before repainting is required suitable for use on internal and external joinery, timber and metal. Available in a range of subtle natural colours.

NATURAL DECO LTD.
David Kitching
The Manor, Manor Lane, Loxley, Warwickshire CV35 9JX
T: 01789 470040
E: davidk@naturaldeco.co.uk
www.naturaldeco.co.uk
Web based suppliers of Aglaia, Auro and Beeck natural breathable paints for walls, wood and metal, including silicate paints, hydrophobing agents and glazes, plasters, natural woodcare products and an extensive library of technical data and application guides. DIY and Professional.

ROUNDED DEVELOPMENTS
Peter Draper
Sustainable Building Centre, Unit 93 Portmanmoor Road Ind. Est., Splott, Cardiff CF24 5HB
T: 029 2040 3399
E: info@rounded-developments.org.uk
www.rounded-developments.org.uk
Rounded Developments Enterprises runs a Sustainable Building Centre in Cardiff that promotes all aspects of sustainable building. We stock a range of goods that includes Earthborn and Auro paints and wood treatments. Online orders and payments are available but we encourage people to come to the centre to find out more about sustainable building in the round.

VENTS FOR THE ENERGY CONSCIOUS

THE PASSYFIER VENT
FOR CONDENSATION CONTROL, BACKGROUND, PASSIVE VENTILATION

THIS VENTILATION ACTS AS AN EXHAUST FOR AIDING CONDENSATION CONTROL WHILST RETAINING AS MUCH HEAT POSSIBLE

THE ARRESTAIR-PRO VENT
FOR VENTING OF HEATING APPLIANCES AND ROOM VENTILATION

USING BI-PLANNAR VANE TECHNOLOGY FOR CONTROLLING THE DREADED DRAUGHT WHILST STILL ALLOWING A TRICKLE OF AIR FOR COMBUSTION

Web: www.condensationshop.com
E-mail: sales@condensationshop.com

Condensation Shop Ltd., Business & Technology Centre, Shire Hill, Saffron Walden, Essex, CB11 3AQ

Tel: 01799 - 528528 Fax: 01799 - 524080

© Green Building Press

EARTH BUILDERS

ABEY SMALLCOMBE
Jill Smallcombe
West Ford Farm, Cheriton Bishop,
Exeter EX6 6HP
T: 01647 24145
E: jackie@abeysmallcombe.com
www.abeysmallcombe.com
We design and create traditional
and contemporary cob buildings
and sculptures, including the cob
shelter at the Eden project and art
for the Met Office. We run practical
courses on cob construction in
both repairs and new build.

ENVIRONMENTAL MONITORING

CLOUDS ENVIRONMENTAL CONSULTANCY LTD.
Carl Peat
327 Copnor Road,
Portsmouth PO3 5EG
T: 023 9263 9858
E: carl.peat@cloudsenvironmental.
co.uk
www.cloudsenvironmental.co.uk
We use an industry leading system
for monitoring and analysing your
energy usage. This system enables
us to provide you with highly
detailed reports that will assist
you in reducing your overheads
and improving the environmental
performance of your business.

GLASS PANELS

THE GREENHOUSE EFFECT LTD.
Andrew Savile
Coach House, High Street, Alfriston
BN26 5TD
T: 01323 871399
E: greenhouseeffectltd@hotmail.co.uk
www.greenhouseeffect.co.uk
Designers and distributors of
Structuran 100% recycled float
glass (without resins) as a sustainable and bio-gas fired glass sheet
formed into 2.8m x 1.2m sizes for
facades, stairs, memorials, kitchen
surfaces, backlit screens, vanity
tops etc.

GREEN ROOFS

FLAG UK LTD.
Tony Mellon
Marlborough House, Beacon Hill
Road, Beacon Hill, Hindhead,
Surrey GU26 6QL
T: 01428 604500
E: greenbible@flaguk.co.uk
www.flaguk.co.uk
Flag UK is one of the largest
manufacturers of TPO single ply
membrane, providing a range of
solutions on green roof projects

throughout UK. Flagon TPO high
performance synthetic liners
provide exceptional weldabil-
ity and flexibility with very high
resistance to weathering, and ultraviolet rays. Flagon TPO membranes
do not contain harmful chlorines,
bromide or halogens.

TRELLEBORG BUILDING SYSTEMS
Ailsa Irwin
Suite 3D, Willow House, Strathclyde
Business Park, Bellshill, Lanarkshire
ML4 3PB
T: 01698 464620
E: ailsa.irwin@trelleborg.com
www.tbselastomers.com
www.greengridroofs.co.uk
Distributor of Ecoseal Single Ply
Roofing System, an environmen-
tal alternative to PVC. Worlds
most used TPO membrane. Also
GreenGrid Modular Green Roof
System. Additional benefits over
standard green roof systems.
Flexibility in cost and design. Can
install on existing roofs

HEATING APPLIANCES

DRAGON STOVES
Kaye Derwas
Dragon Works, Henfaes Lane,
Welshpool, Powys SY21 7BE
T: 01938 5522461
E: kayederwas@aol.com
www.dragon-stoves.co.uk
Suppliers of the Gerkros (Ireland)
Woodpecker range of woodpel-
let boilers. 20-50kW output with
300kg hopper motorised auger
with prices starting at £3500. Fully
automated, approved appliances
for EST grants. Outdoor housing
available. Soon to be launching
utility room boiler and wood pellet
room heaters.

EARTHENERGY LTD.
Brian Kennelly
Falmouth Business Park, Falmouth,
Cornwall TR11 4SZ
T: 01326 310650
E: kennelly@earthenergy.co.uk
www.earthenergy.co.uk
EarthEnergy Limited is the UK's
leading Geothermal Energy
company, specialising in Ground
Source Heat Pump systems to
provide Renewable Heating and
Cooling for buildings across the
country. EarthEnergy+ Systems are
suitable for both domestic and
commercial installations.

GREENER LIVING
Simon Burnett
327 Copnor Road, Portsmouth,

Hampshire PO3 5EG
T: 023 9266 4700
E: sales@greenerliving.co.uk
www.greenerliving.co.uk
Supplier of environmentally friendly
building and decorating products:
Insulations, Lime Plasters and
Mortars, Clay plasters and Clay
boards, Clay and Oil based Paints,
Wood Treatments, Oils and Waxes.
Wooden and Natural Floor cover-
ings. Solar Heating Systems and
Micro power generation.

JUPITER UNDERFLOOR HEATING LTD.
Chris Smith
110 New Haw Road, Addlestone,
Surrey KT15 2DF
T: 01932 858838
E: info@jupiter-system.com
www.jupiter-system.com
Jupiter manufacture an ecological
UFH system comprising of 30mm
high recycled wood fibre panels
that contain the 16mm water pipes
and unique T and G clay tiles that
are used instead of screed. Fast
installation and reaction time.

POUJOULAT (UK) LTD.
Susan Jordan
Unit 1A Quadrum Park, Old
Portsmouth Road, Guildford, Surrey
GU3 1LU
T: 01932 343934
E: sue.jordan@poujoulat.co.uk
www.poujoulat.co.uk
Poujoulat, Europe's largest chimney
manufacturer, now also offers a
secondary heating concept that
achieves 10% of the government
required 20% energy savings for
newbuild homes. Cheaper, more
efficient, flexible contemporary or
traditional design - typical system
cost £3,500.00

INSULATION SUPPLIERS

ECOFIRST
Jody Moorat
The Tithe Office, Abbey Manor
Business Centre, Yeovil, Somerset
BA20 2FJ
T: 0845 257 5064
E: info@ecofirst.net
www.ecofirst.net
Ecofirst supplies and installs sheep's
wool insulation - a renewable and
environmentally friendly product.
We carry out cavity wall surveys
and install CFC and HCFC free
Ecobeads if required. We provide
a nationwide service using our
professional installers.

ECOMERCHANT LTD.
Paul Whitlock
Head Hill Road, Goodnestone, nr
Faversham, Kent ME13 9BU
T: 01795 530130
E: info@ecomerchant.co.uk
www.ecomerchant.co.uk
Ecomerchant is an environmentally friendly builders merchant based in Kent. We supply high performance doors and windows, paints, sunpipes and traditional building restoration materials. We are a national distributor of wool, hemp/cotton, recycled textile and cellulose insulations.

LHOIST UK
Mike Haynes
Hindlow, Buxton,
Derbyshire SK17 0EL
T: 01298 768646
E: mike.haynes@lhoist.com
www.lhoist.co.uk
Lhoist UK manufactures Tradical® Hemcrete, the high carbon capture, biocomposite construction product using lime and hemp. Tradical® Hemcrete provides breathing thermal insulation, benefits occupant health and offers reductions in energy consumption, whilst delivering sustainable buildings and insulation in one product.

NATURAL DECO LTD.
David Kitching
The Manor, Manor Lane, Loxley,
Warwickshire CV35 9JX
T: 01789 470040
E: davidk@trueperspective.com
www.naturaldeco.co.uk
Web based suppliers of Thermafleece wool, Warmcell 100 cellulose and Isonat hemp natural insulation, in all sizes, for convenient ordering online. Also paints, plaster, woodcare and an extensive library of technical data and application guides. DIY and Professional.

GREENER LIVING
Simon Burnett
327 Copnor Road, Portsmouth,
Hampshire PO3 5EG
T: 023 9266 4700
E: sales@greenerliving.co.uk
www.greenerliving.co.uk
Supplier of environmentally friendly building and decorating products: Insulations, Lime Plasters and Mortars, Clay plasters and Clay boards, Clay and Oil based Paints, Wood Treatments, Oils and Waxes. Wooden and Natural Floor coverings. Solar Heating Systems and

Micro power generation.

HERAKLITH
James Muir
Broadway House 21, Broadway,
Maidenhead, Berkshire SL6 1NJ
T: 01628 784330
E: muirwork@btinternet.com
Wood wool boards for external cladding and internal lining of timber frame structures allowing direct application of renders and plasters. Acoustic ceiling and wall panels of wood wool for sports halls, leisure centres, schools etc. External wall insulation system for existing and new solid masonry walls.

KINGSPAN INSULATION LTD
Rachael Morris
Pembridge, Leominster,
Herefordshire HR6 9LA
T: 01544 387209
E: rachael.morris@insulation.kingspan.com
www.insulation.kingspan.com
Kingspan Insulation is Europe's largest manufacturer of flexible faced polyurethane and phenolic insulation. As a responsible manufacturer, Kingspan Insulation was the first insulation manufacturer to carry out an LCA on its sustainable Thermal zero ODP insulation.

PITTSBURGH CORNING (UK) LTD.
Michael Kennett
63 Milford Road, Reading, Berkshire
RG1 8LG
T: 0118 950 0655
E: michael.kennett@pcunet.com
www.foamglas.co.uk
Foamglas® Insulation is manufactured from 66% recycled waste glass cellular glass insulation. It is unique and the only insulation material which is totally impervious to water or water vapour and is non-combustible. Foamglas® products are available for roof, wall and floor.

SECOND NATURE UK LTD
Penny Randell
Soulands Gate, Dacre, Penrith,
Cumbria CA11 0JF
T: 01768 486285
E: info@secondnatureuk.com
www.secondnatureuk.com
Thermafleece uses wool from British hill sheep to create an exceptionally efficient insulation material in new build and refurbishment projects. Completely safe to handle, breathable, remains effective for the life of the building in which it is installed. BBA certified.

SKANDA (UK) LTD
Tony Carroll
64/65 Clywedog Road North,
Wrexham Industrial Estate,
Wrexham LL13 9XN
T: 01978 664255
E: info@skanda-uk.com
www.skanda-uk.com
Skanda are the exclusive sole distributors for Heraklith materials for the UK and Ireland. Heraklith manufacture woodwool boards for external and internal cladding of timber frame structures which allows direct application of renders and plasters. Laminated insulation boards and Acoustic Ceiling panels. Heraklith also manufacture flax insulation.

SPRINGVALE EPS LTD.
Judith Hampton
Dinting Vale Business Park, Glossop,
Derbyshire SK13 6LG
T: 01457 863 211
E: sales@springvale.com
www.springvale.com
Springvale is a leading manufacturer of expanded polystyrene insulation. Our high performance Platinum range offers suitable products for floors, walls and roofs. Most are recyclable and have a very high recycled content. Visit www.sapsonline.co.uk or ecohomesonline.co.uk for energy efficiency assessments.

STEVE ALLIN
Hemp building insulation
Rusheens,
Kenmare,
Co. Kerry
Tel : 00 353 (0) 64 41747
email : steveallin@eircom.net
www.hempbuilding.com
Consultant and training in the use of hemp in buildings. Author of 'Hemp in Buildings'.

JOINERY AND FURNITURE

ECO INTERIORS
Stephen Edwards
39d Effra Road, Brixton,
London SW2 1BZ
T: 020-7737 8110
E: stephenedwards61@hotmail.com
www.ecointeriors-uk.com
Eco Interiors offers consultancy, design and construction for domestic and commercial spaces. Furniture, kitchens, retail displays, office work stations and other interior projects produced with expert knowledge and experience of eco-materials and eco-design.

© Green Building Press

ECOMERCHANT LTD.
Joe Wild
Head Hill Road, Goodnestone, Nr
Faversham, Kent ME13 9BU
T: 01795 591919
E: joinery@ecomerchant.co.uk
www.ecomerchant.co.uk
Ecomerchant is an environmentally
friendly builders merchant based in
Kent. We supply high performance
doors and windows, including a
Passive Haus range, complimented
by our range of internal doors and
staircases. See our listing under
builders merchant for our other
products.

HOWARTH TIMBER (WINDOWS AND DOORS) LTD.
Keith Topliss
The Dock, New Holland,
Lincolnshire DN19 7RT
T: 01469 535314
E: ktopliss@howarth-timber.co.uk
www.howarth-timber.co.uk
Manufacturers of softwood
windows, Conservatories and Door
sets, (full chain of custody).

RECYCLE8
Carwyn Lloyd Jones
Maes Awelon, Pen Y Garn, Bow
Street, Aberystwyth, SY24 5BQ
T: 01970 820027
E: carwynljones@aol.com
www.recycle8.co.uk
A small business using reclaimed,
recycled or environmentally sensitive materials to create items for
the home or garden e.g. decking,
kitchen installation, floor laying.
Repairs and draught proofing
undertaken for boxed sash
windows.

ROY TAM DESIGN
Roy Tam
27 Kings Road, Sherborne,
Dorset DT9 4HU
T: 07808 535 863
E: roytamdesign@btinternet.com
www.eco-furniture.co.uk
Roy trained at John Makepeaces
Hooke Park and the RCA. He
produces a range of domestic
eco furniture as well as one-off
commissions for corporations
including Wessex Water, Kings Fund
and Natural History Museum. He is
also a senior lecturer at Plymouth
University and give eco talks to
many universities and schools.

TEKNION UK LTD.
Kathy Knowles
101 Goswell Road,
London, EC1V 7
T: +44 (0)20 7490 2101
E: kathy.knowles@teknion.com
www.teknion.com
Leading International Designer,
Manufacturer and Marketer of
office systems and related office
furniture products. Extensive portfolio encompasses several lines of
systems furniture, mobile furniture,
desking systems, architectural wall
system, seating, storage, filing and
freestanding casegoods.

LIVING SPACE DESIGN
Bob Mousley
Cedarfield , Five Acres, Funtington,
Chichester, West Sussex PO18 9LX
T: 01243 572604
E: bobmousley@aol.com
livingspacedesign.com
Living Space Joinery are a traditional environmentally conscious
company specializing in anything
to do with wood. Nothing is to
complicated or difficult. We love
one off projects and can offer full
design services if required. We
create the dream, live long and
dance with life.

MODULAR BUILDINGS

ENERGY SPACE LTD.
Aaron Priestman
62 Marmora Road, London, London
SE22 0RY
T: 07979 797471
E: info@energy-space.co.uk
www.energy-space.co.uk
Design and installation of modular
garden buildings that harvest
the suns energy for their power,
heating, cooling and lighting.
A low/zero energy home office
that features building integrated
photovoltaics, AECB silver standard
envelope performance, and
complementary landscape design.

ROUND HOMES UK LTD.
Bob Hughes
Moorlinch Vineyard, Moorlinch,
Somerset TA7 9DD
T: 01458 210099
E: roundhomesuk@aol.com
www.roundhomes.co.uk
Round Homes UK Ltd. build eco-
friendly sustainable SIP Round
Houses as a basic shell, complete
package or full design and build.
Our range of models from 26m^2
to 185m^2 one and two storey are
fast to build with superb insulation
properties.

MORTGAGES

ECOLOGY BUILDING SOCIETY
Jenny Barton
7 Belton Road, Silsden, Keighley
BD20 0EE
T: 01535 650770
E: info@ecology.co.uk
www.ecology.co.uk
Ecology specialises in green
savings and mortgages for the
construction of ecological new
builds and the renovation or
conversion of dilapidated properties. Mortgages are advanced
against the land or the unimproved
property value, and funds can be
released in stages.

RAINWATER SYSTEMS

DALES FABRICATIONS LTD.
Paul Scott
Crompton Road Industrial Estate,
Ilkeston, Derbyshire DE7 4BG
T: 0115 930 1521
E: sales@dales-eaves.co.uk
www.dales-eaves.co.uk/products/
nordal
Nordal Low Cost Aluminium
Rainwater System. Nordal is a
robust Half Round, low mainte-
nance system, which has been
used in Norway for over 40 years.
Nordal offers a low cost alternative
to uPVC and being Aluminium it
meets sustainability criteria.

ECOFIRST
Jody Moorat
The Tithe Office, Abbey Manor
Business Centre, Yeovil, Somerset
BA20 2FJ
T: 0845 257 5064
E: info@ecofirst.net
www.ecofirst.net
Ecofirst supplies and installs rain
water harvesting systems. Our
systems are individually designed
using high quality components. For
domestic applications they can
save 50% of the mains water usage.
We have a nationwide network of
highly trained installation teams.

KLARGESTER ENVIRONMENTAL
Richard Bolton
College Road North,
Aston Clinton,
Buckinghamshire HP22 5EW
T: 01296 633000
E: sales@klargester.co.uk
www.klargester.com
Klargester are the UK market
leaders in off-mains sewage
treatment with a product range
including the BioDisc® Treatment
Plant, Septic Tanks, Cesspools, Oil
Separators and Pump Stations.
Klargester also manufacture the
Envireau Rainwater Harvesting
System for domestic and commer-
cial applications.

RAINHARVESTING SYSTEMS LTD
Derek Hunt
Holbrook Garage, Cheltenham Road, Bisley, Stroud, Gloucestershire GL6 7BX
T: 01452 772000
E: sales@rainharvesting.co.uk
www.rainharvesting.co.uk
Specialist suppliers of rainwater harvesting equipment for domestic, commercial and industrial applications. UK agents for Wisy rainwater products. Also suppliers of Ifo sanitary ware and Lindab steel guttering.

RENEWABLE POWER

BIO PEMBROKESHIRE
Mathew Hawkins
5 Priory Avenue, Haverfordwest, Pembrokeshire SA61 1SG
T: 07870 263771
E: info@biopembrokeshire.co.uk
www.biopembrokeshire.co.uk

Renewable Energy installations for hot water and heating. Past work has been undertaken with Filsol and Aqualec. Heating installations also undertaken including wood pellet stoves and ground source heat pumps. Domestic and commercial work carried out. Corgi registered.

ECONERGY LTD.
Dawn Riggett
Unit 12, St Georges Tower, Hatley St George, Sandy, Bedfordshire SG19 3SH
T: 08700 545554
E: sales@econergy.ltd.uk
www.econergy.ltd.uk
Econergy is the UK market leader in the supply of woodfuelled heating services. We deliver a full range of products to our customers from log, chip or pellet boilers for individual premises to larger turnkey installations, heat networks and CHP.

ELEMENTAL
Peter Ross
The Forge, The Square, Forest Row, East Sussex RH18 5AZ
T: 01342 826111
E: peter@forgeworks.biz
www.elementalplanet.com
Consultants, designers and installers of renewable resource technologies. Elemental work across a wide range of technologies including: Solar water and space heating (including swimming pools), Underfloor heating, Rainwater and Greywater systems, Wind turbines, Photovoltaics, and vegetable oil fuelled CHP units.

GREENSHOP SOLAR LTD.
Eddie Tottle
Bisley, Stroud GL6 7BX
T: 01452 770629
E: solar@greenshop.co.uk
www.greenshop.co.uk
Local installer of solar thermal hot water systems. UK Distributor of Consolar Solar Thermal Stores and Evacuated tube collectors. Supplier of insulation materials, Sunpipes and other energy conservation products.

ISO ENERGY
Justin Broadbent
The Stables, Meath Green Lane, Horley, Surrey RH6 8JA
T: 01293 822100
E: justin@iso.co.uk
www.isoenergy.co.uk
ISO energy consults, recommends, specifies and installs all types of sustainable energy systems including Ground Source Heat pumps (GSHP), Air Source Heat Pumps (Air to water), Biomass Heating Systems, Wind Turbines, Solar Panels (water heating) and Photovoltaic (PV) Electric.

ISKRA WIND TURBINES LTD.
Pat Everett
Unit 13, Loughborough Innovation Centre, Epinal Way, Loughborough, Leicestershire LE11 3EH
T: 0845 8380588
E: enquiries@iskrawind.com
www.iskrawind.com
Iskra Wind Turbines Limited manufacture a high efficiency 5kW wind turbine for powering community and local authority projects, farms, country estates, industrial units, rural domestic properties, offices, schools, and many other applications. IskraWind market the AT5-1 turbine through a network of distributors who are fully trained to

WEST WALES RENEWABLE ENERGY

Electricity from the sun, wind and water

* Photovoltaic Panels from BP Solar
* Small and medium sized wind generators
* Micro hydro systems
+ Full installation service
+ Workshop and demonstration site
+ Advice to 'DIY' Installers
+ ATA Member

Llech Padarn
Llangeitho
Tregaron
Ceredigion
SY25 6TZ

Phone   01974 298851
Fax   01974 298060
Mobile   07977 057723

E mail: Charles@solawind.demon.co.uk

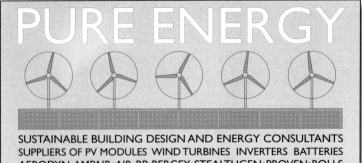

PURE ENERGY

SUSTAINABLE BUILDING DESIGN AND ENERGY CONSULTANTS
SUPPLIERS OF PV MODULES WIND TURBINES INVERTERS BATTERIES
AERODYN•AMPAIR•AIR•BP•BERGEY•STEALTHGEN•PROVEN•ROLLS
OUTBACK•STUDER•TRACE•STECA•SUN-MAR COMPOST TOILETS
SHOREPOWER 16 POPES LANE WELLINGTON SOMERSET TA21 9DQ
TEL-FAX: 01823 666177 www.shorepower.co.uk 37 years experience

© Green Building Press

sell, install and support the turbine.

REHAU LTD.
Tony Sweet
The Building Centre, 26 Store Street,
London, WC1E 7BT
T: 020 7518 6155
E: tony.sweet@rehau.com
www.rehau.co.uk
Manufacturer and design
consultants of renewable energy
systems. Certified by the Zero
Energy House (Passivhaus Institute).
Photovoltaics, ground source
heating/cooling. biomass, ground
air heat exchange, 0.7 U-value
curtain wall, rain water recovery
and A rated energy windows and
doors.

RENEWABLE SOURCES LTD.
Liam Harris
21 Bartholemew Street, Hythe, Kent
CT21 5BY
T: 07706 313134
E: info@renewablesourcesltd.co.uk
www.renewablesourcesltd.co.uk
Wind turbine supply and installation. A complete service for
domestic and light commercial
customers from choice of product
to installation. We offer a detailed
site survey and independent
advice to give you accurate costs,
not just an estimate.

SHOREPOWER
John Shore
16 Popes Lane, Wellington,
Somerset
TA21 9DQ
T: 01823 666177
www.shorepower.co.uk
Wind and Solar energy systems,
including lights, controls and inverters. Air, Whisper, Bergey and Proven
wind turbines, Trace, BP and Elecsol
systems. Independent servicing
consultants and designers - education and training. Over 30 years
experience with wind energy and
ecological building.

SURFACE POWER
TECHNOLOGIES
Frank Trill
Udaras Industrial Park,
Tourmakeady, Mayo, Ireland
T: 353-87-2111722
E: sales@surfacepower.com
www.surfacepower.com
Premium Supplier of Domestic and
Commercial Wind/Solar Electricity
and Heating systems. Please see
our website for full brochures and
pricelists and lots of additional
information.

THE SOLAR DESIGN COMPANY
Chris Laughton
Old Station, Doll Street,
Machynlleth SY20 8BL
T: 01654 700324
E: software@solardesign.co.uk
www.solardesign.co.uk
Engineering support for solar
thermal and wood heating.
Technical authoring, design of
hydraulic and control systems and
presentations to live audiences of
all categories. Sales and service
back-up for energy simulation
products Tsol and PV Sol simulation
softwares.

WIREFREEDIRECT LTD.
Alex Kennedy
26 Woodmere Way, Beckenham,
Kent BR3 6SL
T: 0208 663 3273
E: sales@wirefreedirect.com
www.wirefreedirect.com
We supply and sell a wide range
of solar panels, wind turbines, and
renewable energy products and
accessories.

SOLAR CLADDING

CA GROUP
Andrew Brewster
Evenwood Industrial Estate,
Copeland Road, Evenwood,
Durham DL14 9SF
T: 01388 830 257
E: andrew.brewster@cagroup.ltd.uk
www.cagroup.ltd.uk
CA Building Products are involved
in supplying a range of products
to satisfy the complete metal
building envelope. Included in
their products is the revolutionary

SolarWall, Metal Solar Cladding
System, which converts solar
energy into heat, without producing any CO_2.

SOLAR POWER (PV) INSTALLERS

ECOFIRST
Jody Moorat
The Tithe Office, Abbey Manor
Business Centre, Yeovil BA20 2FJ
T: 0845 257 5064
E: info@ecofirst.net
www.ecofirst.net
Ecofirst is an accredited installer of
solar PV systems. Our systems are
designed by C and G PV qualified
personnel using software simulation systems. The full range of PV
systems (Grid connected or stand-
alone) can be installed by our
highly trained teams.

NORFOLK SOLAR
Lee Rose
26 Gunton Lane, Costessey,
Norwich NR5 0AE
T: 01603 734851
E: lee@norfolksolar.co.uk
www.norfolksolar.co.uk
Specialists in the design, installation and servicing of domestic solar
hot water systems. Also provide
training services to self builders and
professional
installers.

MECH SERVICES
Supply, design & install Solar water heating equipment
Tel./Fax : 01522 520146
Email:matthew@memech.co.uk
41 Cross O'Cliff Hill, Lincoln, LN5 8PR   www.memech.co.uk

PLUG INTO THE SUN

Andrew Tanner
Trebehor Farm Cottage, St. Levan,
Penzance TR19 6LX
T: 01736 871291
E: info@plugintothesun.co.uk
www.plugintothesun.co.uk
Solar PV and solar thermal instal-
lations. Full consultation, design,
installation and commissioning of
solar systems. Fully accredited with
Low Carbon Building Programme
grants system. Based in West
Cornwall, working throughout the
South West region.

SOLARCENTURY

Oliver Sylvester-Bradley
91-94 Lower Marsh, London,
SE1 7AB
T: 020 7803 0100
E: enquiries@solarcentury.com
www.solarcentury.com
Solarcentury is the UK's leading
solar solutions company. We work
directly with architects, housing
developers and engineers throughout Europe to deliver large scale
renewable energy and carbon
reduction solutions.

SPECIFICATION SOFTWARE

NBS

Michael Smith
The Old Post Office, St. Nicholas
Street, Newcastle upon Tyne
NE1 1RH
T: 0191 2445619
E: michael.smith@theNBS.com
www.theNBS.com
NBS produces the National Building
Specification and other related
software products for construction
industry specifiers. NBS offers a
library of clauses for selection and
editing that allow green issues to
be integrated within project specifications. Users may also add their
own clauses. Clauses are accompanied by extensive guidance.

TIMBER FRAME

BENFIELD ATT

Paul Tappin
Castle Way, Caldicot,
Monmouthshire NP26 5PR
T: 01291 437050
E: info@benfieldatt.co.uk
www.benfieldatt.co.uk
Award-winning FSC-Certified
timber frame company Benfield
ATT is the highest qualified building
company in the UK. Led by long-
term environmental construction
expert Professor Michael Benfield,
Benfield ATT engineer, manufacture

and build bespoke timber frame
structures. Free project estimates
by return.

FRAMEWORKS

Paul Thomas
Trewalter Farm Trefeinon,
Brecon LD3 0PS
T: 01874 658586
E: paul.thomas99@btinternet.com
www.oakframeworks.com
Traditional timber framed buildings in oak and other timbers.
Specialising in the medieval
style with halls for sale and hire
for events and festivals where
an outstanding venue may be
required. All timber is sustainably
sourced from well managed forests
and woodland.

HOWARTH TIMBER
ENGINEERING LTD.

Edward Robinson
Railway Sawmills, Burbeary Road,
Lockwood, Huddersfield,
West Yorkshire HD1 3UN
T: 01484 513377
E: sales@howarthengineering.co.uk
www.howarth-timber.co.uk
We design and manufacture struc-
tural timber components, trussed
rafter roofs, timber framed housing
and I beam floors using materials
from certified sources FSC - TRADA-
Trak Chain of Custody Registration
No TT-COC-2206, PEFC - Chain of
Custody Registration No BMT-
PEFC-0267, SFI, CSA, MTCC - BM
TRADA Forest Products Certification
Registration No BMT-COC-0068.

MARLOWS TIMBER
ENGINEERING LTD.

Mike Chester
Howarth House, Hollow Road, Bury
St Edmunds, Suffolk IP32 7QW
T: 01284 772700
E: sales@marlows.com
www.marlows.com
We design and manufacture structural timber components, trussed
rafter roofs, timber framed housing
and I beam floors using materials
from certified sources. We supply
builders, developers and housing
associations, (not one offs or self
build projects). Part of the Howarth
Timber Group.

PIONEER ENVIRONMENTAL
BUILDINGS

Tim Stirrup
Mount Pleasant Ecological,
Porthtowan Park, Truro TR4 8HL
T: 01209 891500
E: enquiries@pioneercabins.co.uk
www.pioneercabins.co.uk

Sustainable, energy efficient
construction. Mainly timber homes
and barns and commissions.

SQUEAKY DESIGN

Mark James
The Wheelhouse, Northampton
NN12 7XU
T: 0790 454 0583
E: squeakydesign@aol.com
www.squeakydesign.info
Traditional carpenter and
woodland craftsman. DIY
guidance to full project management. Bespoke an historic
woodwork. Trees to furniture, round-
house, cruck frame, water wheels
and other timber structures. Owner,
researcher, restorer of "Sea Prince"
registered historic vessel of the
United Kingdom fleet. R.Y.A coastal
and inland skipper.

WESSEX OAK FRAME
CONSTRUCTION LTD.

James Reid
9 Longleaze Cottages, Lower
Wadswick, Box,
Corsham SN13 8JF
T: 01225 812484
E: info@wessexoakframe.co.uk
www.wessexoakframe.co.uk
Incorporating Radicle Oak Frame
Design. 25 years experience in
the Design and Fabrication of
Original Oak-framed Structures
to Traditional or Contemporary
specifications. Conservation of
time-served frames and Glazing of
new-build are specialities.

TIMBER MERCHANTS

ASSOCIATION OF SCOTTISH
HARDWOOD SAWMILLERS

Nick Marshall
Inzievar Woods, Oakley,
Dunfermline, Fife KY12 8HB
T: 01383 851328
E: coordinator@ashs.co.uk
www.ashs.co.uk
The Association of Scottish
Hardwood Sawmillers has 23
member sawmills in all parts of
Scotland. They produce fresh-
sawn and kiln-dried timber from
Scottish-grown hardwoods, plus
high-quality larch and douglas
fir, as well as cladding, shingles,
beams, flooring, worktops, and
other finished wood.

CHRISTINA MEYER WOOD
PRODUCTS

Christina Meyer
Unit 17a, Soho Mills Industrial Estate,
Wooburn Green, Buckinghamshire
HP10 0PF
T: 08456 446588

E: cmeyer@christinameyer.com
www.christinameyer.com
For healthy, beautiful and environmentally friendly flooring, Christina Meyer offers 100% FSC (Forestry Stewardship Council) certified European solid flooring and ecological wood finishes. Wood products with the FSC certification are sourced from sustainable and managed forests and are endorsed by FoE.

ECOCHOICE LTD.
Mike Bekin
18 Charlton Lodge, London,
NW11 7TY
T: 08456 381340
E: info@ecochoice.co.uk
www.ecochoice.co.uk
Importers and agents of FSC certified hardwood products: rough sawn, machined, decking, joists, bollards, fences, beams, sleepers, cladding, piling, bridges, pontoons and water related projects. Species include Massaranduba, Angelim, Garapa, Ekki, Opepe and others. Free quotes and advice on species.

HOWARTH TIMBER GROUP LTD.
Nicholas Howarth
Prince Edward Works, Pontefract Lane, Leeds, LS9 0RA
T: 0113 240 7198
E: info@howarth-timber.co.uk
www.howarth-timber.co.uk
Howarth Timber Group is one of the UK's largest privately owned timber companies. With over 165 years experience in importing, merchanting, manufacturing and timber engineering. With full Chain of Custody certification across the board, our dedication to the industry is evident.

WATER AND WASTE

BIOLOGIC DESIGN
Jay Abrahams
Archenhills, Stanford Bishop,
Bryn Sty, Herefordshire
WR6 5TZ
T: 01886 884721
www.biologicdesign.co.uk
We design and create wetland ecosystem treatment systems, integrated waste water purification, resource production and habitat creation to purify a wide range of effluents.

CRESS WATER LTD.
Rick Hudson
18 Forcefield Road,
Cullumpton EX15 1QB
T: 01884 839000
E: info@cresswater.co.uk

www.cresswater.co.uk
We specialise in the design and installation of reed-beds, ponds and wetlands for sewage and wastewater treatment, recycling treated effluent, water conservation, rainwater harvesting and water management, and the creation of attractive aquatic garden features. We provide a nation-wide service.

ROTALOO UK
Jonathan Cooke
Stocking Green farm, Saffron Walden, Essex CB10 2SS
T: 01799 598086
E: jonathan @rotaloo.co.uk
www.rotaloo.co.uk
Sole importer of waterless and odourless composting loos from Australia made from recycled plastics. Operate without mains electricity . Would need 12V 8W photovoltaic panel to operate fan.

TAPMAGIC LTD.
Andrew Ray
Allens House, Tuddenham, Ipswich, Suffolk IP6 9DA
T: 01473 252043
E: ajr@tapmagic.co.uk
www.tapmagic.co.uk
Tapmagic manufactures a range of low cost water saving tap inserts for hand basins. Simple DIY fitting, quick payback through water and energy saving makes them suitable for private homes, hotels and offices. Fits most round and threaded outlets.

ECO-WORKS LTD.
Chip Rimmer
3 Edgar Buildings, George Street, Bath, Somerset BA1 2FJ
T: 08700 777575

E: info@eco-works.co.uk
www.eco-works.co.uk
Eco-cube reduces unnecessary water consumption by 99%. Eco-cube is a proven system for washroom urinals that uses microbial technology to turn washrooms into a more healthy and hygienic environments as well as radically reducing water, sewage and maintenance charges.

RICHARD IAIN WILKINSON
17 Hamsey Road, Sharpthorne, East Grinstead RH19 4PA
T: 01342 810885
E: iainwilkinson@tiscali.co.uk
www.reedbeds-treatment.co.uk
Reed beds and manufactured treatment units for domestic, industrial and agricultural waste waters. We offer a design, design with supervision, or design with installation service for projects throughout the UK.

WATERPROOFING SYSTEMS

TRELLEBORG BUILDING SYSTEMS
Ailsa Irwin
Suite 3D, Willow House, Strathclyde Business Park, Bellshill, Lanarkshire ML4 3PB
T: 01698 464620
E: ailsa.irwin@trelleborg.com
www.tbselastomers.com
www.greengridroofs.co.uk
Distributor of Ecoseal Single Ply Roofing System, an environmental alternative to PVC. Worlds most used TPO membrane. Also GreenGrid Modular Green Roof System. Additional benefits over standard green roof systems. Flexibility in cost and design. Can install on existing roofs.

 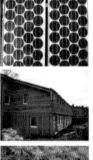

Impetus Consulting Ltd
Creating the environment for change

Impetus specialises in helping organisations to achieve their potential in terms of their environmental performance. Our consultancy and design service provides environmentally sensitive solutions acting as a catalyst to help companies, public sector organisations and individuals reduce their ecological footprint.

To find out more, please contact us: T: 020 7924 9988, E: info@impetusconsult.co.uk, W: www.impetusconsult.co.uk

Appendix A
Useful resources

Specific trade associations are under their relevant category.

AECB (the sustainable building association). *www.aecb.net*

Architects and Engineers for Social Responsibility *Working for peace, ethical values and a better environment. www.sgr.org.uk/*

Beacon Energy *Increasing public awareness about climate change. www.beaconenergy.co.uk*

BioRegional Development Group *Independent environmental organization that develops commercially viable products and services. www.bioregional.com*

Building For a Future magazine (BFF) *BFF is an excellent, quarterly magazine giving an overview of the green construction industry in the UK, with a large range of articles describing experiences and case studies, technical information on building materials and technologies, as well as green building news. Free downloads of BFF recent and back issues are also available . www.buildingforafuture.co.uk*

Building Research Establishment Ltd. (BRE) *01923 664100 - centre of expertise on buildings, construction, energy, environment, fire and risk. www.bre.co.uk*

Business in the Community (BITC) *0870 600 2482 - UK companies committed to improving their positive impact on society. www.bitc.org.uk*

Centre for Alternative Technology *01654 705950 - environmental charity offering practical solutions to environmental problems. www.cat.org.uk*

Centre for Earthen Architecture *01752 233608 - focus for UK earth building activity with links to similar centres across the world. www. tech.plym.ac.uk/soa/arch/earth. htm*

Constructing Excellence *0845 605 5556 The organisation influences the government in the formula-tion of construction policies. www. constructingexcellence.org.uk*

Construction Industry Council (CIC) *020 7399 7400 the CIC is the representative forum for the industry's professional bodies, research organisations and specialist trade associations. www.cic.org.uk*

Construction Skills *01485 577577 CITB-Construction Skills provides assistance in all aspects of recruiting and training the construction workforce. www.citb.org.uk*

Cornwall Sustainable Building Trust *01726 68654 CSBT exists to raise awareness and so minimise the impacts of construction on the Cornish and Global environments. It runs training courses in traditional and sustainable building skills, offers information, advice, and promotes and shares best practice in sustainable construction. admin@csbt.org.uk www.csbt.org.uk*

DTI - Sustainable Construction Resources *The Sustainable Construction page of the Department of Trade & Industry gives access to a broad range of documents and studies on green construction and legislation in a downloadable format. www.dti.gov.uk*

Engineering for a Sustainable Future (IEE) *020 7240 1871 Group of engineers, aiming at developing a sustainable society. www.iee.org/ OnComms/pn/sustainability*

Green Building Press *An online resource built up over the last 16 years and the main website of the Green Building Press. Freely downloadable back issues of Building for a Future magazine. GreenPro, the on-line green building products database. Regular news and artices from leading experts in the field of sustainable building. Forum for discussions and questions. www.newbuilder.co.uk*

Green Street. *Information and advice on improving energy efficiency; water efficiency; material use; waste reduction; and health and wellbeing in the home. www.greenstreet.org.uk*

Hockerton Housing Project *01636 816902   The UK's first earth sheltered, self-sufficient ecological housing development. Tours and workshops. www.hockertonhousingproject.co.uk*

International Ecological Engineering Society *A forum for anyone involved in ecological engineering projects. www.iees.ch*

NBS Green Construction *Keeping you up to date with green building developments. www.greenconstruction.co.uk*

Renewable Energy Association *The Renewable Energy Association and **British BioGen** have joined forces to represent renewable energy producers and promote the use of sustainable energy in the UK. www.r-p-a.org.uk*

Scottish Ecological Design Association (SEDA) *SEDA promotes ecological building design and construction in Scotland. www.seda2.org*

Sponge *Sponge is a network for young professionals who share an interest in sustainable construction. www.spongenet.org*

Straw Bale Building Association *An informal, grassroots association for those who have an interest in strawbale building. www.strawbalebuildingassociation.org.uk*

Sustainable Homes *020 8973 0429 A project for housing asociations and their partners. It provides training and advice. www.sustainablehomes.co.uk*

Square One *Information on energy efficient and sustainable design. www.squ1.com*

The Somerset Trust for Sustainable Development *01458 259400 To make sustainable building the norm by 2010. Organise the popular Homes for Good event each year. www.sustainablehousing.org.uk*

The Green Register (TGR) *0117 377 3490 Providing training and registration for professionals who are interested in sustainable building. www.greenregister.org*

UK Rainwater Harvesting Association *01865 285717 Representing the rainwater harvesting industry in the UK. www.ukrha.org*

Walter Segal Self Build Trust *A newtwork promoting the benefits of community self build using the*

© Green Building Press

Segal method of construction.
www.segalselfbuild.co.uk

Well Built! Sustainable construction
info for local authorities.
www.wellbuilt.org.uk

WWF Reports variety of downloadable reports and studies related to
sustainable construction.
www.wwf.org.uk/sustainable-
homes/reports.asp

ASSESSMENT TOOLS

BREEAM (BRE Environmental
Assessment Method) - sustainability
evaluation method for offices,
retail, and industrial buildings and
residential developments.
www.breeam.org

BRE Sustainable Construction
BRE offers many tools to help
assessing and reducing the
environmental impacts of the built
environment. www.bre.co.uk/
services/Sustainable_construction.
html

Civil Estate Benchmarking Tool
Energy managers can calculate
the energy performance of a
building periodically, and compare
it against benchmarks for similar
public buildings.
http://projects.bre.co.uk/gpg286

Envest 2 Software tool assesses
the environmental impacts of a
building at its early design stage.
www.bre.co.uk/service.jsp?id=52

Environmental profiles Universal
method of measuring the
sustainability of all construction
products and materials over their
entire life cycle. http://cig.bre.
co.uk/envprofiles/document.jsp?js
essionid=3058031159269515515

Office Scorer BRE's sustainable
refurbishment/redevelopment
decision support tool enables users
to systematically compare and test
the environmental and economic
impacts of different office design
concepts, using BRE's Ecopoints
system. www.officescorer.info

**Standard Assessment Procedure
(SAP)** The SAP specification may
be downloaded free of charge,
in PDF format. The SAP is the
Government's recommended
procedure for an energy rating
of dwellings, with a final rating
ranging between 1 to 120 - from
worst to best- based on the annual
energy costs for space and water
heating. SAP also calculates the
Carbon Index, on a scale of 0 to 10,
based on the annual CO_2 emissions

associated with space and water
heating. A SAP rating for every new
dwelling has become compulsory
to fulfil the Building Regulations
requirements of notifying and
displaying an energy rating in new
dwellings. http://projects.bre.
co.uk/sap2001

Sustainability Works 2005
Specifically designed to help
housing professionals and their
partners deliver sustainable development efficiently, from policy
level to project delivery.
www.sustainabilityworks.org.uk

AWARDS

For a full list of awards
www.environmentawards.net

Ashden Awards open to schemes
within the UK that can boast
significant CO_2 savings through
the provision of renewable energy
technologies or energy efficiency
measures.
www.ashdenawards.org

BUILDING - GENERAL

Key Performance Indicators
Department of Trade & Industry
Construction Industry Key
Performance Indicators (KPIs).
KPIs are national data sets against
which a project or a company can
benchmark its performance.
www.dti.gov.uk/
sectors/construction/
ConstructionStatistics/KPIs/
page16440.html

Considerate Constructors Scheme
The Considerate Constructors
Scheme is a code of practice for
improved construction sites.
www.ccscheme.org.uk

Construction Industry Council
Sustainability studies, including
'Constructing for Sustainability';
'Brownfields - building on previ-
ously developed land'; and 'Water
Conservation in Business'.
www.cic.org.uk

Managing Sustainable Companies
(MaSC) MaSC facilitates the introduction and development of more
sustainable business practices.The
site includes guides and site visits.
http://projects.bre.co.uk/masc

Women and Manual Trades
020 7251 9192 Women and
Manual Trades is the national
organisation for tradeswomen and
women training in the trades.
www.wamt.org

BUSINESS & ETHICS

Ethical Consumer magazine
0161 226 2929 Promoting change
by informing and empowering the
consumer.
www.ethicalconsumer.org

Carbon Trust Helping business cut
carbon emissions through carbon
trading. www.thecarbontrust.
co.uk/energy

Ethiscore Identifying the best and
worse products, rated against
environmental, human rights and
animal rights issues.
www.ethiscore.org

Green Futures magazine
Green Futures provides a lively
snapshot of the latest news and
opinion. www.greenfutures.org.uk

COMMUNITY PROJECTS

**Findhorn Foundation Ecovillage
Project** 01309 690311 The ecovillage model is a conscious response
to the extremely complex problem
of how to transform our human
settlements.
www.ecovillagefindhorn.com

Sherwood Energy Village
01623 860222 A 91-acre former
colliery site being transformed
into an environmental enterprise;
industry, commerce, housing,
education, recreation, tourism and
leisure. www.sev.org.uk

COURSES

See Chapter 2, Training and
Education.

DIY & GARDENING

Greenhouse Trust 01603 631007
A key aim of this Trust was the
renovation and conversion of the
building as a DIY model of what
can be done to improve old and
listed housing stock. Lots of information on environmental issues.
www.greenhousetrust.co.uk

Garden Organic (HDRA)
024 7630 3517The national charity
for organic growing.
www.gardenorganic.org.uk

Organic Way 024 7630 3517 The
magazine of the Garden Organic
organisation (HDRA).
www.gardenorganic.org

Soil Association 0117 314 500
promoting organic gardening and
farming. www.soilassociation.org

ENERGY SAVING ADVICE

Bright ideas *Light bulb calculator which reveals the very positive cost benefits of low energy lighting. www.cyberium.co.uk/bright.html*

Building lifecycle carbon calculator *A simple five-step interactive questionnaire, which, alternatively, can also use the output of a SAP assessment. www.cyberium.co.uk/carboncalculator*

Industrial Estate Benchmarking Tool *Helps determine heating and lighting efficiencies by comparison with good practice benchmarks. www.industrialbuildingsbench-mark.info*

National Home Energy Rating (NHER) *Energy rating scheme and energy efficiency advice. www.nher.co.uk*

Office benchmarking tool *Assessing the energy consumption of an office building, by comparing an office consumption with national benchmark levels for UK office buildings. http://217.10.129.104/Energy_Benchmarking/Offices/default.asp*

Save energy *How much money and energy is your home consuming and how can you make reductions? www.saveenergy.co.uk 0845 1207799*

Save money on your gas and electricity *A calculator for comparing all energy suppliers' prices for renewable electricity in your location and supply details, compare the results, and use the application links to switch to a green supplier. http://212.241.173.29/greenpower/domestic-input.asp*

ENVIRONMENTAL ORGANISATIONS

Council for the Protection of Rural England *020 7981 2800 CPRE campaigns for the protection of the countryside. www.cpre.org.uk*

Countryside Voice magazine *The magazine of the Campaign for the Protection of Rural England (CPRE). www.cpre.org.uk*

Energy 21 *01376 333137 - a national network of grassroots renewable energy groups. www.energy21.org.uk*

Environ *0116 222 0222 Leicester charity working to improve the environment and the communities we live in. www.environ.org.uk*

Environment Agency *Leading public body for protecting and improving the environment in England and Wales. www.environment-agency.gov.uk*

Envirowise *0800 585794 Government-funded programme that offers UK businesses free, independent, confidential advice to reduce environmental impact. The online 'Waste Minimisation Guide' can help businesses identify where waste occurs in the supply chain and audit business premises. www.envirowise.gov.uk*

Friends of the Earth *020 7490 1555 Friends of the Earth aims to provide solutions to environmental problems which make life better for people. www.foe.co.uk*

Greenpeace UK *020 7865 8100 Greenpeace is an independent non-profit global campaigning organization that uses non-violent, creative confrontation to expose global environmental problems and their causes. We research the solutions and alternatives to help provide a path for a green and peaceful future. www.greenpeace.org.uk*

National Energy Foundation *020 7820 6300 Promoting renewable energy and sustainable lifestyles. www.nef.org.uk/greenenergy*

National Trust *01793 817400 Portecting historical buildings and gardens. www.nationaltrust.org.uk*

Natural World magazine *The magazine of the UK Wildlife Trusts. www.wildlifetrusts.org*

New Economics Foundation (NEF) *01908 665555 Promotes innovative solutions that challenge mainstream thinking on economic, environment and social issues. www.neweconomics.org*

Reforesting Scotland *0131 554 4321 A network group of those active in the ecological and social regeneration of Scotland. www.reforestingscotland.org*

Women's Environmental Network *020 7481 9004 Campaigning organisation, which represents women and campaigns on issues, which link women, environment and health. www.wen.org.uk*

World Land Trust (WLT) *0845 054 4422 International conservation charity that purchases and protects threatened areas. www.worldlandtrust.org*

World Wildlife Fund (WWF) *01483 426444 At the World Summit on Sustainable Development in August 2002, WWF launched its One Million Sustainable Homes (OMSH) campaign to bring sustainable homes from the fringes of the housing sector to the mainstream. WWF is working with government, industry and consumers to ensure that one million sustainable homes are developed across the UK by 2012 (refurbished as well as new homes). www.wwf.org.uk*

EVENTS

Ecobuild *020 7153 4569 The definitive showcase for sustainable design and construction. Comprehensive conference and seminar programmes and exhibition. www.ecobuild.co.uk*

Greener Homes and Buildings *01654 703064 Encouraging greener building in Wales. www.ghb.org.uk*

Homes for Good exhibition *01458 259400 Exhibits, talks and demos on ecological building and lifestyle. www.sustainablehousing.org.uk*

GRANT SCHEMES

Eaga Partnership Charitable Trust *0800 316 2808 Grants for heating and energy saving measures for those on low incomes. www.eaga.co.uk*

Heat Project UK *0800 093 4050 Grants for all home owners and private tenants for discounted loft and cavity wall insulation. www.heatproject.co.uk*

Low Carbon Buildings Programme *0800 298 3978 Government programme launched April 2006, providing grants for solar PV and other renewable technologies. www.est.org.uk*

Warm Front *Contact your local council for details of grants under this government funded scheme for insulation and heating for those on low incomes*

HEALTH CONCERNS

London Hazards Centre *020 7794 5999 Resource centre dedicated to fighting health and safety hazards in the workplace and community. www.lhc.org.uk*

Pesticide Action Network UK (PAN

© Green Building Press

UK) 020 7065 0905 Support group for anyone whose health has been affected by exposure to pesticides. www.pan-uk.org

LIFESTYLE

Clean Slate magazine
01654 705950 The magazine for members of the Centre for Alternative Technology (CAT). www.cat.org.uk

Green Guide Online Directories on sustainable living and Pure magazine. www.greenguide.co.uk

Green Parent magazine
Green lifestyle magazine for the whole family. www.thegreenparent.co.uk

Grown up Green, on-line resource Encouraging people to protect and improve the natural environment. www.grownupgreen.org.uk

Juno magazine A natural approach to family life. www.hhm.com/juno

New Internationalist magazine
Reporting on issues of world poverty and equality. Debates and campaigns for radical change. www.newint.org

Permaculture magazine
01730 823 311 Solutions for sustainable living. www.permaculture.co.uk

Positive News and Living Lightly magazines 01588 640022
Two publications that report on events and influences around the world that are positive in terms of encouraging a sustainable future. www.positivenews.org.uk

The Positive Network an on-line resource 01460 249 204 Information exchange network promoting sustainable living. www.thepositivenetwork.co.uk

Resurgence magazine 01208 841824 dedicated to the service of the soil, soul and society; helping to create a world based on justice, equity and respect for all beings. www.resurgence.org

PLANNING

Chapter 7 01460 249204 campaigns for a planning system which actively encourages sustainable, low impact and affordable homes. www.tlio.org.uk

The Land magazine 01460 249 204 Campaigning for access to land. Supporting low impact development. www.thelandisours.org

PRODUCT DIRECTORIES

GreenPro Online resource of over 1000 green building products plus case studies, articles and research information. www.newbuilder.co.uk/greenpro/

GreenSpec GreenSpec is a BRE website allowing constructors to design greener materials specifications for their developments. www.greenspec.co.uk

Materials Information Exchange (MIE) Free materials 'dating agency' for the construction and landscaping sectors; especially for waste materials. www.salvomie.co.uk

REGULATORY AND ADVISORY

DEFRA – Sustainable Energy The Department for Environment, Food, and Rural Affairs, - UK and EU regulations and initiatives regarding the energy use in buildings and construction. www.defra.gov. uk/environment/energy/index.htm

Energy Saving Trust (EST) Free guides to help produce energy efficient homes. www.est.org. uk/bestpractice/index.cfm

Sustainable Development Commission 020 7238 4995 The government's independent advisory body on sustainable development. www.sd-commission.gov.uk

UK Climate Impacts Programme 01865 285717 Scenarios that show how climate change will affect our future. www.ukcip.org.uk

RENEWABLE ENERGY

British Hydropower Association Information on site suitability

for water power, and energy potentials. www.british-hydro. org/infopage.asp?infoid=186

Heat pumps Useful basic information about heating-only applications with heat pumps. www.heatpumps.co.uk

Home Power magazine. Input data for your electricity loads, and helps determine what PV panels, batteries, and other equipment are needed. The same information can be used for wind or water generators. The site is that of the Home Power magazine, with US expertise. www.homepower.com/resources/energy_master.cfm

Other power. Lots of practical information about renewable energy sources from alternative energy enthusiasts. www.otherpower.com

Renew Information and comment regarding UK energy supplies and the renewable sector. http://eeru. open.ac.uk/natta/rol.html

Renewable Energy World Renewable energy news, technologies, and case studies from around the globe. www.jxj.com/magsandj/rew

SOLAR ENERGY

British Photovoltaic Association The British Photovoltaic Association (PV-UK) and guide to PV systems. www.greenenergy.org.uk/pvuk2/technology

Benefits, costs, installation information on solar water heating systems. www.thecei.org.uk/solarHeating/default.htm

Degree Days How much solar energy falls in different regions across the UK throughout the year. www.vesma.com/ddd

the **very efficient** HEATING company

● Central heating and controls ● Solar panels for hot water
● Log and pellet boilers ● www.effco.co.uk

North and mid Wales -
Old Station, Machynlleth, Powys
Tel: 01654 700324

Insolation tables *Solar calculators for electric and thermal (water) panels. www.powertech-solar.com*

Loads calculator, *an array size calculator, a battery calculator to help design a basic solar electric system. www.solar-power-answers. co.uk/solar_panel.html*

Soltherm Europe *Stimulating market growth of solar thermal products. Tools and calculators for small and large scale solar water heating projects. Registration is required, but it is free and quick. www.soltherm.org/tools_guide-lines.asp*

The Solar Trade Association *07760 163559 Promoting solar hot water in the UK. www.greenenergy. org.uk*

TIMBER FORESTS AND WOODLAND

BRE - Timber *A variety of links to best practice projects. involving timber constructions. http://projects.bre.co.uk/default. htm#Anchor-Timber-47857*

Forest Stewardship Council (FSC) *01686 413 916 International organi-sation dedicated to promoting responsible management of the world's forests. www.fsc-uk.org*

Soil Association (Woodmark) *0117 314 500 The Woodmark programme (FSC accredited since 1996) is concerned with responsi-ble forest management and the labelling and promotion of forest products. Woodmark provides a full FSC-accredited certification service. www.soilassociation.org*

Span calculator *Calculator for different types of timber for various purposes. This is a North American tool, but to our knowledge, there is no equivalent tool for British species. www.cwc.ca/design/ tools/calcs/SpanCalc_2002*

Timber Research and Development Association (TRADA) *01494 569600 Centre of excellence for the specificartion of timber and wood products. www.trada.co.uk*

Welsh Timber Forum *0845 4560342 For those working in wood-based industries in Wales. www.welshtimberforum.co.uk*

Wood detailing *The Canadian Wood Council website contains a tool which helps determines-wood dimensional changes due to changes in moisture contents. www.cwc.ca/design/tools/calcs/*

dimension_calc

Woodland Trust *National charity protecting our native woodland heritage. www.woodland-trust. org.uk*

WASTE & RECYCLING

BREWEB *BRE's Waste & Environmental Body facilitates ongoing environmental improve-ment in the waste and construction industries by the use of landfill tax sponsorship in high-profile demon-stration and research projects. www.breweb.org.uk*

Centre for Resource Management *01923 664100 - disseminating information on reclaimed/recycled construction materials. www.bre.co.uk*

DEFRA – recycling & waste *Information about UK regulations with regards to waste. www.defra. gov.uk/environment/waste/index. htm*

Design quality indicators (DQI) *DQI online, an interactive tool for designing buildings. www.dqi.org. uk*

EcoConstruction *Information and case studies of recycled & reclaimed material use. www.ecoconstruction.org*

ScopeRecycling *schemes for printer/toner cartridges, phones, IT equipment, CDs and books, across England and Wales, to raise funds for charity www.scope.org. uk/recycling 020 7619 7100*

Recycle more *Hints and tips for managing household rubbish. www.recycle-more.co.uk*

Resource magazine *0117 9077245 Providing a new perspective on*

waste. www.resourcepublishing.co.uk

Salvo *Online directory for antique, reclaimed, salvaged, and green building materials for gardens and homes. www.salvo.co.uk*

SMARTWaste System *Set of tools to help sustainable waste manage-ment. www.smartwaste.co.uk*

Warmer Bulletin *01756 709800 international journal of sustainable waste management and resource recovery. www.residua.com/ Warmer Bulletin/index.html*

Waste Watch *020 7549 0300 National organisation promoting and encouraging action on the 3Rs - waste reduction, reuse and recy-cling. www.wastewatch.org.uk*

WATER

BRE – water *Practical guidance, assessments, and testing in water systems and appliances includ-ing a pdf leaflet on the eco-bio process for cleaning waste water. www.bre.co.uk/services/Water. html*

WIND POWER

Database of wind characteristics. *Categories of wind data for wind turbine design purposes and site analysis. www.winddata.com*

Windpower website *Hugh Pigott is a guru of the small scale wind power world. His website contains numerous links summarizing all of his knowledge. www.scoraigwind. com*

Windpower *This Danish Wind Industry Association's website is excellent for understanding wind power. www.windpower.org/en/ stat/units.htm*

graham bond VISUAL COMMUNICATIONS

DESIGN FOR PRINT

WEB SITE DESIGN

CREATIVE GRAPHICS

DIGITAL IMAGING

TECHNICAL WRITING

T~ 01453 758279
E~studio@gbvisual.com

Appendix B
Author profiles

About the publisher

The Green Building Press is an independent publishing business run by people who are committed to sustainable living. It was established in 1990 to encourage and promote sustainable and environmentally responsible construction with the aim of delivering this information to as wide an audience as possible. Its website (which includes masses of free information) and publications help people create healthy and ecological homes and buildings. Its publications include the quarterly magazine, 'Building for a Future', the 'Green Building Bible' and 'GreenPro', the online eco building database. At the free web forum anyone can ask questions about any aspect of eco building. The information is presented in a user-friendly manner to appeal to both professionals and the general public. The business model also follows the same philosophy and all work is to a strict environmental policy. The offices are in a building renovated to high environmental standards on a farm managed for timber and wildlife. The majority of its energy requirements are from renewables (wind, sun and water).
www.greenbuildingpress.co.uk

Adam Wiseman & Katy Bryce

Adam and Katy completed an apprenticeship in natural building with the Cob Cottage Company, Oregon, USA. Adam is from the US and Katy from the UK. On returning to the UK they started their company, Cob in Cornwall, specialising in the new build and restoration of earth structures in the south-west of England. In 2003 they won a 'Pioneers to the Nation' award for their work with cob.
adamweismann@hotmail.com

Adrian Birch

Adrian originally trained as a chartered building surveyor and for over 15 years worked in various architects and building surveying firms in London and Bristol, managing new-build and refurbishment projects in all property sectors. He now heads the Building Surveying courses at the University of the West of England. In addition to teaching and research in the field of sustainable design and construction, he also provides consultancy advice to individuals and organisations seeking to design, construct or refurbish buildings in a sustainable way. Current projects include a village shop/cafe/business centre in Brockweir, Glos and a nursery school in Llandogo, Monmouthshire.
Adrian.Birch@uwe.ac.uk

Anita Bradley

Anita has an architecture degree from Liverpool University. She regularly reviews books for 'Building for a Future' magazine. Her particular interests are electro-pollution and geopathic stress. She is currently investigating sustainability issues regarding the built environment.

Ben Bamber

Ben is an author who specialises in both clinical psychology and architectural literature, which reflect his interests in a wide variety of other subjects, including politics and religion as well as works of fiction. He also has an interest in graphic design and computer generated art.
dedicate@blueyonder.co.uk

Cath Hassell

Cath is an expert in sustainable water strategies formed from a background of 14 years experience in the conventional plumbing industry and 10 years in environmental building. She uses her extensive experience of conventional and sustainable building services to successfully incorporate both water efficient and carbon efficient systems into the built environment, working with councils, developers, housing associations, architects and engineers. She lectures extensively on the sustainable use of water and carbon efficient energy systems, both in the UK and abroad.
cath.hassell@ech2o.co.uk

Chris Laughton

Chris is one of the leading solar engineers in the UK. With a wide experience in all aspects of the building trade and a variety of environmental and ecological projects, Chris is a fellow of the Institute of Domestic heating and Environmental Engineers (Chair of renewable group), CORGI/HETAS registered installer, SHINE21 trained solar installer and active in the National standards committees. His articles are regularly published in technical and environmental publications and he is experienced in the media of television & radio.
chrisl@effco.co.uk

Chris Morgan

Chris gained 2 first class degrees in architecture at Newcastle University before working both as a builder and architect. He gained experience with Christopher Day in Wales, Malcolm Newton in Northumberland, working on the Earth Balance project, across New Zealand and, from 1997 to 2004, with Gaia Architects in Edinburgh. At Gaia, Chris was responsible for a number of projects, including the Glencoe Visitor Centre. In 2004, Chris set up Locate Architects to continue work on ecological design projects and sustainable development related consultancy, research and teaching. The practice aims always for innovative and contemporary design, with particular expertise in healthy specification, timber and other low impact material based construction, low energy solutions and a desire to 'locate' buildings more fully into their surroundings. Chris has qualifications in permaculture and building biology and is accredited by the RIAS to a 3* level in sustainable design.
mail@chrismorgan.fsnet.co.uk

Clive Fewins

Clive has been a journalist for nearly 40 years and specialises in self-build and architectural subjects. He has lived with his family in a thatched cottage in Oxfordshire for 31 years and this has led to a keen interest in traditional building materials – cob, thatch

and daub in particular. He is the author of two books on church architecture.
zen114600@zen.co.uk

Dave Barton

Dave has worked in sustainable energy for over 12 years, and is an expert on product marketing, project management and policy development with recent experience on utility, local authority and fuel poverty programmes. Dave's interests include building and transport technologies, sustainable communities, natural systems, Zero Emissions Research and Initiatives (ZERI) principles, creative problem solving and helping people and organisations reduce their environmental impact whilst addressing core values. Prior to setting up his own consulting company, Impetus, Dave worked as an associate for the Energy Saving Trust , where he helped to manage the HECAction programme as well as assisting EST in fuel poverty and other policy areas. Before this, Dave worked at BRE for nearly 5 years on the Energy Efficiency Best Practice Programme. Dave has worked in marketing and business development for four private companies, developing existing markets and moving into other markets. He has also managed a number of public and private sector Research and Development projects.
dave@impetusconsult.co.uk

Dave Elliott

Dave has written extensively on renewable energy issues over the years. His book, 'Energy, Society and Environment', now in its second edition, combines an analytical overview of the policy issues, with assessments of the practical deployment opportunities and problems. In his contributions to Building for a Future magazine he has focused on the latter, looking at examples of successful initiatives and programmes in the domestic housing and built environment field. He is director of the Open University Energy and Environment Research Unit and editor of Renew, the journal on renewable energy policy and developments.
D.A.Elliott@open.ac.uk

David Olivier

David is principal of Energy Advisory Associates. He is an energy consultant specialising in the efficient use of energy in buildings. He has helped to design many energy-efficient buildings, including several with record low energy bills for the UK. He is also the author of numerous reports and papers on the subject and gives regular lectures to seminars and conferences.
dolivier@energyadvisoryassociates.co.uk

Doug Stewart

Doug started his own construction company 40 years ago and has a BSc in Building Processes. He is very interested in environmental issues and as Director of DGS Construction, has been pioneering the construction of genuinely sustainable buildings. DGS Construction was shortlisted for the Building Magazine Sustainability Award and in 2005 and was awarded a Caradon Council Design Award for the construction of an energy efficient and environmentally friendly super–e home

in Cornwall. Another recent project was the extensive rebuilding of a 16th century timber frame cottage in Buckinghamshire, which is also being considered for an architectural award
doug@dgsconstruction.co.uk

Gavin Harper

Gavin is a professional author who has written a number of titles including 'Solar Energy Projects for the Evil Genius'. He will shortly be writing 'Domestic Solar Energy'. Gavin is currently finishing an MSc: Architecture Advanced Environmental & Energy Studies at the Centre for Alternative Technology in Machynlleth. He is an affiliate member of the Chartered Institute of Building Services Engineers and a Science and Engineering Ambassador for the SETNET group.
gavindavidjamesharper@gmail.com

Gavin Killip

Gavin is Senior Researcher at Lower Carbon Futures, Environmental Change Institute, Oxford University Centre for the Environment. Gavin's MSc thesis was on the prospects for sustainable energy use in English housing, addressing what is required to reduce carbon dioxide emissions from the domestic sector by 60% by 2050. Gavin has worked for 9 years in the voluntary and public sector on energy efficiency and renewable energy projects in urban areas. Gavin's research interests include the social and economic policy changes that are implicit in the climate change agenda. His refurbishment of a terraced house in Oxford helped reduce energy consumption by 50%.
gavin.killip@environmental-change.oxford.ac.uk

Gideon Richards

Gideon has, over the past ten plus years, advised companies, organisations and individuals on ways to maximise their resources and profits as a management consultant. With a Diploma in Management Studies and an HND in Electrical and Electronic Engineering, Gideon started his career as a project manager in the passenger lift industry. He moved on to have successful posts as a regional sales manager and business development manager, before starting Consulting With A Purpose in 1996. Gideon currently sits on a number of European Standards Working Groups for TC335 Solid Biofuels and TC343 Solid Recovered Fuels and is the chair of the British Standards Institute's PTI/17 mirror committee for TC335 and TC343. He is also on the executive board of The British Pellet Club and a Trustee of the charity CREATE (Create for Research Education and Training in Energy).
gideon.richards@btinternet.com

Howard Liddell

Howard is principal in the Scottish/ Norwegian Ecological Design practice Gaia Architects, and visiting Professor at Oslo University. He is the RIAS Sustainability spokesman and a principal adviser to the Scottish Executive on Sustainability. Primarily he is a practising architect with many international award winning projects to his name, but he is also an author of original think-piece articles, runs CPD courses throughout the UK for the RIBA and lectures and acts as a consultant

© Green Building Press

on eco-building and urban ecology worldwide.
howard@gaiagroup.org

Iain Calderwood

Iain is a City & Guilds qualified heating & ventilation engineer with 28 years experience in the solar thermal industry. Iain is a director of Secon Solar Limited, which imports and distributes a range of solar thermal products. He has extensive knowledge of both sealed and pressurised and drainback systems, mostly with flat plate collectors but also experience of heat pipe and direct flow vacuum tube collectors. Iain is a director of the Solar Trade Association and, with fellow directors, has represented the Association on various technical issues.
iainc@seconsolar.com

Isabel Carmona

Isabel is a fully qualified architect; she is an EcoHomes assessor and accredited to provide SAP ratings. She holds an MSc in Environmental Design and Engineering. She runs CA Sustainable Architecture, an architecture practice combining architecture, sustainability consultancy and research. Isabel is interested in the real outcome of architecture, both in terms of energy performance in use, and the user's appreciation of the building, including comfort. She is convinced of the need for more and better feedback on buildings, and published in Building Research and Information the article 'Architects need Feedback'. Her research in sustainability includes an 'Environmental Management System for Designers' for an architect's firm, and 'A scoping study for developing the criteria for sustainability in commercial buildings' for DTI in collaboration with the Usable Building Trust and British Property Federation.
isabel@ca-sa.co.uk

Jay Abrahams

Jay was introduced to sustainable technologies (photovoltaics, windmills and anaerobic digestion) as a member of his university's 'Alternative Research Group'. His interest in 'waste to energy' technology was furthered by postgraduate work on anaerobic digestion. He gained experience of a wide range of conventional 'energy-intensive' treatment processes within the wastewater treatment industry. Following a Permaculture Design Course he established his company, Biologic Design' to create WET systems; multi-species constructed wetlands for sustainable wastewater purification. His company views wastewater not as a problem to be disposed of, but as an unused resource, purifying wastewater with minimal non-renewable energy use, creating a species-rich wildlife habitat and biomass resource (the coppiced willow can be used in both traditional and contemporary crafts and as a fuel for ceramic and other types of stove. Biologic Design is a home-based business, which, having no mains services, is run on renewable systems - a windmill, photovolatics, wood burner and WET system.
01886 884721

Jerry Clark

Jerry has had a long interest in matters environmental, developing a concern for endangered wildlife as a child during the sixties. He spent many years as a cabinet-maker, and injected his environmental concerns into which timbers and finishes were used, often turning down commissions where the customer insisted on the use of an inappropriate timber. Latterly Jerry has gained a first class honours degree in Environmental Sciences and put a lot of his new-found knowledge into practise while creating a super-insulated, eco-home on a smallholding in Wales. He works on a freelance basis, that includes work for the Green Building Press. He is now in Cornwall where he lives in a multi-generation house with his wife, daughter and father (his son has long since flown the nest). Other interests include listening to music (mostly loud), and kayaking around the estuaries and coasts of Cornwall.
jerry@newbuilder.co.uk

John Cantor

John set up John Cantor Heat Pumps in 1980 and in the early days had close links with The Centre for Alternative Technology in Wales. Since then his company has designed, manufactured and installed a wide variety of water-to-water heat pumps with power-output capabilities from 1kW to 70kW.
www.heatpumps.co.uk

John Garbutt

John has been in the insulation manufacturing industry for seventeen years and is currently Marketing Director at Kingspan Insulation Ltd. He has worked for manufacturers of mineral wool, extruded polystyrene, rigid urethane and phenolic insulation. He is widely respected in the field for his technical expertise and has played a major role in the UK Government's consultation process for the next revision to Approved Document L of Building Regulations for England & Wales. In his role at Kingspan Insulation, John has been responsible for steering the business into carrying out the first independently certified Ecoprofile for any insulation material (via BRE) and the first independent three pillar sustainability appraisal for the manufacture of a building material to be published (using Arup's SPeAR tool). John was also instrumental in the publishing of the ground breaking work 'Insulation for Sustainability' by sustainability consultants XCO2. With a BA Hons in Natural Science from Cambridge University, and a Masters in Earth Sciences from the University of Minnesota, John is an avid environmentalist in his private life and has family membership of Friends of the Earth. He is professionally and personally interested in the topic of sustainability and believes with a passion that manufacturers need to be open and honest about what they do, and that they should be responsible about what they make and how they make it.
john.garbutt@insulation.kingspan.com

Jon Broome

Jon is an architect specialising in low energy housing, sustainable construction, timber frame construction and prefabrication. He wrote 'The Self Build Home' with Brian Richardson back in 1991 and his most recent

book is 'The Green Self-Build Book'. He has self-built two of his own houses. For many years he was a Director of Architype and now he runs his own consultancy specialising in sustainable construction. He is a regular contributor to 'Housing & the Environment', published by the Chartered Institute of Housing.
jon.broome@btconnect.com

John Shore

John Shore graduated from the Architectural Association, specialising in Ecological Design and Renewable Energy. He was responsible for designing, building and monitoring the Integrated Solar Dwelling at Brighton in the 1970s – the UK's first Self-Sufficient, Zero-Heat House. He has been involved with pioneering research, development and demonstration with sustainable buildings and energy systems since the 1960s. As well as writing extensively on self-building and sustainable design and running the wind and solar energy company Aerodyn Shorepower, he has lectured at schools of architecture and worked at Croydon College of Art, Brighton Polytechnic and Somerset College of Arts and Technology. Current projects include designing low-cost, zero-heat sustainable housing and workspace schemes.
resourceresearch@ukonline.co.uk

Judith Thornton

Judith worked at the Centre for Alternative Technology for 5 years, focusing largely on water and sewage systems. She now works part time as a lecturer on CAT's MSc in Architecture and part time as a water and waste management consultant. Judith is author of 'The Water Book', a guide to small scale water supply systems and has worked on a wide range of small scale water and sewage treatment systems.
info@water-works.org.uk

Keith Hall

Keith completed a three year City & Guilds apprenticeship in carpentry and joinery way back in 1974! In the early 1980s he formed his own building business that included general building, renovation and new housing. In 1988 he became concerned about environmental issues, particularly the use of unsustainable tropical timber. From that concern he launched a magazine called Building for a Future and founded the Association for Environment Conscious Building (AECB) in an effort to promote the concept of green and sustainable building. In 1990 he established the Green Building Press, a business dedicated to promoting and providing information about eco and healthy building. He is now Editor of both Building for a Future magazine and the Green Building Bible. He has designed and built many sustainable building projects.
keith@newbuilder.co.uk

Kevin Boniface

Kevin has worked at a company called Sustain, an energy and environmental consultancy in Bristol since January 2006, in the role of Senior Technical Consultant. He is involved primarily in carrying out detail design as well as sustainable energy feasibility and scoping studies for clients in the social housing sector and commercial sectors. Kevin is degree qualified in Mechanical Engineering and worked previously as a Senior Consultant at BRE, managing projects for the Governments Energy Efficiency Best Practice Programme. He has written and project managed publications on sustainable energy, and was instrumental in developing new Best Practice Standards for new housing in the light of tighter Building Regulations.
kevin.boniface@sustain.co.uk

Louise Zass-Bangham

Louise specialises in sustainable garden design, particularly integrating house with garden, sustainable materials and ecological planting. Work includes complete design services, rejuvenation and consultancy. Louise is an experienced writer and lecturer. Changing career after 10 years in fashion design and marketing, Louise brings her eye for colour, texture and form to garden design. Louise and her husband live in Twickenham.
louise@zass-bangham.com

Mark Gorgolewski

Mark is an Associate Professor at the School of Architectural Science at Ryerson University in Toronto, Canada, where he recently moved from the UK. Mark is a fully qualified architect in the UK who has worked for many years as an environmental consultant in the UK construction industry. He has worked on a wide variety of research projects for government, local authorities, housing associations, private developers, materials producers and others, focusing on sustainable construction issues and new technologies and processes. He has published widely on construction technology and environmental issues. Mark is a past chair of the AECB.
mgorgo@ryerson.ca

Michael Littlewood

Michael is a natural landscape architect and environmental planner with extensive experience of successfully designing and implementing sustainable land use projects. His mission has been the introduction of ecological design and planning into the mainstream and is founded on years of practice in a wide variety of situations, landscapes, climates and uses of land for public and private amenities on scales ranging from the residential garden to a village or town. His outstanding international reputation derives from work over many years in England Wales, Australia New Zealand, Saudi Arabia, Malaysia, Greece and Portugal. His clients have included national, regional and local governments, landowners, developers, schools, colleges and universities, farms and estates. Michael is the author of several publications, including a series of technical books on Landscape Detailing, covering all aspects of construction, also a Guide to the Maintenance and Management of School Grounds. He has also produced several posters and calendars on Organic Gardening and a series of brochures covering his concepts of the Forest Village, Forest Farm Forest School and Forest Home/Garden to promote sustainable self sufficiency by communities and individuals.
michael@ecodesignscape.co.uk

Michael Smith

Michael is a mechanical engineer and chartered information professional, working for NBS as an information specialist on the Information Services Team. His responsibilities include: an editorial role on the Construction Information Service (CIS) and the RIBA Office Library Service products. Michael also edits and maintains the information content of Green Construction (a stand alone green building website) and Green Construction Round-Up (a twice monthly newsletter).
Michael.Smith@theNBS.com

Mike George

Mike has more than twenty years experience in the construction industry, having trained as a plasterer and progressing to building maintenance and small building works. In 2004 he obtained a first class honours degree in Architectural Technology from Glamorgan University, where he now works as a Lecturer in the thermal analysis of buildings, and 3D architectural CAD.
mike.george6@btinternet.com

Mischa Hewitt

Mischa has always had a passion for the environment. For the last 3 years he has been working on the Earthship Brighton project, a pioneering 'green' development in Brighton to build a sustainable community centre. Prior to this he worked in Finance. In his spare time he enjoys playing the piano and composing classical music. He has just started writing a book about earthships in the UK which will be published early next year.
mischahewitt@hotmail.com

Oliver Lowenstein

Oliver runs the green cultural review, Fourth Door Review - www.fourthdoor.co.uk - the annual cross-disciplinary art, architecture, design and craft, new music and new media journal. He co-ordinates the Cycle Station Project, as part of Fourth Door Research. He writes regularly for Building for a Future, as well as many other magazines. The Fourth Door web-magazine, Unstructured, can be found at www.unstructured.co.uk. He is also currently working on a book on twenty first century timberbuild.
fourthdoor@pavilion.co.uk

Olwyn Pritchard

Olwyn is on-line news editor for the Green Building Press, and occasional contributor to Building for a Future magazine. She has a varied background including some time spent experiencing social housing, community living, low impact living and a long standing interest in green issues. She is interested in buildings and architecture generally, is a competent handywoman and dreams of one day building the ultimate low impact, energy efficient and funky home for herself.
olwyn@newbuilder.co.uk

Paola Sassi

Paola is a partner of Sassi Chamberlain Architects and a lecturer at the Welsh School of Architecture at Cardiff University. She is the author of 'Strategies for Sustainable Architecture' published by Taylor & Francis Group, an illustrated overview of sustainable design approaches and technologies exemplified through 60 case study buildings in UK, US, Australia, Germany and Austria.
sassip@Cardiff.ac.uk

Paul Jennings

Paul studied Engineering Design & Appropriate Technology at Warwick where he developed an interest in energy and sustainability. He provided technical support to the local welfare rights advice centre. He went on to do a Masters in Energy Resources Management at South Bank. He has been testing ever since and has carried out over 10,000 tests upon buildings and parts thereof for a wide range of applications, particularly energy efficiency (both Building Regulations Part L and the more demanding green and eco standards, such as Canadian Super-E housing), checking advanced ventilation systems, testing for fire separation and containment. Paul has tested across the UK and overseas, including Europe, Africa and the Middle and Far East for a vast range of clients. He has also delivered numerous presentations to builders, architects, local authorities and insurance bodies. Specific buildings that he has tested include the AtEIC building at the Centre for Alternative Technology, Sue Roaf's Oxford Solar House and the Nottingham Ecohouse.
paul.jennings@retroteceurope.co.uk

Peter Acteson-Rook

Peter had developed a keen interest in the environment over many years. After completing two house renovations this naturally moved into the area of renovation and self build. A high interest in green roofs has grown after completing the MSc in Architecture, Advanced Environmental and Energy studies at the Centre of Alternative Technology with UEL. For the Past two years Peter has been conducting experiments on green roof run off, and is also a qualified EcoHomes assessor.
peter@acteson-rook.com

Rachel Shiamh Whitehead

Rachel lives in a straw bale home in woodland near Pembrokeshire with her partner Ravi. She has been living in the woodland for ten years, growing herbs, making flower essences, jewellery and exploring natural healing. Since self building and project managing her house, she has set up the 'Quiet Earth Project' and started to give tours, consultations and courses in straw bale and natural building.
www.quietearth.org.uk

Richard Nicholls

Richard is an applied physicist who began his career in buildings as a research assistant engaged in field trials of low energy houses and condensing boiler heating systems. He then spent time in industry as an energy manager with the role of reducing the energy and water consumption of a large group of local authority buildings. He is currently a senior lecturer in the department of Architecture, Huddersfield University, where he teaches environment and services to all under-

graduate and postgraduate pathways and is course leader for the MSc. in Sustainable Architecture. Writing credits include the book 'Heating, Ventilation and Air-Conditioning' and editor of the website www.info4study.co.uk

Richard Oxley

Richard is a chartered surveyor and an independent historic building's consultant with RICs Diploma in building conservation. He is RICs accredited in Building Conservation. He has an active interest in developing the link between sustainability and historic buildings. He lectures widely on this subject and is author of the book, 'Survey and Repair of Traditional Buildings'.
oxleyconservation@btinternet.com

Rob Scot McLeod

Rob studied as a student on the UEL/ CAT MSc Architecture: Advanced Environmental Energy Studies course. He wrote a paper titled 'Ordinary Portland Cement- Extraordinarily high CO_2 Emissions' which assessed the cumulative effects of growing CO_2 emissions from the cement industry and practical alternatives that might help this sector maintain Kyoto targets.
rob_scot@hotmail.com

Sally Hall

In 1989 Sally co-founded the AECB (the sustainable building organisation). She still works for this organisation on a part-time and voluntary basis. She has many years experience of practical eco-building and renovating, writing for Building for a Future and other publications. She worked full time in finance and personnel management until 1996 when she downshifted to live a more sustainable life on a 140 acre farm in West Wales. Here she helps run the farm which is managed mainly for wildlife using organic principles. She helps care for a diverse range of habitats, including ancient woodland, marshland, traditional hay meadows, orchard and ponds. Her passion is wildlife and conservation and she undertakes regular surveying work for the British Trust for Ornithology.
Sally@aecb.net

Stephen Lowndes

Stephen is a Chartered Engineer with over 20 years experience working as a Building Services Engineer. During this time he has worked for some of the UK's top services design and energy consultancy organisations and has been involved in a variety of projects in both the private and public sectors in the UK and Europe. Stephen has extensive experience in undertaking designs for low energy buildings that optimise the utilisation of natural ventilation and passive solar heating, as well as engineered schemes encompassing biofueled community heating systems, small-scale combined heat and power (CHP) and solar / wind powered rain water harvesting systems.
s.lowndes@ntlworld.com

Steve Allin

Steve runs a successful hemp building consultancy in Kerry, Ireland. He has enthusiastically pioneered the use of hemp in building for the last 10 years & is the author of 'Building with Hemp' 2005. He was a director of Hemp Ireland Ltd. (1998-2003) which was set up to research and develop a hemp processing facility in Ireland.
steveallin@eircom.net

Stuart Barlow

As Technical Manager of REID architecture Stuart is responsible for sustainable & environmental support and initiatives within the company across a wide range of commercial sectors. Stuart has overseen the development of their Environmental Management System for Designing Buildings and was also responsible for delivering the refurbishment of their natural ventilated offices at West End House located in central London. A study of occupants' perceptions of comfort resulted in the publication of a joint paper on how adaptive comfort opportunities might influence refurbishment strategies at a 2006 conference organized by the Network for Comfort & Energy Use in Buildings (NCEUB) and the Low Energy Architecture Research Unit (LEARN). Additional research work has included being part of the steering group for developing a protocol for encouraging office buildings to operate more efficiently and with greater occupant satisfaction (BRE Digest 474) and the Building Sustainable Communities programme led by University College London.
stuart.barlow@ra-lond.com

Sue Roaf

Sue is currently working as a private Consultant with the Green Consultancy and the Carbon Trust, and in research and teaching with Arizona State University and in association with the Open University. She is an author, an Oxford City Councillor for Wolvercote ward, holds a number of honorary positions for a range of organisations and charities, and is occasionally engaged to design eco-buildings. She is Chair of the 2008 Oxford Conference on Resetting the Agenda for Architectural Education and in 2006 Chaired the 2nd International Conference on Solar Cites.
s.roaf@btopenworld.com

Tom MacKeown

Tom has spent many years in the construction industry, from design to completion; working as a contractor in UK, Turkey, Switzerland, Russia, Azerbaijan and Ireland. Projects have included restoration of a Welsh longhouse, sustainable tourism resorts, dry stone walling, design of a straw-bale school and restoration of a Spanish village house. All of these projects involved the use of natural, local materials and processes learned from local craftsmen, which have been adapted for modern applications and needs. In recent years, Tom has specialized in Straw bale and timber-frame construction, developing a system of straw panels to enable precision engineering of straw and widening its potential as a construction material in larger projects. Tom founded Uncle Tom's Cabins and has developed a number of innovations for the use of natural materials in quirky ways to suit modern living.
tom_mackeown@yahoo.co.uk

© Green Building Press

Appendix C
Glossary of terms

Absorb: the ability to soak up by chemical or physical action - usually slowly.

ACH: air changes per hour, stated as the volume of air changed per hour / volume of room.

Airtightness: of increasing importance within the building regulations, energy efficient building design should ensure that ventilation only occurs as desired by the occupants, and not through unwanted draughts and air leakage through or around the building elements.

Alternative energy: the use of energy produced using non-carbon resources, e.g solar, wind, water, thermal etc.

Biomass: biomass is the organic materials produced by plants and trees. The term "biomass" is intended to refer to materials that do not go directly into foods or consumer products but may have alternative industrial uses. Common sources of biomass are; (1)agricultural wastes, e.g straw and manure from cattle, poultry, etc, (2) wood materials, e.g wood or bark, sawdust, mill scrap; (3) municipal waste, such as waste paper and (4) energy crops, such as poplar and willow. In some cases, microbial and animal metabolic wastes are also considered biomass.

Biofuel: biofuel is any fuel that is derived from biomass. It is a renewable energy source, unlike petroleum, coal and nuclear fuels.

Like coal and petroleum, biomass is a form of stored solar energy. The energy of the sun, during the growth of the plants, is 'captured' through the process of photosynthesis. Biofuel is commonly known as biodiesel when used in vehicles.

Biofuels can be made from oil rich crops such as rapeseed, linseed etc. Some companies also make biodiesel from waste vegetable oil from restaurants and chip shops. In South America biofuel has been made for many years from the distilation of sugar cane.

Biological oxygen demand (BOD): the amount of oxygen required by aerobic microorganisms to decompose the organic matter in a sample of water and used as a measure of the degree of water pollution. (Also called biochemical oxygen demand).

Borax/boron/borates: a family of natural mineral based products which have the ability to protect timber from rot, insect attack and fire (spread of flame) if applied and used correctly. Harmless to humans at normal concentrations.

Breathable sheathing: many boards are now available which are sufficiently vapour permeable to allow them to be used externally on a timber frame and allow vapour generated within the building to pass through to the outside without risk of condensation within the fabric.

Breather membrane: usually paper or a woven membrane which is used to prevent water entry to the construction, whilst allowing vapour to escape.

Breathing construction: a term used to describe vapour resistant layers within a wall or roof construction to ensure that moisture is allowed to pass safely (e.g without condensing) from the interior to the exterior of a building.

Brown roof: a roof covering comprising rubble and earth which is designed to be wildlife friendly in urban environments where certain species have adapted to inner city living.

Capilliary action/attraction: the tendency of liquid to rise as a result of surface forces.

Carbon/Carbon dioxide C0$_2$: CO_2 is a colourless, odorless, tasteless gas, about 1.5 times as heavy as air. Under normal conditions it is stable, inert, and nontoxic. The decay (slow oxidation) of all organic materials produces CO_2. Fresh air contains approximately 0.033% CO_2 by volume. In the respiratory action (breathing) of all animals and humans, CO_2 is exhaled.

Carbon index: an addendum to the SAP rating (see later in glossary) which measures the CO_2 'created' in use, expressed as a measure of the CO_2 / m^2 of floor area. One method of satisfying the building regulations re thermal properties.

Carbon neutral: a term used to describe a building design that consumes no fuels that will release-carbon dioxide or uses renewable fuels as energy sources to ensure that the total production of CO_2 related to a building or project is zero.

Cellulose insulation: can be manufactured from recycled newspapers (pre or post consumer waste), cellulose is shredded and treated with borax against insect and rot attack. Can be installed as loose fill, damp spray, or dry-blown to a specified density.

Closed panel construction: panels built on site with sheathing to both sides (internal and exernal) usually with insulated cavity - often using breathing wall technology and materials. Differs from panels used in typical timber frame construction which are sheathed to one side only.

Coefficient of performance (COP): an example of COP; a geothermal heat pump, operating at COP 3.5 is able to move 3.5kWh (11,946BTUh) of heat for every 1kWh it consumes. This can also be viewed as an efficiency of 350%, which compares very favourably to high efficiency (condensing) gas burning furnaces (90-99% efficient), and electric heating (100%). The COP of an air source heat pump may be 2.0 (200% efficiency) at low outdoor air temperatures before its backup electric resistance heating coils are turned on.

Cold bridge: a building term used to describe a heat loss path through a material which has a much lower thermal resistance than the surrounding material and is placed so as to create a 'bridge' from the inner (warm space) to the outer (cold space) of a structure.

Desorb: to cause the relase of an absorbed substance.

District heating: heat which is generated at a central source and stored either as steam or hot water, then delivered on demand to a group of buildings. Most district heating systems in Europe distribute hot water from 'energy centres', where combined heat and power generation (CHP) equipment make heat and electricity at the same time.

Embodied energy: the energy required to produce a material, through extraction, manufacture, transport or installation.

Facade: the face of a building, especially the principal face.

Facultative: capable of functioning under varying environmental conditions. Used by certain organisms, such as bacteria that can live with or without oxygen.

Future proofing: to design-in an ability to adapt to future trends. this may be in the form of lifestyle trends or the availablility of resources such as fuel.

Geenhouse effect: a term used to describe the heating up of the earth by radiation from the sun being trapped with the atmosphere by atmospheric gases. These gases act as insulators preventing radiated heat from the warming of the earth from escaping to space. The gases are found naturally in the atmosphere but in recent decades, levels of some (carbon dioxide and methene in particular) have been bolstered by human activity.

Green roof: a description of a 'living' roof finish of some kind, usually grasses or sedum.

Heat recovery: the use of heat exchangers to extract heat from waste air or water, and transfer it into an incoming air supply.

Humidity: see Relative humidity

Hygroscopic: a feature of natural insulants such as wool or cellulose, it allows vapour to be 'held' within

the material without condensing, and later to release it into the atmosphere. A key principle of a breathing wall specification.

Interstitial condensation: created where warm moisture laden air migrates through the building fabric and condenses onto a cold surface within the fabric, potentially leading to both damage to the fabric, and to an unhealthy internal environment.

Life cycle analysis (LCA): this is a methodology that identifies the environmental impacts associated with the life cycle of a material or product in a specific application, thus identifying opportunities for improvement in environmental performance. Abbreviated LCA.

Lignin: naturally ocurring 'adhesive' in wood. High levels of lignin in woods used for some compressed wood fibre boards reduces the need to use synthetic adhesives.

Low-e glazing: low-e (low emittance) refers to a metallic oxide coating applied to the inner face of a double or triple glazed unit, and which reduces heat loss through the glass, thereby improving the thermal perfomance of the unit. Can also reduce solar overheating and light levels.

Microporous finishes: usually attributed to paints, stains and waxes, which may be naturally produced or petrochemical based, which allow vapour to be released from the material they cover, whilst remaining impermeable to water.

Moisture content: most natural materials will contain moisture to some extent - for example seasoned timber can still contain between 8 and 18% moisture in use, but at these levels will not rot or suffer insect or mould attack.

Natural: a very imprecise term which is used to describe a variety of products, some of which may have a petro-chemical base, but which would on the whole be manufactured from non-petro-chemical ingredients.

Organic: an often misleading term which has come to be a little abused in recent years. Two descriptions follow:

1. chemical term relating to or defining material that contains carbon, chiefly of biological origin. For instance coal and oil are organic compounds as are humans. Organic compounds are often not safe or toxin free as the term has come to suggest.

2. used to describe food or farming methods where chemicals are avoided in the production of food and even non-food crops such as cotton, wood and other fibres.

Ozone: a colourless, toxic, unstable gas formed from oxygen and electrical discharge or ultraviolet light. It differs from oxygen by having three atoms rather than two. Ozone is a pollution when it occours at ground level usually as a result of high traffic concentrations. However, natural ozone at high levels in the atmosphere prevents harmful ultraviolet rays from reaching the surface of the earth. (see ODP below).

Ozone depletion potential ODP: the potential for the manufacturing process of a material (usually the 'blowing' of foam based insulants) to release chemicals that are known to destroy the ozone layer around the earth. CFCs and HCFCs are the most common, and have largely been replaced by air.

Passive: a building term describing a structure or component that needs no mechanical assistance to operate. For instance: passive solar design uses the structure of the building and it's solar orientation to collect energy from the sun. A further example would be a thermostatic radiator valve where the air temperature in a room will cause a wax capsule to expand or contract, thus allowing hot water to flow or not.

Passive stack ventilation: the use of building shape and design to produce sufficient natural ventilation without the use of electrically powered fans. Stack ventilation uses vertical ducts to stimulate natural airflow due to the 'flue' effect.

Recycling: the reprocessing (breaking down and reforming) of an existing material to manufacture a new material for a new use.

Re-use or reclaimed: the re-use of whole and intact building materials in their originally produced form.

Often refered to as architectural salvage.

Relative humidity: this is the amount of moisture within the atmosphere, or a material, expressed as a % of the total saturation moisture content that could be contained.

Renewable resources: materials or energy sources which can be replaced, hopefully within the lifetime of the product e.g timber can be re-grown.

Renewables / non-renewables: material from a source that is renewable (e.g wood) versus that which is not or which has a finite non-renewable supply (e.g fossil fuels).

Resource depletion: the specification of certain materials, products or processes can lead to habitat damage, environmental degredation, and rarity e.g fossil fuels, peat, Welsh slates.

SAP rating: an energy rating system for housing which measures the cost in £ / m^2 floor area. Now a pre-requisite for calculating the Carbon Index which is one method of satisfying the building regulations re thermal performance of housing.

SIPs: structurally Insulated Panels, or prefabricated wall or roof elements produced from petro-chemical based insulation boards bonded to timber based boards.

SUDS: sustainable Urban Drainage System. Aims to reduce the water load on the man-made drainage systems, and to reduce flood risk, by designing the external environment to redistribute rainwater falling onto a site via porous surfaces, etc.

Thermal conductivity: Is a measure of the rate of energy or heat flow through a material, stated as W/mK.

Thermal properties: the characteristics of a building material which define how heat, or energy, passes through the material e.g thermal resistance and density.

Thermal resistance: this is a measure of resistance to heat flow given a specified thickness of a material and a temperature difference each side.

Urban heat island effect (UHI): an urban heat island (UHI) is an urban area which is significantly warmer than its surroundings. As population centres grow in size from village to town to city, they tend to have a corresponding increase in average air temperature, due to the mass of the buildings.

U-value: a measure of heat transmission through a building part or a given thickness of insulating material, expressed as (W/m^2K) that will flow in 1 hour through 1 square metre of the structure or material from air to air with a temperature differential of 1°C.

Vapour barrier: usually in sheet or brush-on form, used in 'non-breathing' construction to prevent water vapour from entering the construction. Unreliable due to difficulties in effecting a seal.

Vapour permeability: vapour permeable materials allow moisture to migrate from inside to outside of building fabric in a controlled manner. BS5250 suggests that vapour should permeate through external sheathing materials at a rate 5 times that of the internal sheathing or lining material so as to reduce the risk of interstitial condensation.

Volatile organic compounds (VOCs): VOCs are organic chemical compounds that have high enough vapour pressures under normal conditions to significantly vaporize and enter the atmosphere during use, application or drying out of a paint or other coating.

Water conservation: the design of water useage and waste systems to minimise wasteage, reduce flooding and un-necessary re-processing to ensure that an essential primary resource remains readily available.

Appendices & Index

Appendix D
List of advertisers

Advertising: *Jerry Clark 01208 895103*
jerry@greenbuildingpress.co.uk

© Green Building Press

Index

*For building professionals
and products please go to
page 415*

Appendices & Index

© Green Building Press

LEEDS COLLEGE OF BUILDING
LIBRARY
NORTH STREET
LEEDS LS2 7QT
TEL: (0113) 222 6097 and 6098

Appendices & Index

© Green Building Press